ADDITIONAL
MATHEMATICS

- **H H Heng**
- **Khoo Cheng**
- **J F Talbert**

PEARSON
Longman

Pearson Education South Asia Pte Ltd
23/25, First Lok Yang Road, Singapore 629733

Associated companies, branches and
representatives throughout the world

First published 2001
Eleventh reprint 2011

ISBN   978-981-235-211-8
ISBN 10   981-235-211-2

Produced by Pearson Education South Asia Pte Ltd
Printed in Singapore

Acknowledgements

The examination questions have been reproduced
By permission of the University of Cambridge Local
Examinations Syndicate and SNP Publishing Pte Ltd.

Preface

This book is written based on the **2001 syllabus** issued by the **Ministry of Education**, Singapore. It is written in a straightforward manner to allow rapid progress in grasping the concepts, with sufficient exercises for practice. The topics are arranged largely in the order of the syllabus for convenience.

The features of this book are:
- Numerous **worked examples** to illustrate the concepts taught
- **Exercises** to give students extensive practice
- **Revision Papers** after every few chapters for further practice
- **Activities** to stimulate students' thinking skills
- **Maths Booster** to challenge students with more difficult questions
- **Maths Bulletin** to provide students with some information on famous mathematicians

Contents

Graphmatica Courseware: Navigation Guide

Activity: To plot graphs of absolute value functions (page 68).

Step 1: Insert the diskette 'Graphmatica' Courseware into Drive A.

Step 2: Double click on 'My Computer' icon.

Step 3: Double click on '$3\frac{1}{2}$ Floppy (A:)' icon.

Step 4: Double click on the file 'Graphmatica.exe' icon.

Step 5: On the menu bar, click on 'Options' menu and select 'Settings'.

Step 6: On the 'Options Panel' screen:
    (i) Click on 'Colors'
    Select 'Background Colors' as 'Dark Gray', then click on 'OK'.
    (ii) Click on 'Graph Paper'
    Select background graph paper type as 'Rectangular' and grid detail level as 'Gridlines', then click on 'OK'.
    (iii) Click on 'Change Range'
    Enter Range of Grid:
    Left: –5   Right: 5
    Bottom: –5   Top: 5
    Click on 'OK'.

Step 7: Type the equation 'y = abs x' in the space. Press 'Enter' key.
(The graph of $y = |x|$ is plotted on the screen.)

Step 8: Type another equation 'y = abs x + 2' in the space.
Press 'Enter' key.
(The graph of $y = |x| + 2$ is then plotted.)

Step 9: Type a third equation 'y = abs x – 2' in the space.
Press 'Enter' key.
(The graph of $y = |x| - 2$ is plotted.)
(You may print a copy of each graph by clicking on the 'Print' button.)
[Make some observations about how the graph of $y = |x|$ is 'moved' or 'translated' by the addition or subtraction of 2.]

Step 10: On the menu bar, click on 'File' menu and select 'New'. Repeat Steps 5 to 9 and type the following equations.
    (i) y = abs x for the graph of $y = |x|$
    (ii) y = abs $(x + 2)$ for the graph of $y = |x + 2|$.
    (iii) y = abs $(x – 2)$ for the graph of $y = |x - 2|$.

    [Make some observations about how the graph of $y = |x|$ is translated by addition or subtraction of 2.]

Note: To use the mathematical operators, functions and variables, click the 'Help' menu and select 'Operator Table'.

Activity: To plot graphs of quadratic functions (page 78)

Similarly, follow the steps described in the Activity for page 68.

Type the following sets of equations:

Group I

$y = 4x^2$	for the graph of $y = 4x^2$
$y = 2x^2$	for the graph of $y = 2x^2$
$y = x^2$	for the graph of $y = x^2$
$y = \dfrac{1}{2}x^2$	for the graph of $y = \dfrac{1}{2}x^2$

Group II

$y = -4x^2$	for the graph of $y = -4x^2$
$y = -2x^2$	for the graph of $y = -2x^2$
$y = -x^2$	for the graph of $y = -x^2$
$y = -\dfrac{1}{2}x^2$	for the graph of $y = -\dfrac{1}{2}x^2$

What can you induce from the relation between the coefficient of x^2 and the shape of the curve of a quadratic function $f(x) = ax^2 + bx + c$?

Activity: To plot graphs of logarithmic functions (page 166)

Similarly, follow the steps described in the Activity for page 68.
Type the following sets of equations:

(a)
$y = \log x$	for the graph of $y = \lg x$
$y = \log (x + 2)$	for the graph of $y = \lg (x + 2)$
$y = \log (x - 2)$	for the graph of $y = \lg (x - 2)$

(b)
$y = \log x$	for the graph of $y = \lg x$
$y = \log x + 2$	for the graph of $y = \lg x + 2$
$y = \log x - 2$	for the graph of $y = \lg x - 2$

Observe how the graph of $y = \lg x$ is moved or translated.

Activity: To plot graphs of exponential functions (page 169)

Similarly, follow the steps described in the Activity for page 68.
Type the following sets of equations:

(a)
$y = 2^x$	for the graph of $y = 2^x$
$y = 2^{(-x)}$	for the graph of $y = 2^{-x}$

(b)
$y = 2^x$	for the graph of $y = 2^x$
$y = -(2^x)$	for the graph of $y = -2^x$

(c)
$y = 2^{(1 - x)}$	for the graph of $y = 2^{1-x}$
$y = 2^{(x - 1)}$	for the graph of $y = 2^{x-1}$

Are the pairs of graphs reflections of each other? If so, what is the line of reflection?

Chapter 1
Sets

We often sort and classify things in our daily lives.

For example, people may be categorised by sex, age group or race.

Do you know why we want to categorise?

Categorisation helps us to put things in order.

It allows us to sort a large group of people or objects into smaller groupings.

1.1 Set Concepts

1.1.1 Set Language and Notation

In everyday speech, we say a *herd* of cows, a *team* of soccer players or a *group* of people. In mathematics, we say a *set* of cows, a *set* of players and a *set* of people.

A **set** is a well-defined collection of objects. These objects are called **elements** or **members** of the set.

For example, Fig. 1.1 shows a set of prime numbers less than 10. The elements in this set are 2, 3, 5 and 7.

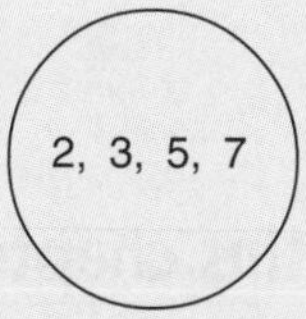

Sets are generally denoted by capital letters. If the set in Fig. 1.1 is denoted by A, we can write the set as follows:

$$A = \{2, 3, 5, 7\}$$

The elements are listed in a pair of curly brackets { }, with commas separating the elements. The order in which the elements is listed is immaterial. Hence the set can also be writen as $A = \{5, 2, 7, 3\}$.

Note that round brackets ( ) and square brackets [ ] should not be used because they are not notations for sets.

If a set contains many elements and these elements follow a specific order, then dots are used to represent part of these elements. For example, set N, which is the set of natural numbers, can be written as

$$N = \{1, 2, 3, 4, 5, ...\}$$

A set can also be written using variables to represent the elements. For example,

$$N = \{x: x \text{ is a natural number}\}$$

It is important that a set be well defined so that the contents can be clearly determined.

For example, if set B is defined as the set of natural numbers less than 4, then set B is

$$B = \{x: x \text{ is a natural number}, x < 4\}$$
$$= \{1, 2, 3\}$$

▶ **Example 1**

Write a description of the set containing 'spring', 'summer', 'autumn' and 'winter'.

▶ **Solution . . .**

The set is the seasons of the year.

▶ **Example 2**

Write the following sets by listing the elements in curly brackets { }:
(a) Set A is the set of letters in the word *computer*.

2, 3, 5, 7

Fig. 1.1

(b) $B = \{x: x$ is an even number, $5 < x < 15\}$

(c) $C = \{x: x$ is a multiple of 3, $x \geq 12\}$

(d) $D = \{(x, y): y = 2x - 3, x$ is an integer and $1 \leq x \leq 4\}$

▶ **Solution . . .**

(a) $A = \{c, o, m, p, u, t, e, r\}$

(b) $B = \{6, 8, 10, 12, 14\}$

(c) $C = \{12, 15, 18, ...\}$

(d) $D = \{(1, -1), (2, 1), (3, 3), (4, 5)\}$

1.1.2   The Symbols $\in$ and $\notin$

The symbol $\in$ is used to indicate membership in a set. In Fig. 1.1, 2 is an element of set A and we write this as $2 \in A$. This may also be written as $2 \in \{2, 3, 5, 7\}$.

Since 4 is **not** an element of set A, we write it as $4 \notin A$, where the symbol $\notin$ means 'is not an element of'.

▶ **Example 3**

State whether each of the following is true or false. Explain your answer.

(a) $A = \{x: x$ is a factor of 15$\}$ and $3 \in A$

(b) $8 \in \{x: x$ is an odd number, $1 < x < 10\}$

▶ **Solution . . .**

(a) True, because $3 \in \{1, 3, 5, 15\}$.

(b) False, because $8 \notin \{3, 5, 7, 9\}$.

1.1.3   Number of Elements in a Set

We use $n(A)$ to denote the number of elements in set A.
In Fig. 1.1, there are four elements in set A. Hence we write $n(A) = 4$.

▶ **Example 4**

Given that $H = \{x: x$ is a multiple of 7, $x < 50\}$, find $n(H)$.

▶ **Solution . . .**

$H = \{7, 14, 21, 28, 35, 42, 49\}$
$n(H) = 7$

1.1.4   Empty Set

Some sets do not contain any elements. For example, the set of months that has 32 days.

A set that contains no elements is called an **empty set** or **null set**, and is denoted by $\{ \ \}$ or $\varnothing$. Hence $n(\varnothing) = 0$.

Note that $\{0\}$ and $\{\varnothing\}$ are not empty sets as they contain the element 0 and $\varnothing$ respectively.

▶ Example 5

Determine which of the following is/are empty sets.
(a) $X = \{$quadrilaterals that have 5 sides$\}$
(b) $Y = \{x : x$ is an integer, $3 - x > 5\}$

▶ Solution . . .

(a) $X = \varnothing$ because quadrilaterals have 4 sides only.
(b) $Y \neq \varnothing$ because $Y = \{-3, -4, -5, \ldots\}$.

1.1.5   Equal Set

Let us consider the following sets:
$$A = \{w, o, r, d, s\}$$
$$B = \{s, w, o, r, d\}$$

Notice that A and B contain exactly the same elements, so we say that A and B are **equal sets** and we write $A = B$.

▶ Example 6

Determine whether the pairs of sets are equal or not.
(a) $M = \{8, 2, 1, 4\}$ and $N = \{x : x$ is a factor of 8$\}$
(b) $P = \{l, o, t\}$ and $Q = \{$letters in the word *lost*$\}$

▶ Solution . . .

(a) $M = \{8, 2, 1, 4\}$ and $N = \{1, 2, 4, 8\}$, $\therefore M = N$.
(b) $P = \{l, o, t\}$ and $Q = \{l, o, s, t\}$, $\therefore P \neq Q$.

1.1.6   Universal Set

Suppose A is the set of odd numbers less than 10, i.e. $A = \{1, 3, 5, 7, 9\}$. If B is the set of factors of 12, of which the elements must be chosen from set A, then $B = \{1, 3\}$.

Notice that only the elements in set A may be considered when working the problem. Set A is called a **universal set**.

> A **universal set** is a set that contains all the elements for any specific discussion and is denoted by the **symbol ε.**

▶ Example 7

Given that $\varepsilon = \{x : x$ is an integer, $1 \leq x \leq 10\}$,
$$A = \{x : x - 2 \geq 4\},$$
$$B = \{x : x \text{ is a multiple of } 3\},$$
find A and B.

► **Solution . . .**

$\varepsilon = \{1, 2, 3, 4, 5, 6, 7, 8, 9, 10\}$

$A = \{x: x - 2 \geq 4\}$

    $= \{x: x \geq 6\}$

    $= \{6, 7, 8, 9, 10\}$

$B = \{x: x \text{ is a multiple of } 3\}$

    $= \{3, 6, 9\}$

Exercise 1A (*Answers on page 493*)

1. Write a description of the following sets:
   (a) Set A is the set containing 'metre', 'inch', 'kilometre' and 'nautical mile'.
   (b) Set B is the set containing 'square', 'rectangle', 'parallelogram', 'trapezium', 'rhombus' and 'kite'.
   (c) $C = \{$mouth, oesophagus, stomach, small intestine, large intestine, rectum$\}$
   (d) $D = \{$Singapore, Malaysia, Indonesia, Brunei, Thailand, the Philippines, Myanmar, Vietnam, Cambodia, Laos$\}$
   (e) $E = \{5, 10, 15, 20, ...\}$
   (f) $F = \{t, r, a, i, n\}$

2. Write the following sets by listing the elements in curly brackets:
   (a) Set P is the set of vowels in the English alphabet.
   (b) Set Q is the set of colours in the rainbow.
   (c) Set R is the set of planets in the earth's solar system.
   (d) Set S is the set of months that has more than 30 days.
   (e) Set T is the set of letters in the word *history*.
   (f) Set U is the set of factors of 12.

3. Write the following sets by listing the elements in curly brackets:
   (a) $A = \{x: x \text{ is an odd number}\}$
   (b) $B = \{x: x \text{ is an integer}, 5 \leq x \leq 12\}$
   (c) $C = \{x: \sqrt{x} \text{ is a positive integer}, x^2 < 20\}$
   (d) $D = \{x: x \text{ is an even number}, x - 1 > 4\}$
   (e) $E = \{x: x \text{ is a multiple of } 3, 6 < 2x < 30\}$
   (f) $F = \{(x,y): y = 3x - 2, x \text{ is a positive integer}, x < 4\}$

4. State whether each of the following is true or false. Explain your answer.
   (a) $A = \{x: x \text{ is a positive integer}, x < 5\}$ and $2 \in A$
   (b) $B = \{x: x \text{ is an even number}, 3 < x < 15\}$ and $2 \notin B$
   (c) $31 \in \{x: x \text{ is a prime number}, 10 < x < 30\}$
   (d) $9 \notin \{x: x \text{ is a perfect square}, 1 < x \leq 16\}$

5. $P = \{x: x$ is a natural number, $x < 10\}$
    $Q = \{x: x$ is an odd number, $5 < x < 15\}$
    $R = \{x: x$ is an integer, $3 < 2x - 1 \leq 12\}$
    $S = \{x: x$ is a multiple of $5\}$

    Copy and fill in the boxes with $\in$ or $\notin$ to make the following statements true:

    (a) 6 ☐ P (b) 10 ☐ P

    (c) 7 ☐ Q (d) 12 ☐ Q

    (e) 8 ☐ R (f) 3 ☐ R

    (g) 25 ☐ S (h) 40 ☐ S

6. (a) A is the set of letters in the word *honest*, find $n(A)$.
    (b) $B = \{x: x$ is an integer, $5 \leq x < 15\}$, find $n(B)$.
    (c) $C = \{x: x$ is an odd number, $2x + 5 < 10\}$, find $n(C)$.
    (d) $D = \{x: x^2$ is a two-digit number$\}$, find $n(D)$.
    (e) $E = \{2, 4, 6, 8, ..., 20\}$, find $n(E)$.

7. Determine which of the following is/are empty sets.
    (a) $H = \{$cuboids that have 8 faces$\}$
    (b) $J = \{x: x$ is a multiple of 11, $16 < 3x - 1 < 30\}$
    (c) $K = \{x: x$ is an even number, $11 < \dfrac{x-3}{2} < 12\}$
    (d) $M = \{x: x$ is a factor of 21, $11 < x < 21\}$

8. Determine whether the following pairs of sets are equal or not:
    (a) $A = \{5, 6, 7\}, B = \{6, 5, 7\}$
    (b) $C = \{1, 2, 3, 4\}, D = \{3, 4, 5, 1, 2\}$
    (c) $E = \{$letters in the word *meat*$\}, F = \{$letters in the word *team*$\}$
    (d) $G = \{1, 7, 14, 21, 28\}, H = \{x: x$ is a multiple of 7, $x < 30\}$

9. Given that $\varepsilon = \{x: x$ is an integer, $10 \leq x \leq 50\}$,
    $A = \{x: 2x - 9 < 15\}$,
    $B = \{x: x$ is a factor of $40\}$,
    $C = \{x: x$ is a multiple of $6\}$,
    find A, B and C.

10. Given that $\varepsilon = \{x: x$ is an even number, $10 \leq x \leq 30\}$,
    $P = \{x: x$ is a prime number$)$,
    $Q = \{x: \sqrt{x}$ is an integer$\}$,
    find $n(\varepsilon)$, $n(P)$ and $n(Q)$.

1.2 Subsets

1.2.1 Proper Subset

A large set is often broken down into smaller more manageable sets, called **subsets**. For example, human knowledge which is a large set, is subdivided into certain areas of study: physical sciences, social sciences and liberal arts. Each of these areas may be considered as a subset.

> Set A is a **subset** of set B if and only if all the elements of set A are also elements of set B. This relationship is written as $A \subseteq B$.

If set A is not a subset of set B, we write set $A \nsubseteq B$. To show that set A is not a subset of set B, we must find at least one element of set A that is not an element of set B.

▶ Example 8

Determine whether set A is a subset of set B.

(a) $A = \{$letters in the word *slow*$\}$
$B = \{$letters in the word *vowels*$\}$

(b) $A = \{x: x$ is a factor of 12, $x < 20\}$
$B = \{x: x$ is a factor of 16, $x < 20\}$

(c) $A = \{x: x$ is a multiple of 2, $x \leq 10\}$
$B = \{x: x$ is an even number, $x \leq 10\}$

▶ Solution . . .

(a) $A = \{s, l, o, w\}$
$B = \{v, o, w, e, l, s\}$
Since every element of set A is also an element of set B, thus $A \subseteq B$.

(b) $A = \{1, 2, 3, 4, 6, 12\}$
$B = \{1, 2, 4, 8, 16\}$
Since the elements 3, 6 and 12 in set A are not elements in set B, thus $A \nsubseteq B$.

(c) $A = \{2, 4, 6, 8, 10\}$
$B = \{2, 4, 6, 8, 10\}$
Since every element in set A is also an element of set B, thus $A \subseteq B$.

Note that in (c), although $A = B$, we can still say that A is a subset of B. However, in (a), $A \neq B$, since the elements v and e in set B are not found in set A. In this case, set A is called the **proper subset** of set B.

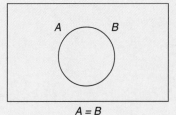

$A = B$

> Set A is a **proper subset** of set B if and only if all the elements of set A are elements of set B and $A \neq B$ (i.e. set B must contain at least one element not in set A). This relationship is denoted by $A \subset B$.

However, set A is not a proper subset of set B if $A = B$.

If $A \nsubseteq B$, it could be $A = B$ or $A \cap B \neq \varnothing$. (See diagrams on the right.)

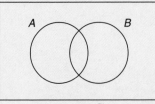

$A \cap B \neq \varnothing$

▶ **Example 9**

Determine whether set A is a proper subset of set B.

(a) $A = \{$red, blue, yellow$\}$
      $B = \{$red, orange, yellow, green, blue, violet$\}$

(b) $A = \{a, b, c, d\}$
      $B = \{a, c, d, b\}$

▶ **Solution . . .**

(a)   All elements of set A are also elements of set B and $A \neq B$, thus $A \subset B$.

(b) $A = B$, so $A \not\subset B$.
      Note, however, that $A \subseteq B$.

1.2.2   Number of Subsets

How many distinct subsets can be made from a given set?

Deduction and Induction

Let us look at the information given in Table 1.1. How many subsets will a set with 4 elements contain? Hence, induce the number of subsets in a set with n elements.

Set	Number of elements in a set	Subsets	Number of subsets
$\varnothing$	0	$\varnothing$	$1 = 2^0$
$\{a\}$	1	$\varnothing, \{a\}$	$2 = 2^1$
$\{a, b\}$	2	$\varnothing, \{a\}, \{b\}, \{a, b\}$	$4 = 2^2$
$\{a, b, c\}$	3	$\varnothing, \{a\}, \{b\}, \{c\},$ $\{a, b\}, \{a, c\}, \{b, c\},$ $\{a, b, c\}$	$8 = 2^3$

Table 1.1

Note: $\varnothing$ is a subset of every set, including $\varnothing$.

From the table above, we notice that the number of subsets in sets with 0, 1, 2 and 3 elements are 2^0, 2^1, 2^2 and 2^3 respectively.

Hence, we can deduce that the number of subsets in a set with 4 elements is 2^4, i.e. 16 subsets.

We can also induce that:

The **number of subsets** in a set with n elements is 2^n

▶ **Example 10**

How many subsets does the following set contain?

(a) $G = \{$letters in the word *creation*$\}$

(b) $H = \{x: x$ is a perfect square, $10 < x < 80\}$

▶ **Solution . . .**

(a) $G = \{c, r, e, a, t, i, o, n\}$
 $n(G) = 8$
 ∴ Number of subsets $= 2^8$
 $= 256$

(b) $H = \{16, 25, 36, 49, 64\}$
 $n(H) = 5$
 ∴ Number of subsets $= 2^5$
 $= 32$

Exercise 1B (Answers on page 493)

1. Determine whether set A is a subset of set B.
   (a) $A = \{2, 4, 6,\}$, $B = \{x: x$ is an integer, $x < 10\}$
   (b) $A = \{$letters in the word *triangle*$\}$
       $B = \{$letters in the word *rectangle*$\}$
   (c) $A = \{11, 13, 17, 19\}$, $B = \{x: x$ is a prime number, $10 < x < 20\}$

2. Given that $P = \{x: x$ is a multiple of 2$\}$,
   $Q = \{x: x$ is a multiple of 3$\}$,
   $R = \{x: x$ is a multiple of 6$\}$,
   which of the following statements are true and which are false?
   (a) $R \subset P$ (b) $R \subset Q$ (c) $Q \subset P$

3. Determine whether set X is a proper subset of set Y.
   (a) $X = \{3, 6, 9\}$, $Y = \{x: x$ is multiple of 3, $x < 15\}$
   (b) $X = \{x: x$ is a multiple of 13, $x < 80\}$
       $Y = \{x: x$ is a multiple of 13, $x < 90\}$
   (c) $X = \varnothing$, $Y = \{0\}$

4. Given that $P = \{x: x$ is a multiple of 8, $x < 30\}$,
   $Q = \{x: x$ is a multiple of 4, $x < 30\}$,
   $R = \{x: x$ is a multiple of 2, $x < 30\}$,
   $T = \{x: x$ is a multiple of 30, $x < 30\}$,
   which of the following statements are true and which are false?
   (a) $P \subset Q$ (b) $P \subseteq Q$ (c) $Q \subset R$
   (d) $T \subset R$ (e) $T \not\subset P$ (f) $P \not\subseteq R$

5. List all the subsets of the sets given.
   (a) $\{1, 2, 3\}$ (b) $\{a, b, c, d\}$

6. How many subsets does each set contain?
   (a) $P = \{$letters in the word *honesty*$\}$
   (b) $Q = \{x: x$ is an integer, $2 \leq \dfrac{x-1}{3} < 5\}$

MATHS BULLETIN

Geometrical diagrams were used in the eighteenth century by Leonhard Euler, a Swiss mathematician, to represent sets.

However, the diagrams were named 'Venn diagrams' to commemorate John Venn, an English mathematician who used the diagrams widely to illustrate the relationships of sets.

1.3 Venn Diagrams and Set Operations

1.3.1 Venn Diagrams

A useful technique for picturing set relationships is the **Venn diagram**, named after John Venn (1834 – 1923), an English mathematician.

In a Venn diagram, the universal set is usually represented by a rectangle and the subsets are usually represented by circles, which are inside the rectangle. Dots, sometimes labelled, are used to represent the elements.

▶ Example 11

Given that $\varepsilon = \{x: x$ is a natural number, $10 \leq x < 18\}$,

$A = \{x: x$ is an odd number$\}$,

draw a Venn diagram to show the relationship between the sets ε and A.

▶ Solution . . .

$\varepsilon = \{10, 11, 12, 13, 14, 15, 16, 17\}$
$A = \{11, 13, 15, 17\}$
The Venn diagram is shown in Fig. 1.2.

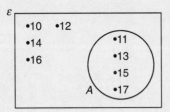

Fig. 1.2

1.3.2 Complement

In the solution of Example 11, note that 10, 12, 14 and 16 are elements of the universal set but **not** the elements of set A. This set of numbers $\{10, 12, 14, 16\}$ is called the **complement** of set A and is written as A'. Thus we can write $A' = \{10, 12, 14, 16\}$.

In the Venn diagram in Fig. 1.3, the complement of set A is represented by the shaded region outside set A but within the universal set.

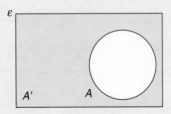

Fig. 1.3

> The **complement** of set A is the set of all the elements in the universal set that are not in set A.

▶ Example 12

Given that $\varepsilon = \{x: x$ is an integer, $10 < x < 20\}$,
and $A = \{x: x$ is a multiple of $3\}$, find A' and $n(A')$.

▶ Solution . . .

$\varepsilon = \{11, 12, 13, 14, 15, 16, 17, 18, 19\}$
$A = \{12, 15, 18\}$
The elements in ε but not in set A are 11, 13, 14, 16, 17 and 19.
Thus $A' = \{11, 13, 14, 16, 17, 19\}$.
As there are six elements in set A', thus $n(A') = 6$.

From the above example we notice that $n(\varepsilon) = 9$, $n(A) = 3$ and $n(A') = 9 - 3 = 6$.

Thus $\boxed{n(A') = n(\varepsilon) - n(A)}$.

1.3.3   Intersection

Consider the following two sets A and B:

$A = \{1, 2, 3, 4, 5\}$

$B = \{2, 4, 6, 8\}$

Note that the elements 2 and 4 are found in both sets A and B. This set of numbers $\{2, 4\}$ is known as the **intersection** of sets A and B and is written as $A \cap B = \{2, 4\}$.

In a Venn diagram, the intersection of set A and B is represented by the overlapping of the two sets, as shown by the shaded region in Fig. 1.4.

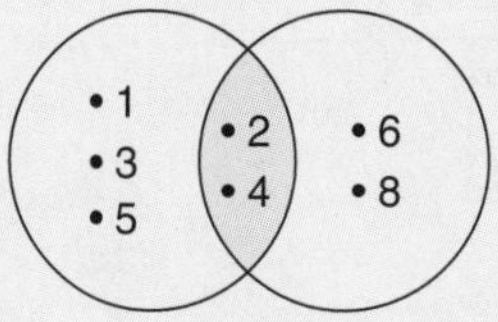

> The **intersection** of sets A and B, $A \cap B$, is the set containing all the elements that are common to both set A and set B.

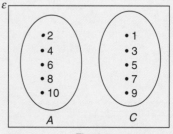

Fig. 1.4

▶ **Example 13**

Given $\varepsilon = \{1, 2, 3, 4, 5, 6, 7, 8, 9, 10\}$,

$A = \{2, 4, 6, 8, 10\}$,

$B = \{1, 2, 4, 8\}$,

$C = \{1, 3, 5, 7, 9\}$,

find

(a) $A \cap B$,   **(b)** $A \cap C$,   **(c)** $A' \cap B$,   **(d)** $n(A \cap B)'$.

▶ **Solution . . .**

(a) $A \cap B = \{2, 4, 6, 8, 10\} \cap \{1, 2, 4, 8\}$
$= \{2, 4, 8\}$

(b) $A \cap C = \{2, 4, 6, 8, 10\} \cap \{1, 3, 5, 7, 9\}$
$= \varnothing$

(c) $A' = \{1, 3, 5, 7, 9\}$
$A' \cap B = \{1, 3, 5, 7, 9\} \cap \{1, 2, 4, 8\}$
$= \{1\}$

(d) From (a), $A \cap B = \{2, 4, 8\}$.
Thus $(A \cap B)' = \{1, 3, 5, 6, 7, 9, 10\}$.
$\therefore n(A \cap B)' = 7$

In (b), $A \cap C = \varnothing$ means there are no elements common to both set A and set C. A and C are **disjoint sets**, i.e., there is no overlapping between sets A and C (Fig. 1.5).

Fig. 1.5

1.3.4   Union

Consider the following two sets P and Q:

$P = \{1, 2, 5, 10\}$

$Q = \{5, 10, 15\}$

Note that the elements 1, 2, 5, 10 and 15 are found in either set P or set Q. This set of numbers $\{1, 2, 5, 10, 15\}$ is known as the **union** of sets P and Q and is written as $P \cup Q$. Thus we can write $P \cup Q = \{1, 2, 5, 10, 15\}$.

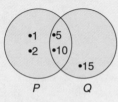

Fig. 1.6

In a Venn diagram, the union of sets P and Q is represented by the region occupied by **both** sets P and Q, as shown by the shaded region in Fig. 1.6.

> The **union** of sets P and Q, $P \cup Q$, is the set containing all the elements that are members of the sets P or Q or both.

▶ ## Example 14

Given that $\varepsilon = \{1, 2, 3, 4, 5, 6, 7, 8, 9, 10\}$,
$$P = \{1, 2, 3, 6\},$$
$$Q = \{3, 6, 9\},$$
$$R = \{1, 2, 3\},$$
find
(a) $P \cup Q$, **(b)** $P \cup R$, **(c)** $P' \cup Q$, **(d)** $(P \cup Q)'$.

▶ ## Solution . . .

(a) $P \cup Q = \{1, 2, 3, 6\} \cup \{3, 6, 9\}$
$$= \{1, 2, 3, 6, 9\}$$

(b) $P \cup R = \{1, 2, 3, 6\} \cup \{1, 2, 3\}$
$$= \{1, 2, 3, 6\}$$

(c) $P' = \{4, 5, 7, 8, 9, 10\}$
$$P' \cup Q = \{4, 5, 7, 8, 9, 10\} \cup \{3, 6, 9\}$$
$$= \{3, 4, 5, 6, 7, 8, 9, 10\}$$

(d) From (a), $P \cup Q = \{1, 2, 3, 6, 9\}$
$$(P \cup Q)' = \{4, 5, 7, 8, 10\}$$

In (b), $P \cup R = P$ which occurs when $R \subseteq P$.

▶ ## Example 15

Using the Venn diagram in Fig. 1.7, find
(a) $A \cap B$, **(b)** $A \cup B$,
(c) $A \cap B'$, **(d)** $(A \cap B)'$.

Fig. 1.7

▶ ## Solution . . .

(a)

$A \cap B = \{3, 4, 5\}$

(b)

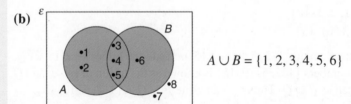

$A \cup B = \{1, 2, 3, 4, 5, 6\}$

(c)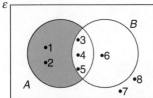

$A \cap B' = \{1, 2\}$

(d)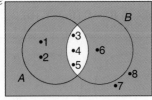

$(A \cap B)' = \{1, 2, 6, 7, 8\}$

▶ ## Example 16

Construct a Venn diagram to illustrate the following sets:

$\varepsilon = \{x: x$ is an integer, $1 \le x \le 10\}$
$A = \{x: x$ is a multiple of 3$\}$
$B = \{x: x$ is a factor of 6$\}$

▶ ## Solution . . .

$\varepsilon = \{1, 2, 3, 4, 5, 6, 7, 8, 9, 10\}$
$A = \{3, 6, 9\}$
$B = \{1, 2, 3, 6\}$

To construct the Venn diagram (Fig. 1.8), first find the intersection of two sets $A \cap B = \{3, 6\}$, then complete sets A and B. Finally determine $(A \cup B)' = \{4, 5, 7, 8, 10\}$.

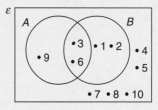

Fig. 1.8

1.3.5 Relationship between $n(A \cup B)$, $n(A)$, $n(B)$ and $n(A \cap B)$

▶ ## Example 17

Given that $A = \{a, b, c, d, e\}$,
$B = \{d, e, f, g, h, i\}$,
find
(a) $n(A \cup B)$, **(b)** $n(A \cap B)$.

Is $n(A \cup B) = n(A) + n(B)$? If not, what can you conclude, about the relationship between $n(A \cup B)$, $n(A)$, $n(B)$ and $n(A \cap B)$?

▶ ## Solution . . .

(a) $(A \cup B) = \{a, b, c, d, e\} \cup \{d, e, f, g, h, i\}$
$= \{a, b, c, d, e, f, g, h, i\}$
$\therefore n(A \cup B) = 9$

(b) $(A \cap B) = \{a, b, c, d, e\} \cap \{d, e, f, g, h, i\}$
$= \{d, e\}$
$\therefore n(A \cap B) = 2$

Since $n(A) = 5$ and $n(B) = 6$,

$n(A) + n(B) = 5 + 6 = 11$.

Hence $n(A \cup B) \neq n(A) + n(B)$.

Since $n(A) + n(B) - n(A \cap B) = 5 + 6 - 2 = 9$,

hence $n(A \cup B) = n(A) + n(B) - n(A \cap B)$.

Note that $n(A \cup B) \neq n(A) + n(B)$ when $n(A \cap B) \neq 0$ (Fig. 1.9).
However, $n(A \cup B) = n(A) + n(B)$ when $n(A \cap B) = 0$ (Fig. 1.10).

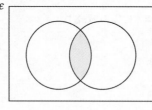

Fig. 1.9   Fig. 1.10

▶ **Example 18**

Set A contains 16 elements, set B contains 10 elements, and 8 elements are common to both sets A and B. How many elements are there in $A \cup B$?

▶ **Solution . . .**

Given $n(A) = 16$, $n(B) = 10$

$n(A \cap B) = 8$

$n(A \cup B) = n(A) + n(B) - n(A \cap B)$

$\qquad = 16 + 10 - 8 = 18$

There are 18 elements in $A \cup B$.

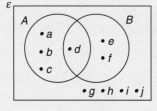

Fig. 1.11

1.3.6 *Relationship between $n(\varepsilon)$, $n(A \cup B)$ and $n(A \cup B)'$*

▶ **Example 19**

Given that $\varepsilon = \{a, b, c, d, e, f, g, h, i, j\}$,

$\qquad A = \{a, b, c, d\}$,

$\qquad B = \{d, e, f\}$,

find

(a) $n(\varepsilon)$,   **(b)** $n(A \cup B)$,   **(c)** $n(A \cup B)'$.

What can you conclude about the relationship between $n(\varepsilon)$, $n(A \cup B)$ and $n(A \cup B)'$ from the results obtained above?

▶ **Solution . . .**

(a) Since there are ten elements in ε, $n(\varepsilon) = 10$.

(b) $(A \cup B) = \{a, b, c, d\} \cup \{d, e, f\}$

$\qquad\qquad = \{a, b, c, d, e, f\}$

$\quad \therefore \ n(A \cup B) = 6$

(c) $(A \cup B)' = \{g, h, i, j\}$

$\qquad \therefore \ n(A \cup B)' = 4$

From the results on page 14, we notice that

$$n(A \cup B) + n(A \cup B)' = 6 + 4$$
$$= 10$$
$$= n(\varepsilon)$$

Hence we can conclude that $n(\varepsilon) = n(A \cup B) + n(A \cup B)'$.

▶ **Example 20**

Given $n(\varepsilon) = 30$, $n(A) = 22$, $n(B) = 17$ and $n(A \cup B)' = 3$, find $n(A \cap B)$.

▶ **Solution . . .**

As $n(\varepsilon) = n(A \cup B) + n(A \cup B)'$
         $30 = n(A \cup B) + 3$
   $n(A \cup B) = 27$

As $n(A \cup B) = n(A) + n(B) - n(A \cap B)$
         $27 = 22 + 17 - n(A \cap B)$
   $\therefore \ n(A \cap B) = 12$

▶ **Example 21**

Given $n(\varepsilon) = 40$, $n(A) = 26$ and $n(B) = 22$, find
(a) the least possible value of $n(A \cap B)$,
(b) the largest possible value of $n(A \cup B)'$.

▶ **Solution . . .**

(a) Since $n(A) + n(B) = 26 + 22 = 48$ and given $n(\varepsilon) = 40$,
   $n(A) + n(B) > n(\varepsilon)$.
   Hence $(A \cap B) \neq \varnothing$, that is, sets A and B overlap.
   The overlapping is minimum,
   i.e. $n(A \cup B) = n(\varepsilon)$
                  $= 40$
   As $n(A \cup B) = n(A) + n(B) - n(A \cap B)$
         $40 = 26 + 22 - n(A \cap B)$
   $\therefore \quad n(A \cap B) = 8$
   Hence the least possible value of $n(A \cap B)$ is 8 (Fig. 1.12).

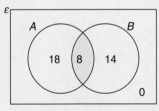

Fig. 1.12

(b) $n(A \cup B)'$ has the largest possible value when $n(A \cup B)$ is minimum
   which means $B \subseteq A$.
   Hence $n(A \cup B) = n(A)$
                  $= 26$
   As $n(\varepsilon) = n(A \cup B) + n(A \cup B)'$
         $40 = 26 + n(A \cup B)'$
   $\therefore \ n(A \cup B)' = 14$
   Hence the largest possible value of $n(A \cup B)'$ is 14 (Fig. 1.13).

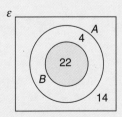

Fig. 1.13

▶ **Example 22**

Given $\varepsilon = \{a, b, c, d, e, f, g\}$,

$\quad A = \{a, c, e, g\}$,

$\quad B = \{a, b, c, f\}$,

$\quad C = \{c, d, e\}$,

find

(a) $(A \cup B) \cap C$, **(b)** $A \cup (B \cap C)$, **(c)** $(A \cup B) \cap (A \cup C)$.

▶ **Solution . . .**

(a) $\quad A \cup B = \{a, c, e, g\} \cup \{a, b, c, f\} = \{a, b, c, e, f, g\}$

$(A \cup B) \cap C = \{a, b, c, e, f, g\} \cap \{c, d, e\}$

$\qquad\qquad = \{c, e\}$

(b) $\quad B \cap C = \{a, b, c, f\} \cap \{c, d, e\} = \{c\}$

$A \cup (B \cap C) = \{a, c, e, g\} \cup \{c\}$

$\qquad\qquad = \{a, c, e, g\}$

(c) $A \cup B = \{a, c, e, g\} \cup \{a, b, c, f\} = \{a, b, c, e, f, g\}$

$A \cup C = \{a, c, e, g\} \cup \{c, d, e\} = \{a, c, d, e, g\}$

$(A \cup B) \cap (A \cup C) = \{a, b, c, e, f, g\} \cap \{a, c, d, e, g\}$

$\qquad\qquad\qquad = \{a, c, e, g\}$

From (a) and (b) above, we notice that

$$(A \cup B) \cap C \neq A \cup (B \cap C).$$

Exercise 1C (Answers on page 493)

1. Draw a Venn diagram to show the relationship between the given sets.

   (a) $\varepsilon = \{2, 4, 6, 8, 10\}$

   $\quad A = \{2, 4, 8\}$

   (b) $\varepsilon = \{x: x \text{ is an odd number, } 10 < x < 20\}$

   $\quad B = \{x: x \text{ is a prime number}\}$

   (c) $\varepsilon = \{x: x \text{ is a positive integer and } 20 \leq x \leq 30\}$

   $\quad C = \{x: \text{just one digit of } x \text{ is } 2\}$

   (d) $\varepsilon = \{\text{letters in the word } universal\}$

   $\quad D = \{\text{letters in the word } real\}$

2. **(a)** Given $\varepsilon = \{1, 2, 3, 4, 5, 6, 7, 8, 9, 10\}$ and $A\{2, 3, 5, 7\}$, find A' and $n(A')$.

   (b) Given $\varepsilon = \{\text{letters in the word } triangle\}$ and $B = \{\text{letters in the word } angel\}$, find B' and $n(B')$.

   (c) Given $\varepsilon = \{x: x \text{ is a positive integer}\}$ and $C = \{x: x \geq 5\}$, find C' and $n(C')$.

   (d) Give $\varepsilon = \{x: x \text{ is a natural number, } 30 \leq x \leq 40\}$ and $D = \{x: x \text{ is divisible by } 3\}$, find D' and $n(D')$.

3. **(a)** Given $\varepsilon = \{$letters of the English alphabet$\}$
   and $Q = \{$letters in the word *singapore*$\}$, find $n(Q')$.

   (b) Given $\varepsilon = \{x: x$ is an integer, $1 \leq x \leq 50\}$
   and $P = \{$multiples of 5$\}$, find $n(P')$.

   (c) Given $\varepsilon = \{x: x$ is an integer, $20 \leq x \leq 100\}$
   and $R = \{$perfect squares$\}$, find $n(R')$.

   (d) Given $\varepsilon = \{x: x$ is an integer, $1 < x \leq 20\}$
   and $S = \{x: x$ is a prime number$\}$, find $n(S')$.

4. Given $\varepsilon = \{1, 2, 3, 4, 5, 6, 7, 8, 9, 10\}$,
   $A = \{1, 2, 3, 6\}$,
   $B = \{2, 3, 5, 7\}$,
   $C = \{4, 8\}$,
   find
   (a) $A \cap B$,   **(b)** $B \cap C$,   **(c)** $A' \cap B$,   **(d)** $(A \cap B)'$.

5. Given that $\varepsilon = \{x: x$ is an integer, $2 \leq x \leq 10\}$,
   $A = \{x: x$ is a prime number$\}$,
   $B = \{x: x$ is a multiple of 3$\}$,
   $C = \{x: x$ is a factor of 10$\}$,
   find
   (a) $A \cap B$,   **(b)** $B \cap C$,   **(c)** $A \cap B'$,   **(d)** $A' \cap C'$.

6. Given $\varepsilon = \{x: x$ is a positive integer$\}$,
   $P = \{x: x < 10 \}$,
   $Q = \{x: x \geq 6\}$,
   list the elements of $P \cap Q$.

7. Given $\varepsilon = \{x: x$ is an integer and $30 \leq x \leq 100\}$,
   $P = \{x: x$ is divisible by 3$\}$,
   $Q = \{x: x$ is a perfect square$\}$,
   $R = \{x:$ units digit of x is 7$\}$.
   find
   (a) $n(P \cap Q)$,   **(b)** $n(P \cap R)$,   **(c)** $n(Q \cap R)$.

8. Given $\varepsilon = \{1, 2, 3, 4, 5, 6, 7, 8, 9, 10\}$,
   $P = \{2, 3, 5, 7\}$,
   $Q = \{1, 2, 4, 8\}$,
   $R = \{4, 8\}$,
   find
   (a) $P \cup Q$,   **(b)** $Q \cup R$,   **(c)** $P' \cup R$,   **(d)** $(P \cup Q)'$.

9. Given $\varepsilon = \{x: x$ is an integer, $1 < x \leq 6\}$,
   $A = \{x: x$ is a perfect square$\}$,
   $B = \{x: x$ is a multiple of 3$\}$,
   $C = \{x: x$ is a prime number$\}$,
   find
   (a) $A \cup B$,   **(b)** $B \cup C$,   **(c)** $A \cup C'$,   **(d)** $B' \cup C'$.

10. Given $\varepsilon = \{2, 3, 4, 5, 6, 7, 8, 9, 10\}$,
$\qquad P = \{x: x \text{ is a factor of } 12\}$,
$\qquad Q = \{x: x \text{ is an odd integer}\}$,
find
(a) $n(P \cup Q)$, **(b)** $n(P' \cup Q)$, **(c)** $n(P \cup Q')$.

11. Given $\varepsilon = \{x: x \text{ is an integer, } 1 < x < 10\}$,
$\qquad A = \{x: x - 1 \geq 3\}$,
$\qquad B = \{x: 8 < 4x < 30\}$,
$\qquad C = \{x: x \text{ is divisible by } 3\}$,
find
(a) $A \cap B$, **(b)** $B \cup C$, **(c)** $A \cap C'$, **(d)** $A' \cup B'$.

12. Copy the Venn diagram in Fig. 1.14 and on each of your copies, shade the region represented by
(a) $A \cap B$, **(b)** $A \cup B$, **(c)** $A' \cap B$,
(d) $A \cup B'$, **(e)** $(A \cup B)'$, **(f)** $(A \cap B)'$.

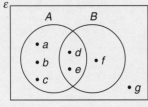

Fig. 1.14

13. Using the Venn diagram in Fig. 1.15, find the following:
(a) A **(b)** B **(c)** $A \cap B$ **(d)** $A \cup B$
(e) A' **(f)** B' **(g)** $A' \cup B$ **(h)** $A \cap B'$
(i) $(A \cap B)'$ **(j)** $(A \cup B)'$

Fig. 1.15

14. Write, in set notation, the set represented by the shaded region.
(a) **(b)**

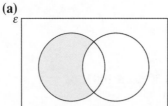 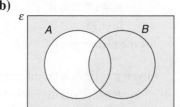

15. Construct Venn diagrams to illustrate the following sets:
(a) $\varepsilon = \{x: x \text{ is an integer, } 3 \leq x \leq 12\}$
$\qquad A = \{x: 5 \leq x \leq 8\}$
$\qquad B = \{x: x \text{ is a prime number}\}$

(b) $\varepsilon = \{x: x \text{ is a natural number, } 1 \leq x \leq 10\}$
$\qquad P = \{x: x \text{ is a multiple of } 10\}$
$\qquad Q = \{x: 2x - 1 < 10\}$

16. Set A contains 12 elements, set B contains 8 elements, and 6 elements are common to both sets A and B. How many elements are there in $A \cup B$?

17. If $n(A \cup B) = 40$, $n(A \cap B) = 12$ and $n(A) = 30$, find $n(B)$.

18. Given that $n(\varepsilon) = 30$, $n(A) = 18$, $n(B) = 12$ and $n(A \cap B) = 5$,
(a) contruct a Venn diagram to illustrate this given information,
(b) find $n(A' \cup B)$.

19. Given that $n(\varepsilon) = 35$, $n(A) = 20$, $n(B) = 22$ and $n(A \cup B)' = 5$, find $n(A \cup B)$.

   (b) Given $n(A) = 28$, $n(B) = 18$, $n(A \cap B) = 6$ and $n(A \cup B)' = 10$, find $n(\varepsilon)$.

   (c) Given $n(\varepsilon) = 38$, $n(A) = 20$, $n(B) = 15$ and $n(A \cap B) = 5$, find $n(A \cup B)'$.

   (d) Given $n(\varepsilon) = 32$, $n(B) = 14$, $n(A \cap B) = 2$ and $n(A \cup B)' = 10$, find $n(A)$.

20. In each of the following cases, find
   (i) the least possible value of $n(A \cap B)$ and of $n(A \cup B)'$,
   (ii) the largest possible value of $n(A \cap B)$ and of $n(A \cup B)'$.
   (a) $n(\varepsilon) = 40$, $n(A) = 18$ and $n(B) = 26$
   (b) $n(\varepsilon) = 50$, $n(A) = 34$ and $n(B) = 22$
   (c) $n(\varepsilon) = 30$, $n(A) = 12$ and $n(B) = 15$
   (d) $n(\varepsilon) = 60$, $n(A) = 30$ and $n(B) = 18$

21. In the Venn diagram in Fig. 1.16, ε is the set of all children in a certain chosen group, $A = \{$children in Youth Club $A\}$ and $B = \{$children in Youth Club $B\}$.

   The letters p, q, x and y in the diagram represent the number of children in each subset. Given that $n(\varepsilon) = 200$, $n(A) = 75$ and $n(B) = 35$,
   (a) express p in terms of x,
   (b) find the smallest possible value of y,
   (c) find the largest possible value of x,
   (d) find the value of q if $p = 45$. (C)

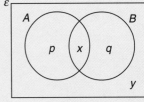

Fig. 1.16

22. Given $\varepsilon = \{p, q, r, s, t, u, v\}$,
   $A = \{p, q, r, s\}$,
   $B = \{r, t, u, v\}$,
   $C = \{r, s, u, v\}$,
   (a) find $n(A \cap C)$,
   (b) list the elements of
       (i) $(B \cup C)'$,   **(ii)** $(A \cup C) \cap B$. (C)

23. Given $\varepsilon = \{a, b, c, d, e, f\}$,
   $A = \{a, c, d, f\}$,
   $B = \{b, c, e\}$,
   $C = \{a, d, g\}$,
   find
   (a) $(A \cup B) \cap C$,   **(b)** $A \cup (B \cap C)$,   **(c)** $(A \cup B) \cap \{A \cup C\}$.

1.4 Venn Diagrams with Three Sets

Venn diagrams can be used to illustrate three or more sets.

▶ **Example 23**

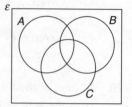

Copy the given Venn diagram and on each of
your copies, shade the region represented by
(a) $A \cup (B \cap C)$, **(b)** $A \cap (B \cup C)'$.

▶ **Solution . . .**

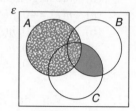

(a) First, shade $B \cap C$, then shade A. Both
shaded regions represent $A \cup (B \cap C)$.

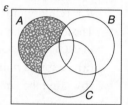

(b) First shade $(B \cup C)'$, then shade A. The
overlapping between A and $(B \cup C)'$
represents $A \cap (B \cup C)'$.

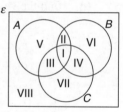

When constructing a Venn diagram with three
sets, we generally start with region I, then
regions II, III and IV, followed by regions V,
VI and VII, and finally proceed to determine
region VIII.

▶ **Example 24**

Construct a Venn diagram illustrating the following sets:
$\varepsilon = \{x : x \text{ is a natural number}, x \leq 12\}$
$A = \{x : x \leq 6\}$
$B = \{x : 4 < x \leq 10\}$
$C = \{x : x \text{ is a multiple of } 3\}$

▶ **Solution . . .**

$\varepsilon = \{1, 2, 3, 4, 5, 6, 7, 8, 9, 10, 11, 12\}$
$A = \{1, 2, 3, 4, 5, 6,\}$
$B = \{5, 6, 7, 8, 9, 10\}$
$C = \{3, 6, 9, 12\}$
Step 1: Find the intersection of three sets.
$$A \cap B \cap C = \{6\}$$

Step 2: Find the intersection of two sets.

$$A \cap B = \{5, 6\}$$
$$A \cap C = \{3, 6\}$$
$$B \cap C = \{6, 9\}$$

Step 3: Complete sets A, B and C.

Step 4: Determine $(A \cup B \cup C)' = \{11\}$.

The Venn diagram is shown in Fig. 1.17.

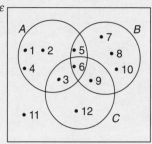

Fig. 1.17

▶ **Example 25**

A, B and C are three sets and $\varepsilon = A \cup B \cup C$. The number of elements in each subset is shown in the Venn diagram in Fig. 1.18.

(a) Find $n(C)$.

(b) If $n(A) = 41$, find x.

(c) Find $n(A' \cap B \cap C)$.

(C)

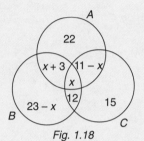

Fig. 1.18

▶ **Solution . . .**

(a) $n(C) = 15 + 12 + x + (11 - x)$
$\quad = 38$

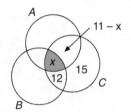

(b) $n(A) = 22 + (x + 3) + x + (11 - x)$
$\quad = 36 + x$

Given $n(A) = 41$
$\quad 36 + x = 41$
$\quad\quad\quad x = 5$

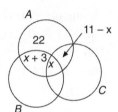

(c) $n(A' \cap B \cap C) = 12$

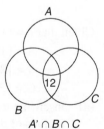

$A' \cap B \cap C$

Exercise 1D (Answers on page 493)

1. Copy the Venn diagram in Fig. 1.19 and on each of your copies, shade the region represented by the following:

   (a) $A \cap B \cap C$ **(b)** $A \cup B \cup C$ **(c)** $(A \cap B) \cup C$

   (d) $(A \cup B) \cap C$ **(e)** $B \cup (A \cap C)$ **(f)** $A \cap (B \cup C)$

   (g) $(A \cup B) \cap C'$ **(h)** $(B \cap C) \cap A'$ **(i)** $A \cap (B \cup C)'$

   (j) $(A \cap C) \cup (B \cap C)$ **(k)** $(A \cup C) \cap (B \cup C)$

Fig. 1.19

2. Three sets A, B and C are represented by the given Venn diagram. Copy the diagram and shade **(a)** the regions representing the set $(A \cap B) \cup C$, and **(b)** the region representing the set $A \cap (B \cup C)$.

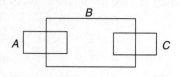

3. Write, in set notation, the set represented by the shaded region in each of the following Venn diagrams:

(a)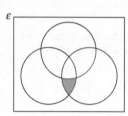

(b)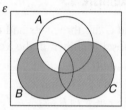

(c)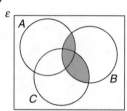

(d)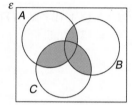

4. Using the Venn diagram in Fig. 1.20, find the following:

(a) $(A \cap B) \cup C$ **(b)** $(B \cup C) \cap A$

(c) $B \cap (A \cup C)$ **(d)** $A' \cap (B \cup C)$

(e) $B \cup (A' \cap C)$ **(f)** $B \cap (A \cup C)'$

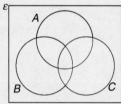

Fig. 1.20

5. Given that $\varepsilon = \{1, 2, 3, 4, 5, 6, 7, 8,\}$,

$\qquad A = \{1, 4, 5, 6\}$,

$\qquad B = \{2, 4, 5, 7\}$,

$\qquad C = \{3, 4, 6, 7\}$,

(a) insert the numbers 1, 2, 3, 4, 5, 6, 7 and 8 in the appropriate regions of the Venn diagram shown in Fig. 1.21,

(b) find the value of $n(A \cap B)'$,

(c) list the elements of $(A \cup B) \cap C$.

Fig. 1.21

6. Construct a Venn diagram illustrating the following sets:

(a) $\varepsilon = \{a, b, c, d, e, f, g, h, i, j, k, l, m, n\}$

$\qquad A = \{a, c, d, e, f, h\}$

$\qquad B = \{b, c, e, f, i, j, m, n\}$

$\qquad C = \{c, g, h, i, j\}$

(b) $\varepsilon = \{x: x$ is a natural number, $2 < x \le 12\}$
   $P = \{x: x$ is an even number$\}$
   $Q = \{x: x$ is a multiple of $3\}$
   $R = \{x: x$ is a prime number$\}$

7. $\varepsilon = \{x: x$ is an integer, $1 \le x \le 100\},$
   $A = \{x: x$ is divisible by $13\},$
   $B = \{x: x$ is divisible by $26\},$
   $C = \{x: x$ is divisible by $39\}.$
   (a)   State the value of $n(A)$.
   (b)   Add the sets B and C to the
       Venn diagram given.   (C)

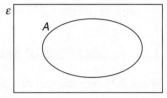

8.   **(a)** $P = \{$Parallelograms$\}, R = \{$Rectangles$\}$ and $H = \{$Rhombuses$\}$.
       Draw a Venn diagram to show the relation between the sets P, R
       and H.
   (b)   The universal set $\varepsilon = \{x: x$ is an integer and $x \ge 2\}$.
       $A = \{$prime numbers$\}, B = \{$perfect squares$\}$ and
       $C = \{$integers with final digit $7\}$.
       Illustrate these three sets on a Venn diagram.   (C)

9. A, B and C are three sets and $\varepsilon = A \cup B \cup C$.
   The number of elements in some of the subsets are shown in the
   Venn diagram in Fig. 1.22 and $n(\varepsilon) = 50$.
   Find
   (a) $n(A \cup B)$,   **(b)** $n(C)$,   **(c)** $n(A \cap B')$.

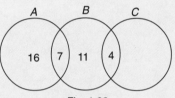

Fig. 1.22

10. A, B and C are three sets and $\varepsilon = A \cup B \cup C$.
   The number of elements in each subset is shown in the Venn diagram
   in Fig. 1.23.
   (a)   Find $n(A)$.
   (b)   If $n(B) = 32$, find x.
   (c)   Find $n[(A \cap B) \cup C]$.

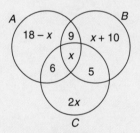

Fig. 1.23

11. A, B and C are three sets and the
   numbers of elements are shown in
   the Venn diagram.
   Given that $\varepsilon = A \cup B \cup C$ and that
   $n(\varepsilon) = 34$, find
   (a)   the value of x,
   (b) $n(A \cap B \cap C')$.

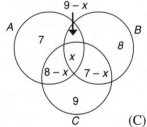

   (C)

12. P, Q and R are sets such that $\varepsilon = P \cup Q \cup R$.
   The number of elements in each subset is shown in the Venn diagram
   in Fig. 1.24.
   (a)   Find x, given that $n(P) = n(Q)$.
   (b)   Find y, given that $n((P \cup Q)') = n(P \cap Q)$.
   (c)   Find $n(\varepsilon)$.   (C)

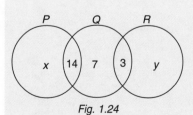

Fig. 1.24

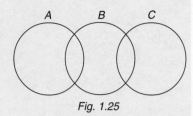

Fig. 1.25

13. A, B and C are three sets and $\varepsilon = A \cup B \cup C$. It is given that $n(\varepsilon) = 80$, $n(A \cap B) = 8$, $n(B \cap C) = 6$, $n(A) = 32$ and $n(B) = 26$.

   (a) On the Venn diagram in Fig. 1.25, write the number of elements in each subset.

   (b) Find the value of $n(B')$.

   (c) Find the value of $n[A \cup (B \cap C)]$.

1.5 Applications of Sets

When solving practical problems involving sets, we should look for key words or phrases like '*only* set A', 'set A *or* set B', 'set A *and* set B', 'set A and set B and *not* set C'. The word '*or*' is generally interpreted to mean **union**, the word '*and*' is generally interpreted to mean **intersection**, and the word '*not*' means **complement**. The problems to be solved can be represented in the form of Venn diagrams.

▶ **Example 26**

Problem Solving

There are 40 boys in a class. Of these, 24 play football, 18 play basketball and 6 play neither football nor basketball.

How many boys play both football and basketball?

▶ **Solution . . .**

Let $\varepsilon = \{$boys in a class$\}$, $n(\varepsilon) = 40$.

Let $F = \{$boys who play football$\}$, $n(F) = 24$.

Let $B = \{$boys who play basketball$\}$, $n(B) = 18$.

Given that 6 boys play neither football nor basketball, thus $n(F \cup B)' = 6$.

Let the number of boys who play both football and basketball be x.

A diagram is then constructed as follows:

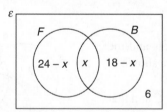

$$n(\varepsilon) = (24 - x) + x + (18 - x) + 6$$
$$40 = 48 - x$$
$$x = 8$$

∴ There are 8 boys who play both football and basketball.

▶ **Example 27**

Problem Solving

There are 120 students in secondary three express level.

Of these, 57 students study Physics,

58 students study Chemistry,

69 students study Biology,

32 students study both Physics and Chemistry,

38 students study both Chemistry and Biology,

35 students study both Physics and Biology,

20 students study all three subjects.

How many students

(a) study Biology only,

(b) study exactly two subjects,

(c) study at least one of the subjects,

(d) do not study any of the subjects?

▶ **Solution . . .**

Let ε = {students in secondary three express level},

P = {students who study Physics},

C = {students who study Chemistry},

B = {students who study Biology}.

The above information can be illustrated with a Venn diagram as shown in Fig. 1.26.

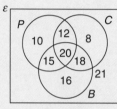

Fig. 1.26

(a) There are 16 students who study Biology only.

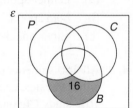

(b) The number of students who study exactly two subjects is $12 + 15 + 18 = 45$.

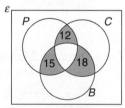

(c) The number of students who study at least one of the subjects is
$10 + 12 + 8 + 15 + 20 + 18 + 16 = 99$.

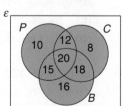

(d) The number of students who do not study any of the subjects is 21.

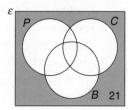

Exercise 1E (Answers on page 493)

1. There are 40 students in a class. 32 study Mathematics, 17 study Science and 5 study neither Mathematics nor Science.
    By drawing a Venn diagram, or otherwise, find the number of students who study both Mathematics and Science.

2. In a survey carried out for a television company, the viewing choices of 200 families on a particular evening were recorded.

    144 families said they had watched programme A,

    92 families said they had watched programme B,

    26 families said they had not watched either programme.

    By drawing a Venn diagram, or otherwise, find
    (a) the number of families who had watched both programmes,
    (b) the number of families who had watched programme B only.

3. There are 42 members in a sports club.
    Of these, 25 members play cricket,

    22 members play tennis,

    two times as many members play both cricket and tennis compared to members who play neither.

    Find how many play
    (a) neither sport,
    (b) both sports,
    (c) either one of the two sports but not both.

4. All 150 students in secondary three express level of a school study either Physics, Chemistry or both. Given that 40% study Physics and 70% study Chemistry, how many students study
    (a) both Physics and Chemistry,
    (b) Chemistry only?

5. There are 24 children on a school outing. At lunch time, 11 of them ate a sandwich, 9 of them ate a banana, n of them ate neither a sandwich nor a banana.
    By drawing Venn diagrams, or otherwise, find
    (a) the smallest possible value of n,
    (b) the largest possible value of n.   (C)

6. In a school, 120 boys play cricket.
    ε is the set of all boys who play cricket,
    X is the set of batsmen,
    Y is the set of bowlers.
    The letters a, b and c in the Venn diagram represent the number of boys in each subset of X and Y.

    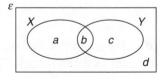

    The letter d represents the number of boys who are neither batsmen nor bowlers. Given that $n(\varepsilon) = 120$, $n(X) = 80$ and $n(Y) = 48$, find

(a) the value of *b* if *d* = 0,
(b) the value of *d* if *b* = *c*,
(c) the largest possible number of boys who are neither batsmen nor bowlers.   (C)

7. A travel agent interviewed 180 people to determine whether they preferred travelling long distances by airplane, train or bus, and learnt that

     122 preferred to travel by airplane,

     68 preferred to travel by train,

     47 preferred to travel by bus,

     35 preferred to travel by both airplane and train,

     32 preferred to travel by both airplane and bus,

     25 preferred to travel by both train and bus,

     20 preferred to travel by all three means of transport.

Of these interviewed, how many preferred to travel by

(a) airplane only,
(b) both airplane and bus but not by train,
(c) at least one means of transport,
(d) none of the means of transport?

8. 300 people staying at a resort hotel can go sailing, swimming and play golf.

     16 people take part in all three activities,

     36 people go sailing and swim,

     45 people swim and play golf but do not go sailing,

     18 people play golf and go sailing but do not swim,

     65 people go sailing only,

     22 people do not take part in any of these activities.

If the number of people who play golf only is 8 less than those who swim only, find the number of people who

(a) swim only,
(b) do not swim.

9. Each of the 56 pupils in the fourth year of a small school studies one of the subjects History, English and Agriculture.

Of the 14 pupils who study Agriculture,

     4 also study History and English,

     3 study neither History nor English and

     5 study English but not History.

Of the 42 pupils who do not study Agriculture,

     6 study both History and English,

     x study only History and

     2*x* study only English.

Copy the Venn Diagram in Fig. 1.27 and on your copy, show the number of pupils in each subset.

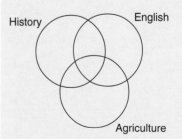

Fig. 1.27

Hence find

(a) the value of x,

(b) the total number of pupils studying English,

(c) the total number of pupils who do not study History.   (C)

10. A number of travellers were questioned about the transport they used on a particular day. Each of them used one or more of the methods shown in the Venn diagram in Fig. 1.28.

Of those questioned, 6 said that they travelled by bus and train only, 2 by train and car only, and 7 by bus, train and car.

The number x who travelled by bus only was equal to the number who travelled by bus and car only.

(a) Given that 35 people used buses and 25 people used trains, find

    (i) the value of x,

    (ii) the number who travelled by train only,

    (iii) the number who travelled by at least two methods of transport.

(b) Given also that 85 people were questioned altogether, calculate the number who travelled by car only.   (C)

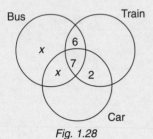

Fig. 1.28

Summary

1. A **set** is a collection of objects.
   These objects are called **elements** of the set.

2. **Set Notations**:

Symbol	Meaning
$\in$	'is an element of'
$\notin$	'is not an element of'
$n(A)$	the number of elements in set A
$\varnothing$	the empty set
$A = B$	A and B are equal sets
$A \neq B$	A and B are not equal sets
ε	universal set
$A \subseteq B$	A is a subset of B
$A \nsubseteq B$	A is not a subset of B
$A \subset B$	A is a proper subset of B
$A \not\subset B$	A is not a proper subset of B
A'	complement of set A
$A \cup B$	union of sets A and B
$A \cap B$	intersection of sets A and B

3. The number of subsets in a set with n elements is 2^n.

4. Venn diagrams

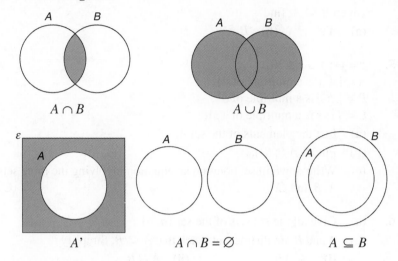

$A \cap B$

$A \cup B$

A'

$A \cap B = \varnothing$

$A \subseteq B$

5. $n(A \cup B) = n(A) + n(B) - n(A \cap B)$

6. $n(\varepsilon) = n(A \cup B) + n(A \cup B)'$

Revision Exercise 1 (*Answers on page 494*)

1. $\varepsilon = \{p, q, r, s, t, u, v, w\}$,
$A = \{r, t, v, w\}$,
$B = \{q, r, s, u, v\}$,
$C = \{q, s, u\}$.
Find
   (a) $n(A \cap B)$,   **(b)** $n(B \cup C)$,   **(c)** $(A \cup B)'$,
   (d) $A \cap B'$,   **(e)** $A \cap (B \cap C')$.

2. $\varepsilon = \{a, b, c, d, e, f\}$. The sets A, B and C each contains 1, 4 and 2 elements respectively, and $A \cup B \cup C = \varepsilon$.
Given that $A \cap B = \{a\}$, $C \cap (A \cup B) = \varnothing$ and $(A \cup B)' = \{e, f\}$, find A, B and C.

3. $\varepsilon = \{x: x \text{ is an integer}, 10 \leq x \leq 100\}$,
$A = \{x: x + 7 < 57 < x + 41\}$,
$B = \{x: \sqrt{x} \text{ is a positive integer}\}$,
$C = \{x: x \text{ is a multiple of } 12\}$.
   (a) Find **(i)** $n(A)$,   **(ii)** $n(B')$,   **(iii)** $n(A \cup C)$.
   (b) List the elements of
         (i) $A \cap B$,   **(ii)** $A' \cap C$,   **(iii)** $B \cap (A \cup C)'$.
   (c) List the elements of x such that $x \in B \cup C$ and $x \notin A$.

4. $\varepsilon = \{x: x$ is an integer, $5 < x < 20\}$,
   $A = \{x: 8 \le x < 18\}$,
   $B = \{x: x$ is a prime number$\}$.
   Given $B \subset A$, find
   (a) A',   (b) B.

5. $\varepsilon = \{x: 1 \le x \le 30\}$,
   $A = \{x: x$ is a multiple of $4\}$,
   $B = \{x: x$ is a multiple of $3\}$,
   $C = \{x: x$ is a multiple of $12\}$.
   (a) List the elements of the set A.
   (b) Find $n(A \cap B')$.
   (c) Write down in set notation an equation involving the three sets A, B and C.   (C)

6. (a) Give all the subsets of the set $\{a, b\}$.
   (b) A and B are distinct sets such that $A \subset B$. Simplify
       (i) $A \cap B$,   (ii) $A \cup B$.

7. (a) If $R = \{$rhombuses$\}$ and $P = \{$parallelograms$\}$, simplify $R \cap P$.
   (b) The sets C and D are such that $n(C \cup D) = 44$, $n(C \cap D) = 11$ and $n(C) = 31$.
       Find the value of $n(D)$.   (C)

8. Given that $n(\varepsilon) = 100$, $n(A) = 75$ and $n(B) = 65$.
   Find
   (a) the smallest value of $n(A \cap B)$,
   (b) the largest value of $n(A \cup B)'$.

9. (a) In the Venn diagram (i), shade $A \cap B'$.
   (b) In the Venn diagram (ii), shade $P \cup (Q \cap R')$.
   (c) Express in set notation, as simply as possible, the subset shaded in the Venn diagram (iii).

(i)   (ii)

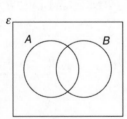 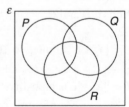

(iii)

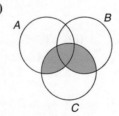

10. (a) The Venn diagram in Fig. 1.29 represents three sets A, B and C. Express, in set notation, three *different* conditions which would lead to this diagram.

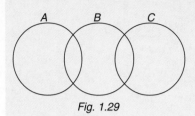

Fig. 1.29

(b) Copy the Venn diagram in Fig. 1.30 and add to your diagram a set N such that $N \subset L$, and $N \cap M = \varnothing$.

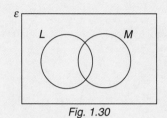

Fig. 1.30

(c) The three sets, P, Q and R are such that $P \cap Q \neq \varnothing$, $P \cup R = \varnothing$ and $R \subset Q$. Draw a Venn diagram to illustrate the three sets P, Q and R.

11. In the Venn diagram in Fig. 1.31,
ε represents the set of all triangles,
I represents the set of isosceles triangles, and
R represents the set of right-angled triangles.

(a) Add the set E to the Venn diagram where E represents the set of equilateral triangles.

(b) A triangle has sides 3 m, 4 m and 5 m. On the diagram, mark and label a point T to represent this triangle. **(C)**

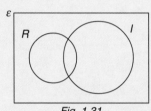
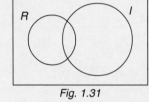

Fig. 1.31

12. In Fig. 1.32, A, B, C are three sets and $\varepsilon = A \cup B \cup C$. The number of elements in some of the subsets are shown. Given that $n(\varepsilon) = 40$, find

(a) $n(B)$,   **(b)** $n(A \cup C)$,

(c) $n[A \cap (B \cup C)]$,   **(d)** $n(A' \cap C')$.

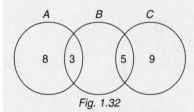

Fig. 1.32

13. A, B and C are three sets and the numbers of elements are as shown in the Venn diagram in Fig. 1.33.
The universal set $\varepsilon = A \cup B \cup C$.

(a) State the value of $n((B \cup C)')$.

(b) If $x \in (A \cup B) \cap C$, find the probability that $x \in A$.

(c) If $n(C) = n(A)$, find the two possible values of k. **(C)**

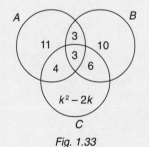

Fig. 1.33

14. There are 38 students in a class. Of these, 25 study History and 27 study Geography.

(a) Find the smallest possible number of students who study both History and Geography.

(b) Express in set notation {students who neither study History nor Geography}.

15. 250 people were interviewed to find out whether they spoke French, Spanish, French and Spanish, or neither French nor Spanish. It was found that 80 people spoke French and 220 people spoke Spanish. Find

    (a) the largest possible number of people who spoke French only,

    (b) the largest possible number of people who spoke both French and Spanish,

    (c) the largest possible number of people who spoke neither French nor Spanish.

16. Each of a group of 20 students studies at least one of the three subjects Chemistry, Physics and Biology.

    All those who study Physics also study Chemistry,

    3 students study all three subjects,

    4 students study only Chemistry,

    8 students study Physics,

    14 students study Chemistry.

    (a) Draw a Venn diagram to illustrate this information.

    (b) How many students study only Biology?

    (c) How many students study Chemistry and Biology but not Physics?   (C)

17. At an international college, students have to be proficient in at least one of the languages English, French or German.

    In a particular group of 33 students, 2 are proficient in all three languages, 3 in English and French only, 4 in French and German only and 5 in German and English only. The number proficient in English only is x, in French only is x, and in German only is $(x + 1)$. Illustrate this information by a Venn diagram, showing the number in each separate region.

    Find x and hence find the total number proficient in English.   (C)

18. In a school, some of the subjects that students can take are Mathematics, Additional Mathematics and Physics. The Venn diagram in Fig. 1.34 shows the combinations of these subjects that are possible, and the numbers and letters represent the number of students in each subset.

    (a) Given that the number of students taking Physics is 123, calculate the value of x.

    (b) Given that one sixth of those taking Mathematics also take Additional Mathematics, calculate the value of y and hence find the total number of students taking Mathematics.   (C)

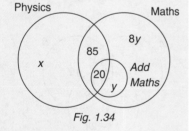

Fig. 1.34

Maths Booster

In set theory, De Morgan's Laws are symbolised as

1. $(A \cup B)' = A' \cap B'$,   2. $(A \cap B)' = A' \cup B'$.

The laws were expressed verbally by William of Ockham in the fourteenth century. In the nineteenth century, Augustus De Morgan expressed them mathematically. Can you verify the laws?

Chapter 2

Functions

In everyday life, we see a variety of situations where one quantity is linked to another:

- The distance travelled by a car is linked to its speed.
- The number of schools needed is linked to the size of the population.
- The cost of a bus ticket is linked to the distance travelled.

In these situations, the linking is based on a specific rule called a **function**.

2.1.1 Relations and Functions

A **relation** links the members of two sets together. Relations can be of many kinds, for example, 'is the father of', 'is the square of', 'is the square root of', 'is divisible by', etc.

Let us consider a set of men, {Mr Li, Mr Amin} and a set of children {Li Beng, Johari, Ramli}. The relation 'is the father of' linking the set of men to the set of children can be illustrated by an arrow diagram as shown in Fig. 2.1.

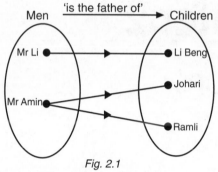

Fig. 2.1

In the diagram, an arrow identifies the relation between a father and child. It shows that Mr Li is the father of Li Beng and Mr Amin is the father of Johari and Ramli. Therefore, one arrow leaves from Mr Li and two arrows from Mr Amin.

Fig. 2.2 shows an arrow diagram of the relation 'is the square root of' linking set A {1, 2, 3, 4} and set B {1, 4, 9, 16}.

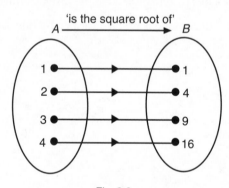

Fig. 2.2

Note that only **one** arrow leaves **each** element in set A, i.e. **every** element in set A is linked to only **one** element in set B. This is an example of a special type of relation called a **function**.

The relation in Fig. 2.1 is **not** a function since the element in the set of men 'Mr Amin' is linked to the elements, 'Johari' and 'Ramli' in the set of children.

A function is also called a **mapping**. In Fig. 2.2, we say that set A is mapped onto set B by the relation 'is the square root of'.

▶ **Example 1**

Analysis and Classification

Which of the relations illustrated by the arrow diagrams below is a function? Give reasons for your answer.

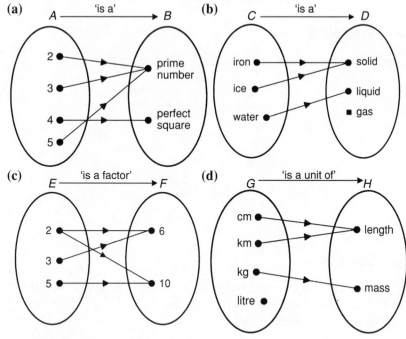

(a) A 'is a' B

(b) C 'is a' D

(c) E 'is a factor' F

(d) G 'is a unit of' H

▶ **Solution . . .**

(a) This relation is a function because every member in set A is linked to only one member in set B.

(b) This relation is a function because every member in set C is linked to only one member in set D even though the member 'gas' in set D is not linked to any member in set C.

(c) This relation is **not** a function because the member '2' in set E is linked to **two** members '6' and '10' in set F.

(d) This relation is not a function because not every member in set G is linked to set H, i.e. the member 'litre' in set G, is not linked to any member in set H.

2.1.2 Domain and Range

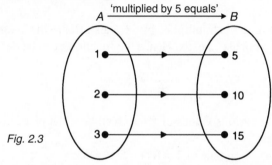

A 'multiplied by 5 equals' B

Fig. 2.3

Fig. 2.3 illustrates the relation 'multiplied by 5 equals' linking set A to set B. This relation is a function.

In this function, the members 1, 2 and 3 are called the **objects**. The set of objects {1, 2, 3}, i.e. set *A*, is called the **domain**. The objects 1, 2 and 3 in set *A* are linked to the members 5, 10 and 15 in set *B* respectively. These members 5, 10 and 15 in set *B* are called the **images**, i.e. 5 is the image of 1, 10 is the image of 2, and 15 is the image of 3. The set of images {5, 10, 15}, i.e. set *B*, is called the **range**.

▶ **Example 2**

State the domain, images and range of the following function:

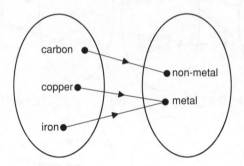

▶ **Solution . . .**

The domain is {carbon, copper, iron}. 'Non-metal' is the image of 'carbon', and 'metal' is the image of 'copper' and 'iron'.
The range is {non-metal, metal}.

2.1.3   *Function Notation*

A function is usually denoted by a lower case letter such as f, g and h. The function f in Fig. 2.2 can be written as

$$f : A \longmapsto B.$$

We read this as 'a function f maps set *A* onto *B*'.

If *x* is an object in set *A*, then the image of *x* can be written as f(*x*). Hence the function f can also be written as

$$f : x \longmapsto f(x).$$

f(*x*) is read as 'f of *x*'.

Function f in Fig. 2.3 is 'multiplied by 5 equals'. Hence the image of *x* is '*x* multiplied by 5 equals', i.e. 5*x*. Hence the function f can be defined as

$$f : x \longmapsto 5x$$
$$\text{or} \quad f(x) = 5x.$$

By substituting various values of *x* into f(*x*) = 5*x*, the respective images can be obtained.

$$\text{image of } 1 = f(1) = 5(1) = 5$$
$$\text{image of } 2 = f(2) = 5(2) = 10$$
$$\text{image of } 3 = f(3) = 5(3) = 15$$

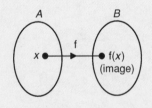

Leonhard Euler (1707 – 1783) was the first person to use f(*x*).

Summarising,
- a function f maps **every** object in the domain onto only **one** image in the range.
- $f : x \longmapsto f(x)$
- a function may be defined algebraically.

  Eg. $f : x \longmapsto 2x^2 - 3$. It may be stated in words such as the function 'Y is the father of X' or given in the form of a table such as a table of square roots.

▶ **Example 3**

A function f is defined by $f : x \longmapsto x^2 - 2x - 3$. Find the images of 3 and –2.

▶ **Solution . . .**

Given $f : x \longmapsto x^2 - 2x - 3$

i.e. $\quad f(x) = x^2 - 2x - 3$

image of 3 $= f(3)$

$\qquad = 3^2 - 2(3) - 3$

$\qquad = 0$

image of –2 $= f(-2)$

$\qquad = (-2)^2 - 2(-2) - 3$

$\qquad = 5$

▶ **Example 4**

A function f is defined by $f : x \longmapsto x^2 + x - 1$.

(a) Find the values of x which have an image of 5.

(b) Find the values of x which map onto themselves.

▶ **Solution . . .**

(a) Given $f(x) = x^2 + x - 1$

and image = 5,

i.e. $\quad f(x) = 5$.

Hence $\quad x^2 + x - 1 = 5$

$\qquad x^2 + x - 6 = 0$

$\qquad (x + 3)(x - 2) = 0$

$\qquad\qquad x = -3 \text{ or } x = 2$

Hence the values of x that have an image 5 are –3 and 2.

(b) Let a be the object that maps onto itself.

Hence $\quad f(a) = a$

$\qquad a^2 + a - 1 = a$

$\qquad\quad a^2 - 1 = 0$

$\quad (a + 1)(a - 1) = 0$

$\qquad\qquad a = -1 \text{ or } a = 1$

Hence the objects that map onto themselves are –1 and 1.

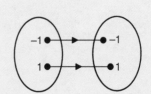

▶ Example 5

Given function $f : x \longmapsto ax + b$ where a and b are constants, $f(2) = 1$ and $f(-2) = -11$, find the value of a and of b.

▶ Solution . . .

$$
\begin{aligned}
\text{Given } f(x) &= ax + b \\
\text{and } f(2) &= 1 \\
2a + b &= 1 \qquad \ldots\ldots (1) \\
\text{Given } f(-2) &= -11 \\
-2a + b &= -11 \qquad \ldots\ldots (2)
\end{aligned}
$$

$(1) - (2)$:
$$
\begin{aligned}
4a &= 12 \\
a &= 3
\end{aligned}
$$

Substitute $a = 3$ into (1):
$$
\begin{aligned}
2(3) + b &= 1 \\
b &= -5
\end{aligned}
$$

Hence $a = 3$ and $b = -5$.

▶ Example 6

The function h is given by $h(x) = \dfrac{2x+1}{x-1}$, $x \neq 1$.
Solve the equation $h(2p) = \dfrac{1}{2}$.

▶ Solution . . .

$$
h(2p) = \frac{1}{2}
$$

$$
\frac{2(2p)+1}{2p-1} = \frac{1}{2}
$$

$$
\frac{4p+1}{2p-1} = \frac{1}{2}
$$

$$
8p + 2 = 2p - 1
$$

$$
6p = -3
$$

$$
p = -\frac{1}{2}
$$

2.1.4   Domain of a Function

In a function, the domain can be any set of numbers. It could be just a few selected numbers or all positive numbers or all real numbers. If it is not specified, it is taken to be all real numbers. However some numbers may have no image and these must be stated. They are excluded from the domain.

▶ Example 7

State the domain for the function $f : x \longmapsto \dfrac{2x}{x-3}$.

▶ Solution . . .

The domain of the function f is {all real values of x, $x \neq 3$}.

If $x = 3$, $f(x) = \dfrac{2(3)}{x-3} = \dfrac{6}{0}$ which is impossible as division by zero is
undefined. Hence this function is often stated as $f : x \longmapsto x - \dfrac{2x}{x-3}$, $x \neq 3$.

2.1.5 Graphical Representation of Functions

A simple way of illustrating a function graphically is to use two parallel
number lines, one for values of the domain, the other for the range. The
diagrams below show the function $f(x) = 2x + 1$ with domain $\{-1, 0, 1, 2\}$.
An arrowed line joins x in the domain to $f(x)$ in the range.

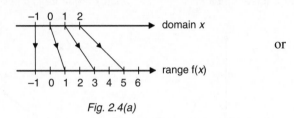

or

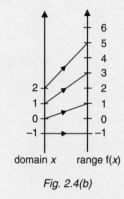

Fig. 2.4(a)

Fig. 2.4(b)

▶ Example 8

Illustrate the function $f : x \longmapsto x^2 - x + 2$ on two number lines for the
domain $\{-1, 0, 1, 2, 3\}$.

▶ Solution . . .

Given

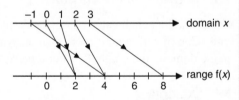

$f(x) = x^2 - x + 2$
$f(-1) = (-1)^2 - (-1) + 2 = 4$
$f(0) = 0^2 - 0 + 2 = 2$
$f(1) = 1^2 - 1 + 2 = 2$
$f(2) = 2^2 - 2 + 2 = 4$
$f(3) = 3^2 - 3 + 2 = 8$

This number line method is only suitable if the domain consists of a few
values. If the domain is all real numbers for example, it would be impossible
to show all the arrowed lines. Furthermore, the pattern of the arrowed lines
gives no idea of the type of function.

A far better method is to use a **Cartesian graph**. Here we use two
perpendicular lines, the x-axis and the y-axis (Fig. 2.5). Values of the domain
are placed on the x-axis and the range on the y-axis. Then x and its image
$f(x)$ give the coordinates (x, y) of a point. If sufficient points are plotted and
joined up, we have the **graph** of the function. $y = f(x)$ is the Cartesian
equation of the curve.

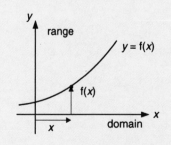

Fig. 2.5

Using this method of representing a function, we find that the graphs of
various kinds of functions have characteristic shapes. Hence functions can
be recognised from their graphs.

2.1.6 Common Functions and their Graphs

Fig. 2.6 shows the graphs of some common functions.

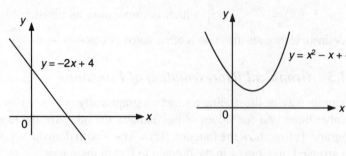

(a) linear function   (b) quadratic function

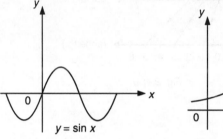 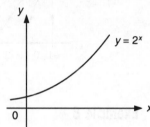

(c) trigonometric function   (d) exponential function

Fig. 2.6

2.1.7 Graph of a Function

For a function, **each** value of x in the domain must give just **one and only one** value of y. If there is more than one value of y for the same value of x in the domain, the graph does not represent a function.

▶ Example 9

Classification

Which of the following is the graph of a function?

(a)   (b)

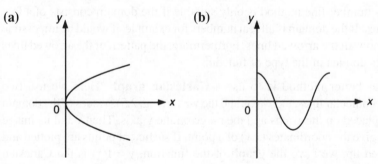

▶ Solution . . .

(a) This is not the graph of a function because there are two values of y for each value of x.

(b) This is the graph of a function because there is only one value of y for each value of x.

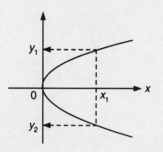

2.1.8 Types of Functions

In a function, each object has only one image. However, there may be more than one object which map onto the same image.

Steps:
Draw vertical lines parallel to the y-axis.

In Fig. 2.7, there is only one arrow reaching each member of set B, i.e. only one object maps onto an image. This function is a **one-to-one** function.

If any of these lines cuts the graph at more than one point, then the graph does not illustrate a function.

In Fig. 2.8, there is more than one arrow reaching some members of set D, i.e. more than one object map onto the same image, e.g. –2 and 2 map onto 5, and –1 and 1 map onto –1. This function is called a **many-to-one** function.

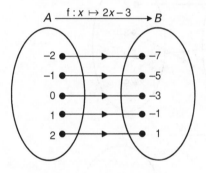

Fig. 2.7

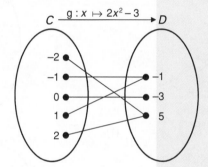

Fig. 2.8

Classification

Classify the type of function shown in Fig. 2.6.

Exercise 2A (Answers on page 494)

1. Which of the relations illustrated by the arrow diagrams below is a function? Give reasons for your answer.

(a)

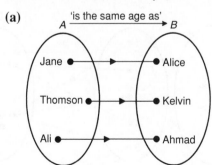

(b)

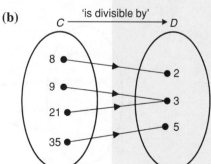

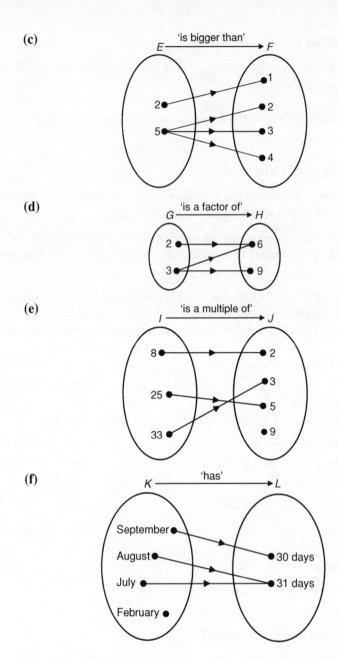

(c) 'is bigger than' $E \longrightarrow F$

(d) 'is a factor of' $G \longrightarrow H$

(e) 'is a multiple of' $I \longrightarrow J$

(f) $K \longrightarrow L$ 'has'

2. State the domain, images and range of the following functions.

(a)   **(b)**

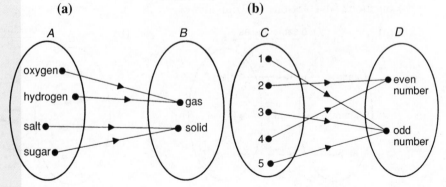

3. In each of the following functions, find the images of –3, 0, 2 and 5.
   (a) $f : x \longmapsto x^2 - x - 5$ (b) $g : x \longmapsto 2x - x^2$

4. The domain for the function $f : x \longmapsto 2x^2 + 1$ is $\{-2, -1, 0, 1, 2\}$. Find the range of the function f.

5. The domain of the function $g : x \longmapsto \dfrac{2x+1}{x-1}$ is $\{0, 2, 4\}$. Find the range of the function g.

6. A function is defined by $f : x \longmapsto \dfrac{2x-1}{3}$. Find the objects which have images –3, 0, 1 and 3.

7. The function g is given by $g(t) = 7t - 2t^2$. Find the values of t which have an image of 5.

8. If $h(x) = 3x + 2$, what is the value of x which is mapped onto 8?

9. The function g is given as $g : x \longmapsto x^2 - 5x + 9$.
   (a) Find the values of x which have an image of 15.
   (b) Find the value of x which maps onto itself.

10. The function h is defined by $h : x \longmapsto 2^x$.
    (a) Find the values of h(3) and h(–2).
    (b) If $h(x) = 16$, find the value of x.

11. If the range of the function $f(x) = x^2 - 2$ is $\{-2, -1, 7\}$, find the domain.

12. The range of the function $g(x) = 1 - \dfrac{2}{x}$ is $\{-1, 2, 4\}$. Find the domain.

13. The function f is defined by $f : x \longmapsto ax + b$, where a and b are constants, $f(-2) = 7$ and $f(2) = -1$. Find the value of a and of b.

14. $f(x) = ax^2 + bx + c$, where a, b and c are constants. If $f(0) = 7$, what is the value of c? Given also that $f(1) = 6$ and $f(-1) = 12$, find the value of a and of b.

15. Given the function $f : x \longmapsto \dfrac{9}{ax+b}$ where a and b are constants, $f(2) = 3$ and $f(-4) = -1$, find the value of a and of b.

16. Given that $f(x) = x^2 - 4x + 1$, solve the equations
    (a) $f(x) = x - 3$,   (b) $f(2x) = 13$.

17. Functions f and g are given as $f(x) = x^2 - x$ and $g(x) = 2x - 3$.
    (a) If $f(x) + g(x) = 3$, find x.
    (b) If $f(p) + g(-p) = 1$, find p.

18. If $f(x) = \dfrac{x+1}{x^2 - x + 1}$, find the value of k (other than $k = 1$) such that $f(k) = f(1)$.

19. If $f(x) = 3x + 1$, find $f(a)$, $f(b)$ and $f(a + b)$. Is $f(a + b) = f(a) + f(b)$?

20. Given the function $f(x) = x^2 - 3x - 2$, express $f(2a) - f(a)$ in its simplest form in terms of a.

21. A function h is defined by $h(x) = \dfrac{x-1}{x+1}$.

    (a) Find $h(-3)$, $h(-1)$, $h(0)$ and $h(2)$.
    (b) State the domain which defines the function.

22. State the domain for the following functions:

    (a) $f : x \longmapsto \dfrac{5}{x-2}$ **(b)** $g : x \longmapsto \dfrac{x+2}{3x+2}$

    (c) $h : x \longmapsto \dfrac{x+1}{x^2+x-2}$ **(d)** $i : x \longmapsto 3 - \dfrac{2}{x+3}$

    (e) $j : x \longmapsto \sqrt{x}$ (positive root)

23. Given the function $f(x) = \dfrac{x+3}{x-1}$,

    (a) find the value of x for which f is undefined,
    (b) find the positive value of x for which $f(x) = x$.

24. The number of diagonals in a polygon with n sides is given by the function $D(n) = \dfrac{n(n-3)}{2}$.

    (a) State the domain of this function.
    (b) Find the number of diagonals in polygons with 4, 5 and 10 sides.
    (c) What is the polygon with 20 diagonals?

25. Illustrate the following function on two number lines for the domain $\{-1, 0, 1, 2\}$:
    (a) $f : x \longmapsto 3 - 2x$ **(b)** $g : x \longmapsto 2x^2 - 2x$
    (c) $h : x \longmapsto 4 - 2x^2$

26. Which of the following is the graph of a function? Give reasons for your answer. Classify the type of function.

    (a)   **(b)**

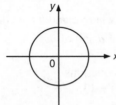 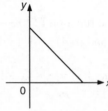

    (c)   **(d)**

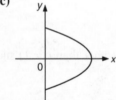 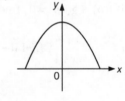

2.2 Composite Functions

2.2.1 Composition of Functions

Consider two functions f and g which are defined by the arrow diagrams in Fig. 2.9 and Fig. 2.10.

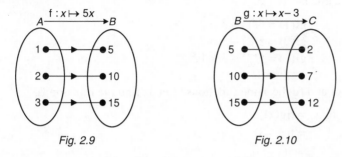

Fig. 2.9   Fig. 2.10

Combining the two arrow diagrams, we obtain the arrow diagram as shown in Fig. 2.11.

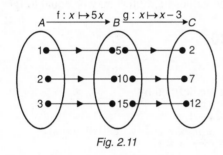

Fig. 2.11

Note that every member in set A is linked to only one member in set C. Hence we can obtain a new function h linking set A to set C (Fig. 2.12).

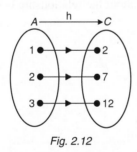

Fig. 2.12

This new function h is a composition of the two functions f and g. Hence h is known as the **composite function** of f and g and is denoted by gf or gof.

Hence $h(x) = gf(x)$

second   first

Note that $gf(x)$ means that we find function f **first** and then find function g. Algebraically, we can find the composite function gf from the given functions f and g.

$$gf(x) = g[f(x)]$$

$$= g(5x)$$

$$= 5x - 3$$

first find f

then find g

We can verify the range of the function gf by substituting various values of x into $gf(x) = 5x - 3$.

$$gf(1) = 5(1) - 3 = 2$$
$$gf(2) = 5(2) - 3 = 7$$
$$gf(3) = 5(3) - 3 = 12$$

Are gf and fg the same functions? Let us find the function fg.

$$fg(x) = f[g(x)]$$
$$= f(x - 3)$$
$$= 5(x - 3)$$
$$= 5x - 15$$

Since $gf(x) \neq fg(x)$, gf and fg are different functions.
However for some values of x, $gf(x)$ may be equal to $fg(x)$.

▶ **Example 10**

Deduction

Functions f and g are defined by

$$f : x \longmapsto 2x - 1,$$

$$g : x \longmapsto \frac{5x}{x - 1}, x \neq 1.$$

(a) Find in similar form, fg and gf.
(b) For what values of x is $fg(x) = gf(x)$?

What can you conclude about the relationship between the two functions fg and gf?

▶ **Solution . . .**

(a) Given $f(x) = 2x - 1$

and $g(x) = \dfrac{5x}{x - 1}$

$$fg(x) = f[g(x)]$$

$$= f\left[\frac{5x}{x - 1}\right]$$

$$= 2\left(\frac{5x}{x - 1}\right) - 1$$

$$= \frac{10x - (x - 1)}{x - 1}$$

$$= \frac{9x + 1}{x - 1}$$

$$\therefore fg : x \longmapsto \frac{9x + 1}{x - 1}, x \neq 1.$$

$$gf(x) = g[f(x)]$$
$$= g(2x - 1)$$
$$= \frac{5(2x - 1)}{(2x - 1) - 1}$$
$$= \frac{10x - 5}{2x - 2}$$
$$\therefore gf : x \longmapsto \frac{10x - 5}{2x - 2}, x \neq 1.$$

(b) If $fg(x) = gf(x)$,

$$\frac{9x + 1}{x - 1} = \frac{10x - 5}{2x - 2}$$
$$(9x + 1)(2x - 2) = (10x - 5)(x - 1)$$
$$18x^2 - 18x + 2x - 2 = 10x^2 - 10x - 5x + 5$$
$$8x^2 - x - 7 = 0$$
$$(8x + 7)(x - 1) = 0$$
$$x = -\frac{7}{8} \text{ or } x = 1$$

Since fg and gf are not defined when $x = 1$, $\therefore x = -\frac{7}{8}$.

From the results above, we can conclude that $fg \neq gf$ for all the values of x except $x = -\frac{7}{8}$.

▶ **Example 11**

If $f : x \longmapsto \frac{3x + 2}{x + 3}$, $x \neq -3$, and $g : x \longmapsto \frac{x^2}{2 - 3x}$, $x \neq \frac{2}{3}$, find gf(4).

▶ **Solution . . .**

Given $f(x) = \frac{3x + 2}{x + 3}$, $x \neq -3$

and $g(x) = \frac{x^2}{2 - 3x}$, $x \neq \frac{2}{3}$

$$gf(4) = g[f(4)]$$
$$= g\left[\frac{3(4) + 2}{4 + 3}\right]$$
$$= g(2)$$
$$= \frac{2^2}{2 - 3(2)}$$
$$= -1$$

An alternative method is to find the composite function $gf(x)$ and then substitute $x = 4$ into the function. However this is a rather complicated method when the functions f and g are not simple algebraic expressions.

2.2.2 Composition of a Given Function and Itself

The composite of a function f and itself can be written as f^2, i.e.

$$f^2 = ff$$

Hence $\quad f^3 = fff = ff^2 = f^2f$

$\qquad f^4 = ffff = ff^3 = f^3f = f^2f^2$

and so on for $f^5, f^6, \ldots,$ etc.

▶ **Example 12**

Prediction and Induction

Given that $f : x \longmapsto \dfrac{x}{x+1}, x \neq -1$, find in similar form f^2 and f^3.

Hence predict an expression for f^4 and induce an expression for f^n.

▶ **Solution . . .**

Given $\qquad f(x) = \dfrac{x}{x+1}$

$\qquad\quad f^2(x) = ff(x)$

$\qquad\qquad\quad = f[f(x)]$

$\qquad\qquad\quad = f\left[\dfrac{x}{x+1}\right]$

$\qquad\qquad\quad = \dfrac{\frac{x}{x+1}}{\frac{x}{x+1}+1}$

$\qquad\qquad\quad = \dfrac{\frac{x}{x+1}}{\frac{x+x+1}{x+1}}$

$\qquad\qquad\quad = \dfrac{x}{2x+1}$

$\therefore f^2 : x \longmapsto \dfrac{x}{2x+1}, x \neq -1, -\dfrac{1}{2}$

domain of f^2 = domain of f

$f^3(x) = f[f^2(x)]$

$\qquad\quad = f\left[\dfrac{x}{2x+1}\right]$

$\qquad\quad = \dfrac{\frac{x}{2x+1}}{\frac{x}{2x+1}+1}$

$\qquad\quad = \dfrac{\frac{x}{2x+1}}{\frac{x+2x+1}{2x+1}}$

$\qquad\quad = \dfrac{x}{3x+1}$

$\therefore f^3 : x \longmapsto \dfrac{x}{3x+1}, x \neq -1, -\dfrac{1}{2}, -\dfrac{1}{3}$

domain of f^3 = domain of f^2 = domain f

From the above results

$f : x \longmapsto \dfrac{x}{x+1}, x \neq -1$

$f^2 : x \longmapsto \dfrac{x}{2x+1}, x \neq -1, -\dfrac{1}{2}$

$f^3 : x \longmapsto \dfrac{x}{3x+1}, x \neq -1, -\dfrac{1}{2}, -\dfrac{1}{3}$

we can predict that f^4 can be defined as

$$f^4 : x \longmapsto \frac{x}{4x+1}, x \neq -1, -\frac{1}{2}, -\frac{1}{3}, -\frac{1}{4}.$$

We can also induce that

$$f^n : x \longmapsto \frac{x}{nx+1}, x \neq -1, -\frac{1}{2}, -\frac{1}{3}, -\frac{1}{4}, -\frac{1}{5}, \ldots, -\frac{1}{n}.$$

▶ **Example 13**

Comparison

If $f : x \longmapsto ax + b \ (a > 0)$ and $f^2 : x \longmapsto 4x - 9$, find the value of a and of b.

▶ **Solution . . .**

Given
$$\begin{aligned}
f(x) &= ax + b \\
f^2(x) &= f[f(x)] \\
&= f(ax + b) \\
&= a(ax + b) + b \\
&= a^2x + ab + b
\end{aligned}$$

Given $\qquad f^2(x) = 4x - 9,$

hence $\qquad a^2x + ab + b = 4x - 9.$

Comparing coefficients of x, we obtain
$$a^2 = 4$$
$$a = 2 \qquad (\text{since } a > 0)$$

Comparing the constant terms, we obtain
$$ab + b = -9$$
Substituting $a = 2$,
$$2b + b = -9$$
$$b = -3$$

Hence $a = 2$ and $b = -3$.

▶ **Example 14**

Given $f : x \longmapsto 2x - 5$, find a function g such that $fg : x \longmapsto 6x - 1$.

▶ **Solution . . .**

Given $\qquad f(x) = 2x - 5$

and $\qquad fg(x) = 6x - 1$
$$\begin{aligned}
f[g(x)] &= 6x - 1 \\
2g(x) - 5 &= 6x - 1 \\
g(x) &= 3x + 2 \\
g : x &\longmapsto 3x + 2
\end{aligned}$$

▶ **Example 15**

Given that $g : x \longmapsto 1 - 3x$, find a function f such that $fg : x \longmapsto 7 - 6x$.

▶ **Solution . . .**

Given $\quad g(x) = 1 - 3x$

and $\qquad fg(x) = 7 - 6x$

$\qquad f(1 - 3x) = 7 - 6x$

Substituting $y = 1 - 3x$, $x = \dfrac{1 - y}{3}$

$$f(y) = 7 - 6\left(\dfrac{1 - y}{3}\right)$$

$$= 5 + 2y$$

$$f : y \longmapsto 5 + 2y$$

Replacing y by x,

$$f : x \longmapsto 5 + 2x.$$

▶ **Example 16**

Given $f : x \longmapsto x + 3$ and $g : x \longmapsto x^2$, express the following composite functions in terms of f and g.

(a) $\quad h : x \longmapsto x^2 + 3$

(b) $\quad i : x \longmapsto x^2 + 6x + 9$

(c) $\quad j : x \longmapsto x + 6$

▶ **Solution . . .**

Given $\quad f(x) = x + 3$

and $\qquad g(x) = x^2$

(a) Given $h(x) = x^2 + 3$

$$= g(x) + 3 \qquad g(x) = x^2$$

$$= f[g(x)] \qquad f[g(x)] = g(x) + 3$$

$$= fg(x)$$

$\therefore$ The function h is $fg : x \longmapsto x^2 + 3$.

(b) Given $i(x) = x^2 + 6x + 9$

$$= (x + 3)^2$$

$$= [f(x)]^2 \qquad f(x) = x + 3$$

$$= g[f(x)] \qquad f[f(x)] = [f(x)] + 3$$

$$= gf(x)$$

Hence the function i is $gf : x \longmapsto x^2 + 6x + 9$.

(c) Given $j(x) = x + 6$

$$= x + 3 + 3 \qquad f(x) = x + 3$$

$$= f(x) + 3$$

$$= f[f(x)] \qquad g[f(x)] = [f(x)]^2$$

$$= f^2(x)$$

Hence the function j is $f^2 : x \longmapsto x + 6$.

Exercise 2B (Answers on page 494)

1. Functions f and g are defined as follows. Find, in similar form, the composite functions fg and gf.
   (a) $f : x \longmapsto x + 5$; $g : x \longmapsto 3x - 2$
   (b) $f : x \longmapsto 4 - x$; $g : x \longmapsto 2x + 5$
   (c) $f : x \longmapsto x^2 + 2$; $g : x \longmapsto 3 - x$
   (d) $f : x \longmapsto 1 + 2x$; $g : x \longmapsto \dfrac{6}{3 - x}$, $x \neq 3$
   (e) $f : x \longmapsto 2 - 3x$; $g : x \longmapsto \dfrac{x}{x - 1}$, $x \neq 1$

2. Given that $f : x \longmapsto x^2 - 2$ and $g : x \longmapsto x + 3$,
   (a) find fg and gf;
   (b) for what value(s) of x is $fg(x) = gf(x)$?

3. Given that $f : x \longmapsto 3x + 2$ and $g : x \longmapsto \dfrac{1}{x}$, $x \neq 0$, find the value(s) of x for which $fg(x) = gf(x)$.

4. Given that $g : x \longmapsto x + 2$ and $h : x \longmapsto x^2 - 3$, find the value of x for which $gh(x) = hg(x)$.

5. If $f : x \longmapsto \dfrac{x}{x + 2}$, $x = -2$ and $g : x \longmapsto \dfrac{1 + 2x}{1 - x}$, $x \neq 1$, find fg(4) and gf(4).

6. Given that $f : x \longmapsto 4x - 5$ and $g : x \longmapsto \dfrac{2x - 4}{x - 2}$, $x \neq 2$, find gf(3) and fg(3).

7. Given that $f : x \longmapsto \dfrac{3x + 1}{x - 2}$, $x \neq 2$ and $g : x \longmapsto \dfrac{2x - 3}{x - 1}$, $x \neq 1$, find fg(2) and ffg(2).

8. Given the functions $f : x \longmapsto 2x - 5$ and $g : x \longmapsto \dfrac{3}{x}$ $(x \neq 0)$, find, in similar form, fg. Hence solve the equation $fg(x) = g(x)$.

9. Given that $f : x \longmapsto 2x - 3$, $g : x \longmapsto ax - 5$ and $fg(2) = 3$, find the value of a.

10. $f : x \longmapsto \dfrac{2x}{x - 4}$, $x \neq 4$ and $g : x \longmapsto ax^2 + bx$. Given that $g(3) = 9$ and that $gf(2) = 14$, find the values of a and b. \qquad (C)

11. Given $f : x \longmapsto 3x - 4$, $g : x \longmapsto ax + b$ and $gf : x \longmapsto 11 - 6x$, find the values of a and b.

12. $f : x \longmapsto ax + b$ and $g : x \longmapsto 2x + 3$ are two functions. If $fg(x) = gf(x)$, find a relation between a and b.

13. Given that $f : x \longmapsto x + 1$, find in similar form, f^2 and f^3. Hence predict an expression for f^4 and induce an expression for f^n.

14. Given that $g : x \longmapsto \dfrac{x}{1-x}$, $x \neq 1$, find in similar form, f^2 and f^3. Hence induce an expression for f^n.

15. Given that $h : x \longmapsto \dfrac{x}{x-1}$, $x \neq 1$, find in similar form, f^2, f^3 and f^4. Hence obtain an expression for f^{10} and f^{11}.

16. Given that $f : x \longmapsto \dfrac{2x+2}{x-2}$, $x \neq 2$, find $f^2(4)$ and $f^4(4)$.

17. $f : x \longmapsto \dfrac{x-2}{x+1}$, $x \neq -1$.

    (a) Find f^2.
    (b) If $f^2(x) = -1$, find the value of x.

18. If $f : x \longmapsto \dfrac{x-1}{x+2}$, $x \neq -2$, find f^2 and f^3. Solve the equation $f^3(x) = 1$.

19. If $f : x \longmapsto ax + b \ (a > 0)$ and $f^2 : x \longmapsto 25x - 18$, find the values of a and b.

20. The function g is defined by $g : x \longmapsto 2x + a$. Given that $g^2(4) = 7$, find the value of a. (C)

21. Functions f and g are defined by $f : x \longmapsto 4x - 17$ and
    $g : x \longmapsto \dfrac{5}{2x-7}$, $x \neq 3.5$. Solve the equation $f^2(x) = gf(7)$.

    (C)

22. Given $f : x \longmapsto 2x + 3$, find a function g such that
    $fg : x \longmapsto 2x - 1$.

23. Given that $f : x \longmapsto \dfrac{2}{x+1}$, $x \neq -1$, find a function g such that
    $fg : x \longmapsto \dfrac{2}{3x-1}$, $x \neq \dfrac{1}{3}$.

24. Given that $f : x \longmapsto x^2 + 2$, find a function g such that
    $fg : x \longmapsto 4x^2 - 12x + 11$.

25. Given that $g : x \longmapsto 3x + 1$, find a function f such that
    $fg : x \longmapsto 3x + 2$.

26. If $g : x \longmapsto x - 3$, what is the function f which makes
    $fg : x \longmapsto x^2 - 6x + 10$?

27. Given that $g : x \longmapsto \dfrac{2}{x}$, $x \neq 0$, find a function f such that
    $fg : x \longmapsto \dfrac{1-x}{1+x}$, $x \neq -1$.

28. Given $f : x \longmapsto x + 2$ and $g : x \longmapsto 3x$, express the following composite functions in terms of f and g:

(a) $h : x \longmapsto 3x + 2$

(b) $i : x \longmapsto 3x + 6$

(c) $j : x \longmapsto x + 4$

(d) $k : x \longmapsto 3x + 12$

29. Given $f : x \longmapsto x - 3$ and $g : x \longmapsto x^2 - 1$, state the following in terms of f and g:

(a) $x \longmapsto x^2 - 4$

(b) $x \longmapsto x^2 - 6x + 8$

(c) $x \longmapsto x - 9$

(d) $x \longmapsto x^2 - 12x + 35$

2.3 Inverse Functions

2.3.1 Inverse of a Function

Fig. 2.13 shows a one-to-one function $f : x \longmapsto 3x - 2$ which maps set A (the domain) onto set B (the range).

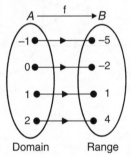

Fig. 2.13

Is there any function that will map the range (set B) back onto the domain (set A) (Fig. 2.14).

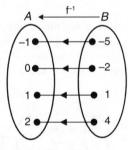

Fig. 2.14

The arrow diagram shown in Fig. 2.14 is a function since each member in set B maps onto only one member in set A. This new function is called the **inverse function** of f and is denoted by $\mathbf{f}^{-1}$.

However, some functions do not have an inverse.

Consider the function $g : x \longmapsto x^2$ which maps set P onto set Q (Fig. 2.15).

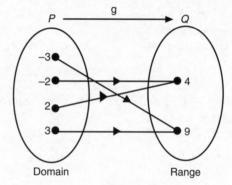

Fig. 2.15

Is there any function that will map the range back onto the domain (Fig. 2.16)?

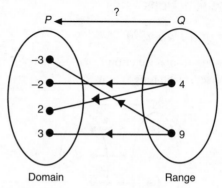

Fig. 2.16

The mapping shown in Fig. 2.16 is not a function because the elements in set Q maps onto more than one element in set P, i.e. 4 maps onto -2 and 2, and 9 maps onto -3 and 3.

An inverse function can exist only if the original function is a **one-to-one** function (Fig. 2.13).

There will be no inverse if the function is not a one-to-one function, for example, the many-to-one function in Fig. 2.15.

In general, if $f(x) = y$, then $f^{-1}(y) = x$, and vice versa, if $f^{-1}(y) = x$, then $f(x) = y$.

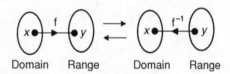

Fig. 2.17

Note that the range under f now becomes the domain under f^{-1} and the domain under f becomes the range under f^{-1} (Fig. 2.17).

▶ **Example 17**

Classification

Which of the following functions have an inverse? Give reasons for your answer.

(a)

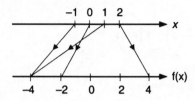

(b)

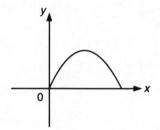

(c)

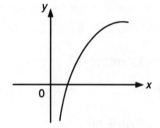

▶ **Solution . . .**

(a) This has no inverse because it is a many-to-one function, i.e. −1 and 1 map onto −4.

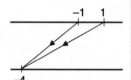

(b) This has no inverse because it is a many-to-one function, i.e. there are two values of *x* that map onto the same value of *y*.

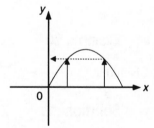

(c) This has an inverse because it is a one-to-one function, i.e. only one value of *x* maps onto one value of *y*.

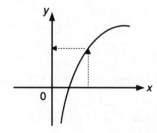

▶ **Example 18**

Given that $f : x \longmapsto \dfrac{x+2}{3}$, find f^{-1}.

▶ **Solution . . .**

Let $f^{-1}(y) = x$

then $f(x) = y$

$\dfrac{x+2}{3} = y$

Rearranging the equation to make x the subject,

$x = 3y - 2$

$\therefore f^{-1}(y) = 3y - 2$

$f^{-1} : y \longmapsto 3y - 2$

Replacing y by x, $f^{-1} : x$ a $3x - 2$.

▶ **Example 19**

Given $f^{-1} : x \longmapsto 5 - 2x$, find f.

▶ **Solution . . .**

Let $f(x) = y$

then $f^{-1}(y) = x$

$5 - 2y = x$

Rearranging the equation to make y the subject,

$y = \dfrac{5 - x}{2}$

$\therefore f(x) = \dfrac{5 - x}{2}$

$f : x \longmapsto \dfrac{5 - x}{2}$

▶ **Example 20**

Given that $f : x \longmapsto \dfrac{2x + 3}{x + 3}$, $x \neq -3$, find $f^{-1}(3)$.

▶ **Solution . . .**

Let $f^{-1}(3) = x$

then $f(x) = 3$

$\dfrac{2x + 3}{x + 3} = 3$

$x = -6$

$\therefore f^{-1}(3) = -6$

Alternatively we can first find $f^{-1}(x)$ and then substitute $x = 3$.

Let $f^{-1}(y) = x$

then $f(x) = y$

$\dfrac{2x + 3}{x + 3} = y$

Rearranging the equation to make x the subject,

$$x = \frac{3 - 3y}{y - 2}$$

$$\therefore \; f^{-1}(y) = \frac{3 - 3y}{y - 2}$$

Replacing y by x,

$$f^{-1}(x) = \frac{3 - 3x}{x - 2}$$

$$f^{-1}(3) = \frac{3 - 3(3)}{3 - 2}$$

$$= -6$$

▶ **Example 21**

Given the function $f : x \longmapsto \dfrac{x + p}{x + 3}$ $(x \neq -3)$ and $f^{-1}(3) = 4$, find the value of p.

▶ **Solution . . .**

Given $\qquad f(x) = \dfrac{x + p}{x + 3}$

and $\qquad f^{-1}(3) = 4$

$$f(4) = 3$$

$$\frac{4 + p}{4 + 3} = 3$$

$$p = 17$$

2.3.2   *Composition of a Function and its Inverse*

▶ **Example 22**

Deduction

Given that $f : x \longmapsto \dfrac{2}{x - 3}$, $x \neq 3$, find **(a)** ff^{-1} and **(b)** $f^{-1}f$. What can you conclude about the relationship between ff^{-1} and $f^{-1}f$?

▶ **Solution . . .**

Given $\qquad f(x) = \dfrac{2}{x - 3}$,

we obtain its inverse function $f^{-1}(x) = \dfrac{3x + 2}{x}$.

(a) $\quad ff^{-1}(x) = f\!\left(\dfrac{3x + 2}{x} \right)$

$$= \frac{2}{\left(\frac{3x+2}{x} \right) - 3}$$

$$= x$$

$$\therefore \;\; ff^{-1} : x \longmapsto x$$

(b) $f^{-1}f(x) = f^{-1}\left(\dfrac{2}{x-3}\right)$

$$= \dfrac{3\left(\frac{2}{x-3}\right)+2}{\left(\frac{2}{x-3}\right)}$$

$$= x$$

$$\therefore \quad f^{-1}f : x \longmapsto x$$

Hence we conclude that $ff^{-1} = f^{-1}f$.

Note that $ff^{-1}(x) = f^{-1}f(x) = x$.

▶ ## Example 23

Deduction

Functions f and g are defined as $f : x \longmapsto \dfrac{2}{x+1}, x \neq -1$, and

$g : x \longmapsto 3x - 2$. Find **(a)** $g^{-1}f^{-1}$ and **(b)** $(fg)^{-1}$. What can you conclude about the relationship between $(fg)^{-1}$ and $g^{-1}f^{-1}$?

▶ ## Solution . . .

(a) Given $\qquad f(x) = \dfrac{2}{x+1},$

we can obtain $\quad f^{-1}(x) = \dfrac{2-x}{x}.$

Given $\qquad g(x) = 3x - 2,$

we obtain $\quad g^{-1}(x) = \dfrac{x+2}{3}.$

Hence $\qquad g^{-1}f^{-1}(x) = g^{-1}\left(\dfrac{2-x}{x}\right)$

$$= \dfrac{\frac{2-x}{x}+2}{3}$$

$$= \dfrac{x+2}{3x}$$

(b) $\qquad fg(x) = f[3x - 2]$

$$= \dfrac{2}{(3x-2)+1}$$

$$= \dfrac{2}{3x-1}$$

Let $(fg)^{-1}(y) = x$

then $(fg)(x) = y$

$$\dfrac{2}{3x-1} = y$$

$$x = \dfrac{y+2}{3y}$$

$\therefore (fg)^{-1}(y) = \dfrac{y+2}{3y}$

$\therefore (fg)^{-1} : x \longmapsto \dfrac{x+2}{3x}$

Hence we can conclude that $(fg)^{-1} = g^{-1}f^{-1}$.

2.3.3 Graph of an Inverse Function

Given a function f : $x \longmapsto 2x - 3$, we can verify that its function f^{-1} is
$f^{-1} : x \longmapsto \dfrac{x+3}{2}$.

Fig. 2.18 shows the graphs of the function f : $x \longmapsto 2x - 3$ and its
inverse function $f^{-1} : x \longmapsto \dfrac{x+3}{2}$. Add the line $y = x$ (shown as a dotted line).

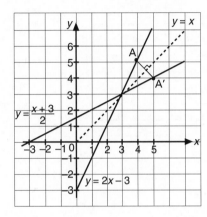

Fig. 2.18

How do the two lines $y = 2x - 3$ and $y = \dfrac{x+3}{2}$ appear in relation to the line $y = x$?

Analysing and Inferring

1. Consider point A on the line $y = 2x - 3$ where $x = 4$. The image of 4 under f is 5, so the coordinates of A are (4,5).

2. Now if we take $x = 5$, its image under f^{-1} will be 4. This gives point A'(5,4) which lies on the line $y = \dfrac{x+3}{2}$.

3. Notice that A and A' are reflections of each other in the line $y = x$.

4. We can repeat this for other points. The coordinates will be interchanged by the inverse function, so the two points are reflections of each other. Hence the lines $y = 2x - 3$ and $y = \dfrac{x+3}{2}$ are reflections of each other in the line $y = x$. (You can also test this by folding the graph paper along the line $y = x$.)

> The graphs of $y = f(x)$ and $y = f^{-1}(x)$ are reflections of each other in the line $y = x$.

▶ **Example 24**

The diagram shows the graph of a function $y = f(x)$ for the domain $0 \le x \le 3$.

(a) Copy the diagram and sketch the graph of $y = f^{-1}(x)$ on it.

(b) State the domain and range of f^{-1}.

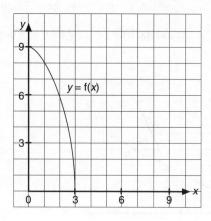

▶ **Solution . . .**

Steps:

1. Copy the graph $y = f(x)$.

2. Draw the line $y = x$.

3. Mark the images:
   image for (3,0) is (0,3);
   image for (0,9) is (9,0).

4. Sketch the graph $y = f^{-1}(x)$, which is a reflection of $y = f(x)$ in the line $y = x$. The two graphs $y = f(x)$ and $y = f^{-1}(x)$ will intersect on the line $y = x$.

(a)

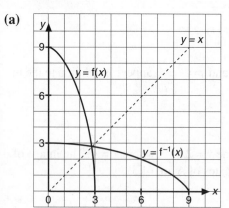

(b) The domain of f^{-1} is $0 \le x \le 9$.
The range of f^{-1} is $0 \le f^{-1}(x) \le 3$.

Note that the two graphs $y = f(x)$ and $y = f^{-1}(x)$ in this example meet at a point on the line $y = x$. The x-coordinate of this point gives the solution to the equation $f(x) = f^{-1}(x)$.

Note also that the domain of f^{-1} equals the range of f.

Exercise 2C (*Answers on page 495*)

1. Which of the following functions have an inverse?
   Give reasons for your answer.

   (a)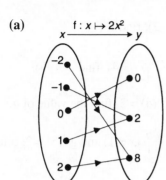

   (b)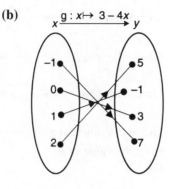

   (c)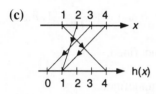

   (d)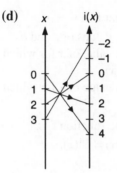

   (e)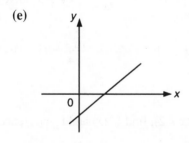

   (f)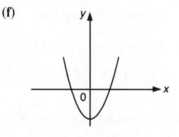

Deduction and IT Skills

Use Graphmatica courseware to plot the following sets of graphs:

(a) $y = 2x - 4$, $y = \frac{1}{2}x + 2$ and $y = x$

(b) $y = x^3$, $y = \sqrt[3]{x}$ and $y = x$

(c) $y = e^x$, $y = \ln x$ and $y = x$

(d) $y = \frac{1}{x} - 2$, $y = \frac{1}{x+2}$ and $y = x$

What can you deduce about the relationship between the first two graphs in each of the cases above?

2. Find the inverse of the following functions in similar form:

   (a) $f : x \longmapsto 3x + 4$

   (b) $g : x \longmapsto \dfrac{5 - 2x}{3}$

   (c) $h : x \longmapsto \dfrac{5}{x+1}, x \neq -1$

   (d) $i : x \longmapsto \dfrac{3}{x} + 2, x \neq 0$

   (e) $j : x \longmapsto \dfrac{2x + 1}{x - 3}, x \neq 3$

3. Given $f : x \longmapsto \dfrac{6 - 5x}{x}, x \neq 0$, find the values of x for which $f(x) = f^{-1}(x)$.

4. If $f^{-1} : x \longmapsto 3 - \dfrac{4}{x}$, $x \neq 0$, find f in a similar form.

5. If $g^{-1} : x \longmapsto \dfrac{3-x}{5+x}$, $x \neq -5$, find g in a similar form.

6. Given that $f : x \longmapsto \dfrac{x+6}{x+2}$ $(x \neq -2)$, find $f^{-1}(-1)$.

7. Given the function $g : x \longmapsto \dfrac{1-x}{x-4}$ $(x \neq 4)$, find $g^{-1}(-3)$.

8. Given that $f : x \longmapsto a - x$ and $f^{-1}(4) = 3$, find the value of a.

9. Given the function $g : x \longmapsto \dfrac{x+b}{x-1}$ $(x \neq 1)$ and $g^{-1}(5) = 2$, find
   (a) the value of b,
   (b) g^{-1}.

10. Given that $f : x \longmapsto \dfrac{x+c}{x+d}$, $f(4) = 6$ and $f^{-1}\left(-\dfrac{1}{4}\right) = -1$. Find
    (a) the values of c and d,
    (b) the value of x for which f is undefined,
    (c) $f^{-1}(x)$,
    (d) the value of x for which f^{-1} is undefined.

11. Given the function $f : x \longmapsto 4 - \dfrac{3}{x}$, $x \neq 0$, find the values of x for which $f(x) = f^{-1}(x)$.

12. Given $f : x \longmapsto 4x - 17$ and $g : x \longmapsto \dfrac{5}{2x-7}$, $x \neq 3.5$, solve the equation $f^{-1}(x) = g^{-1}(x)$. (C)

13. Given $g : x \longmapsto \dfrac{x+1}{x-2}$ $(x \neq 2)$, $h : x \longmapsto \dfrac{ax+3}{x}$ $(x \neq 0)$, and $hg^{-1}(4) = 6$, find the value of a. (C)

14. Given that $f : x \longmapsto \dfrac{1}{x-2}$ $(x \neq 2)$, find $f^{-1}(x)$ and $f^2(x)$. Hence solve the equation $f^2(x) + 2f^{-1}(x) = 5$.

15. If $g : x \longmapsto \dfrac{a}{x-2}$ $(x \neq 2)$, find the values of a if $g^2(-1) + 2g^{-1}(-1) = -3$.

16. Given that $f : x \longmapsto \dfrac{3}{2x+1}$, $x \neq -\dfrac{1}{2}$, find
    (a) f^{-1},
    (b) ff^{-1},
    (c) $f^{-1}f$.
    What can you conclude about the relationship between ff^{-1} and $f^{-1}f$?

17. Given that $f : x \longmapsto \dfrac{x-3}{x+2}, x \neq -2$, find

    (a) f^{-1},

    (b) $f^{-1}f^{-1}$,

    (c) f^2,

    (d) $(f^2)^{-1}$.

What can you conclude about the relationship between $(f^2)^{-1}$ and $f^{-1}f^{-1}$?

18. Given that $f : x \longmapsto x - 4$ and $g : x \longmapsto 3x - 2$, find

    (a) f^{-1},

    (b) g^{-1},

    (c) $f^{-1}g^{-1}$,

    (d) $g^{-1}f^{-1}$.

What can you conclude about the relationship between $f^{-1}g^{-1}$ and $g^{-1}f^{-1}$?

19. Given that $f : x \longmapsto 2x + 1$ and $g : x \longmapsto 1 - 3x$, find

    (a) $(fg)^{-1}$,

    (b) $g^{-1}f^{-1}$.

What is the relationship between $(fg)^{-1}$ and $g^{-1}f^{-1}$?

20. Given that $f : x \longmapsto \dfrac{3}{x-1} + 2 \ (x \neq 1)$ and $g : x \longmapsto x + 4$, find

    (a) $(gf)^{-1}$,

    (b) $f^{-1}g^{-1}$.

What is the relationship between $(gf)^{-1}$ and $f^{-1}g^{-1}$?

21. Given that $f : x \longmapsto \dfrac{2}{1-x} \ (x \neq 1)$ and $g : x \longmapsto 3x - 1$, find

    (a) $(fg)^{-1}$,

    (b) $f^{-1}g^{-1}$.

What can you conclude about the relationship between $(fg)^{-1}$ and $f^{-1}g^{-1}$?

22. Copy each of the following diagrams showing the graph of a function $y = f(x)$, and sketch the graph $y = f^{-1}(x)$. In each case, state the domain and range of f^{-1}.

(a)

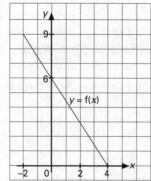

(b)

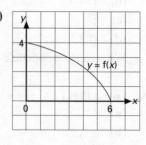

(c)

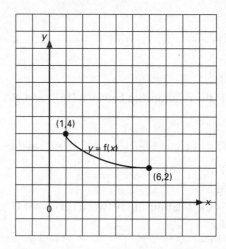

(d)

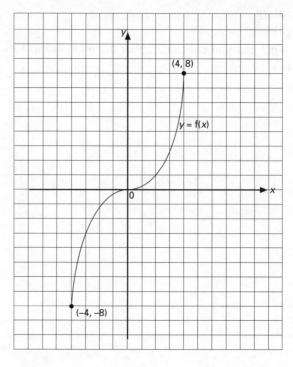

23. The function f is defined by $f : x \longmapsto 6 - 2x, 0 \leq x \leq 3$.
    (a) Sketch, on the same diagram, the graphs of f and f^{-1}.
    (b) State the domain and range of f^{-1}.

24. The function is defined by $f : x \longmapsto 3 - \dfrac{2}{x}, \dfrac{1}{2} \leq x \leq 2$.

    (a) Solve the equation $f(x) = x$.
    (b) Sketch, on the same diagram, the graphs of f and f^{-1}.
    (c) State the domain and range of f^{-1}.

25. The function f is defined by
$$f : x \longmapsto \begin{cases} x + 3, & x \geq 0 \\ 2x + 3, & x < 0 \end{cases}$$
Sketch, on the same diagram, the graphs of f and f^{-1}.

26. On graph paper, draw axes of x and y for $0 \leq x \leq 8$ and $0 \leq y \leq 8$, using the same scale on each axis. Plot the graph of $f : x \longmapsto 1 + \dfrac{6}{x}$ for the domain $1 \leq x \leq 4$, using integer values of x. By drawing a suitable line on your diagram, find the value of x for which $f(x) = f^{-1}(x)$. State the domain of f^{-1} and on your diagram plot the graph of f^{-1} for this domain.

(C)

2.4 Absolute Value Functions

2.4.1 Absolute Value of a Function

The **absolute value** of a number x is the numerical value of x and is denoted by $|x|$ (read as **modulus** of x).

For example, the numbers 3 and –3 have the same numerical value of 3. Hence we can say that the absolute value of 3 and –3 is 3 and is written as

$|3| = 3$ (read as 'modulus of 3 is 3')

$|-3| = 3$ (read as 'modulus of –3 is 3')

So we can define the absolute value of x as

$$|x| = \begin{cases} -x \text{ if } x < 0 \\ x \text{ if } x \geq 0 \end{cases}$$

Similarly the absolute value of a function $f(x)$, written as $|f(x)|$, is the numerical value of $f(x)$.

▶ **Example 25**

State the values of

(a) $|-10|$,

(b) $|\cos 150°|$,

(c) $|2^2 - 3^2|$.

▶ **Solution . . .**

(a) $|-10| = 10$

(b) $|\cos 150°| = |-0.866| = 0.866$

(c) $|2^2 - 3^2| = |4 - 9| = |-5| = 5$

▶ **Example 26**

Given $f(x) = |5 - 2x|$, find

(a) $f(-3)$,

(b) $f(3)$,

(c) $f\left(\dfrac{5}{2}\right)$.

▶ **Solution . . .**

(a) $f(-3) = |5 - 2(-3)|$

$\qquad = |11|$

$\qquad = 11$

(b) $f(3) = |5 - 2(3)|$

$\qquad = |-1|$

$\qquad = 1$

(c) $f\left(\dfrac{5}{2}\right) = |5 - 2\left(\dfrac{5}{2}\right)|$

$\qquad = |0|$

$\qquad = 0$

▶ **Example 27**

Given $f(x) = |3x - 8|$, find the values of x if $f(x) = 7$.

▶ **Solution . . .**

Given $\qquad\qquad f(x) = 7$

$\qquad\qquad |3x - 8| = 7$

$\qquad\qquad 3x - 8 = -7 \qquad$ or $\qquad 3x - 8 = 7$

$\qquad\qquad\qquad x = \dfrac{1}{3} \qquad$ or $\qquad\qquad x = 5$

2.4.2　Graph of an Absolute Value Function

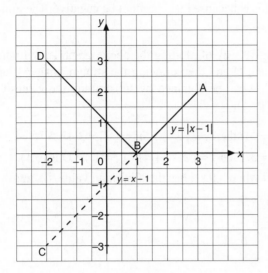

Fig. 2.19

Consider a function $f : x \longmapsto x - 1, -2 \leq x \leq 3$. Fig. 2.18 shows the graph of $y = f(x)$ (line ABC) and $y = |f(x)|$ (which is made up of two straight lines AB and BD).

Notice that BD is the reflection of BC in the x-axis. Hence we can draw the graph of $y = |f(x)|$ by drawing $y = f(x)$ first and then reflect any negative part in the x-axis.

▶ **Example 28**

Draw the graph of $y = |2 - x|$ for the domain $-1 < x < 3$ and state the range of y.

▶ **Solution . . .**

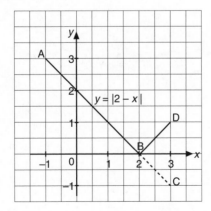

Steps:
1. Draw the line $y = 2 - x$ for $-1 \leq x \leq 3$ (line ABC).

2. Reflect the negative part in the x-axis (dotted line BC is reflected onto BD).

Hence the graph of $y = |2 - x|$ consists of two lines AB and BD.

Range of y is $0 \leq y \leq 3$.

Note that the graph of an absolute value function $|\,f(x)\,|$ always lies above the x-axis. This is because $|\,f(x)\,|$ cannot be negative. The minimum value of $|\,f(x)\,|$ is zero.

So an alternative way of plotting the above graph is by finding the three points A, B and D and then drawing the straight lines AB and BD. The points A and D can be obtained by substituting the values of x into the equation $y = |\,2 - x\,|$.

Substitute $x = -1$, then $y = |\,2 - (-1)\,| = |\,3\,| = 3$, so A is $(-1, 3)$.

Substitute $x = 3$, then $y = |\,2 - 3\,| = |\,-1\,| = 1$, so D is $(3, 1)$.

B is the point where $|\,f(x)\,|$ has the minimum value, i.e. zero.

$$|\,f(x)\,| = 0$$
$$|\,2 - x\,| = 0$$
$$2 - x = 0$$
$$x = 2$$

B is $(2, 0)$.

Hence the graph is

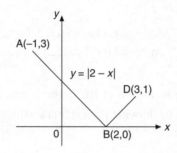

► **Example 29**

Draw the graph of $y = |\,6 - 2x\,| + 2$ for $1 \le x \le 5$.

(a) Find the values of x for which $y = 4$.

(b) Find the range of values of x for which $y \le 4$.

Analysis

Use Graphmatica courseware to plot the following set of graphs:

(a) $y = |\,x\,|, y = |\,x\,| + 2, y = |\,x\,| - 2$

(b) $y = |\,x\,|, y = |\,x + 2\,|, y = |\,x - 2\,|$

Make some observations about how the graph of $y = |\,x\,|$ is 'moved' or 'translated' by the addition or subtraction of 2.

▶ **Solution . . .**

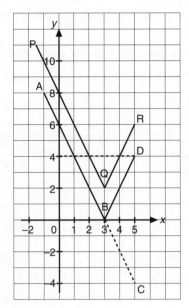

Steps:
1. Draw the line $y = 6 - 2x$ for $-1 \le x \le 5$ (line ABC).
2. Reflect BC onto BD to obtain the graph of $y = |\,6 - 2x\,|$ (lines AB and BD).
3. Translate the graph of $y = |\,6 - 2x\,|$ by $\binom{2}{0}$ to obtain the graph of $y = |\,6 - 2x\,| + 2$ (lines PQ and QR).

(a) When $y = 4$, $x = 2$ and 4. (Line $y = 4$ cuts the graph at $x = 2$ and $x = 4$.)

(b) When $y \le 4$, $2 \le x \le 4$.

Exercise 2D (*Answers on page 495*)

1. State the values of

(a) $|-8|$,　　(b) $|-\frac{1}{2}|$,　　(c) $|\cos 120°|$,　　(d) $|3^2 - 6^2|$.

2. Given $f(x) = |\,3x - 1\,|$, find

(a) $f(2)$,　　(b) $f(-2)$,　　(c) $f\left(\frac{1}{3}\right)$.

3. State the values of $|\,1 - x\,|$ for $x = -3, 2, 4$.

4. Given $f(x) = x^2 - x - 6$, find the values of $|\,f(x)\,|$ for $x = -3, 0, 3, 6$.

5. If $f(x) = 2\,|\,x - 1\,| - 3$, find $f(3)$, $f(1)$, $f(0)$ and $f(-1)$.

6. Given $f(x) = |\,2x - 5\,|$, find the values of x if $f(x) = 3$.

7. Given $g(x) = |\,1 - 3x\,|$, find the values of x for which $g(x) = x$.

8. Given $h(x) = |\,4 - 3x\,|$, find the values of x when $h(x) = 2x$.

9. Draw the graph of $y = |\,2x - 4\,|$ for the domain $0 \le x \le 3$ and state the range of y.

10. Draw the graph of $y = |\,3 - 2x\,|$ for the domain $-1 \le x \le 3$ and state the range of y.

11. Draw the graph of $y = |\frac{2}{3}x + 2|$ for the domain $-6 \le x \le 3$. State the minimum value of y and the value of x when y is minimum.

12. On the same graph paper, draw the graphs of $y = |2x|$ and $y = -\frac{2}{3}(x - 4)$ for the domain $-3 \le x \le 4$. Hence solve the equation $|2x| = -\frac{2}{3}(x - 4)$.

13. Copy each of the following diagrams showing the graph of a function $y = f(x)$, and on it sketch the graph $y = |f(x)|$. In each case state the range of $|f(x)|$.

    (a)

    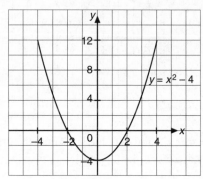

    (b)

    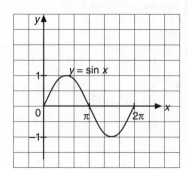

    (c)

    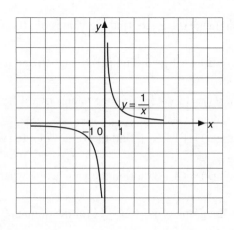

14. **(a)** Draw the graph of $y = |\,2x - 1\,|$ for $-2 \le x \le 4$.

   (b) On the same diagram, draw the graph of $y = |\,2x - 1\,| + 2$ for the same domain.

   (c) State the range of $y = |\,2x - 1\,| + 2$.

15. Draw the graph of $y = |\,2x - 3\,| - 3$ for the domain $-2 \le x \le 4$.
   (a) State the range of y for $-2 \le x \le 4$.
   (b) Find the range of x if $y \le 0$.

16. Draw the graph of $y = 4 - |\,x - 3\,|$ for the domain $-2 \le x \le 6$.
   (a) State the range of y for $-2 \le x \le 6$.
   (b) Find the values of x for which $y = 2$.
   (c) Find the range of x for which $y \ge 2$.

17. The diagram shows part of the graph of $y = 3 - |\,x - 2\,|$. Find the coordinates of the points A and B. (C)

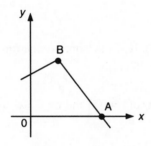

18. Sketch the graphs of $3y = 4x + 2$ and $3y = |\,4x - 8\,|$ on the same diagram. Solve the following simultaneous equations:

$$3y = 4x + 2$$
$$3y = |\,4x - 8\,|$$

(C)

Summary

1. **Function**

   A function f maps every object (x) in the domain onto only one image (y) in the range.

   $$f : x \longmapsto y$$
   or $\quad f(x) = y$

   Domain   Range

2. **Composite Function**

(a) If f maps set A onto set B and g maps set B onto set C, then the composite function gf maps set A onto set C.

gf

(b) In general, gf ≠ fg.

(c) f^2 means ff, f^3 means fff, and so on.

3. **Inverse Function**

(a) An inverse function f^{-1} maps every image (y) in the range back onto only one object (x) in the domain.

If $f : x \longmapsto y$,
then $f^{-1} : y \longmapsto x$.

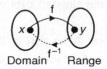

Domain   Range

(b) f^{-1} exists only if f is a one-to-one function.

(c) $ff^{-1}(x) = f^{-1}f(x) = x$

(d) $(fg)^{-1} = g^{-1}f^{-1}$; $(gf)^{-1} = f^{-1}g^{-1}$.

(e) The graphs of $y = f(x)$ and $y = f^{-1}(x)$ are reflections of each other in the line $y = x$.

4. **Absolute Value Function**

(a) $|f(x)| = \begin{cases} f(x) & \text{if} \quad f(x) \geq 0 \\ -f(x) & \text{if} \quad f(x) < 0 \end{cases}$

(b) To draw the graph of $y = |f(x)|$, first draw the graph of $y = f(x)$ and then reflect any negative parts in the x-axis.

Revision Exercise 2 (Answers on page 495)

1. The function f is defined by $f : x \longmapsto 3x - \dfrac{10}{x}$, $x \neq 0$. Find
   (a) the value of f(2),
   (b) the values of x which have an image of 1 under f.

2. The function R maps x onto the remainder when 16 is divided by x. If the domain is {2, 3, 5, 7}, find the range. Does R^{-1} exist?

3. Given the function $g : x \longmapsto 2x - 3$, find the domain of x if $-5 \leq g(x) \leq 3$.

4. The arrow diagram represents part of the function $f : x \longmapsto y$, where $y = ax + b$. Calculate the value of a and of b.

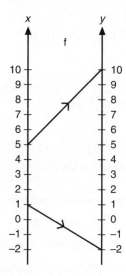

Find the endpoints of the shortest arrow that can be drawn for this function.

5. The function f is defined by $h : x \longmapsto \dfrac{tx + 9}{1 - x}, x \neq 1$. Find the value of t for which the equation $h(x) = x$ has the solution $x = 3$.

6. The functions f and g are defined by
$f : x \longmapsto$ remainder when x^2 is divided by 7, and
$g : x \longmapsto$ remainder when x^2 is divided by 5.
(a) Show that $f(5) = g(3)$.
(b) If n is an integer, prove that $f(7n + x) = f(x)$ and state the corresponding result for g. (C)

7. Given the function $g : x \longmapsto \dfrac{2x + 3}{x - 2}, x \neq 2$, show that $gg(x) = x$ for all values of x except $x = 2$.

8. A function f is defined as $f : x \longmapsto \dfrac{x}{x - 3}, x \neq 3$.

Show that $f^2 = x \longmapsto \dfrac{x}{-2x + 9}, x \neq 3, x \neq \dfrac{9}{2}$. Obtain a similar expression for f^3 and hence suggest a possible expression for f^6.

9. If $f : x \longmapsto ax + b \ (a > 0)$ and $f^2 : x \longmapsto 9x - 8$, find
(a) the values of a and b,
(b) f^3,
(c) f^4,
and hence deduce f^5.

10. Given that $f : x \longmapsto x + 2$ and $gf : x \longmapsto x^2 + 4x + 2$, find the function g. Hence express $h : x \longmapsto x^2 - 4x + 2$ in terms of f and g.

11. Functions f and g are defined by

$$f : x \longmapsto \frac{3x-1}{x-2}, x \neq 2, \text{ and } g : x \longmapsto \frac{2x-1}{x-3}, x \neq 3.$$

(a) Show that $fg : x \longmapsto x$.

(b) Evaluate $f^{-1}(5)$, $g^{-1}(4)$ and $ffg(7)$.

(C)

12. Given that $f : x \longmapsto \frac{x+p}{x-3}, x \neq 3$ and that $f(4) = 9$, find the value of p. Hence,

(a) find $f^{-1}(-3)$,

(b) obtain a similar expression for f^2,

(c) find the values of x which have the same image under f^2 and f^{-1}.

13. (a) Functions f and g are defined by

$$f : x \longmapsto \frac{6}{x-2}, x \neq 2, \text{ and}$$
$$g : x \longmapsto kx^2 - 1, \text{ where } k \text{ is a constant.}$$

(i) Given that $gf(5) = 7$, evaluate k.

(ii) Express $f^2(x)$ in the form $\frac{ax+b}{c-x}$, stating the values of a, b and c.

(b) On graph paper, using the same scale on each axis, draw the graph of $h : x \longmapsto \frac{2x+2}{x+2}$ for the domain $-1 \leq x \leq 3$.

(i) By drawing the appropriate straight line on the graph, obtain a solution to the equation $h(x) = h^{-1}(x)$.

(ii) State the domain of $h^{-1}(x)$.

(iii) Using the same axes for $h(x)$, draw, on the same diagram, the graph of $h^{-1}(x)$.

(C)

14. The function f is defined by

$$f : x \longmapsto \begin{cases} 2 & \text{for} \quad x \geq 0 \\ x + 2 & \text{for} \quad x < 0 \end{cases}$$

Sketch the graphs of f and f^{-1}.

15. On the same graph paper, sketch the graphs of $y = |x + 1|$ and $y = |3 - x|$. Hence solve the equation $|x + 1| = |3 - x|$.

16. Find the distance between the two points of intersection of the graphs of $y = |x - 1|$ and $y = -\frac{1}{2}x + 5$.

(C)

17. Solve the simultaneous equations $3x - 2y = 13$, and $|x + y| = 1$.

(C)

1. Draw the graph of $y = \left| \, 1 - \left| \, 2 - x \, \right| \, \right|$ for the domain $-3 < x < 5$.

2. For the domain $-3 \le x \le 3$, sketch the graph of $y = |\,[x]\,|$, where $[x]$ means the greatest integer less than or equal to x (for example, $[3.4] = 3$, and $[-3.4] = -4$). State the range of this function for this domain.

3. If $\left| \, a \, \right| < 1$ and $\left| \, b \, \right| < 1$, prove that $\left| \dfrac{a+b}{1+ab} \right| < 1$.

Chapter 3

Quadratic Functions

In everyday life, many things and activities are related to curves, for example, a satellite dish, a suspension bridge, and even the way a ball moves in the air when you kick it. These curves can be represented by specific algebraic functions called **quadratic functions**.

3.1 Quadratic Functions

The expression $f(x) = ax^2 + bx + c$, where $a \neq 0$, is called a **quadratic function**. Some examples are $f(x) = 3x^2 - 5x + 2$, $g(x) = 4x - x^2$ and $h(x) = 5x^2$. Note that the highest power of x in a quadratic function is 2. So $f(x) = 6x^2 - x^3$ is not a quadratic function. Do you know why?

3.1.1 Quadratic Function and its Graph

Analysis

Below are graphs of two quadratic functions. Do you know the properties of the two curves?

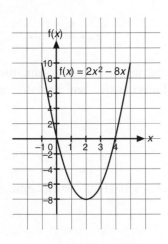

Fig. 3.1   Fig. 3.2

Compare and Contrast

Draw the graphs of
$f(x) = x^2 - 2x + 4$ for $-2 \leq x \leq 4$ and
$g(x) = 1 - 4x - x^2$ for $-5 \leq x \leq 1$.
Compare and contrast the two graphs you have obtained.

The graph of $f(x) = 2x^2 - 8x$ in Fig. 3.1 has a characteristic shape. It is called a **parabola**. This parabola has a **minimum** value at the bottom of the curve. This minimum value is -8. It occurs when $x = 2$. Note also that the curve is symmetrical about the line $x = 2$. The line $x = 2$ is called the **line of symmetry**.

The graph of $g(x) = 9 + 6x - 3x^2$ in Fig. 3.2 is also a parabola. This parabola has a **maximum** value at the top of the curve. This maximum value is 12 which occurs when $x = 1$. The line of symmetry is $x = 1$.

3.1.2 Maximum or Minimum Values of Quadratic Functions

Induction

The following are graphs of some quadratic functions. What can you induce about the relation between the coefficient of x^2 (i.e., value of a) and the maximum or minimum value a quadratic function $f(x) = ax^2 + bx + c$ has?

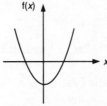

$f(x) = x^2 - 4x - 5$

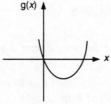

$g(x) = 3x^2 - 6x$

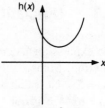

$h(x) = 2x^2 + 5$

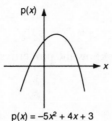

$p(x) = -5x^2 + 4x + 3$

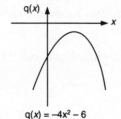

$q(x) = -4x^2 - 6$

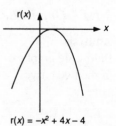

$r(x) = -x^2 + 4x - 4$

From the graphs above, it can be induced that a quadratic function $f(x) = ax^2 + bx + c$ has a minimum value if a is positive, and a maximum value if a is negative.

▶ **Example 1**

Which of the following quadratic functions has a maximum or a minimum value?

(a) $f(x) = (2 - x)(3x + 4)$

(b) $g(x) = (x - 2)^2 - 8$

▶ **Solution . . .**

To find out whether a quadratic function has a maximum or a minimum value,

(1) express the quadratic function in the form $f(x) = ax^2 + bx + c$,

(2) if $a > 0$, $f(x)$ has a minimum value;
     if $a < 0$, $f(x)$ has a maximum value.

(a) $\begin{aligned} f(x) &= (2 - x)(3x + 4) \\ &= -3x^2 + 2x + 8 \end{aligned}$

Since $a < 0$ ($a = -3$), $f(x)$ has a maximum value.

(b) $\begin{aligned} g(x) &= (x - 2)^2 - 8 \\ &= x^2 - 4x - 4 \end{aligned}$

Since $a > 0$ ($a = 1$), $g(x)$ has a minimum value.

Analysis and Induction

Below are graphs of 2 quadratic functions expressed in the form of $f(x) = a(x - h)^2 + k$. What can you induce from the values of h and k?

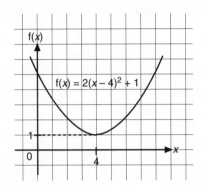 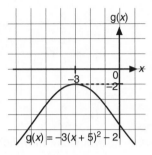

It is observed that:

The graph of $f(x) = 2(x - 4)^2 + 1$ has a minimum value of 1 when $x = 4$.

The graph of $g(x) = -3(x + 5)^2 - 2$ has a maximum value of -2 when $x = -5$.

From the graphs above, it can be induced that a quadratic function expressed in the form of $f(x) = a(x - h)^2 + k$ has a maximum or minimum value (depending on the value of a) of k when $x = h$.

Note that the minimum point of $f(x) = 2(x - 4)^2 + 1$ is $(4,1)$, and the maximum point of $g(x) = -3(x + 5)^2 - 2$ is $(-5,-2)$. The maximum and minimum points of quadratic functions are also called **turning points** of the curves.

▶ ## Example 2

State the maximum or minimum value of the following functions and the corresponding value of x.

(a) $f(x) = (x + 5)^2 - 1$

(b) $g(x) = 6 - \dfrac{x^2}{3}$

▶ ## Solution . . .

(a) $f(x) = (x + 5)^2 - 1 \equiv a(x - h)^2 + k$

$a = 1, h = -5, k = -1$

As $a > 0$, $f(x)$ has a minimum value. The minimum value is -1 when $x = -5$.

(b) $g(x) = 6 - \dfrac{x^2}{3}$

$= -\dfrac{1}{3}(x - 0)^2 + 6$

$\equiv a(x - h)^2 + k$

$a = -\dfrac{1}{3}, h = 0, k = 6$

As $a < 0$, $g(x)$ has a maximum value. The maximum value is 6 when $x = 0$.

A quadratic function has to be expressed in the form $f(x) = a(x - h)^2 + k$ in order to find the maximum or minimum value.

We can express a given quadratic function $f(x) = ax^2 + bx + c$ in the form of $f(x) = a(x - h)^2 + k$ using the **completing square** method.

$$f(x) = ax^2 + bx + c$$

$$= a\left(x^2 + \frac{b}{a}x\right) + c$$

$$= a\left[x^2 + \frac{b}{a}x + \left(\frac{b}{2a}\right)^2 - \left(\frac{b}{2a}\right)^2\right] + c$$

$$= a\left[\left(x + \frac{b}{2a}\right)^2 - \frac{b^2}{4a^2}\right] + c$$

$$= a\left(x + \frac{b}{2a}\right)^2 - \frac{b^2}{4a} + c$$

Hence the maximum or minimum value of $f(x)$ is $-\dfrac{b^2}{4a} + c$ when $x = -\dfrac{b}{2a}$.

▶ **Example 3**

What is the minimum value of $3x^2 - 4x + 1$ and for what value of x does it occur?

▶ **Solution . . .**

Method 1 (using the formula $f(x) = a\left(x + \dfrac{b}{2a}\right)^2 - \dfrac{b^2}{4a} + c$)

Let $f(x) = 3x^2 - 4x + 1$; $a = 3$, $b = -4$, $c = 1$

Minimum value of $f(x) = -\dfrac{b^2}{4a} + c$

$$= -\frac{(-4)^2}{4(3)} + 1$$

$$= -\frac{1}{3}$$

The minimum value occurs when x is $-\dfrac{b}{2a}$

$$= -\frac{(-4)}{2(3)}$$

$$= \frac{2}{3}$$

Method 2 (using the completing square method)

$$f(x) = 3x^2 - 4x + 1$$

$$= 3\left(x^2 - \frac{4}{3}x\right) + 1$$

$$= 3\left[x^2 - \frac{4}{3}x + \left(\frac{2}{3}\right)^2 - \left(\frac{2}{3}\right)^2\right] + 1$$

$$= 3\left[\left(x - \frac{2}{3}\right)^2 - \frac{4}{9}\right] + 1$$

$$= 3\left(x - \frac{2}{3}\right)^2 - \frac{4}{3} + 1$$

$$= 3\left(x - \frac{2}{3}\right)^2 - \frac{1}{3}$$

The minimum value is $-\dfrac{1}{3}$ when $x = \dfrac{2}{3}$.

▶ **Example 4**

Find the maximum point of the graph $f(x) = 5 - x - 2x^2$.

▶ **Solution . . .**

$$f(x) = 5 - x - 2x^2$$
$$= -2x^2 - x + 5$$
$$= -2\left(x^2 + \frac{1}{2}x\right) + 5$$
$$= -2\left[x^2 + \frac{1}{2}x + \left(\frac{1}{4}\right)^2 - \left(\frac{1}{4}\right)^2\right] + 5$$
$$= -2\left[\left(x + \frac{1}{4}\right)^2 - \frac{1}{16}\right] + 5$$
$$= -2\left(x + \frac{1}{4}\right)^2 + \frac{41}{8}$$

The maximum point is $\left(-\frac{1}{4}, \frac{41}{8}\right)$.

3.1.3   Sketching the Graph of a Quadratic Function

To sketch a graph, we need to know:
(1)   the shape of the curve, $\cup$ or $\cap$,
(2)   the turning point,
(3)   where it cuts the y-axis. (This is given by $f(0)$.)

▶ **Example 5**

Sketch the graph of $f(x) = 2x^2 - 3x - 4$. State the range of the function for all real values of x.

▶ **Solution . . .**

(1)   As $a > 0$ $(a = 2)$, the shape is $\cup$.
(2) $f(x) = 2x^2 - 3x - 4$
$$= 2\left(x - \frac{3}{4}\right)^2 - \frac{41}{8}.$$

So the minimum point is $\left(\frac{3}{4}, -\frac{41}{8}\right)$.
(3) $f(0) = -4$.
So the curve cuts the y-axis at $(0, -4)$.

The curve can now be sketched through these points.

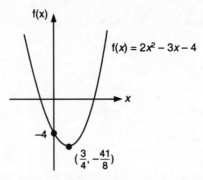

The range of f(x) is $f(x) \geq -\dfrac{41}{8}$.

3.1.4   Range of a Quadratic Function for a given Domain

To find the range of a quadratic function for a given domain $a \leq x \leq b$, we need to know:

(1) the maximum or minimum value of the function,
(2) f(a) and f(b),
(3) the sketch of the graph.

▶ ## Example 6

Find the range of $f(x) = x^2 - 2x - 3$ for the domain $-2 \leq x \leq 5$.

▶ ## Solution . . .

(1) $f(x) = x^2 - 2x - 3$
$\qquad = (x - 1)^2 - 4$.
So f(x) has a minimum value of -4 where $x = 1$.

(2) $f(-2) = (-2)^2 - 2(-2) - 3$
$\qquad\quad = 5$
$f(5) = 5^2 - 2(5) - 3$
$\qquad = 12$

(3) Sketch of the graph:

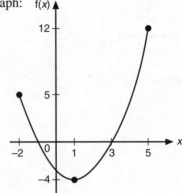

The range of f(x) is $-4 \leq f(x) \leq 12$.

Exercise 3A (Answers on page 496)

1. Which of the following quadratic functions has a maximum or a minimum value?
   - **(a)** $f(x) = 6 - x^2 + 2x$
   - **(b)** $g(x) = 2x(3x - 1)$
   - **(c)** $h(x) = (x - 3)(4 - 3x)$
   - **(d)** $i(x) = 3(2x - 5)^2 - 11$

2. State the maximum or minimum value of the following functions and the corresponding value of x at which the maximum or minimum value occurs:

   - **(a)** $f(x) = (x - 3)^2 - 2$
   - **(b)** $g(x) = 3 - 2(x - 4)^2$

   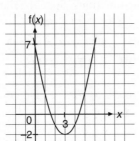
   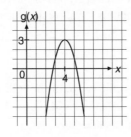

   - **(c)** $h(x) = -3(x - 2)^2$
   - **(d)** $i(x) = (x + 6)^2 + 2$

   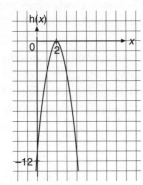
   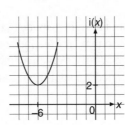

3. State the maximum or minimum value of the following functions and the corresponding value of x:
   - **(a)** $f(x) = 2(x - 1)^2 - 8$
   - **(b)** $g(x) = 5 - (x + 3)^2$
   - **(c)** $h(x) = 3(x + 5)^2$
   - **(d)** $i(x) = 6 - x^2$
   - **(e)** $j(x) = 5 + (2x + 1)^2$
   - **(f)** $k(x) = -(4 - 3x)^2 - 12$

4. Find the maximum or minimum values of the following functions and the corresponding values of x where this occurs:
   - **(a)** $x^2 - 6x - 1$
   - **(b)** $2x^2 + 8x - 5$
   - **(c)** $1 - 4x - 2x^2$
   - **(d)** $(1 - x)(x + 2)$
   - **(e)** $x^2 + 3x$
   - **(f)** $x^2 + 2bx + c$

5. Find the minimum point of the graph $f(x) = 2x^2 - x - 4$.

6. Find the maximum point of the graph $g(x) = 3 - x - 2x^2$.

7. Express $5 - x - 2x^2$ in the form $a(x - h)^2 + k$ and hence or otherwise, find its maximum value and the value of x where it occurs.

8. If the minimum value of $x^2 + 4x + k$ is -7, find the value of k.

9. The function $f(x) = ax^2 + bx + 1$ has a minimum value of 4 where $x = -1$. Find the value of a and of b.

10. Sketch the graphs of the following functions. State the range of each function for all real values of x.
    (a) $f(x) = x^2 + 2x - 3$ (b) $g(x) = 2x^2 - 4x + 5$
    (c) $h(x) = 3 - 8x - 2x^2$ (d) $i(x) = x(2 - x)$

11. Find the range of the following functions for the given domains:
    (a) $f(x) = x^2 - 4x - 1$ for $-1 \le x \le 3$
    (b) $g(x) = 3 - 4x - 2x^2$ for $-4 \le x \le 4$

12. The height (h cm) of a ball above the ground is given by the function $h(t) = 15t - 5t^2$, where t is the time in seconds since the ball left ground level. Find the range of the height for $1 \le t \le 3$.

13. A spot of light is made to travel across a computer screen in a straight line so that, at t seconds after starting, its distance from the left-hand edge (d cm) is given by the function $d(t) = 7t - t^2 + 2$. Find the furthest distance the spot travels and how long it takes to travel this distance.

3.2   Quadratic Equations

3.2.1 *Solving Quadratic Equations*

There are various methods of solving a quadratic equation:

(I)   By factorisation

This is the simplest method if it is possible. In this method, the quadratic equation is first rewritten in the form $ax^2 + bx + c = 0$ and then factorised completely.

▶ **Example 7**

Solve $x(6x + 5) = 4$

► **Solution . . .**

$$x(6x + 5) = 4$$
$$6x^2 + 5x = 4$$
$$6x^2 + 5x - 4 = 0$$
$$(2x - 1)(3x + 4) = 0$$
$$2x - 1 = 0 \quad \text{or} \quad 3x + 4 = 0$$
$$x = \frac{1}{2} \quad \text{or} \quad x = -\frac{4}{3}$$

(II) By completing the square

Some quadratic equations cannot be solved by factorisation because the quadratic expression $ax^2 + bx + c$ cannot be factorised completely. These quadratic equations can be solved by completing the square.

► **Example 8**

Solve $2x^2 - 3x - 1 = 0$

► **Solution . . .**

$$2x^2 - 3x - 1 = 0$$
$$x^2 - \frac{3}{2}x - \frac{1}{2} = 0$$
$$x^2 - \frac{3}{2}x = \frac{1}{2}$$
$$x^2 - \frac{3}{2}x + \left(\frac{3}{4}\right)^2 = \frac{1}{2} + \left(\frac{3}{4}\right)^2$$
$$\left(x - \frac{3}{4}\right)^2 = \frac{17}{16}$$
$$x - \frac{3}{4} = \pm\sqrt{\frac{17}{16}}$$
$$x - 0.75 = \pm 1.03$$
$$x - 0.75 = 1.03 \quad \text{or} \quad x - 0.75 = -1.03$$
$$x = 1.78 \quad \text{or} \quad x = -0.28$$

(III) By formula

We can derive a formula for the solutions or **roots** of any quadratic equation using the completing square method as follows :

$$ax^2 + bx + c = 0$$
$$x^2 + \frac{b}{a}x + \frac{c}{a} = 0$$
$$x^2 + \frac{b}{a}x = -\frac{c}{a}$$
$$x^2 + \frac{b}{a}x + \left(\frac{b}{2a}\right)^2 = -\frac{c}{a} + \left(\frac{b}{2a}\right)^2$$

$$\left(x + \frac{b}{2a}\right)^2 = \frac{b^2 - 4ac}{4a^2}$$

$$x + \frac{b}{2a} = \frac{\pm\sqrt{b^2 - 4ac}}{2a}$$

$$x = \frac{-b \pm \sqrt{b^2 - 4ac}}{2a}$$

▶ **Example 9**

Solve $2x^2 - 3x - 4 = 0$.

▶ **Solution . . .**

Here $a = 2$, $b = -3$, $c = -4$

$$x = \frac{-(-3) \pm \sqrt{(-3)^2 - 4(2)(-4)}}{2(2)}$$

$$= \frac{3 \pm \sqrt{41}}{4}$$

$$= 2.35 \quad \text{or} \quad -0.85$$

3.2.2 Types of Roots of $ax^2 + bx + c = 0$

For any quadratic equation $ax^2 + bx + c = 0$, the roots are given by $x = \frac{-b \pm \sqrt{b^2 - 4ac}}{2a}$. The expression $b^2 - 4ac$ is called the **discriminant**, D, where

$$D = b^2 - 4ac \quad .$$

D determines the types of roots the equation has.

(I)   If $D > 0$, the equation has two different real roots.

(II)   If $D = 0$, the equation has two equal real roots.

(III) If $D < 0$, the equation has no real roots.

▶ **Example 10**

What types of roots do the following equations have?

(a) $2x^2 + 3x - 4 = 0$

(b) $9x^2 - 12x + 4 = 0$

(c) $5x^2 - 3x + 1 = 0$

▶ **Solution . . .**

(a) $2x^2 + 3x - 4 = 0$; $a = 2$, $b = 3$, $c = -4$

      $D = b^2 - 4ac$

        $= 3^2 - 4(2)(-4)$

        $= 41$

      As $D > 0$, the equation has two different real roots.

(b) $9x^2 - 12x + 4 = 0$; $a = 9$, $b = -12$, $c = 4$

$D = (-12)^2 - 4(9)(4)$

$ = 0$

As $D = 0$, the equation has two equal real roots.

(c) $5x^2 - 3x + 1 = 0$; $a = 5$, $b = -3$, $c = 1$

$D = (-3)^2 - 4(5)(1)$

$ = -11$

As $D < 0$, the equation has no real roots.

▶ **Example 11**

Find the values of p for which the equation $(p + 3)x^2 - 12x + 2p = 0$ has equal real roots.

▶ **Solution . . .**

Here $a = p + 3$, $b = -12$, $c = 2p$.

For equal real roots, $D = 0$.

$$b^2 - 4ac = 0$$
$$(-12)^2 - 4(p + 3)(2p) = 0$$
$$144 - 8p^2 - 24p = 0$$
$$18 - p^2 - 3p = 0$$
$$p^2 + 3p - 18 = 0$$
$$(p + 6)(p - 3) = 0$$
$$p = -6 \text{ or } 3$$

▶ **Example 12**

The equation $qx^2 - 2(q + 3)x + q - 1 = 0$ has two different real roots. What is the range of values of q?

▶ **Solution . . .**

Here $a = q$, $b = -2(q + 3)$, $c = q - 1$.

For two different real roots, $D > 0$.

$$[-2(q + 3)]^2 - 4(q)(q - 1) > 0$$
$$4q^2 + 24q + 36 - 4q^2 + 4q > 0$$
$$28q + 36 > 0$$
$$q > -\frac{9}{7}$$

▶ **Example 13**

Find the range of values of k for which the equation $kx^2 + 3x + k = 2kx + 5$ has no real roots.

► **Solution . . .**

$$kx^2 + 3x + k = 2kx + 5$$
$$kx^2 + (3 - 2k)x + k - 5 = 0$$
$$a = k, b = 3 - 2k, c = k - 5.$$

For no real roots, $D < 0$.

$$(3 - 2k)^2 - 4(k)(k - 5) < 0$$
$$9 - 12k + 4k^2 - 4k^2 + 20k < 0$$
$$9 + 8k < 0$$
$$k < -\frac{9}{8}$$

3.2.3 Conditions for the Intersection of a Line and a Curve

When a line and a curve are drawn on the same graph, the line may intersect, touch or not intersect the curve. To find out, we first solve the equation of the line and the curve simultaneously and then find out what type of roots the resulting equation has.

(1) When a line intersects a curve at two distinct points, the resulting equation has two different real roots, i.e. $b^2 - 4ac > 0$.

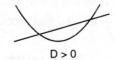

(2) When a line touches a curve (i.e. the line is a tangent to the curve), the resulting equation has two equal real roots, i.e. $b^2 - 4ac = 0$.

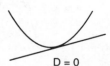

(3) When a line does not intersect a curve, the resulting equation has no real roots, i.e. $b^2 - 4ac < 0$.

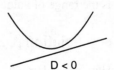

► **Example 14**

Find the range of values of m for which the line $y = mx + 6$ intersects the curve $2x^2 - xy = 3$ at two distinct points.

► **Solution . . .**

$$y = mx + 6 \quad \ldots \ldots (1)$$
$$2x^2 - xy = 3 \quad \ldots \ldots (2)$$

Substitute (1) into (2),

$$2x^2 - x(mx + 6) = 3$$
$$2x^2 - mx^2 - 6x = 3$$
$$(2 - m)x^2 - 6x - 3 = 0$$

Since the line intersects the curve at two distinct points, the above equation has two different real roots, i.e.

$$b^2 - 4ac > 0$$
$$(-6)^2 - 4(2 - m)(-3) > 0$$
$$36 + 24 - 12m > 0$$
$$-12m > -60$$
$$m < \frac{-60}{-12}$$
$$m < 5$$

▶ **Example 15**

Find the values of k if the line $x + y = k$ is a tangent to the curve $x^2 + y^2 = 8$.

▶ **Solution . . .**

$$x + y = k \qquad \ldots \ldots (1)$$
$$x^2 + y^2 = 8 \qquad \ldots \ldots (2)$$
Rearranging (1), $\quad y = k - x \quad \ldots \ldots (3)$
Substitute (3) into (2),
$$x^2 + (k - x)^2 = 8$$
$$x^2 + k^2 - 2kx + x^2 = 8$$
$$2x^2 - 2kx + k^2 - 8 = 0$$

Since the line is a tangent to the curve, the above equation has equal real roots, i.e.

$$b^2 - 4ac = 0$$
$$(-2k)^2 - 4(2)(k^2 - 8) = 0$$
$$4k^2 - 8k^2 + 64 = 0$$
$$k^2 = 16$$
$$k = \pm 4$$

Exercise 3B (Answers on page 496)

1. Solve the following equations by factorisation:
   (a) $x^2 + 3x = 10$
   (b) $2x^2 = 6 - 11x$
   (c) $(2x - 1)(x - 3) = 18$
   (d) $(3x + 10)(x - 1) = 20x$

2. Solve the following equations by completing the square:
   (a) $x^2 + 4x - 3 = 0$
   (b) $x^2 - 5x + 2 = 0$
   (c) $2x^2 + 3x - 6 = 0$
   (d) $2x(1 - 2x) + 5 = 0$

3. Solve the following equations by formula:
   (a) $4x^2 - 3x - 2 = 0$
   (b) $3x^2 = x + 3$
   (c) $(5x - 2)(x + 1) = 10$
   (d) $(x - 1)(x - 3) = 2x + 5$

4. What types of roots do the following equations have?
   (a) $x^2 - 6x + 10 = 0$ (b) $4x^2 - 20x + 25 = 0$
   (c) $3x^2 + x = 1$ (d) $2x^2 = px + p^2$

5. Find the values of p if the following equations have equal real roots:
   (a) $x^2 - 6x - p - 2 = 0$ (b) $x^2 - 2px + p + 2 = 0$
   (c) $x^2 + (p - 2)x + 10 - p = 0$ (d) $x^2 - 2x + 1 = p(x - 3)$

6. Find the range of values of q for which the following equations have two different real roots:
   (a) $x^2 + 3x + q - 2 = 0$ (b) $3qx^2 - 4x + 1 = 0$
   (c) $3 - 8x - 2qx^2 = 0$ (d) $x^2 - 2qx + q^2 = 2q - 6$

7. Find the range of values of k for which the following equations have no real roots:
   (a) $3kx^2 + 6x - 1 = 0$ (b) $2x^2 - 4x + k + 3 = 0$
   (c) $(2k - 3)x^2 + 4x = 5$ (d) $2x^2 - 5x = kx^2 + x - 3$

8. The equation $(p + 3)x^2 + 2px + p = 1$ has real roots. Find the range of values of p.

9. If the equation $x^2 - (p - 2)x + 1 = p(x - 2)$ is satisfied by only one value of x, what are the possible values of p?

10. What is the largest value m can have if the roots of $3x^2 - 4x + m = 0$ are real?

11. Show that the equation $a^2x^2 + ax + 1 = 0$ can never have real roots.

12. Find the range of values of m for which the line $y = mx + 12$ intersects the curve $x^2 + xy = 12$ at two distinct points.

13. Find the range of values of k for which the line $y = x + k$ does not intersect the curve $y^2 = 4x$.

14. Find the values of t for which the line $y = t(1 - 2x)$ is tangent to the curve $y = x^2 + 2$.

15. Find the relation between m and c if the line $y = mx + c$ is a tangent to the curve $y^2 = 2x$.

16. The line $y = mx + c$ is a tangent to the curve $x^2 + y^2 = 9$. Show that $9m^2 = c^2 - 9$.

17. The equation $kx^2 + 2(k + a)x + k = a$ has equal roots. Express k in terms of a. Show that the line $y = k(x - 3)$ is a tangent to the curve $y = k(x^2 - 3x + 1)$ for any values of k except 0.

3.3 Quadratic Inequalities

There are various methods of solving a quadratic inequality:

(I) By graph

(1) Rewrite the quadratic inequality in the form $ax^2 + bx + c > 0$ or $ax^2 + bx + c < 0$.

(2) Factorise completely the quadratic expression.

(3) Find out where the curve cuts the x-axis. This is given by $f(x) = 0$.

(4) Sketch the graph, 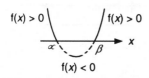 or 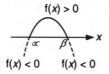 .

(5) The part of the curve above the x-axis indicates $f(x) > 0$, and that below the x-axis indicates $f(x) < 0$.

$f(x) > 0$ $f(x) > 0$ $f(x) > 0$

α β x α β x

$f(x) < 0$ $f(x) < 0$ $f(x) < 0$

▶ **Example 16**

Find the range of values of x for which $x^2 + 5x > 6$.

▶ **Solution . . .**

(1) $\qquad x^2 + 5x > 6$

$\qquad x^2 + 5x - 6 > 0$

(2) $\quad$ Let $\quad f(x) = x^2 + 5x - 6$

$\qquad\qquad\qquad = (x + 6)(x - 1)$

(3) When $\quad f(x) = 0$

$\qquad (x + 6)(x - 1) = 0$

$\qquad\qquad\qquad x = -6 \text{ or } 1$

(4) Sketch the graph:

$f(x) = x^2 + 5x - 6$

$f(x) > 0$ $f(x) > 0$

-6 1 x

(5) For $f(x) > 0$, the range of values of x is $x < -6$ or $x > 1$.

(II) By number line

Here a number line is drawn instead of a graph.

► **Example 17**

Find the range of values of x for which $x^2 + 2 < 3x$.

► **Solution . . .**

$$x^2 + 2 < 3x$$
$$x^2 - 3x + 2 < 0$$
$$(x - 1)(x - 2) < 0$$

Consider the range of values of x for which both factors are positive.

$$x - 1 > 0 \quad \text{and} \quad x - 2 > 0$$
$$x > 1 \quad \text{and} \quad x > 2$$

A number line is drawn to represent the range of values.

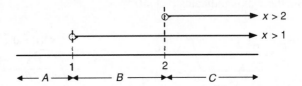

In region C, $(x - 1)(x - 2)$ is positive (as indicated by two arrow lines).
In region B, $(x - 1)(x - 2)$ is negative (as indicated by one arrow line).
In region A, $(x - 1)(x - 2)$ is positive (as indicated by no arrow lines).
For $(x - 1)(x - 2) < 0$, the range of values of x lies in region B,
i.e. $1 < x < 2$.

► **Example 18**

For what range of values of p will the equation
$x^2 - (p + 2)x + p^2 + 3p - 3 = 0$ have real roots?

► **Solution . . .**

Here $a = 1$, $b = -(p + 2)$, $c = p^2 + 3p - 3$.
For real roots, $D \geq 0$.

$$[-(p + 2)]^2 - 4(1)(p^2 + 3p - 3) \geq 0$$
$$p^2 + 4p + 4 - 4p^2 - 12p + 12 \geq 0$$
$$-3p^2 - 8p + 16 \geq 0$$
$$3p^2 + 8p - 16 \leq 0$$
$$(p + 4)(3p - 4) \leq 0$$

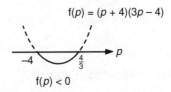

For $f(p) \leq 0$, the range of values of p is $-4 \leq p \leq \dfrac{4}{3}$.

▶ **Example 19**

Find the range of values of p if the curve $f(x) = (p+1)x^2 + 4px + 9$ does not intersect the x-axis.

▶ **Solution . . .**

When the curve $f(x)$ does not intersect the x-axis, $f(x) = 0$ has no real roots, i.e. $D < 0$.

$$(4p)^2 - 4(p+1)(9) < 0$$
$$16p^2 - 36p - 36 < 0$$
$$4p^2 - 9p - 9 < 0$$
$$(4p+3)(p-3) < 0$$

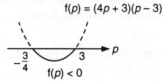

$f(p) = (4p + 3)(p - 3)$

$f(p) < 0$

For $f(p) < 0$, the range of values of p is $-\dfrac{3}{4} < p < 3$.

▶ **Example 20**

Find the range of values of x for which $|x^2 - 3x - 7| \le 3$.

▶ **Solution . . .**

If $|x^2 - 3x - 7| \le 3$,

then $-3 \le x^2 - 3x - 7 \le 3$.

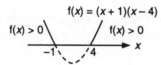

$f(x) = (x + 1)(x - 4)$

$f(x) > 0$ $f(x) > 0$

(a) For
$$-3 \le x^2 - 3x - 7$$
$$x^2 - 3x - 4 \ge 0$$
$$(x+1)(x-4) \ge 0$$

For $f(x) \ge 0$, the range of values of x is
$$x \le -1 \text{ or } x \ge 4.$$

(b) For
$$x^2 - 3x - 7 \le 3,$$
$$x^2 - 3x - 10 \le 0$$
$$(x+2)(x-5) \le 0.$$

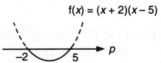

$f(x) = (x + 2)(x - 5)$

$f(x) \le 0$

For $f(x) \le 0$, the range of values of x is
$$-2 \le x \le 5.$$

Now x must satisfy both sets of conditions.

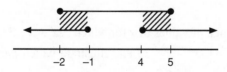

Therefore, the range of x must lie in the shaded regions,

i.e. $-2 \le x \le -1$ or $4 \le x \le 5$.

1. Find the range of values of x which satisfies the following inequalities:
   (a) $x^2 - x > 2$ (b) $x^2 + x < 6$
   (c) $3x^2 > 4 - 11x$ (d) $2x^2 - 1 \geq x$
   (e) $x(6x - 5) \leq -1$ (f) $4x - x^2 < 0$

2. Find the range of values of t if the equation $3x^2 - 3tx + (t^2 - t - 3) = 0$ has two different real roots.

3. If the roots of $p(x^2 + 2) = 1 - 2x$ are real, find the range of values of p.

4. If the equation $qx(x - 1) + q + 3 = 0$ has no real roots, find the range of values of q.

5. Show that the equation $(r + 3)x^2 + (2r + 5)x + r + 2 = 0$ has real roots for all real values of x.

6. Find the range of x for which $x^2 - 6x + 5$ lies between -3 and 12.

7. What is the range of values of c if the line $y = 2x + c$ intersects the curve $x^2 + 2y^2 = 8$ at two distinct points?

8. What is the range of values of m if the line $y = mx + 1$ does not intersect the curve $y^2 = 2x - 3$?

9. Find the range of values of p if the curve $f(x) = 4x^2 + (4 + p)x + p + 1$ does not intersect the x-axis.

10. Find the range of values of q if the curve $f(x) = 4x^2 + 12x + 15 - q(4x + 5)$ intersects the x-axis at two distinct points.

11. Find the range of values of x for which
    (a) $|x^2 + x - 7| < 5$,   (b) $|x^2 - 5x - 10| \geq 4$,
    (c) $|4 + x - x^2| \leq 2$.

12. Find the range of values of x for which $|2x^2 - x - 3| \leq 3$. Sketch the graph $f(x) = |2x^2 - x - 3|$ and illustrate which parts of the graph satisfy $|2x^2 - x - 3| \leq 3$.

13. A rectangle has sides of length $(2x + 3)$ cm and $(x + 1)$ cm. What is the range of values of x if the area of the rectangle lies between 10 cm^2 and 36 cm^2 inclusive?

Summary

1. A quadratic function $f(x) = ax^2 + bx + c$ has a maximum value if $a < 0$ and a minimum value if $a > 0$.

2. The maximum or minimum value of a quadratic function can be determined by using completing the square method in the form $f(x) = a(x - h)^2 + k$, where the maximum or minimum value of $f(x)$ is k when $x = h$.

3. A quadratic equation can be solved by factorisation, by completing the square or by the formula $x = \dfrac{-b \pm \sqrt{b^2 - 4ac}}{2a}$.

4. Types of roots (where $D = b^2 - 4ac$):
   If $D > 0$, there are two different real roots.
   If $D = 0$, there are two equal real roots.
   If $D < 0$, there are no real roots.

5. When a line intersects a curve, $D > 0$.
   When a line is a tangent to a curve, $D = 0$.
   When a line does not intersect a curve, $D < 0$.

6. A quadratic inequality can be solved by graph or number line.

Revision Exercise 3 (*Answers on page 496*)

1. (a) A function V is given by $V(t) = 2t^2 - 8t + 30$. Find the minimum value of V and the value of t where this occurs.
   (b) What is the range of this function for $0 \le t \le 3$?

2. Convert $y = \dfrac{1}{2}\left[(x + 4)^2 + (x - 2)^2\right]$ to the form $y = (x + p)^2 + q$ and hence, find the minimum value of y and the value of x where this occurs.

3. The function $g(x) = ax^2 + bx + c$ has a minimum value of $-5\dfrac{1}{4}$ where $x = \dfrac{1}{4}$, and $g(0) = -5$. Find the value of a, of b and of c.

4. The function $2ax^2 - 4x - a$ has a maximum value of 3. Find the values of a.

5. The graph of a quadratic function meets the x-axis where $x = 3$ and $x = k$. If the turning point of the function occurs where $x = \dfrac{1}{2}$, find the value of k.

6. A rectangular enclosure is made against a straight wall using three lengths of fencing, two of length x m. The total length of fencing available is 50 m.

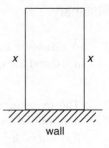
wall

  (a) Show that the area enclosed is given by $50x - 2x^2$.

  (b) Hence, find the maximum possible area which can be enclosed and the value of x for this area.

7. If the equation $x^2 - 2kx + 3k + 4 = 0$ has equal roots, find the possible values of k and solve the two equations.

8. Show that the equation $(p + 1)x^2 + (2p + 3)x^2 + (p + 2) = 0$ has real roots for all values of p.   (C)

9. The quadratic equation $x^2 + px + q = 0$ has roots –2 and 6. Find

  (a) the value of p and of q,

  (b) the range of values of r for which the equation $x^2 + px + q = r$ has no real roots.   (C)

10. (a) The quadratic equation $kx^2 + 2(k + a)x + (k + b) = 0$ has equal roots. Express k in terms of a and of b.

  (b) The quadratic equation $(p + 1)x^2 + 2px + (p + 2) = 0$ has real roots. Find the range of values of p.   (C)

11. The roots of the quadratic equation $x^2 + 2x + 3 = p(x^2 - 2x - 3)$ are real. Show that p cannot have a value between –1 and $\frac{1}{2}$.

12. (a) Solve the equation $x^2 + 2ax + 2 = 2a^2 + 5a$ to obtain x in terms of a.

  (b) If these values of x are real, find the range of values of a.

13. (a) Find the range of values of m for which the line $y = mx + 5$ meets the curve $y = x^2 + 9$ in two distinct points.

  (b) If this line is to be a tangent, find the two possible equations of the tangents and the coordinates of the points of contact.

14. (a) Find the range of values of x for which $6x^2 - 11x \geq 7$.

  (b) Find the coordinates of the turning point of the curve $y = (2x - 3)^2 + 6$ and sketch the curve.   (C)

15. The equation of a curve is $y = 4x^2 - 8x - 5$. Find

  (a) the range of values of x for which $y \geq 0$,

  (b) the coordinates of the turning points of the curve.

State the coordinates of the maximum points of the curve $y = |\,4x^2 - 8x - 5\,|$ and sketch the curve $y = |\,4x^2 - 8x - 5\,|$.

16. The function $x^2 + 3x + k$ is never negative. Find the least whole number value of k. If $k = 4$, find the minimum value of the function.

17. The function $x^2 + px + q$ is negative for $2 < x < 4$. Find
    (a) the value of p and of q,
    (b) the range of values of x if $15 \le x^2 + px + q \le 48$.

18. Find the range of values of x if $\sqrt{5x - 2 - 2x^2}$ is real.

19. Find the range of values of x if $2 < \sqrt{2x^2 + x + 3} < 3$.

20. The two shortest sides of a right-angled triangle have lengths $(x + 1)$ cm and $(x + 2)$ cm. If the area A cm^2 of the triangle is such that $15 \le A \le 28$, find the range of values of x.

21. A square has sides x cm and a rectangle has sides x cm and $2(x + 1)$ cm. For what range of values of x is the total area not less than 1 cm^2 and not more that 5 cm^2?

Maths Booster

1. Find the smallest value of x which satisfies the equation
   $(2x + 1)^2 + (2x + 1)(3x^2 - 4x - 7) + (3x^2 - 4x - 7)^2 = (3x^2 - 2x - 6)^2$

2. If the perimeter of a rectangle is $8\sqrt{2}$ cm, what is the smallest possible value of the length of one of its diagonals in cm?

3. Solve the inequality $(x - 1)(x - 2)(x - 3) > 0$.

4. If the solution of the inequality $x^2 + ax + 6 \le 0$ is $2 \le x \le k$, find the value of k.

5. What is the smallest positive integer n such that
$$\sqrt{n - 2} - \sqrt{n - 3} < 0.02?$$

Chapter 4

Indices And Surds

Scientists often deal with extremely large and extremely small numbers. For example:

- The distance from the Earth to the sun is approximately 150 000 000 kilometres.

- The mass of one atom of iron is approximately 0.000 000 000 000 000 000 000 1 g.

The large number of zeros in these numbers makes them difficult to read and hard to remember. They can be simplified by expressing them in the form of indices.

For example, $150\ 000\ 000 \text{ km} = 1.5 \times 100\ 000\ 000 \text{ km}$
$$= 1.5 \times 10^8 \text{ km},$$

and $0.000\ 000\ 000\ 000\ 000\ 000\ 000\ 1 \text{ g} = 1 \times 10^{-22} \text{ g}.$

4.1 Indices

4.1.1 Definition of Indices

When a number 3 is multiplied by itself 5 times, we get 3^5 , i.e.
$$3 \times 3 \times 3 \times 3 \times 3 = 3^5.$$

The digit 3 in 3^5 is called the **base** and the digit 5 is the **index**, **exponent** or **power**.

base $\rightarrow a^n \leftarrow$ index

In general, a^n means a is multiplied by itself n times, i.e.

$$a^n = \underbrace{a \times a \times a \times \ldots \ldots \times a}_{n \text{ factors}}$$

Examples:

1. $2^6 = 2 \times 2 \times 2 \times 2 \times 2 \times 2$
    $= 64$

2. $\left(\dfrac{3}{5}\right)^4 = \dfrac{3}{5} \times \dfrac{3}{5} \times \dfrac{3}{5} \times \dfrac{3}{5}$
    $= \dfrac{81}{625}$

4.1.2 Rules of Indices

Thinking Skill: Induction

There are several important rules for indices:

Rule 1

Simplify $2^3 \times 2^4$.
$$2^3 \times 2^4 = \underbrace{(\underbrace{2 \times 2 \times 2}_{3 \text{ factors}}) \times (\underbrace{2 \times 2 \times 2 \times 2}_{4 \text{ factors}})}_{7 \text{ factors}}$$
$$= 2^7$$

In general, $a^m \times a^n = \underbrace{(\underbrace{a \times a \times \ldots \times a}_{m \text{ factors}}) \times (\underbrace{a \times a \times \ldots \times a}_{n \text{ factors}})}_{(m + n) \text{ factors}}$
$$= a^{m+n}$$

▶ **Example 1**

Simplify (a) $a^3 \times a^8$, (b) $2^{x-y} \times 2^{2y-x}$.

▶ **Solution . . .**

(a) $a^3 \times a^8 = a^{3+8} = a^{11}$

(b) $2^{x-y} \times 2^{2y-x} = 2^{(x-y)+(2y-x)} = 2^y$

Induction

Verify whether the following sets of numbers have the same value:

(a) -2^4 and $(-2)^4$

(b) -2^5 and $(-2)^5$

What can you induce from your verification?

Rule 2

Simplify $3^6 \div 3^2$.

$$3^6 \div 3^2 = \frac{3^6}{3^2}$$

$$= \frac{3 \times 3 \times 3 \times 3 \times 3 \times 3}{3 \times 3} \qquad \text{6 factors}$$
$$\text{2 factors}$$
$$= 3 \times 3 \times 3 \times 3 \qquad \text{6 – 2 factors = 4 factors}$$
$$= 3^4$$

In general, $a^m \div a^n = \dfrac{a \times a \times \ldots \times a}{a \times a \times \ldots \times a} \qquad \begin{array}{l} m \text{ factors} \\ n \text{ factors} \end{array}$

$$= a^{m-n}$$

▶ **Example 2**

Simplify **(a)** $a^8 \div a^2$, **(b)** $\dfrac{a^3 \times a^9}{a^4}$.

▶ **Solution . . .**

(a) $a^8 \div a^2 = a^{8-2} = a^6$

(b) $\dfrac{a^3 \times a^9}{a^4} = \dfrac{a^{3+9}}{a^4} = \dfrac{a^{12}}{a^4} = a^{12-4} = a^8$

Rule 3

Simplify $(5^3)^2$.

$$(5^3)^2 = (5 \times 5 \times 5)^2$$
$$\text{3 factors}$$
$$= (5 \times 5 \times 5) \times (5 \times 5 \times 5) \qquad 3 \times 2 \text{ factors = 6 factors}$$
$$= 5^6$$

In general, $(a^m)^n = (a \times a \times \ldots \times a)^n$
$$\qquad\qquad m \text{ factors}$$
$$= (a \times a \times \ldots \times a) \times \ldots \times (a \times a \times \ldots \times a) \quad (m \times n) \text{ factors}$$
$$= a^{mn}$$

▶ **Example 3**

Simplify **(a)** $(a^7)^3$, **(b)** $(a^2 \times a^3 \div a^4)^5$.

▶ **Solution . . .**

(a) $(a^7)^3 = a^{7 \times 3} = a^{21}$

(b) $(a^2 \times a^3 \div a^4)^5 = (a^{2+3-4})^5 = (a^1)^5 = a^{1 \times 5} = a^5$

Rule 4

Simplify $2^3 \times 5^3$.

$$2^3 \times 5^3 = (2 \times 2 \times 2) \times (5 \times 5 \times 5)$$
$$= (2 \times 5) \times (2 \times 5) \times (2 \times 5)$$
$$= (2 \times 5)^3$$
$$= 10^3$$

In general, $a^m \times b^m = (a \times a \times \ldots \times a) \times (b \times b \times \ldots \times b)$

$\underbrace{\qquad\qquad}_{m \text{ factors}} \quad \underbrace{\qquad\qquad}_{m \text{ factors}}$

$= \underbrace{(a \times b) \times (a \times b) \times \ldots \times (a \times b)}_{m \text{ factors}}$

$= (a \times b)^m$

▶ Example 4

Simplify **(a)** $\quad 3^n \times 6^n$, **(b)** $\quad 2^{6n} \times (3^{3n})^2 \times (4^{2n})^3$.

▶ Solution . . .

(a) $\quad 3^n \times 6^n = (3 \times 6)^n = 18^n$

(b) $\quad 2^{6n} \times (3^{3n})^2 \times (4^{2n})^3 = 2^{6n} \times 3^{6n} \times 4^{6n}$
$= (2 \times 3 \times 4)^{6n}$
$= 24^{6n}$

Rule 5

Simplify $4^3 \div 5^3$.

$$4^3 \div 5^3 = \frac{4^3}{5^3}$$

$$= \frac{4 \times 4 \times 4}{5 \times 5 \times 5}$$

$$= \left(\frac{4}{5}\right) \times \left(\frac{4}{5}\right) \times \left(\frac{4}{5}\right)$$

$$= \left(\frac{4}{5}\right)^3$$

In general, $a^m \div b^m = \dfrac{a \times a \times \ldots \times a}{b \times b \times \ldots \times b} \qquad \begin{matrix} m \text{ factors} \\ m \text{ factors} \end{matrix}$

$$= \left(\frac{a}{b}\right) \times \left(\frac{a}{b}\right) \times \ldots \times \left(\frac{a}{b}\right) \qquad m \text{ factors}$$

$$= \left(\frac{a}{b}\right)^m$$

▶ Example 5

Simplify **(a)** $\quad 24^m \div 8^m$, **(b)** $\quad \dfrac{8^n \times 9^n}{6^n}$

▶ Solution . . .

(a) $\quad 24^m \div 8^m = \left(\dfrac{24}{8}\right)^m = 3^m$

(b) $\quad \dfrac{8^n \times 9^n}{6^n} = \left(\dfrac{8 \times 9}{6}\right)^n = 12^n$

Below is a summary of the rules for indices:

1. $\quad a^m \times a^n = a^{m+n}$

2. $\quad a^m \div a^n = a^{m-n}$

3. $\quad (a^m)^n = a^{mn}$

4. $a^m \times b^m = (a \times b)^m$

5. $a^n \div b^m = \left(\dfrac{a}{b}\right)^m$

▶ **Example 6**

Evaluate $\dfrac{6^3 \times (6^2)^3 \div 6^5}{2 \times 2^3}$ without using a calculator.

▶ **Solution . . .**

$$\frac{6^3 \times (6^2)^3 \div 6^5}{2 \times 2^3} = \frac{6^3 \times 6^6 \div 6^5}{2^1 \times 2^3}$$

$$= \frac{6^{3+6-5}}{2^{1+3}}$$

$$= \frac{6^4}{2^4}$$

$$= \left(\frac{6}{2}\right)^4$$

$$= 3^4$$

$$= 81$$

4.1.3 Zero Index

$a^3 \div a^3 = a^{3-3} = a^0$ (Rule 2)

$a^3 \div a^3 = \dfrac{a \times a \times a}{a \times a \times a} = 1$ (By definition)

Hence we obtain

$\boxed{a^0 = 1}$ where a is any real number and $a \neq 0$.

▶ **Example 7**

Find the value of   **(a)** 3^0,   **(b)** $\left(\dfrac{1}{2}\right)^0$,   **(c)** $\dfrac{a^3 \times a^6}{a^4 \times a^5}$.

▶ **Solution . . .**

(a) $3^0 = 1$

(b) $\left(\dfrac{1}{2}\right)^0 = 1$

(c) $\dfrac{a^3 \times a^6}{a^4 \times a^5} = \dfrac{a^{3+6}}{a^{4+5}} = \dfrac{a^9}{a^9} = a^{9-9} = a^0 = 1$

4.1.4 Negative Indices

$a^3 \div a^5 = a^{3-5} = a^{-2}$ (Rule 2)

$a^3 \div a^5 = \dfrac{a \times a \times a}{a \times a \times a \times a \times a}$ (By definition)

$$= \frac{1}{a \times a}$$

$$= \frac{1}{a^2}$$

Therefore we obtain $a^{-2} = \dfrac{1}{a^2}$.

In general, $\boxed{a^{-n} = \dfrac{1}{a^n}}$ where $a \neq 0$.

▶ **Example 8**

Find the value of **(a)** 5^{-2}, **(b)** $\left(\dfrac{2}{3}\right)^{-3}$.

▶ **Solution . . .**

(a) $5^{-2} = \dfrac{1}{5^2} = \dfrac{1}{25}$

(b) $\left(\dfrac{2}{3}\right)^{-3} = \dfrac{1}{\left(\frac{2}{3}\right)^3} = \dfrac{1}{\left(\frac{8}{27}\right)} = \dfrac{27}{8}$

4.1.5 Fractional Indices

For $\left(a^{\frac{1}{2}}\right)^2 = a^{\frac{1}{2} \times 2} = a$,

taking the square roots on both sides, we obtain

$\qquad a^{\frac{1}{2}} = \sqrt{a}$.

For $\left(a^{\frac{1}{3}}\right)^3 = a^{\frac{1}{3} \times 3} = a$,

taking the cube roots on both sides, we obtain

$\qquad a^{\frac{1}{3}} = \sqrt[3]{a}$.

In general, $\boxed{a^{\frac{1}{n}} = \sqrt[n]{a}}$.

▶ **Example 9**

Find the value of **(a)** $8^{\frac{1}{3}}$, **(b)** $\left(\dfrac{256}{81}\right)^{\frac{1}{4}}$, **(c)** $27^{-\frac{1}{3}}$.

▶ **Solution . . .**

Method 1　　　　　　　　**Method 2**

(a) $8^{\frac{1}{3}} = \sqrt[3]{8}$　　　　　$8^{\frac{1}{3}} = (2^3)^{\frac{1}{3}}$

$\qquad\quad = 2$　　　　　　　$\qquad = 2^1$

$\qquad\qquad\qquad\qquad\qquad\quad = 2$

(b) $\left(\dfrac{256}{81}\right)^{\frac{1}{4}} = \sqrt[4]{\dfrac{256}{81}}$

$\qquad\qquad = \dfrac{\sqrt[4]{256}}{\sqrt[4]{81}}$

$\qquad\qquad = \dfrac{4}{3}$

$\left(\dfrac{256}{81}\right)^{\frac{1}{4}} = \left(\dfrac{2^8}{3^4}\right)^{\frac{1}{4}}$

$\qquad\qquad = \dfrac{(2^8)^{\frac{1}{4}}}{(3^4)^{\frac{1}{4}}}$

$\qquad\qquad = \dfrac{2^2}{3^1}$

$\qquad\qquad = \dfrac{4}{3}$

(c) $27^{-\frac{1}{3}} = \dfrac{1}{27^{\frac{1}{3}}}$

$\qquad\quad = \dfrac{1}{\sqrt[3]{27}}$

$\qquad\quad = \dfrac{1}{3}$

$27^{-\frac{1}{3}} = (3^3)^{-\frac{1}{3}}$

$\qquad\quad = 3^{-1}$

$\qquad\quad = \dfrac{1}{3}$

Consider $a^{\frac{2}{3}}$ which can be written in two ways:

$$a^{\frac{2}{3}} = (a^2)^{\frac{1}{3}} = \sqrt[3]{a^2}$$

or $\qquad a^{\frac{2}{3}} = (a^{\frac{1}{3}})^2 = (\sqrt[3]{a})^2$

In general, $\boxed{a^{\frac{m}{n}} = \sqrt[n]{a^m} = (\sqrt[n]{a^m})}$.

▶ **Example 10**

Find the value of **(a)** $32^{\frac{2}{5}}$, **(b)** $27^{-\frac{2}{3}}$.

▶ **Solution . . .**

Method 1

(a) $32^{\frac{2}{5}} = (\sqrt[5]{32})^2$

$\qquad\quad = 2^2$

$\qquad\quad = 4$

(b) $27^{-\frac{2}{3}} = \dfrac{1}{27^{\frac{2}{3}}}$

$\qquad\quad = \dfrac{1}{(\sqrt[3]{27})^2}$

$\qquad\quad = \dfrac{1}{3^2}$

$\qquad\quad = \dfrac{1}{9}$

Method 2

$32^{\frac{2}{5}} = (2^5)^{\frac{2}{5}}$

$\qquad\quad = 2^2$

$\qquad\quad = 4$

$27^{-\frac{2}{3}} = (3^3)^{-\frac{2}{3}}$

$\qquad\quad = 3^{-2}$

$\qquad\quad = \dfrac{1}{3^2}$

$\qquad\quad = \dfrac{1}{9}$

To solve more complicated problems involving indices, we usually express the numbers in the form of indices with the same base.

▶ **Example 11**

Find the value of $\dfrac{8^{\frac{1}{2}} \times 2^{\frac{2}{3}}}{4^{\frac{1}{12}}}$.

▶ **Solution . . .**

$$\dfrac{8^{\frac{1}{2}} \times 2^{\frac{2}{3}}}{4^{\frac{1}{12}}} = \dfrac{(2^3)^{\frac{1}{2}} \times 2^{\frac{2}{3}}}{(2^2)^{\frac{1}{12}}}$$

$$= \dfrac{2^{\frac{3}{2}} \times 2^{\frac{2}{3}}}{2^{\frac{1}{6}}}$$

$$= 2^{\frac{3}{2} + \frac{2}{3} - \frac{1}{6}}$$

$$= 2^2$$

$$= 4$$

▶ **Example 12**

Simplify $2^{1-3n} \times 4^{2n-1} \div 8$.

▶ **Solution . . .**

$$2^{1-3n} \times 4^{2n+1} \div 8 = 2^{1-3n} \times (2^2)^{2n+1} \div 2^3$$

$$= 2^{1-3n} \times 2^{4n+2} \div 2^3$$

$$= 2^{(1-3n) + (4n+2) - 3}$$

$$= 2^n$$

▶ **Example 13**

Show that $3^{2x-1} = \dfrac{9^x}{3}$.

▶ **Solution . . .**

$$3^{2x-1} = \dfrac{3^{2x}}{3^1}$$

$$= \dfrac{(3^2)^x}{3}$$

$$= \dfrac{9^x}{3}$$

▶ **Example 14**

If $y = 2^x$, express $2^{2x+3} - 2^{x-1} + 8^x$ in terms of y.

▶ **Solution . . .**

$$2^{2x+3} - 2^{x-1} + 8^x = 2^{2x} \cdot 2^3 - 2^x \cdot 2^{-1} + (2^3)^x$$

$$= (2^x)^2(8) - (2^x)\left(\dfrac{1}{2}\right) + (2^x)^3$$

$$= 8y^2 - \dfrac{1}{2}y + y^3$$

▶ **Example 15**

Show that $3^n + 3^{n+1} + 3^{n+2}$ is divisible by 13 for all positive integer values of n.

▶ **Solution . . .**

$$3^n + 3^{n+1} + 3^{n+2} = 3^n + 3^n(3^1) + 3^n(3^2)$$
$$= 3^n + 3(3^n) + 9(3^n)$$
$$= 13(3^n)$$

As $13(3^n)$ is divisible by 13, $3^n + 3^{n+1} + 3^{n+2}$ is divisible by 13 for all positive integer values of n.

4.1.6 Solving Exponential Equations

We can solve an exponential equation

(1) by expressing both sides in terms of the same base and then equating the indices, i.e. $a^m = a^n \Rightarrow m = n$.

(2) by expressing both sides in terms of the same index and then equating the base, i.e. $a^n = b^n \Rightarrow a = b$.

▶ **Example 16**

Solve the equations   **(a)** $27^x = 81$,   **(b)** $2 \cdot 4^{1-x} = 8^x$.

▶ **Solution . . .**

(a) $27^x = 81$
$$(3^3)^x = 3^4$$
$$3^{3x} = 3^4$$
$$3x = 4$$
$$x = \frac{4}{3}$$

(b) $2 \cdot 4^{1-x} = 8^x$
$$2^1(2^2)^{1-x} = (2^3)^x$$
$$2^1 \cdot 2^{2-2x} = 2^{3x}$$
$$2^{1+2-2x} = 2^{3x}$$
$$2^{3-2x} = 2^{3x}$$
$$\therefore \quad 3 - 2x = 3x$$
$$3 = 5x$$
$$x = \frac{3}{5}$$

▶ **Example 17**

Solve the equations   **(a)** $a^5 = 32$,   **(b)** $b^{-3} = 0.125$.

▶ **Solution . . .**

(a) $a^5 = 32$
$$a^5 = 2^5$$
$$\therefore \quad a = 2$$

(b) $b^{-3} = 0.125$
$$b^{-3} = \frac{1}{8}$$
$$b^{-3} = \frac{1}{2^3}$$
$$b^{-3} = 2^{-3}$$
$$\therefore \quad b = 2$$

► **Example 18**

Solve the equation $2^{2x+1} + 2^{x+4} = 2^x + 8$.

► **Solution ...**

$$2^{2x+1} + 2^{x+4} = 2^x + 8$$
$$2^{2x} \cdot 2^1 + 2^x \cdot 2^4 = 2^x + 8$$
$$2(2^x)^2 + 16(2^x) = 2^x + 8$$
$$2(2^x)^2 + 15(2^x) - 8 = 0$$

Substituting $y = 2^x$,
$$2y^2 + 15y - 8 = 0$$
$$(2y - 1)(y + 8) = 0$$

$$y = \frac{1}{2} \quad \text{or} \quad y = -8$$

$$2^x = \frac{1}{2} \qquad\qquad 2^x = -8$$
$$\quad = 2^{-1} \qquad \text{As } 2^x \text{ is never negative, this part has no solution.}$$
$$x = -1$$

The equation has therefore only one solution, $x = -1$.

► **Example 19**

Given that $y = ax^b - 6$, and that $y = 10$ when $x = 2$, and $y = 48$ when $x = 3$, find the value of a and of b.

► **Solution ...**

Given $\quad y = ax^b - 6$

Substituting $x = 2$ and $y = 10$ into $y = ax^b - 6$,
$$10 = a(2^b) - 6$$
$$a(2^b) = 16 \qquad \ldots\ldots (1)$$

Substituting $x = 3$ and $y = 48$ into $y = ax^b - 6$,
$$48 = a(3^b) - 6$$
$$a(3^b) = 54 \qquad \ldots\ldots (2)$$

$\dfrac{(2)}{(1)}:\qquad \dfrac{a(3^b)}{a(2^b)} = \dfrac{54}{16}$

$$\frac{3^b}{2^b} = \frac{27}{8}$$

$$\left(\frac{3}{2}\right)^b = \left(\frac{3}{2}\right)^3$$

$$\therefore \quad b = 3$$

Substituting $b = 3$ into (1),
$$a(2^3) = 16$$
$$a = 2$$

$\therefore a = 2$ and $b = 3$.

▶ **Example 20**

Solve the simultaneous equations:

$$3^x \times 9^y = 1,$$

$$2^{2x} \times 4^y = \frac{1}{8}.$$

▶ **Solution . . .**

Given $\quad\quad 3^x \times 9^y = 1$

$\quad\quad\quad\quad 3^x \times 3^{2y} = 1$

$\quad\quad\quad\quad 3^{x+2y} = 3^0$

$\quad\quad \therefore \quad x + 2y = 0 \quad\quad\quad \ldots\ldots (1)$

Given $\quad\quad 2^{2x} \times 4^y = \dfrac{1}{8}$

$\quad\quad\quad\quad 2^{2x} \times 2^{2y} = \dfrac{1}{2^3}$

$\quad\quad\quad\quad 2^{2x+2y} = 2^{-3}$

$\quad\quad \therefore \quad 2x + 2y = -3 \quad\quad \ldots\ldots (2)$

$(2) - (1): \quad\quad\quad x = -3$

Substituting $x = -3$ into (1),

$\quad\quad\quad\quad -3 + 2y = 0$

$$y = \frac{3}{2}$$

$\therefore \quad\quad\quad x = -3, y = \dfrac{3}{2}.$

Exercise 4A (Answers on page 496)

1. Evaluate each of the following without using a calculator:

   (a) 3^4 $\quad\quad\quad$ (b) $\left(\dfrac{1}{2}\right)^5$ $\quad\quad\quad$ (c) $\left(\dfrac{2}{3}\right)^6$

2. Simplify

   (a) $a^4 \times a^5$, $\quad\quad$ (b) $a^{\frac{1}{2}} \times a^{\frac{1}{3}} \times a^{\frac{1}{6}}$,

   (c) $2^{5-2x} \times 2^{3x-5}$, $\quad\quad$ (d) $x^{2+n} \times x^{3-n} \times x^{2n-1}$.

3. Simplify the following:

   (a) $a^6 \div a^2$ $\quad\quad$ (b) $\dfrac{3^{2n-1}}{3^{n-1}}$ $\quad\quad$ (c) $a^8 \times a^4 \div a^2$

   (d) $\dfrac{a^{8n} \times a^{3n}}{a^{6n}}$ $\quad\quad$ (e) $\dfrac{5^{2x+1}}{5^{x-4} \times 5^{2-x}}$ $\quad\quad$ (f) $\dfrac{2^{2x+1} \times 2^{3x}}{2^{x-3} \times 4^{4-3x}}$

4. Simplify

   (a) $(a^4)^2$, $\quad\quad$ (b) $(a^3 \times a^5)^4$,

   (c) $(a^2 \times a^5 \div a^6)^3$, $\quad$ (d) $(a^{3n-2} \div a^{n-1})^3$.

5. Simplify
   (a) $3^n \times 7^n$,
   (b) $(2^n)^3 \times (3^3)^n \times 4^{3n}$.

6. Simplify
   (a) $12^n \div 3^n$,
   (b) $\dfrac{36^{2n+1}}{4^{2n+1}}$,

   (c) $\dfrac{4^{3n} \times 9^n}{12^{2n}}$,
   (d) $\dfrac{(4^{2n})^3 \times (9^{3n})^2}{(12^n)^6}$.

7. Evaluate each of the following without using a calculator:
   (a) $2^4 \times (2^3)^4 \div 2^{13}$
   (b) $4^6 \times (3^2)^3 \div (6^3)^2$
   (c) $\dfrac{3^{2n-1} \times 3^{4n+2}}{3^{6n-3}}$
   (d) $\dfrac{12^4 \times (12^3)^4 \div 12^{11}}{6 \times 6^4}$

8. Find the value of the following:
   (a) 8^0
   (b) $\left(\dfrac{3}{4}\right)^0$
   (c) $a^{6n} \div a^{6n}$

   (d) $a^{1-2x} \times a^{2x-1}$
   (e) $\dfrac{a^4 \times a^7}{a^3 \times a^8}$

9. Find the value of
   (a) 4^{-2},
   (b) $\left(\dfrac{1}{2}\right)^{-3}$,
   (c) $\left(\dfrac{4}{3}\right)^{-3}$.

10. Find the value of
    (a) $27^{\frac{1}{3}}$,
    (b) $\left(\dfrac{8}{125}\right)^{\frac{1}{3}}$,
    (c) $16^{-\frac{1}{4}}$

11. Find the value of the following:
    (a) $81^{\frac{3}{4}}$
    (b) $64^{\frac{2}{3}}$
    (c) $16^{-\frac{3}{4}}$
    (d) $\left(\dfrac{8}{27}\right)^{\frac{2}{3}}$
    (e) $\left(\dfrac{4}{25}\right)^{-\frac{3}{2}}$
    (f) $\left(\dfrac{1}{32}\right)^{-\frac{2}{5}}$
    (g) $\left(3\dfrac{3}{8}\right)^{\frac{2}{3}}$
    (h) $\left(\dfrac{1}{9}\right)^{2\frac{1}{2}}$
    (i) $4^{-1.5}$

12. Evaluate each of the following without using a calculator:
    (a) $16^{\frac{2}{3}} \times 2^{\frac{1}{3}}$
    (b) $\dfrac{27^{\frac{3}{2}}}{3^{\frac{1}{2}}}$
    (c) $\dfrac{25^{\frac{1}{3}} \times 5^{\frac{5}{6}}}{125^{\frac{1}{6}}}$
    (d) $\dfrac{49^{\frac{1}{4}}}{7^{\frac{1}{3}} \times 7^{\frac{1}{6}}}$

13. Simplify the following:
    (a) $8^{n-2} \times 4^{3-n}$
    (b) $27^{\frac{x}{3}} \div 9^{\frac{x}{2}}$
    (c) $3^{2n-1} \times 9^{2-n} \div 27$
    (d) $\dfrac{25^{3n+2} \times 5}{5^{2n+5} \times 125^n}$

14. Show that

    (a) $2^{2x+3} = 8 \times 4^x$, (b) $2^{3-x} = \dfrac{8}{2^x}$,

    (c) $4^{2-x} = \dfrac{16}{2^{2x}}$, (d) $5^x \times 25^y = 5^{x+2y}$.

15. If $y = 2^x$, express each of the following in terms of y:

    (a) $2^{2x+1} - 2^{x+2}$ (b) $4^x - 2^{1-x}$

    (c) $4^{x+1} + 8\,(2^{2x-1})$ (d) $2^{2x-1} - 4^{x-1} - 8^{\frac{2}{3}x-1}$

16. Show that, for all positive integer values of n,

    (a) $5^n + 5^{n+1} + 5^{n+2}$ is divisible by 31,

    (b) $2^{n+1} + 2^{n+2} + 2^{n+3}$ is divisible by 7,

    (c) $3^{n+1} - 3^{n-1}$ is divisible by 2.

17. Solve the following equations:

    (a) $2^x = 64$ (b) $9^x = \dfrac{1}{729}$

    (c) $5^x = 1$ (d) $16^x = 0.125$

    (e) $32^x = 8$ (f) $8^{x+1} = 16$

    (g) $3^{2x-1} = 27^{x+1}$ (h) $8^x - 4 = 0$

    (i) $3 \cdot 9^{x+1} = 27^{x-1}$ (j) $2 \cdot 4^{x+1} = 16^{2x}$

18. Solve the following equations:

    (a) $a^3 = 27$ (b) $a^{-4} = \dfrac{1}{16}$

    (c) $a^{-2} = 0.04$ (d) $a^{\frac{1}{2}} = 4$

19. Solve the following equations:

    (a) $3^{2x} - 12(3^x) + 27 = 0$ (b) $2^{2x+3} + 1 = 9(2^x)$

    (c) $5^{2x} + 1 = 26(5^{x-1})$ (d) $2^{x+3} = 2^{1-x} + 15$

20. Given that $y = ax^b$, and that $y = 2$ when $x = 3$, and $y = \dfrac{2}{9}$ when $x = 9$, find the value of a and of b.   (C)

21. The equation of a curve is $y = ax^n$. Given that the points $(2,9)$ and $(3,4)$ lie on the curve, calculate the value of a and of n.   (C)

22. Solve the following simultaneous equations:

    (a) $5^x \times 25^{2y} = 5$ (b) $2^{2x} \times 8^y = 4$

    $3^{2x} \times 9^{y-1} = \dfrac{1}{27}$ $3^x \times 9^{y+1} = \dfrac{1}{81}$

    (c) $\dfrac{5^{3x}}{25^y} = 3\,125$

    $2^x \times 4^{y-1} = 32$ (C)

4.2 Surds

4.2.1 Definition of Surds

A number which can be expressed as a fraction of integers and the denominator is not zero is called a **rational number**. Examples of rational numbers are $\frac{3}{2}, -\frac{4}{5}$ and 6. A number which cannot be expressed as a fraction of integers is called an **irrational number**. Examples of irrational numbers are $\sqrt{2}$, $\sqrt[3]{5}$ and π.

An irrational number involving a root is called a **surd**. Examples of surds are $\sqrt{3}$, $\sqrt{15}$ and $3\sqrt{7}$. Usually the exact value of a surd cannot be determined. However, an approximate value of it can be found using a calculator or mathematical tables.

4.2.2 Rules of Surds

Rule 1 $\quad \boxed{\sqrt{a} \times \sqrt{b} = \sqrt{a \times b}}$

For example, (i) $\sqrt{2} \times \sqrt{5} = \sqrt{2 \times 5} = \sqrt{10}$,

(ii) $\sqrt{3} \times \sqrt{12} = \sqrt{3 \times 12} = \sqrt{36} = 6$.

Rule 2 $\quad \boxed{\sqrt{a} \div \sqrt{b} = \sqrt{\dfrac{a}{b}}}$

For example, (i) $\sqrt{75} \div \sqrt{5} = \sqrt{\dfrac{75}{5}} = \sqrt{15}$,

(ii) $\dfrac{\sqrt{27}}{\sqrt{3}} = \sqrt{\dfrac{27}{3}} = \sqrt{9} = 3$.

When a surd is multiplied or divided by another surd, the result may be a surd or a rational number.

Note, however, that $\sqrt{2} + \sqrt{5} \neq \sqrt{2+5}$ and $\sqrt{75} - \sqrt{5} \neq \sqrt{75-5}$. Can you verify these using a calculator?

In general, $\sqrt{a} + \sqrt{b} \neq \sqrt{a+b}$ and $\sqrt{a} - \sqrt{b} \neq \sqrt{a-b}$.

Rule 1 and Rule 2 can also be expressed as $\sqrt{a \times b} = \sqrt{a} \times \sqrt{b}$ and $\sqrt{\dfrac{a}{b}} = \dfrac{\sqrt{a}}{\sqrt{b}}$.

These rules are useful for simplifying a surd into a simpler term, or combining two or more surds into one single surd.

▶ **Example 21**

Simplify **(a)** $\sqrt{24}$,   **(b)** $\sqrt{72}$,   **(c)** $3\sqrt{50}$,   **(d)** $\dfrac{\sqrt{500}}{10}$.

▶ **Solution . . .**

(a)   Factorise 24, choosing the perfect square factor 4:

$$\sqrt{24} = \sqrt{4\times6} = \sqrt{4}\times\sqrt{6} = 2\sqrt{6}$$

(b)   Factorise 72, choosing the perfect square factors 4 and 9:

$$\sqrt{72} = \sqrt{4\times9\times2} = \sqrt{4}\times\sqrt{9}\times\sqrt{2} = 2\times3\times\sqrt{2} = 6\sqrt{2}$$

(c)   Factorise 50, choosing the perfect square factor 25:

$$3\sqrt{50} = 3\sqrt{25\times2} = 3\times\sqrt{25}\times\sqrt{2} = 3\times5\times\sqrt{2} = 15\sqrt{2}$$

(d)   Factorise 500, choosing the perfect square factor 100:

$$\frac{\sqrt{500}}{10} = \frac{\sqrt{100\times5}}{10} = \frac{\sqrt{100}\times\sqrt{5}}{10} = \frac{10\times\sqrt{5}}{10} = \sqrt{5}$$

▶ **Example 22**

Simplify $\sqrt{50} - 2\sqrt{8} + \sqrt{2}$.

▶ **Solution . . .**

$$
\begin{aligned}
\sqrt{50} - 2\sqrt{8} + \sqrt{2} &= \sqrt{25\times2} - 2\sqrt{4\times2} + \sqrt{2}\\
&= 5\sqrt{2} - 4\sqrt{2} + \sqrt{2}\\
&= 2\sqrt{2}
\end{aligned}
$$

▶ **Example 23**

Using $\sqrt{2} = 1.414$ and $\sqrt{5} = 2.236$, evaluate

(a) $\sqrt{50}$,   **(b)** $10\sqrt{20}$,   **(c)** $\sqrt{98} - \sqrt{45}$.

▶ **Solution . . .**

(a) $\sqrt{50} = \sqrt{25\times2} = 5\times\sqrt{2} = 5\times1.414 = 7.07$

(b) $10\sqrt{20} = 10\sqrt{4\times5} = 20\sqrt{5} = 20\times2.36 = 44.72$

(c) $\sqrt{98} - \sqrt{45} = \sqrt{49\times2} - \sqrt{9\times5}$

$$
\begin{aligned}
&= 7\sqrt{2} - 3\sqrt{5}\\
&= 7\times1.414 - 3\times2.236\\
&= 3.19
\end{aligned}
$$

▶ **Example 24**

Square   **(a)** $\sqrt{8}$,   **(b)** $3\sqrt{5}$,   **(c)** $\dfrac{3}{\sqrt{6}}$.

▶ Solution . . .

(a) $(\sqrt{8})^2 = \sqrt{8} \times \sqrt{8} = \sqrt{64} = 8$

(b) $(3\sqrt{5})^2 = 3^2 \times (\sqrt{5})^2 = 9 \times 5 = 45$

(c) $(\dfrac{3}{\sqrt{6}})^2 = \dfrac{3^2}{(\sqrt{6})^2} = \dfrac{9}{6} = \dfrac{3}{2}$

Note that $(\sqrt{a})^2 = a$.

▶ Example 25

Expand $(5 - \sqrt{3})^2$.

▶ Solution . . .

$$
\begin{aligned}
(5 - \sqrt{3})^2 &= (5 - \sqrt{3})(5 - \sqrt{3}) \\
&= 25 - 5\sqrt{3} - 5\sqrt{3} + (\sqrt{3})^2 \\
&= 25 - 10\sqrt{3} + 3 \\
&= 28 - 10\sqrt{3}
\end{aligned}
$$

Note that when a polynomial that consists of a surd is squared, the result is also a surd.

4.2.3 Conjugate Surds

Study the following examples:

1.
$$
\begin{aligned}
(\sqrt{5} + \sqrt{2})(\sqrt{5} - \sqrt{2}) &= (\sqrt{5})^2 - (\sqrt{5}\,\sqrt{2}) + (\sqrt{2}\,\sqrt{5}) - (\sqrt{2})^2 \\
&= 5 - (\sqrt{10}) + (\sqrt{10}) - 2 \\
&= 3
\end{aligned}
$$

2.
$$
\begin{aligned}
(2\sqrt{3} - 5)(2\sqrt{3} + 5) &= (2\sqrt{3})^2 + 10\sqrt{3} - 10\sqrt{3} - 5^2 \\
&= 12 - 25 \\
&= -13
\end{aligned}
$$

It is observed that in example 1, the product of 2 polynomials $(\sqrt{5} + \sqrt{2})$ and $(\sqrt{5} - \sqrt{2})$ is a rational number.

$(\sqrt{5} + \sqrt{2})$ and $(\sqrt{5} - \sqrt{2})$ are called conjugate surds. $(\sqrt{5} + \sqrt{2})$ is called the conjugate surd of $(\sqrt{5} - \sqrt{2})$, and vice versa.

Similarly, in example 2, $(2\sqrt{3} - 5)$ and $(2\sqrt{3} + 5)$ are conjugate surds.

In general, $(a\sqrt{m} + b)$ and $(a\sqrt{m} - b)$ are a pair of conjugate surds because their product is a rational number, i.e. $(a\sqrt{m} + b)(a\sqrt{m} - b) = a^2 m - b^2$.

4.2.4 Rationalising the Denominator of a Fraction

It is usual not to write surds in the denominator of a fraction. The process of changing the denominator from a surd to a rational number is called **rationalisation**.

Case I:

When the denominator is a surd in its simplest form, multiply both numerator and denominator of the fraction by the surd itself.

▶ ## Example 26

Rationalise the denominator of

(a) $\dfrac{4}{\sqrt{2}}$,   (b) $\dfrac{\sqrt{5}}{\sqrt{10}}$,   (c) $\dfrac{15}{2\sqrt{5}}$,   (d) $\dfrac{4-\sqrt{2}}{\sqrt{2}}$.

▶ ## Solution . . .

(a) $\dfrac{4}{\sqrt{2}} = \dfrac{4}{\sqrt{2}} \times \dfrac{\sqrt{2}}{\sqrt{2}} = \dfrac{4\sqrt{2}}{\left(\sqrt{2}\right)^2} = \dfrac{4\sqrt{2}}{2} = 2\sqrt{2}$

(b) $\dfrac{\sqrt{5}}{\sqrt{10}} = \dfrac{\sqrt{5}}{\sqrt{10}} \times \dfrac{\sqrt{10}}{\sqrt{10}} = \dfrac{\sqrt{50}}{\left(\sqrt{10}\right)^2} = \dfrac{\sqrt{50}}{10}$

(c) $\dfrac{15}{2\sqrt{5}} = \dfrac{15}{2\sqrt{5}} \times \dfrac{\sqrt{5}}{\sqrt{5}} = \dfrac{15\sqrt{5}}{2\left(\sqrt{5}\right)^2} = \dfrac{15\sqrt{5}}{2 \times 5} = \dfrac{3\sqrt{5}}{2}$

(d) $\dfrac{4-\sqrt{2}}{\sqrt{2}} = \dfrac{4-\sqrt{2}}{\sqrt{2}} \times \dfrac{\sqrt{2}}{\sqrt{2}} = \dfrac{4\sqrt{2}-2}{2} = 2\sqrt{2} - 1$

Case II:

Sometimes we need to simplify a surd into its smallest form before rationalising the denominator.

▶ ## Example 27

Rationalise the denominator of

(a) $\dfrac{4}{\sqrt{8}}$,   (b) $\dfrac{8}{\sqrt{72}}$,   (c) $\dfrac{\sqrt{60}-\sqrt{27}}{\sqrt{12}}$.

▶ ## Solution . . .

(a) $\dfrac{4}{\sqrt{8}} = \dfrac{4}{\sqrt{4 \times 2}} = \dfrac{4}{2\sqrt{2}} = \dfrac{2}{\sqrt{2}} = \dfrac{2}{\sqrt{2}} \times \dfrac{\sqrt{2}}{\sqrt{2}} = \dfrac{2\sqrt{2}}{2} = \sqrt{2}$

(b) $\dfrac{8}{\sqrt{72}} = \dfrac{8}{\sqrt{4 \times 9 \times 2}} = \dfrac{8}{2 \times 3 \times \sqrt{2}} = \dfrac{4}{3\sqrt{2}} = \dfrac{4}{3\sqrt{2}} \times \dfrac{\sqrt{2}}{\sqrt{2}} = \dfrac{4\sqrt{2}}{3 \times 2}$

$= \dfrac{2\sqrt{2}}{3}$

(c)
$$\frac{\sqrt{60} - \sqrt{27}}{\sqrt{12}} = \frac{\sqrt{4 \times 15} - \sqrt{9 \times 3}}{\sqrt{4 \times 3}}$$

$$= \frac{2\sqrt{15} - 3\sqrt{3}}{2\sqrt{3}}$$

$$= \frac{2\sqrt{3}(\sqrt{5}) - 3\sqrt{3}}{2\sqrt{3}} \times \frac{\sqrt{3}}{\sqrt{3}}$$

$$= \frac{2 \times 3(\sqrt{5}) - 3 \times 3}{2 \times 3}$$

$$= \frac{2\sqrt{5} - 3}{2}$$

Case III:

If the denominator consists of the sum or difference of two surds, we can rationalise the denominator by multiplying it with its conjugate surd.

▶ Example 28

Rationalise the denominator of

(a) $\dfrac{\sqrt{3}}{\sqrt{3} - \sqrt{2}}$,   **(b)** $\dfrac{\sqrt{5}}{2\sqrt{5} + 3}$.

▶ Solution . . .

(a) The conjugate surd of $\sqrt{3} - \sqrt{2}$ is $\sqrt{3} + \sqrt{2}$.

$$\frac{\sqrt{3}}{\sqrt{3} - \sqrt{2}} = \frac{\sqrt{3}}{\sqrt{3} - \sqrt{2}} \times \frac{\sqrt{3} + \sqrt{2}}{\sqrt{3} + \sqrt{2}}$$

$$= \frac{3 + \sqrt{6}}{3 - 2}$$

$$= 3 + \sqrt{6}$$

(b) The conjugate surd of $2\sqrt{5} + 3$ is $2\sqrt{5} - 3$.

$$\frac{\sqrt{5}}{2\sqrt{5} + 3} = \frac{\sqrt{5}}{2\sqrt{5} + 3} \times \frac{2\sqrt{5} - 3}{2\sqrt{5} - 3}$$

$$= \frac{2 \times 5 - 3\sqrt{5}}{4 \times 5 - 9}$$

$$= \frac{10 - 3\sqrt{5}}{11}$$

Rationalising the denominator simplifies evaluation.

Thus $\dfrac{4}{\sqrt{8}} = \sqrt{2} = 1.414$.

Otherwise $\dfrac{4}{\sqrt{8}} = \dfrac{4}{2.828}$ will lead to a lengthy division.

▶ **Example 29**

Given $\sqrt{2} = 1.414$, $\sqrt{3} = 1.732$ and $\sqrt{5} = 2.236$, evaluate, without using a calculator,

(a) $\dfrac{5}{\sqrt{5}}$, (b) $\dfrac{18}{\sqrt{27}}$, (c) $\dfrac{1}{\sqrt{12}}$, (d) $\dfrac{3+\sqrt{2}}{\sqrt{2}}$.

▶ **Solution . . .**

(a) $\dfrac{5}{\sqrt{5}} = \dfrac{5}{\sqrt{5}} \times \dfrac{\sqrt{5}}{\sqrt{5}} = \dfrac{5\sqrt{5}}{5} = \sqrt{5} = 2.236$

(b) $\dfrac{18}{\sqrt{27}} = \dfrac{18}{\sqrt{9 \times 3}} = \dfrac{18}{3\sqrt{3}} = \dfrac{6}{\sqrt{3}} = \dfrac{6}{\sqrt{3}} \times \dfrac{\sqrt{3}}{\sqrt{3}} = \dfrac{6\sqrt{3}}{3} = 2\sqrt{3}$
$= 2 \times 1.732 = 3.464$

(c) $\dfrac{1}{\sqrt{12}} = \dfrac{1}{\sqrt{4 \times 3}} = \dfrac{1}{2\sqrt{3}} = \dfrac{1}{2\sqrt{3}} \times \dfrac{\sqrt{3}}{\sqrt{3}} = \dfrac{\sqrt{3}}{6} = \dfrac{1.732}{6} = 0.289$
(to 3 decimal places)

(d) $\dfrac{3+\sqrt{2}}{\sqrt{2}} = \dfrac{3+\sqrt{2}}{\sqrt{2}} \times \dfrac{\sqrt{2}}{\sqrt{2}} = \dfrac{3\sqrt{2}+2}{2} = \dfrac{3(1.414)+2}{2} = 3.121$

4.2.5 Solving Surd Equations

To solve a surd equation, we first isolate the surd, square both sides and solve the resulting equation. If there is more than one root, we have to check the roots obtained against the original equation.

▶ **Example 30**

Solve $\sqrt{2x} - 1 = 3$.

▶ **Solution . . .**

$$\sqrt{2x} - 1 = 3$$
$$\sqrt{2x} = 4$$
$$(\sqrt{2x})^2 = 4^2$$
$$2x = 16$$
$$x = 8$$

check: When $x = 8$
$$\text{LHS} = \sqrt{2x} - 1$$
$$= \sqrt{16} - 1$$
$$= 4 - 1$$
$$= 3$$
$$\text{RHS} = 3$$
$$\therefore x = 8$$

▶ **Example 31**

Solve $\sqrt{2x - 1} = \sqrt{5x} - 2$.

▶ **Solution . . .**

$$\sqrt{2x-1} = \sqrt{5x} - 2$$
$$(\sqrt{2x-1})^2 = (\sqrt{5x} - 2)^2$$
$$2x - 1 = 5x - 4\sqrt{5x} + 4$$
$$4\sqrt{5x} = 3x + 5$$
$$(4\sqrt{5x})^2 = (3x + 5)^2$$
$$16(5x) = 9x^2 + 30x + 25$$
$$9x^2 - 50x + 25 = 0$$
$$(x - 5)(9x - 5) = 0$$
$$x = 5 \quad \text{or} \quad x = \frac{5}{9}$$

Check:

Substituting $x = 5$ into both sides of the equation $\sqrt{2x-1} = \sqrt{5x} - 2$, we have:

LHS = $\sqrt{2(5)-1}$ RHS = $\sqrt{5(5)} - 2$

      = $\sqrt{9}$ = $5 - 2$

      = 3   = 3

Since LHS = RHS, $x = 5$ is a possible solution. Substituting $x = \frac{5}{9}$ into both sides of the equation $\sqrt{2x-1} = \sqrt{5x} - 2$, we have:

LHS = $\sqrt{2\left(\frac{5}{9}\right)-1}$ RHS = $\sqrt{5\left(\frac{5}{9}\right)} - 2$

      = $\sqrt{\frac{1}{9}}$ = $\frac{5}{3} - 2$

      = $\frac{1}{3}$ = $-\frac{1}{3}$

Since LHS ≠ RHS, $x = \frac{5}{9}$ is not a possible solution.

∴ $x = 5$ is the only solution.

Exercise 4B (*Answers on page 497*)

1. Simplify the following:

     (a) $\sqrt{7} \times \sqrt{2}$ **(b)** $\sqrt{3} \times \sqrt{10}$ **(c)** $\dfrac{\sqrt{42}}{\sqrt{14}}$

     (d) $\sqrt{2} \times \sqrt{8}$ **(e)** $\sqrt{12} \times \sqrt{3}$ **(f)** $\dfrac{\sqrt{150}}{\sqrt{6}}$

2. Simplify the following:

     (a) $\sqrt{8}$ **(b)** $\sqrt{18}$ **(c)** $\sqrt{75}$ **(d)** $\sqrt{32}$

     (e) $\sqrt{108}$ **(f)** $\sqrt{200}$ **(g)** $\sqrt{128}$ **(h)** $\sqrt{1800}$

     (i) $2\sqrt{45}$ **(j)** $3\sqrt{75}$ **(k)** $\dfrac{\sqrt{27}}{3}$ **(l)** $\dfrac{\sqrt{63}}{6}$

3. Simplify the following:

(a) $\sqrt{8} + \sqrt{50} - 3\sqrt{2}$ **(b)** $\sqrt{75} - \sqrt{27} + 2\sqrt{12}$

(c) $\sqrt{32} + \sqrt{128} - \sqrt{512}$ **(d)** $\sqrt{24} - \sqrt{216} + \sqrt{294} - 3\sqrt{6}$

4. Using $\sqrt{2} = 1.414$, $\sqrt{3} = 1.732$ and $\sqrt{5} = 2.236$, evaluate the following:

(a) $\sqrt{12}$ **(b)** $2\sqrt{18}$ **(c)** $\dfrac{\sqrt{8000}}{4}$ **(d)** $\sqrt{2} + \sqrt{32}$

(e) $\sqrt{75} - \sqrt{8}$ **(f)** $\sqrt{125} + 3\sqrt{18} - \sqrt{27}$

5. Square the following:

(a) $\sqrt{3}$ **(b)** $\sqrt{\dfrac{2}{5}}$ **(c)** $4\sqrt{2}$

(d) $\sqrt{5} \times \sqrt{7}$ **(e)** $\dfrac{\sqrt{12}}{\sqrt{9}}$ **(f)** $\dfrac{\sqrt{12}}{4}$

(g) $\dfrac{6}{\sqrt{8}}$ **(h)** $\dfrac{3}{2\sqrt{6}}$

6. Expand the following:

(a) $(3 + \sqrt{2})^2$ **(b)** $(2 - \sqrt{5})^2$

(c) $(\sqrt{5} + \sqrt{7})^2$ **(d)** $(\sqrt{3} - \sqrt{2})^2$

7. Expand the following and hence deduce whether the two polynomials are conjugate surds:

(a) $(\sqrt{7} + \sqrt{3})(\sqrt{7} - \sqrt{3})$

(b) $(\sqrt{6} + \sqrt{3})(\sqrt{6} + \sqrt{3})$

(c) $(4 - \sqrt{3})(4 - \sqrt{3})$

(d) $(2\sqrt{5} + 4)(2\sqrt{5} - 4)$

8. Rationalise the denominator of the following fractions:

(a) $\dfrac{1}{\sqrt{3}}$ **(b)** $\dfrac{2}{\sqrt{2}}$ **(c)** $\dfrac{3}{\sqrt{6}}$

(d) $\dfrac{10}{\sqrt{5}}$ **(e)** $\dfrac{\sqrt{2}}{\sqrt{3}}$ **(f)** $\dfrac{\sqrt{5}}{\sqrt{15}}$

(g) $\dfrac{10}{3\sqrt{2}}$ **(h)** $\dfrac{12}{5\sqrt{3}}$ **(i)** $\dfrac{6 + \sqrt{3}}{\sqrt{3}}$

(j) $\dfrac{2\sqrt{2} - 6}{\sqrt{2}}$ **(k)** $\dfrac{15 - \sqrt{5}}{\sqrt{5}}$ **(l)** $\dfrac{\sqrt{5} + \sqrt{20}}{\sqrt{10}}$

9. Rationalise the denominator of the following:

(a) $\dfrac{9}{\sqrt{27}}$ **(b)** $\dfrac{10}{\sqrt{50}}$ **(c)** $\dfrac{8}{\sqrt{200}}$

(d) $\dfrac{15}{\sqrt{180}}$ **(e)** $\dfrac{3}{2\sqrt{18}}$ **(f)** $\dfrac{15}{2\sqrt{50}}$

(g) $\dfrac{16 - 2\sqrt{2}}{\sqrt{8}}$ **(h)** $\dfrac{\sqrt{90} - \sqrt{24}}{\sqrt{50}}$

10. Rationalise the denominator of the following:

    (a) $\dfrac{3}{\sqrt{5} - \sqrt{2}}$ (b) $\dfrac{\sqrt{2}}{\sqrt{3} + \sqrt{2}}$ (c) $\dfrac{1}{3 + \sqrt{2}}$

    (d) $\dfrac{2}{\sqrt{6} - 2}$ (e) $\dfrac{\sqrt{3}}{3\sqrt{2} - 2\sqrt{3}}$ (f) $\dfrac{\sqrt{5} + 1}{\sqrt{5} - 1}$

    (g) $\dfrac{\sqrt{2} + 2\sqrt{5}}{\sqrt{5} - \sqrt{2}}$

11. Given $\sqrt{2} = 1.414$, $\sqrt{3} = 1.732$ and $\sqrt{5} = 2.236$, evaluate the following, without using a calculator:

    (a) $\dfrac{2}{\sqrt{2}}$ (b) $\dfrac{12}{\sqrt{3}}$ (c) $\dfrac{40}{\sqrt{8}}$

    (d) $\dfrac{30}{\sqrt{45}}$ (e) $\dfrac{9\sqrt{5}}{\sqrt{15}}$ (f) $\dfrac{12 - \sqrt{3}}{\sqrt{3}}$

    (g) $\dfrac{\sqrt{5} + 1}{\sqrt{5}}$ (h) $\dfrac{\sqrt{20} + \sqrt{5}}{\sqrt{10}}$

12. Solve the following:

    (a) $\sqrt{5x} = 10$ (b) $\sqrt{2x + 3} = 5$

    (c) $2\sqrt{3x} - 5 = 7$ (d) $\sqrt{3x + 4} + 6 = 11$

    (e) $5\sqrt{x} = \sqrt{x} - 12$ (f) $8\sqrt{x} - 9 = \sqrt{x} + 5$

    (g) $\sqrt{x + 1} = \sqrt{2x} - 1$ (h) $\sqrt{5x + 10} - \sqrt{3x} = 2$

    (i) $\sqrt{4x + 5} = \sqrt{3x - 6} + 2$ (j) $\sqrt{5x + 1} - \sqrt{3x - 5} = 2$

Summary

1. Rules for indices:

    (a) $a^m \times a^n = a^{m + n}$

    (b) $a^m \div a^n = a^{m - n}$

    (c) $(a^m)^n = a^{mn}$

    (d) $a^m \times b^m = (ab)^m$

    (e) $a^m \div b^m = \left(\dfrac{a}{b}\right)^m$

2. $a^0 = 1$

   $a^{-n} = \dfrac{1}{a^n}$

   $a^{\frac{m}{n}} = \sqrt[n]{a^m} = (\sqrt[n]{a})^m$

3. Rules for surds:

    (a) $\sqrt{a} \times \sqrt{b} = \sqrt{a \times b}$

    (b) $\dfrac{\sqrt{a}}{\sqrt{b}} = \sqrt{\dfrac{a}{b}}$

Revision Exercise 4 *(Answers on page 497)*

1. Find the value of

   (a) $8^{\frac{5}{3}}$,
   (b) $27^{-\frac{2}{3}}$,
   (c) $\left(\dfrac{1}{16}\right)^{-\frac{3}{2}}$.

2. Solve the following equations:

   (a) $9^x = \dfrac{1}{3}$
   (b) $3^{x+1} = 27^{1-x}$

   (c) $4^{x^2-23} = 16$
   (d) $4^x - 12 \times 2^x + 32 = 0$

   (e) $2^{2x-5} - 3(2^{x-3}) + 1 = 0$
   (f) $4^x = 10 - 4^{x+1}$

3. Solve $7^{x^2} - 49^{6-2x} = 0$. (C)

4. Show that $2^{2x} + 3(2^{x+1}) + 8 = 0$ has no solution.

5. Given that $\dfrac{5^{3x}}{25^y} = 3\,125$ and $2^x 4^{y-1} = 32$, find the value of x and of y.

6. The curve with equation $py = q^x$ passes through the points $(1,-12)$ and $(-2, \dfrac{3}{16})$. Find the value of p and of q. (C)

7. Simplify
   (a) $\sqrt{27} - \sqrt{12} + 2\sqrt{75}$,
   (b) $(2 + \sqrt{3})^2$,
   (c) $(2\sqrt{2} - 3)(3\sqrt{2} - 1)$,
   (d) $(\sqrt{2} - 3)^2(2\sqrt{2} + 5)$.

8. Rationalise the denominator of
   (a) $\dfrac{3\sqrt{5} - \sqrt{2}}{2\sqrt{5} + 3\sqrt{2}}$,
   (b) $\dfrac{1 - \sqrt{2}}{\sqrt{5} + \sqrt{3}} + \dfrac{1 - \sqrt{2}}{\sqrt{5} - \sqrt{3}}$.

9. Solve $\sqrt{x + 4} + \sqrt{x + 10} = \sqrt{8x + 18}$. (C)

10. If $(a - b\sqrt{5})^2 = 49 - 12\sqrt{5}$, find the value of a and of b.

11. Find the value of $(\sqrt[6]{8} - \sqrt{\dfrac{8}{9}})^2$.

12. Solve the equation $\dfrac{6}{5 - \sqrt{x}} = \sqrt{x}$.

Maths Booster

1. Explain how you would help a friend understand that 2^{-3} is not equal to -8.

2. If p and q are positive integers and $p < q$, solve the equation $p^q = q^p$.

3. During bacterial reproduction, the time required for a population to double is called the generation time. If x bacteria are introduced into a medium, after the generation time has elapsed, there will be $2x$ bacteria. Derive an expression for the number of bacteria produced after n generation. Explain what this expression represents when $n = 0$.

4. If a and b are two positive integers such that
$\sqrt{a}(\sqrt{a} + \sqrt{b}) = 3\sqrt{b}(\sqrt{a} + 5\sqrt{b})$, find the value of
$\dfrac{3a + 2\sqrt{ab} + 2b}{a + \sqrt{ab} - b}$.

Chapter 5

Simultaneous Equations

We can use mathematics to solve a wide variety of problems. This is done by using problem-solving strategies. The problem is analysed, variables are used to represent the unknown quantities and equations are formed. The equations are then solved using the most convenient method: graphing, substitution or elimination.

Simultaneous Equations

Simultaneous equations – one linear and one non-linear equation – are normally solved by the method of **substitution**. The steps are as follows:

Step 1: Rearrange the linear equation by expressing one variable in terms of the other.

Step 2: Substitute the equation from step 1 into the non-linear equation to obtain an equation in one variable.

Step 3: Solve the equation obtained in step 2.

Step 4: Substitute the solutions from step 3 into the linear equation to obtain the values of the other variable.

▶ **Example 1**

Solve the simultaneous equations
$$2x + y = 1,$$
$$4x^2 + y^2 = 13.$$

▶ **Solution . . .**

$$2x + y = 1 \qquad \cdots\cdots\cdots \quad (1)$$
$$4x^2 + y^2 = 13 \qquad \cdots\cdots\cdots \quad (2)$$

Rearranging (1):
$$y = 1 - 2x \qquad \cdots\cdots\cdots \quad (3)$$

Substituting (3) into (2):
$$4x^2 + (1 - 2x)^2 = 13$$
$$4x^2 + (1 - 4x + 4x^2) = 13$$
$$8x^2 - 4x - 12 = 0$$
$$2x^2 - x - 3 = 0$$
$$(x + 1)(2x - 3) = 0$$
$$x = -1 \ \text{ or } \ x = \frac{3}{2}$$

Substituting $x = -1$ into (3):
$$y = 1 - 2\,(-1)$$
$$= 3$$

Substituting $x = \frac{3}{2}$ into (3):
$$y = 1 - 2\left(\frac{3}{2}\right)$$
$$= -2$$

∴ The solutions are $x = -1$, $y = 3$ or $x = \frac{3}{2}$, $y = -2$.

Note:

1. The solutions $x = -1$ and $\frac{3}{2}$ must be substituted into the linear equation in (1) or (3) to obtain the values of y. If the solutions of x are substituted

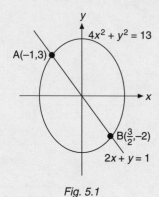

Fig. 5.1

into the non-linear equation in (2), we would obtain 4 values of x, from which 2 values are wrong.

For example, if we substitute $x = -1$ into equation (2), we will obtain

$$4(-1)^2 + y^2 = 13$$
$$y^2 = 9$$
$$y = \pm 3$$

Among the two values of y, $y = -3$ is a wrong answer because it does not satisfy equation (1), i.e. $2(-1) + (-3) \neq 1$.

2. In Example 1, $2x + y = 1$ represents a straight line while $4x^2 + y^2 = 13$ represents a curve. The line meets the curve at two different points, $A(-1,3)$ and $B\left(\frac{3}{2}, -2\right)$.

Hence, we can conclude that the solutions of the simultaneous equations give the points of intersection of a line and a curve (Fig. 5.1).

▶ **Example 2**

Find the coordinates of the points of intersection of the line $2x + 3y = -1$ and the curve $x(x - y) = 2$.

▶ **Solution . . .**

$$2x + 3y = -1 \qquad \text{............ (1)}$$
$$x(x - y) = 2 \qquad \text{............ (2)}$$

Rearranging (1):

$$y = \frac{-1 - 2x}{3} \qquad \text{............ (3)}$$

Substituting (3) into (2):

$$x\left(x - \frac{-1 - 2x}{3}\right) = 2$$
$$x\left(\frac{3x + 1 + 2x}{3}\right) = 2$$
$$x(5x + 1) = 6$$
$$5x^2 + x - 6 = 0$$
$$(x - 1)(5x + 6) = 0$$
$$x = 1 \text{ or } x = -\frac{6}{5}$$

Substituting $x = 1$ into (3):

$$y = \frac{-1 - 2(1)}{3} = -1$$

Substituting $x = -\frac{6}{5}$ into (3):

$$y = \frac{-1 - 2(-\frac{6}{5})}{3} = \frac{7}{15}$$

Hence, the coordinates of the points of intersection are $(1, -1)$ and $\left(-\frac{6}{5}, \frac{7}{15}\right)$.

![Activity]

Verification and IT Skills

We can use the graphing method to solve the simultaneous equations:

$$2x + y = 1$$
$$4x^2 + y^2 = 13$$

Use Graphmatica courseware to plot the graphs of the two equations. The points of intersection give the solutions to the equations.

From the graphs, verify the two sets of solutions.

Can we use the substitution method to solve such a pair of equations? Explain.

The principle of solving simultaneous equations can also be applied in solving practical problems. We would first formulate the linear and non-linear equations and then solve them simultaneously.

▶ Example 3

Problem Solving

The perimeter of a rectangle is 22 cm and its area is 28 cm^2. Find its length and breadth.

▶ Solution . . .

Let the length and breadth of the rectangle be x cm and y cm.

Given   perimeter = 22 cm

$$2x + 2y = 22$$
$$x + y = 11$$
$$y = 11 - x \quad \ldots\ldots\ldots\ldots(1)$$

Given   area = 28 cm^2

$$xy = 28 \quad \ldots\ldots\ldots\ldots(2)$$

Substituting (1) into (2):

$$x(11 - x) = 28$$
$$x^2 - 11x + 28 = 0$$
$$(x - 4)(x - 7) = 0$$
$$x = 4 \text{ or } x = 7$$

Substituting $x = 4$ into (1):

$$y = 11 - 4 = 7$$

Substituting $x = 7$ into (1):

$$y = 11 - 7 = 4$$

Therefore, the length of the rectangle is 7 cm and the breadth is 4 cm.

Problem-solving strategy

Step 1: Analyse the facts in the problem.

Step 2: Use variables to represent the unknown quantities.

Step 3: Form equations involving the variables.

Step 4: Solve the equations.

Exercise 5A (Answers on page 497)

1. Solve the following pairs of simultaneous equations:

(a) $x + y = 5$
     $xy - x = 3$

(b) $x - y = 2$
     $x(x + y) = 9$

(c) $2x + y = 5$
     $x^2 + y^2 = 10$

(d) $x - 2y = 2$
     $x^2 + xy = 20$

(e) $2x + 3y = 5$
     $y(y - x) = 5$

(f) $3x - 2y = 7$
     $x^2 + y^2 = 10$

(g) $3x - y = 7$
     $x^2 + xy - y^2 = 1$

(h) $x + 3y = 1$
     $x^2 - xy + y^2 = 21$

(i) $3x + 4y = 2$
     $x^2 - 3y^2 = 1$

(j) $x + 2y = 7$
     $x^2 - 4x + y^2 = 1$

(k) $\frac{x}{3} - \frac{y}{2} = 1$
     $\frac{3}{x} + \frac{2}{y} = \frac{3}{2}$

(l) $3x - 2y = 11$
     $(x - 1)(y + 3) = 4$

2. Find the coordinates of the points of intersection of the line $x + 2y = 10$ and the curve $2y^2 - 7y + x = 0$. (C)

3. The line $y = 2x + 3$ intersects the curve $xy + 20 = 5y$ at A and B. Find the coordinates of A and of B. (C)

4. The line $3x - 5y = 8$ meets the curve $\dfrac{3}{x} - \dfrac{1}{y} = 4$ at A and B. Find the coordinates of the mid-point of AB.

5. The line $y = x + 2$ intersects the curve $y^2 = 4(2x + 1)$ at A and B. Find
   (a) the coordinates of A and of B,
   (b) the distance AB.

6. A straight line through $(0, -1)$ meets the curve $x^2 + y^2 - 4x - 2y + 4 = 0$ at the point $(3, 1)$. Find
   (a) the equation of the straight line,
   (b) the coordinates of the second point where this line meets the curve.

7. The perimeter of a rectangle is 36 cm and its area is 77 cm^2. Find its length and breadth.

8. Fencing is used to make 3 sides of a rectangular field: two pieces each of length a m and one piece of length b m. The total length of fencing used is 30 m and the area enclosed is 100 m^2. What are the values of a and b?

9. The difference between two positive numbers is 2 and the difference of their squares is 28. Find the numbers.

10. If the sum of two numbers is 4 and the sum of their squares minus three times their product is 76, find the numbers.

Summary

1. To solve simultaneous equations – one linear and one non-linear equation – the steps are:

   Step 1: Make one variable the subject of the linear equation.

   Step 2: Substitute the equation from Step 1 into the non-linear equation.

   Step 3: Solve the quadratic equation obtained.

   Step 4: Find the corresponding values of the second variable.

2. The point of intersection of a line and a curve can be determined by solving the equations simultaneously.

3. To solve a practical problem involving a linear and a non-linear equation, first formulate the equations and then solve them simultaneously.

Revision Exercise 5 (*Answers on page 497*)

1. Solve the simultaneous equations: $2x + 3y = 6$
$$(2x + 1)^2 + 6(y - 2)^2 = 49 \qquad \text{(C)}$$

2. Solve the simultaneous equations: $x + y = 6$
$$\frac{1}{x - 1} = \frac{3}{y} + \frac{1}{4}$$

3. A line through the point (2,1) meets the curve $x^2 - 2x - y = 3$ at A(–2,5) and at B. Find the coordinates of B.

4. P(3,1) lies on the curve $(x - 1)(y + 1) = 4$. A line, perpendicular to $x + 2y = 7$, cuts through P and meets the curve again at Q. Find the coordinates of Q.

5. The line parallel to $y = 2x - 3$ cuts through (–3,8) and meets the curve $(x + 3)(y - 2) = 8$ at R and S. Find the coordinates of the midpoint of RS.

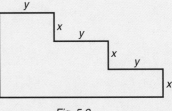

6. The perimeter of the shape (Fig. 5.2) is 90 cm and the area enclosed is 300 cm². All corners are right angled. Find the values of x and y.

Fig. 5.2

7. Two quantities u and v are related by the equation $u + 2v = 7$. A third quantity p is given by $p = u(v - 3)$. Find the values of u and v when $p = -3$.

8. The hypotenuse of a right-angled triangle is $(2y - 1)$ cm long. The other two sides are x cm and $(y + 5)$ cm in length. If the perimeter of the triangle is 30 cm, find the possible values of x and y.

9. In Fig. 5.3, ABE is an isosceles triangle and BCDE is a rectangle. The total length round ABCDEA is 22 cm and the area enclosed is 30 cm².
   (a) State the distance of A from BE in terms of x.
   (b) Find the possible values of x and y.

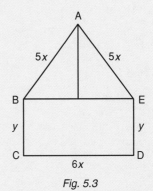

Fig. 5.3

10. P(a,b) is a point on the line passing through A(–1,–2), B(3,0) and PA = $\sqrt{125}$.
    (a) Show that $a - 2b = 3$, and $a^2 + b^2 + 2a + 4b - 120 = 0$.
    (b) Find the values of a and b.

Maths Booster

1. If $x > y > z > 664$ and x, y and z are positive integers, solve the simultaneous equations: $x + y + z = 2001$
$$x + 2y + 3z = 4000$$

2. Solve the simultaneous equations: $w + 2x + 3y + 4z = 12$
$$2w + x + 3y + 6z = 10$$
$$4w + 5x + 2y + 3z = -12$$
$$3w + 4x + 2y - z = -10$$
$$w = -5$$

Revision Paper 1 (Answers on page 512)

1. **(a)** It is given that $n(\varepsilon) = 60$ and that A and B are two sets for which $n(A) = 18$, $n(B) = 24$ and $n(A \cap B) = 10$.
   - **(i)** Draw a Venn diagram to illustrate this information.
   - **(ii)** Find $n(A' \cap B)$.

   (b)

   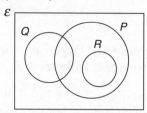

   Copy this Venn diagram and shade the set $P \cap (Q \cup R)'$.

2. $\varepsilon = \{x: 10 \leq x \leq 50, \text{ where } x \text{ is an integer}\}$
   $A = \{x: x \text{ is an even number}\}$
   $B = \{x: x \text{ is a number where the difference between the digits is } 5\}$
   $C = \{x: x \text{ is a number which has a remainder of 3 when divided by 5}\}$

   (a) List the elements of sets B and C.

   (b) Find **(i)** $n(A \cap B)$,   **(ii)** $n(A \cup B)'$,
                (iii) $n(B \cap C)$,   **(iv)** $n(A \cap C')$.

3. **(a)** The function f is defined by $\text{f} : x \longmapsto \dfrac{x+4}{x-2}$ $(x \neq 2)$.
   Find **(i)** $\text{f}^{-1}(3)$ and **(ii)** the values of x for which $\text{f}(x) = x$.

   (b) The function g is given by $\text{g} : x \longmapsto a - \dfrac{3}{x}$ $(x \neq 0)$ where a is a constant. If $\text{g}(2) - \text{g}^{-1}(-2) = 2$, find the values of a.

4. For each of the following functions, find the range of $\text{f}(x)$ corresponding to the domain given:

   (a) $\text{f}(x) = \left| 3 - x \right|$ for $-1 \leq x \leq 4$
   (b) $\text{f}(x) = 4 - x^2$ for $-1 \leq x \leq 3$
   (c) $\text{f}(x) = x^2 - 4x + 3$ for $0 \leq x \leq 3$

5. **(a)** Given that $\text{f}(x) = x - \dfrac{4}{x}$, sketch the graph of $y = \text{f}(x)$ for $1 \leq x \leq 4$.
   Hence sketch the graph of $y = \text{f}^{-1}(x)$ for $-3 \leq x \leq 3$.

   (b) Find the range of values of y for which $\left| y^2 - 5y - 1 \right| \leq 5$.

6. **(a)** For what values of k is the function $x^2 + 2kx + 5$ always positive?

   (b) Given that $\text{f}(x)$ is a quadratice function and that $\text{f}(x)$ is only positive when x lies between -1 and 3, find $\text{f}(x)$ if $\text{f}(-2) = -10$.

7. **(a)** Solve the equation $32^x = 8^{x+1}$.

   (b) Simplify $2^{n+2} - 2^n + 10(2^{n-1})$.

8. Solve the equations:

    (a) $\sqrt{x+4} + \sqrt{x+10} = \sqrt{8x+18}$

    (b) $2^{x+1} + 2^x = 24$

9. Solve the simultaneous equations:

$$2x - 3y = 7$$
$$xy = x^2 - 6$$

10. Given that $f(x) = |2x + 1|$ and $g(x) = \dfrac{x}{2} + 4$.

    (a) Draw the graphs of $y = f(x)$ and $g(x)$ on the same axis for $-4 \le x \le 4$.

    (b) From your graph, find the range of values of x which satisfy the inequality $|2x + 1| < \dfrac{x}{2} + 4$.

Revision Paper 2 (Answers on page 512)

1. **(a)** Express in set notation, as simply as possible, the subset shaded in the Venn diagram.

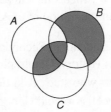

    (b) Given that $n(\varepsilon) = 50$, $n(P) = 28$ and $n(Q) = 26$, find the least possible value of $n(P \cap Q)$.

2. **(a)** The function f is defined as $f : x \longmapsto \dfrac{20}{ax+b}$. Given that $f(1) = 4$ and $f^{-1}(-4) = -4$, find

        (i) the value of a and of b,

        (ii) the values of x for which $f(x) = x$.

    (b) Find the range of values of x for which $(x - 2)(2x + 3) < (x - 2)(x + 2)$.

3. The functions f and g are defined for $x > 0$ as $f : x \longmapsto 3 - x$, $g : x \longmapsto \dfrac{4}{x}$. Show that

    (a) f and g are each self-inverse functions,

    (b) $(fg)^{-1} = gf$.

    (c) Prove that $fg(x) = gf(x)$ has no real solution.

4. On the same diagram, sketch the graphs of $y = |x - 1|$ and $y = |x + 2|$. Hence find the range of values of x for which $|x - 1| > |x + 2|$.

5. **(a)** If $y = 6 - x - x^2$, find
   (i) the range of values of x for which y is positive,
   (ii) the maximum value of y.

   (b) If $f : x \longmapsto \dfrac{x}{x+3}$ $(x \neq -3)$, find in a similar form f^2 and f^3.

   (c) Given that $f : x \longmapsto x^2 + 2$ and $g : x \longmapsto x - 1$, find the value of x for which $fg(x) = gf(x)$.

6. **(a)** Solve the equation $2^x + 2^{1-x} = 3$.

   (b) Simplify $\sqrt{27} - \sqrt{12} + 2\sqrt{75}$.

7. Solve the simultaneous equations
$$2^{2x} \times 8^y = 4,$$
$$3^x \times 9^{y+1} = \frac{1}{81}.$$

8. Solve the simultaneous equations:
$$3y - 2x = 4$$
$$x^2 - 5xy = 1$$

9. The line $2x - 5y = 7$ meets the curve $12x^2 - 5y^2 = 7$ at A and B. Find the coordinates of the midpoint of AB.

10. Each of the 112 students in Secondary Three studies at least one of the three subjects History, Geography and Additional Mathematics.
   Of the 28 students who study Additional Mathematics,
   8 also study History and Geography,
   6 study neither History nor Geography, and
   10 study Geography but not History.

   Of the 84 students who do not study Additional Mathematics,
   12 study both History and Geography,
   x study History, and
   $2x$ study only Geography.

   Draw a Venn diagram to illustrate this information.
   Hence find
   (a) the value of x,
   (b) the total number of students who study Geography.

Chapter 6

Factors of Polynomials

Polynomial equations can be solved using graphs. However, there are theorems that we can use to help solve polynomial equations by dividing and factorising.

In this chapter, you will learn how this is done.

6.1 The Remainder Theorem

When 216 is divided by 5, the quotient is 43 and the remainder is 1 (see the long division below).

$$
\begin{array}{r}
43 \quad \longrightarrow \text{quotient} \\
\text{divisor} \longleftarrow \; 5\overline{)216} \quad \longrightarrow \text{dividend} \\
20 \\
\hline
16 \\
15 \\
\hline
1 \quad \longrightarrow \text{remainder}
\end{array}
$$

The result may be stated as

$$
\begin{array}{ccccccc}
216 & = & 5 & \times & 43 & + & 1 \\
\text{dividend} & = & \text{divisor} & \times & \text{quotient} & + & \text{remainder}
\end{array}
$$

When the polynomial $x^3 - 2x^2 + 4x - 3$ is divided by $x - 3$, the quotient is $x^2 + x + 7$ and the remainder is 18 (see the long division below).

$$
\begin{array}{r}
x^2 + x + 7 \quad \longrightarrow \text{quotient} \\
\text{divisor} \longleftarrow \; x-3\overline{)x^3 - 2x^2 + 4x - 3} \quad \longrightarrow \text{dividend} \\
\underline{x^3 - 3x^2} \\
x^2 + 4x \\
\underline{x^2 - 3x} \\
7x - 3 \\
\underline{7x - 21} \\
18 \quad \longrightarrow \text{remainder}
\end{array}
$$

Similarly, the result may be stated as

$$
x^3 - 2x^2 + 4x - 3 = (x - 3)(x^2 + x + 7) + 18
$$

$$
\begin{array}{cccc}
\downarrow & \downarrow & \downarrow & \downarrow \\
\text{dividend} & \text{divisor} & \text{quotient} & \text{remainder}
\end{array}
$$

If we denote the dividend by f(x), the quotient by $Q(x)$ and the remainder by R, the result may be rewritten as

$$
f(x) = (x - 3) \, Q(x) + R
$$

Let $x = 3$,

$$
f(3) = (3 - 3)Q(3) + R
$$
$$
f(3) = R
$$

i.e. the remainder is f(3).

Now substitute $x = 3$ into $f(x) = x^3 - 2x^2 + 4x - 3$, we get

$$
\begin{aligned}
f(3) &= 3^3 - 2(3)^2 + 4(3) - 3 \\
&= 18
\end{aligned}
$$

Hence, the remainder is 18. (This is consistent with the result obtained earlier by long division.) So we can conclude that when f(x) is divided by $(x - a)$, the remainder is f(a).

In general,

> when a polynomial f(x) is divided by $px + q$, the remainder is $\mathbf{f\left(-\dfrac{q}{p}\right)}$.

This is the **Remainder Theorem**.

▶ ## Example 1

Find the remainder when $x^3 - x^2 + 3x - 2$ is divided by
(a) $x - 1$,   **(b)** $x + 2$,   **(c)** $2x - 1$.

▶ ## Solution . . .

Let f(x) = $x^3 - x + 3x - 2$.

(a) When f(x) is divided by $x - 1$,
  the remainder = f(1)
  $= 1^3 - 1^2 + 3(1) - 2$
  $= 1$

(b) When f(x) is divided by $x + 2$,
  the remainder = f(–2)
  $= (-2)^3 - (-2)^2 + 3(-2) - 2$
  $= -20$

(c) When f(x) is divided by $2x - 1$,

  the remainder = $f\left(\dfrac{1}{2}\right)$

  $= \left(\dfrac{1}{2}\right)^3 - \left(\dfrac{1}{2}\right)^2 + 3\left(\dfrac{1}{2}\right) - 2$

  $= -\dfrac{5}{8}$

▶ ## Example 2

The polynomial $x^3 + ax^2 - 3x + 4$ is divided by $x - 2$ and the remainder is 14. What is the value of a?

▶ ## Solution . . .

Let f(x) = $x^3 + ax^2 - 3x + 4$.
Using the Remainder Theorem,
  f(2) = 14
i.e. $(2)^3 + a(2)^2 - 3(2) + 4 = 14$
  $8 + 4a - 6 + 4 = 14$
  $a = 2$

▶ ## Example 3

The expression $x^3 + ax^2 + bx - 3$ leaves a remainder of 1 when divided by $x - 1$, and a remainder of –9 when divided by $x + 1$. Find the value of a and of b.

▶ **Solution . . .**

Let $f(x) = x^3 + ax^2 + bx - 3$.
Using the Remainder Theorem,
$$f(1) = 1$$
$$1^3 + a(1)^2 + b(1) - 3 = 1$$
$$a + b = 3 \quad \ldots \ldots \ldots (1)$$
and
$$f(-1) = -9$$
$$(-1)^3 + a(-1)^2 + b(-1) - 3 = -9$$
$$a - b = -5 \ldots \ldots \ldots (2)$$
$$(1) + (2) \qquad 2a = -2$$
$$a = -1$$
Substitute $a = -1$ into (1),
$$-1 + b = 3$$
$$b = 4$$
$$a = -1 \text{ and } b = 4.$$

▶ **Example 4**

The remainder when $x^3 - 3x^2 - 2x + a$ is divided by $x + 2$ is twice the remainder when the same expression is divided by $x - 3$. Find the value of a.

▶ **Solution . . .**

Let $f(x) = x^3 - 3x^2 - 2x + a$.
Using the Remainder Theorem,
$$f(-2) = 2f(3)$$
$$(-2)^3 - 3(-2)^2 - 2(-2) + a = 2[3^3 - 3(3)^2 - 2(3) + a]$$
$$-8 - 12 + 4 + a = 2(27 - 27 - 6 + a)$$
$$-16 + a = -12 + 2a$$
$$a = -4$$

Exercise 6A (Answers on page 497)

1. Using long division, find the remainder when
   (a) $x^3 + 2x^2 - x - 1$ is divided by $x - 1$,
   (b) $3x^3 - x^2 - x - 1$ is divided by $x - 4$,
   (c) $x^3 + 3x - 2$ is divided by $x + 2$.
   Check your answers using the Remainder Theorem. (C)

2. Using the Remainder Theorem, find the remainder when $x^3 + 2x^2 - x - 1$ is divided by
   (a) $x + 1$,   (b) $x - 3$,   (c) $3x + 2$.

3. Find the remainder when
   (a) $1 - 2x - 3x^2$ is divided by $x - 2$,
   (b) $x^3 + 3x - 3$ is divided by $3x - 2$,
   (c) $x^4 + x^3 - 2x^2 - 3$ is divided by $x + 3$.

4. The polynomial $2x^3 + px^2 - x - 2$ is divided by $x + 3$. State the remainder in terms of p.

5. When the polynomial $x^3 + ax - 4$ is divided by $x + 4$, the remainder is -28. Find the value of a.

6. Given that $4x^3 - 6x^2 + ax + 3$ leaves a remainder of 7 when divided by $2x - 1$, evaluate a. (C)

7. When the expression $2px^2 - p^2x - 14$ is divided by $x - 3$, the remainder is 10. Find the values of p. (C)

8. The expression $x^3 + ax^2 + bx - 1$ leaves a remainder of 7 when divided by $x - 2$, and a remainder of 4 when divided by $x + 1$. Find the value of a and of b.

9. When $x^4 + 3x^3 + ax^2 + bx - 1$ is divided by $x - 1$ and $x + 2$, the remainders are 4 and 19 respectively. Find the value of a and of b.

10. The remainder when $2x^3 + kx^2 + 7$ is divided by $x - 2$ is half the remainder when the same expression is divided by $2x - 1$. Find the value of k. (C)

11. When the polynomials $x^3 - 4x + 3$ and $x^3 - x^2 + x + 9$ are each divided by $x - a$, the remainders are equal. Find the possible values of a.

12. The remainders obtained when $px^3 + qx^2 + 4x - 2$ is divided by $x - 1$ and by $x + 2$ are equal. Show that $3p - q = -4$.

13. When the expression $x^3 + px^2 + qx + 2$ is divided by $x + 2$, the remainder is double that obtained when it is divided by $x - 1$. Find a relation between p and q. If the remainder is 6 when the expression is divided by $x + 1$, find the value of p and of q.

14. The expression $ax^2 + bx - 1$ leaves a remainder of R when divided by $x + 2$, and a remainder of $3R + 5$ when divided by $x - 3$. Show that $a = 3b - 1$. Given also that the expression is exactly divisible by $2x - 1$, evaluate a and b. (C)

15. The remainder when $x(x + b)(x - 2b)$ is divided by $x - b$ is -16. Find the value of b.

16. (a) If the expression $x^3 + px^2 + qx + r$ gives the same remainder when divided by $x + 1$ and by $x - 2$, show that $p + q = -3$.
    (b) If the remainder is 4 when the expression is divided by $x - 1$, find the value of r.
    (d) Hence, find the value of p and of q if the remainder is -60 when the expression is divided by $x + 3$.

6.2 The Factor Theorem

▶ **Example 5**

Using the remainder theorem, find the remainder when
$4x^3 + 3x^2 - 16x - 12$ is divided by one of its factors, $x - 2$.

▶ **Solution...**

Let $f(x) = 4x^3 + 3x^2 - 16x - 12$.
Using the remainder theorem, when $f(x)$ is divided by $x - 2$,
the remainder $= f(2)$
$$= 4(2)^3 + 3(2)^2 - 16(2) - 12$$
$$= 0$$

From the result above, we see that when a polynomial $f(x)$ is divided by its
factor $x - a$, the remainder $f(a) = 0$.

In general,

> if $px + q$ is a factor of $f(x)$, $f\left(-\dfrac{q}{p}\right) = 0$;
>
> if $f\left(-\dfrac{q}{p}\right) = 0$, $px + q$ is a factor of $f(x)$.

This is the **Factor Theorem**.

▶ **Example 6**

Determine whether $x - 2$ and $x - 4$ are factors of $2x^3 + x^2 - 22x + 24$.

▶ **Solution...**

Let $f(x) = 2x^3 + x^2 - 22x + 24$.

Substituting $x = 2$,
$$f(2) = 2(2)^3 + (2)^2 - 22(2) + 24$$
$$= 0$$
$\therefore x - 2$ is a factor of $f(x)$.

Substituting $x = 4$,
$$f(4) = 2(4)^3 + (4)^2 - 22(4) + 24$$
$$= 80$$
Since $f(4) \neq 0$,
$\therefore x - 4$ is not a factor of $f(x)$.

▶ **Example 7**

If $x + 1$ is a factor of $2x^3 + 3x^2 + kx + 3$, find the value of k.

▶ **Solution...**

Let $f(x) = 2x^3 + 3x^2 + kx + 3$.

Since $x + 1$ is a factor of f(x),
$$f(-1) = 0$$
$$2(-1)^3 + 3(-1)^2 + k(-1) + 3 = 0$$
$$-2 + 3 - k + 3 = 0$$
$$k = 4$$

▶ **Example 8**

The expression $2x^3 + ax^2 + bx - 2$ is exactly divisible by $x - 2$ and $2x + 1$. Find the values of a and b.

▶ **Solution . . .**

Let f(x) = $2x^3 + ax^2 + bx - 2$.
Given f(x) is divisible by $x - 2$,
i.e. $x - 2$ is a factor of f(x),
$$f(x) = 0$$
$$2(2)^3 + a(2)^2 + b(2) - 2 = 0$$
$$4a + 2b = -14$$
$$2a + b = -7 \qquad \ldots . . (1)$$

Given f(x) is divisible by $2x + 1$,
i.e. $2x + 1$ is a factor of f(x),
$$f\left(-\frac{1}{2}\right) = 0$$
$$2\left(-\frac{1}{2}\right)^3 + a\left(-\frac{1}{2}\right)^2 + b\left(-\frac{1}{2}\right) - 2 = 0$$
$$-\frac{1}{4} + \frac{a}{4} - \frac{b}{2} - 2 = 0$$
$$a - 2b = 9 \qquad \ldots . . (2)$$

Solving equations (1) and (2) simultaneously, we obtain $a = -1$ and $b = -5$.

Exercise 6B (Answers on page 498)

1. Determine whether $x + 4$ and $x + 2$ are factors of $x^3 + 5x^2 + 16x + 48$.

2. Show that $2x + 1$ is a factor of $2x^3 + 11x^2 - 7x - 6$.

3. Show that $x^4 + 5x^3 + 5x^2 - 5x - 6$ is divisible by $x + 3$ but not by $x - 3$.

4. If $x + 1$ is a factor of $2x^3 + kx^2 - 2x - 3$, find the value of k.

5. Find the value of m if $(mx + 1)^3 + (x + 1)^7$ has a factor of $x + 2$.

6. Find the value of p if $4x^3 - 16x^2 + px - 4$ is divisible by $2x - 1$.

7. Given that $x + 1$ and $x - 2$ are factors of $3x^3 + ax^2 + bx - 2$, find the value of a and of b. (C)

8. Given that $x + 2$ and $7x - 5$ are factors of $14x^3 + ax^2 + bx + 10$, find the value of a and of b. (C)

9. Find the value of p and of q for which $x^2 - 2x - 3$ is a factor of $2x^3 + px^2 - 12x + q$. [Hint : $x^2 - 2x - 3 = (x + 1)(x - 3)$] (C)

10. $x^3 + ax + b$ and $x^2 + 2ax + 3b$ have a common factor $x + 1$. Find the value of a and of b.

11. If $x - 2$ is a common factor of the expressions $x^2 + (p + q)x - q$ and $2x^2 + (p - 1)x + (p + 2q)$, find the value of p and of q.

12. The expression $f(x) = x^3 + ax^2 + bx + 4$ is exactly divisible by $x - 2$. If the remainder is -24 when $f(x)$ is divided by $x + 2$, find the value of a and of b.

13. Find the value of k ($k \neq 0$) for which $x + k$ and $x - k$ are both factors of $x^3 - x^2 - 9x + 9$.

6.3   Factorisation of Polynomials

When one of the factors of a polynomial is given, we can find the other factors by long division or the inspection method.

▶ **Example 9**

Given that $x - 2$ is a factor of $2x^3 + x^2 - 22x + 24$, find the other two factors.

▶ **Solution . . .**

Method 1 : Long division

$$
\begin{array}{r}
2x^2 + 5x - 12 \\
x - 2 \overline{\smash{\big)}\ 2x^3 + x^2 - 22x + 24} \\
\underline{2x^3 - 4x^2} \\
5x^2 - 22x \\
\underline{5x^2 - 10x} \\
-12x + 24 \\
\underline{-12x + 24}
\end{array}
$$

$\therefore 2x^3 + x^2 - 22x + 24 = (x - 2)(2x^2 + 5x - 12)$
$\qquad\qquad\qquad\qquad\quad = (x - 2)(x + 4)(2x - 3)$

Hence, the other two factors are $x + 4$ and $2x - 3$.

Method 2 : Inspection

As the polynomial is of the third degree and $x - 2$ is a factor, it can be written as

$$2x^3 + x^2 - 22x + 24 = (x - 2)(ax^2 + bx + c)$$

with labels ax^3, $-2c$, and ax^3, $-2c$ indicating terms.

As the first term is $2x^3$, we obtain $\quad a = 2$.
As the last term is 24, we have $\quad -2c = 24$
$$c = -12$$

So the polynomial can be rewritten as

$$2x^3 + x^2 - 22x + 24 = (x-2)(2x^2 + bx - 12)$$

with the x^2 terms: $-4x^2 + bx^2$ and bx^2 (the product giving $-4x^2$).

By comparing the coefficient of x^2 on both sides of the equation, we have
$$-4 + b = 1$$
$$b = 5$$

Hence, $2x^3 + x^2 - 22x + 24 = (x-2)(2x^2 + 5x - 12)$
$$= (x-2)(x+4)(2x-3)$$

The other two factors are $x + 4$ and $2x - 3$.

Note:
Alternatively we can obtain the value of b by comparing the coefficient of x on both sides of the equation.

$$2x^3 + x^2 - 22x + 24 = (x-2)(2x^2 + bx - 12)$$

with the x terms giving $-12x$ and $-2bx$.

Comparing the coefficient of x:
$$-12 - 2b = -22$$
$$b = 5$$

If the first factor of a polynomial is not given, we would find the factor by the trial-and-error method.

▶ Example 10

Factorise $x^3 - 2x^2 - 5x + 6$.

▶ Solution . . .

Let $f(x) = x^3 - 2x^2 - 5x + 6$.
As $f(x)$ is of the third degree, it will have at most three linear factors. Since the coefficient of the first term x^3 is 1, possible factors of $f(x)$ are of the form $x + a$, $x + b$ and $x + c$.

Then $x^3 - 2x^2 - 5x + 6 = (x+a)(x+b)(x+c)$

with abc (constant term) and abc.

As the last term is 6, so $abc = 6$.

Hence possible values of a, b and c are $\pm1, \pm2, \pm3$ and ±6. So possible factors are $x \pm 1$, $x \pm 2$, $x \pm 3$ and $x \pm 6$. The first factor has to be found by trial.

By trying $x + 1$, the remainder $= f(-1) = (-1)^3 - 2(-1)^2 - 5(-1) + 6 = 8$

Since $f(-1) \neq 0$, $x + 1$ is not a factor.

By trying $x - 1$, the remainder $= f(1) = 1^3 - 2(1)^2 - 5(1) + 6 = 0$

Since $f(1) = 0$, $x - 1$ is a factor.

Now we can continue trying other possible factors by this trial-and-error method.

Alternatively we can find other factors by long division or inspection. Let's try the long division method in this example.

$$
\begin{array}{r}
x^2 - x - 6 \\
x - 1 \overline{\smash{\big)}\ x^3 - 2x^2 - 5x + 6} \\
\underline{x^3 - x^2} \\
-x^2 - 5x \\
\underline{-x^2 + x} \\
-6x + 6 \\
\underline{-6x + 6}
\end{array}
$$

Then $x^3 - 2x^2 - 5x + 6 = (x - 1)(x^2 - x - 6)$
$$= (x - 1)(x + 2)(x - 3)$$

▶ **Example 11**

Factorise $x^3 - 3x^2 - 2x + 8$.

▶ **Solution . . .**

The possible factors are $x \pm 1$, $x \pm 2$, $x \pm 4$ and $x \pm 8$.

By trying $x + 1$, the remainder $= -1 - 3 + 2 + 8 \neq 0$, $x + 1$ is not a factor.

By trying $x - 1$, the remainder $= 1 - 3 - 2 + 8 \neq 0$, $x - 1$ is not a factor.

By trying $x + 2$, the remainder $= -8 - 12 + 4 + 8 \neq 0$, $x + 2$ is not a factor.

By trying $x - 2$, the remainder $= 8 - 12 - 4 + 8 = 0$, $x - 2$ is a factor.

The other factor is then found by inspection.

Then $x^3 - 3x^2 - 2x + 8 = (x - 2)(x^2 - x - 4)$

Note that $x^2 - x - 4$ cannot be factorised, so $x^3 - 3x^2 - 2x + 8$ has two factors only — one linear factor and one quadratic factor.

▶ **Example 12**

Factorise $4x^3 - 8x^2 - x + 2$.

▶ **Solution . . .**

As the first term is $4x^3$, the possible factors are of the form $px + a$, $qx + b$ and $rx + c$.

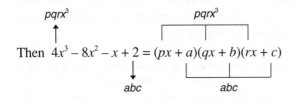

Then $4x^3 - 8x^2 - x + 2 = (px + a)(qx + b)(rx + c)$

Comparing the first terms: $pqr = 4$, the possible values of p, q and r are ± 1, ± 2 and ± 4.

Comparing the last terms: $abc = 2$, the possible values of a, b and c are ± 1 and ± 2.

Hence, the possible factors are $x \pm 1$, $x \pm 2$, $2x \pm 1$ and $4x \pm 1$.

Try $x + 1$, $x - 1$ and $x + 2$ and confirm that they are not factors.

Now try $x - 2$. The remainder $= 32 - 32 - 2 + 2 = 0$, so $x - 2$ is a factor.

Then $\qquad 4x^3 - 8x^2 - x + 2 = (x - 2)(4x^2 - 1)$

Hence $\qquad 4x^3 - 8x^2 - x + 2 = (x - 2)(2x - 1)(2x + 1)$

Exercise 6C (*Answers on page 498*)

1. Given that $x + 2$ is a factor of $x^3 + 2x^2 - x - 2$, find the other two factors.

2. If $2x + 3$ is a factor of $2x^3 - 11x^2 - x + 30$, find the other two factors.

3. Given that $12x^3 - 8x^2 - 3x + 2$ is exactly divisible by $3x - 2$, find the other two factors.

4. Factorise the following:
   (a) $x^3 - 4x^2 + 5x - 2$ (b) $x^3 - 4x^2 + x + 6$
   (c) $x^3 - x^2 + 2x - 2$ (d) $x^3 - 2x^2 - 9x + 18$
   (e) $x^3 + 1$ (f) $3x^3 + 2x^2 - 3x - 2$
   (g) $2x^3 - 3x^2 - 8x + 12$ (h) $6x^3 - 13x^2 + 9x - 2$

5. Given that $f(x) = x^3 - 6x^2 + 11x + p$, find the value of p for which $x - 3$ is a factor of $f(x)$. With this value of p, find the other factors of $f(x)$.

6. The expression $2x^3 + ax^2 + bx + 1$ is exactly divisible by $x + 1$ and $2x - 1$. Find the value of a and of b. Hence find the third factor of the expression.

7. $x^3 + ax^2 + x + b$ is exactly divisible by $x - 3$, and the remainder is -20 when it is divided by $x + 2$. Find the value of a and of b and then factorise the expression.

8. The expression $x^4 + 4x^3 + 6x^2 + 5x + 2$ has only two linear factors. Find these factors.

9. The expression $A(x - 1)^3 + B(x + 3)^2 + 20$ is exactly divisible by $x + 1$, and the remainder is 26 when it is divided by x. Find the value of A and of B. Using these values, rewrite the expression as a polynomial and factorise it completely.

10. Given the expression $ax^3 + bx^2 + cx + d$, show that $x - 1$ is a factor if $a + b + c + d = 0$.
   [This result is worth remembering: if the sum of the coefficients = 0, then $x - 1$ is a factor.]

6.4   Solving Cubic Equations

▶ ## Example 13

Solve the equation $2x^3 + 3x^2 - 3x - 2 = 0$.

▶ ## Solution ...

Let $f(x) = 2x^3 + 3x^2 - 3x - 2$.

Possible factors are $x \pm 1$, $x \pm 2$ and $2x \pm 1$.

Considering $x + 1$: $f(-1) = -2 + 3 + 3 - 2 \neq 0$, $x + 1$ is not a factor.

Considering $x - 1$: $f(1) = 2 + 3 - 3 - 2 = 0$, $x - 1$ is a factor.

Divide $f(x)$ by $x - 1$ to obtain the other factor, $2x^2 + 5x + 2$.

Then $2x^3 + 3x^2 - 3x - 2 = (x - 1)(2x^2 + 5x + 2)$
$$= (x - 1)(x + 2)(2x + 1)$$

Hence $2x^3 + 3x^2 - 3x - 2 = 0$
$$(x - 1)(x + 2)(2x + 1) = 0$$
$$x = 1, x = -2 \text{ or } x = -\frac{1}{2}$$

▶ ## Example 14

Solve the equation $x^3 - 2x^2 + 2x = 4$.

▶ ## Solution ...

Given $x^3 - 2x^2 + 2x = 4$
$$x^3 - 2x^2 + 2x - 4 = 0$$

Let $f(x) = x^3 - 2x^2 + 2x - 4$.

Possible factors are $x \pm 1$, $x \pm 2$ and $x \pm 4$.

Consider $x + 1$, $x - 1$ and $x + 2$, and confirm that they are not factors.

Considering $x - 2$: $f(2) = 8 - 8 + 4 - 4 = 0$, $x - 2$ is a factor.

Divide $f(x)$ by $x - 2$ to obtain the other factor, $x^2 + 2$.

Then $\quad x^3 - 2x^2 + 2x - 4 = (x - 2)(x^2 + 2)$

Hence $\qquad x^3 - 2x^2 + 2x - 4 = 0$

$$(x - 2)(x^2 + 2) = 0$$
$$x - 2 = 0 \quad \text{or} \quad x^2 + 2 = 0$$
$$x = 2 \qquad\qquad x^2 = -2 \text{ (no solution)}$$

▶ Example 15

Solve the equation $x^3 - 3x^2 + x + 2 = 0$, giving your answers correct to 2 decimal places where necessary.

▶ Solution . . .

Let $\quad f(x) = x^3 - 3x^2 + x + 2$.

Possible factors are $x \pm 1$ and $x \pm 2$.

Try $x + 1$, $x - 1$ and $x + 2$, and confirm that they are not factors.

Try $x - 2$: $f(2) = 8 - 12 + 2 + 2 = 0$, $x - 2$ is a factor.

Divide $f(x)$ by $x - 2$ to obtain the other factor, $x^2 - x - 1$.

Hence $\qquad\qquad x^3 - 3x^2 + x + 2 = 0$

$$(x - 2)(x^2 - x - 1) = 0$$
$$x - 2 = 0 \quad \text{or} \quad x^2 - x - 1 = 0$$

$$x = 2 \quad \text{or} \qquad x = \frac{-(-1) \pm \sqrt{(-1)^2 - 4(1)(-1)}}{20}$$

$$= \frac{1 \pm \sqrt{5}}{5}$$

$$= 1.62 \text{ or } -0.62$$

Exercise 6D (Answers on page 498)

1. Solve the following equations:
   (a) $x^3 + 2x^2 - x - 2 = 0$ (b) $x^2 + 6x^2 + 11x + 6 = 0$
   (c) $x^3 = 13x + 12$ (d) $4x^3 = 12x^2 - 5x - 6$
   (e) $x^2(2x + 1) = 13x - 6$ (f) $x^3 + 2x^2 = 2x - 3$

2. Solve the following equations, giving your answers correct to 2 decimal places where necessary:
   (a) $x^3 = 6x + 5$ (b) $2x^3 + 7x^2 = 2x + 1$
   (c) $2x^3 + 3x^2 - 4x = 4$ (d) $x^2 = 5 + \dfrac{2}{x}$ (C)

3. Factorise completely the expression $4x^3 - 13x - 6$ and hence solve the equation $2\left(2x^2 - \dfrac{3}{x}\right) = 13$.

4. Solve the equation $x^3 - 7x + 6 = 0$. Hence state the solutions of the equation $(x - 2)^3 - 7(x - 2) + 6 = 0$.

5. Find the x-coordinates of the points where the line $y = 5x - 1$ meets the curve $y = 2x^3 + x^2 + 1$.

6. Find the coordinates of the points of intersection of the curve $y = x^3$ and the line $y = 7x + 6$.

Summary

1. **Remainder Theorem**
   - If a polynomial f(x) is divided by $x - a$, then the remainder is f(a).
   - If f(x) is divided by $px + q$, the remainder is $f\left(-\dfrac{q}{p}\right)$.

2. **Factor Theorem**
   - If $x - a$ is a factor of f(x), then f(a) = 0.
   - If $px + q$ is a factor of f(x), then $f\left(-\dfrac{q}{p}\right) = 0$.

3. **Factorisation of Polynomials**
   We would find the first factor by the trial-and-error method. The other factors can be found by using the same method, or by using long division or the inspection method.

4. **Solving Cubic Equations**
   To solve the equation f(x) = 0, we first factorise f(x) using the Factor Theorem. If $x - a$ is a factor of f(x), then $x = a$ is a root of the equation.

Revision Exercise 6 (*Answers on page 498*)

1. Find the remainder when $4x^5 + x^3 - 7x^2 + 5$ is divided by $2x + 1$.   C)

2. If $x^2 + (m - 2)x - m^2 - 3m + 5$ is divided by $x + m$, the remainder is -1. Find the values of m.

3. The expression $ax^3 - x^2 + bx - 1$ leaves a remainder of -33 and 77 when divided by $x + 2$ and $x - 3$ respectively. Find the remainder when the expression is divided by $x - 2$.

4. The remainder when $x^2 - 6x - 9$ is divided by $x - p$ is the same as the remainder when the same expression is divided by $x + q$ where $p \neq -q$. Find the value of $p - q$.   (C)

5. If the polynomial $ax^3 + bx^2 + cx - 4$ is divided by $x + 2$, the remainder is double that obtained when the polynomial is divided by $x + 1$. Show that c can have any value and find b in terms of a.

6. The expressions $x^3 - ax + a^2$ and $ax^3 + x^2 - 17$ have the same remainder when divided by $x - 2$. Find the possible values of
   (a) a,   **(b)** the remainder.   (C)

7. When the expression $x^2 + bx + c$ is divided by $x - 2$, the remainder is R. When the expression is divided by $x + 1$, the remainder is also R.
   (a) Find the value of b.

144 *Factors of Polynomials*

(b) When the expression is divided by $x - 4$, the remainder is $2R$. Find the value of c and of R.

(c) When the expression is divided by $x - t$, the remainder is $5R$. Find the two possible values of t. (C)

8. (a) The expressions $x^3 - 7x + 6$ and $x^3 - x^2 - 4x + 24$ have the same remainder when divided by $x + p$.

   (i) Find the possible values of p.

   (ii) Determine whether, for either or both of these values, $x + p$ is a factor of the expression.

(b) Given that $E = x^4 - x^3 + 5x^2 + 4x - 36$, find

   (i) the remainder when E is divided by $x + 1$,

   (ii) the value of a ($a > 0$) for which $x + a$ and $x - a$ are both factors of E. (C)

9. Find, in terms of p, the remainder when $3x^3 - 2x^2 + px - b$ is divided by $x + 2$. Hence write down the value of p for which the expression is exactly divisible by $x + 2$. (C)

10. (a) The expression $6x^2 + x + 7$ leaves the same remainder when divided by $x - a$ and $x + 2a$, where a $\neq 0$. Calculate the value of a.

(b) Given that $x^2 + px + q$ and $3x^2 + q$ have a common factor $x - b$, where p, q and b are non-zero, show that $3p^2 + 4q = 0$. (C)

11. The remainder when $3x^3 + x^2 + 2x + 4$ is divided by $x - a$ is double the remainder when $x^3 + 2x^2 + 6x - 10$ is divided by $x - a$. Find the possible values of a.

12. Find the value of a for which $(1 - 2a)x^2 + 5ax + (a - 1)(a - 8)$ is divisible by $x - 2$ but not by $x - 1$. (C)

13. By first solving the equation $x^3 - 3x + 2 = 0$ or otherwise, find the solutions of the equation $(x + 2)^3 = 3x + 4$.

14. If $f(x) = x^3 - 3x^2 + x - 3$, show that $x - 2$ is a factor of $f(x + 1)$.

15. Given that $2x + p$ is a factor of $2x^3 + px^4 + 2px^2 + 7x + 3$, show that $p^3 - 7p + 6 = 0$. Hence find the possible values of p.

16. Factorise the polynomial $f(x) = x^3 - (2p + 1)x^2 + (2p - q)x + q$ where p and q are constants. If the equation $f(x) = 0$ has three real roots, show that $p^2 + q \geq 0$.

17. Find the x-coordinate of each of the three points of intersection of the curves $y = 6x^2 - 5$ and $y = 17x - \dfrac{6}{x}$. (C)

Maths Booster

If $a + b = 1$ and $a^2 + b^2 = 1$, what is the value of $a^5 + b^5$?

Chapter 7

Logarithmic and Exponential Functions

Man first counted with fingers. When bigger numbers become known, things like shells, stones and knots on a rope were used. As man progressed, the need for more complicated calculations arose. Various calculating machines like the abacus and mechanical calculator were invented to make calculations easier, faster and more accurate.

In 1614, John Napier, a Scottish mathematician, compiled tables of logarithms. The use of these tables made calculations even faster. His invention opened up a whole new field of mathematical knowledge.

7.1 Logarithmic Functions

The inverse of the exponential function is called the **logarithmic function**.

If $y = a^x$, we define x as the **logarithm** of y to the base a ($a > 0$). This logarithmic form is written as $\log_a y$.

Exponential form	Logarithmic form
$y = a^x$ ⟷	$\log_a y = x$

For example,   — index becomes logarithm —

$$8 = 2^3 \qquad\qquad \log_2 8 = 3$$

— base —

$$100 = 10^2 \qquad\qquad \log_{10} 100 = 2$$

$$r = a^3 \qquad\qquad \log_a r = 3$$

Conversely, if $\log_x 10 = 4$, then $10 = x^4$.
if $\log_3 x = 5$, then $x = 3^5$.

▶ Example 1

Write in logarithmic form

(a) $9 = 3^2$, **(b)** $x^3 = 10$, **(c)** $2^{-2} = \dfrac{1}{4}$.

▶ Solution . . .

(a) If $9 = 3^2$, then $\log_3 9 = 2$.

(b) If $x^3 = 10$, then $\log_x 10 = 3$.

(c) If $2^{-2} = \dfrac{1}{4}$, then $\log_2\left(\dfrac{1}{4}\right) = -2$. (Logarithms can be negative.)

▶ Example 2

Write the following in exponential form and hence find the value of x:

(a) $\log_2 x = 3$ **(b)** $\log_x 100 = 2$ **(c)** $x = \log_3 \dfrac{1}{27}$

▶ Solution . . .

(a) If $\log_2 x = 3$, then $x = 2^3 = 8$.

(b) If $\log_x 100 = 2$, then $100 = x^2$
$$10^2 = x^2$$
$$\therefore \quad x = 10.$$

(c) If $x = \log_3 \dfrac{1}{27}$, then $\dfrac{1}{27} = 3^x$

$$3^{-3} = 3^x$$
$$\therefore\ x = -3$$

▶ **Example 3**

Find the value of the following:

(a) $\log_2 32$ (b) $\log_4 \dfrac{1}{16}$ (c) $\log_{27} 3$

(d) $\log_{\frac{1}{2}} 4$ (e) $\log_7 1$ (f) $\log_5 5$

▶ **Solution . . .**

(a) Let $x = \log_2 32$,
then $2^x = 32$
$$2^x = 2^5$$
$$x = 5$$
Hence $\log_2 32 = 5$.

(b) Let $x = \log_4 \left(\dfrac{1}{16} \right)$,

then $4^x = \dfrac{1}{16}$
$$4^x = 4^{-2}$$
$$x = -2$$
$\therefore\ \log_4 \left(\dfrac{1}{16} \right) = -2.$

(c) Let $x = \log_{27} 3$,
then $27^x = 3$
$$3^{3x} = 3^1$$
$$3x = 1$$
$$x = \dfrac{1}{3}$$
$\therefore\ \log_{27} 3 = \dfrac{1}{3}.$

(d) Let $x = \log_{\frac{1}{2}} 4$,

then $\dfrac{1}{2}^x = 4$

$$2^{-x} = 2^2$$
$$-x = 2$$
$$x = -2$$
$\therefore\ \log_{\frac{1}{2}} 4 = -2.$

(e) Let $x = \log_7 1$,
then $7^x = 1$
$$7^x = 7^0$$
$$x = 0$$
$\therefore\ \log_7 1 = 0.$

(f) Let $\quad x = \log_5 5,$

then $\quad 5^x = 5$

$\qquad\quad 5^x = 5^1$

$\qquad\qquad x = 1$

$\therefore\ \log_5 5 = 1$

Note:

(1) Logarithms of 1 to any base is always 0,

i.e. $\qquad\qquad \boxed{\log_a 1 = 0}$

(2) Logarithms of a number to a base of the same is always 1,

i.e. $\qquad\qquad \boxed{\log_a a = 1}$

Exercise 7A (Answers on page 498)

1. Write the following in logarithmic form:

   (a) $16 = 4^2$ **(b)** $21 = 7^x$ **(c)** $2 = 4^{\frac{1}{2}}$

   (d) $3^4 = 81$ **(e)** $10^3 = 1\,000$ **(f)** $x^3 = 64$

   (g) $2^{-3} = \dfrac{1}{8}$ **(h)** $10^{-1} = 0.1$ **(i)** $x^{-3} = 0.3$

2. Write the following in exponential form and hence find the value of x:

   (a) $\log_3 x = 4$ **(b)** $\log_5 x = -2$ **(c)** $\log_{\frac{1}{2}} x = 3$

   (d) $\log_x 8 = 3$ **(e)** $\log_x 0.001 = -3$ **(f)** $\log_x 3 = \dfrac{1}{2}$

   (g) $x = \log_2 16$ **(h)** $x = \log_7\left(\dfrac{1}{49}\right)$ **(i)** $x = \log_{36} 6$

3. Find the value of x in each case:

   (a) $\log_2 x = -3$ **(b)** $\log_4(x-2) = 3$ **(c)** $\log_8(x-2) = \dfrac{1}{3}$

   (d) $\log_x 81 = -4$ **(e)** $\log_{2x} 36 = 2$ **(f)** $\log_{x+1} 27 = 3$

4. Find the value of the following:

   (a) $\log_8 64$ **(b)** $\log_2 64$ **(c)** $\log_3 243$

   (d) $\log_5\left(\dfrac{1}{25}\right)$ **(e)** $\log_2\left(\dfrac{1}{16}\right)$ **(f)** $\log_x\left(\dfrac{1}{x}\right)$

   (g) $\log_9 3$ **(h)** $\log_8 2$ **(i)** $\log_8 4$

   (j) $\log_4 8$ **(k)** $\log_{16} 8$ **(l)** $\log_{27}\dfrac{1}{9}$

   (m) $\log_{\frac{1}{2}} 8$ **(n)** $\log_{\frac{1}{3}} 9$ **(o)** $\log_3 1$

   (p) $\log_5 1$ **(q)** $\log_8 8$ **(r)** $\log_{\frac{1}{2}}\left(\dfrac{1}{2}\right)$

5. Given that $\log_3 x = r$ and $\log_9 y = s$, express xy^2 and $\dfrac{x^2}{y}$ as powers of 3.

   Hence, given that $xy^2 = 81$ and $\dfrac{x^2}{y} = \dfrac{1}{3}$, determine the values of r and s.

   (C)

7.2 Laws of Logarithms

There are three basic laws of logarithms which can be derived from the rules of indices.

Let $P = a^m$, then $m = \log_a P$.

Let $Q = a^n$, then $n = \log_a Q$.

(1)
$$P \times Q = a^m \times a^n$$
$$PQ = a^{m+n}$$
then $\log_a PQ = m + n$

$$\therefore \quad \boxed{\log_a PQ = \log_a P + \log_a Q} \; .$$

(2)
$$P \div Q = a^m \div a^n$$
$$\frac{P}{Q} = a^{m-n}$$
then $\log_a \dfrac{P}{Q} = m - n$

$$\therefore \quad \boxed{\log_a \frac{P}{Q} = \log_a P - \log_a Q} \; .$$

(3)
$$P^n = (a^m)^n = a^{mn}$$
$$\log_a P^n = mn$$

$$\therefore \quad \boxed{\log_a P^n = n \log_a P} \; .$$

▶ **Example 4**

Express each of the following in terms of $\log_a x$ and $\log_a y$:

(a) $\log_a xy^2$ **(b)** $\log_a \dfrac{x}{y^3}$ **(c)** $\log_a \sqrt{\dfrac{ax^2}{y}}$

▶ **Solution . . .**

(a) $\log_a xy^2 = \log_a x + \log_a y^2$
$$= \log_a x + 2 \log_a y$$

(b) $\log_a \dfrac{x}{y^3} = \log_a x - \log_a y^3$
$$= \log_a x - 3 \log_a y$$

(c) $\log_a \sqrt{\dfrac{ax^2}{y}} = \log_a \left(\dfrac{ax^2}{y} \right)^{\frac{1}{2}}$
$$= \frac{1}{2} \log_a \frac{ax^2}{y}$$
$$= \frac{1}{2} (\log_a ax^2 - \log_a y)$$

$$= \frac{1}{2}(\log_a a + \log_a x^2 - \log_a y)$$

$$= \frac{1}{2}(1 + 2\log_a x - \log_a y)$$

▶ Example 5

Given that $\log_5 2 = 0.431$ and $\log_5 3 = 0.683$, find the value of

(a) $\log_5 6$, **(b)** $\log_5 1.5$, **(c)** $\log_5 8$,

(d) $\log_5 60$, **(e)** $\log_5 \frac{1}{18}$.

▶ Solution . . .

(a) $\log_5 6 = \log_5(2 \times 3)$
$\qquad = \log_5 2 + \log_5 3$
$\qquad = 0.431 + 0.683$
$\qquad = 1.114$

(b) $\log_5 1.5 = \log_5 \frac{3}{2}$
$\qquad\quad = \log_5 3 - \log_5 2$
$\qquad\quad = 0.683 - 0.431$
$\qquad\quad = 0.252$

(c) $\log_5 8 = \log_5 2^3$
$\qquad = 3\log_5 2$
$\qquad = 3 \times 0.431$
$\qquad = 1.293$

(d) $\log_5 60 = \log_5(4 \times 3 \times 5)$
$\qquad\quad = \log_5 4 + \log_5 3 + \log_5 5$
$\qquad\quad = \log_5 2^2 + \log_5 3 + \log_5 5$
$\qquad\quad = 2\log_5 2 + \log_5 3 + \log_5 5$
$\qquad\quad = 2(0.431) + 0.683 + 1$
$\qquad\quad = 2.545$

(e) $\log_5 \frac{1}{18} = \log_5 1 - \log_5 18$
$\qquad\quad = \log_5 1 - \log_5(2 \times 3^2)$
$\qquad\quad = \log_5 1 - (\log_5 2 + 2\log_5 3)$
$\qquad\quad = \log_5 1 - \log_5 2 - 2\log_5 3$
$\qquad\quad = 0 - 0.431 - 2(0.683)$
$\qquad\quad = -1.797$

▶ Example 6

Find the value of

(a) $\log_7 49$, **(b)** $\log_3 \frac{1}{9}$, **(c)** $\log_{16} 4$.

▶ **Solution . . .**

(a) $\log_7 49 = \log_7 7^2$
$$= 2\log_7 7$$
$$= 2 \times 1$$
$$= 2$$

(b) $\log_3 \dfrac{1}{9} = \log_3 3^{-2}$
$$= -2\log_3 3$$
$$= -2 \times 1$$
$$= -2$$

(c) $\log_{16} 4 = \log_{16} \sqrt{16}$
$$= \log_{16} 16^{\frac{1}{2}}$$
$$= \frac{1}{2}\log_{16} 16$$
$$= \frac{1}{2}$$

▶ **Example 7**

Find the value of $\log_3 18 + \log_3 21 - \log_3 14$.

▶ **Solution . . .**

$$\log_3 18 + \log_3 21 - \log_3 14 = \log_3\left(\frac{18 \times 21}{14}\right)$$
$$= \log_3 27$$
$$= \log_3 3^3$$
$$= 3\log_3 3$$
$$= 3$$

▶ **Example 8**

Solve the equations
(a) $2\log_3 x = \log_3(x + 6)$,
(b) $\log_5(x^2 - 3x + 2) = 2 + \log_5(x - 1)$.

▶ **Solution . . .**

(a)
$$2\log_3 x = \log_3(x + 6)$$
$$\log_3 x^2 = \log_3(x + 6)$$
$$x^2 = x + 6$$
$$x^2 - x - 6 = 0$$
$$(x - 3)(x + 2) = 0$$
$$x = 3 \text{ or } -2$$

It is essential to check if any of these solutions are invalid. We see that x cannot be -2 because $\log(-2)$ is undefined. Hence the only solution is $x = 3$.

(b)
$$\log_5(x^2 - 3x + 2) = 2 + \log_5(x - 1)$$
$$\log_5(x^2 - 3x + 2) - \log_5(x - 1) = 2$$
$$\log_5\left(\frac{x^2 - 3x + 2}{x - 1}\right) = 2$$

Changing to exponential form,
$$\frac{x^2 - 3x + 2}{x - 1} = 5^2$$
$$x^2 - 3x + 2 = 25x - 25$$
$$x^2 - 28x + 27 = 0$$
$$(x - 27)(x - 1) = 0$$
$$x = 27 \text{ or } x = 1$$

Now check these results:
If $x = 1$, $\log_5(x - 1) = \log_5 0$ which is undefined. So the only solution is $x = 27$.

▶ **Example 9**

If $\log_5 x = a$ and $\log_5 y = b$, express the following in terms of a and b:

(a) xy^3,　　**(b)** $\dfrac{25x}{\sqrt{y}}$.

▶ **Solution . . .**

If $\log_5 x = a$, then $x = 5^a$.
If $\log_5 y = b$, then $y = 5^b$.

(a) $\quad xy^3 = (5^a)(5^b)^3$
$$= 5^{a + 3b}$$

(b) $\quad \dfrac{25x}{\sqrt{y}} = \dfrac{(5)^2(5^a)}{(5^b)^{\frac{1}{2}}}$
$$= 5^{2 + a - \frac{1}{2}b}$$

▶ **Example 10**

Solve the simultaneous equations:

$$\log_2(2x - y) = 3$$
$$\log_3(x + 1) = 1 + \log_3 y$$

▶ **Solution . . .**

$$\log_2(2x - y) = 3$$
$$2x - y = 2^3$$
$$2x - y = 8 \ldots\ldots(1)$$

$$\log_3(x + 1) = 1 + \log_3 y$$
$$\log_3(x + 1) - \log_3 y = 1$$

$$\log_3\left(\frac{x+1}{y}\right) = 1$$

$$\frac{x+1}{y} = 3$$
$$x + 1 = 3y$$
$$x - 3y = -1 \quad\text{.........(2)}$$

$(1) \times 3: \quad 6x - 3y = 24 \quad\text{.........(3)}$

$(3) - (2): \quad\quad 5x = 25$

$$x = 5$$

Substituting $x = 5$ into (1),

$$2(5) - y = 8$$
$$y = 2$$

$\therefore x = 5, y = 2.$

Exercise 7B (Answers on page 498)

1. Express each of the following in terms of $\log_a x$ and $\log_a y$:

    (a) $\log_a x^3 y$ (b) $\log_a \dfrac{x^2}{\sqrt{y}}$ (c) $\log_a \sqrt{\dfrac{x^3 a}{y^2}}$

2. Express each of the following in terms of $\log_a P$, $\log_a Q$ and $\log_a R$:

    (a) $\log_a P^2 Q^3 R$ (b) $\log_a \dfrac{P^2 \sqrt{Q}}{R}$ (c) $\log_a \dfrac{P}{\sqrt{Q^2 R}}$

3. If $\log_a x = p$ and $\log_a y = q$, express the following in terms of p and q:

    (a) $\log_a x^2 y$ (b) $\log_a \sqrt{xy}$

    (c) $\log_a \dfrac{x^3}{y}$ (d) $\log_a \dfrac{a^3 x}{y^2}$

4. If $\log_{10} x = a$ and $\log_{10} y = b$, express $\log_{10} \sqrt{\dfrac{10x}{y^3}}$ in terms of a and b.

5. Given that $\log_a x^2 y = p$ and that $\log_a\left(\dfrac{x}{y^2}\right) = q$, find $\log_a x$ and $\log_a y$ in terms of p and q, and hence express $\log_a xy$ in terms of p and q.

6. Given that $\log_3 4 = 1.262$ and that $\log_3 5 = 1.465$, find the value of the following:

    (a) $\log_3 20$ (b) $\log_3 0.8$ (c) $\log_3 1.25$

    (d) $\log_3 100$ (e) $\log_3 64$ (f) $\log_3 80$

    (g) $\log_3 6.25$ (h) $\log_3 15$ (i) $\log_3 0.25$

7. Given that $\log_7 2 = 0.356$ and that $\log_7 3 = 0.565$, find the value of the following:

    (a) $\log_7 6$ (b) $\log_7 9$ (c) $\log_7 18$

    (d) $\log_7 24$ (e) $\log_7 4.5$ (f) $\log_7 \sqrt{3}$

    (g) $\log_7 14$ (h) $\log_7 42$ (i) $\log_7 4\dfrac{2}{3}$

8. Find the value of the following:

(a) $\log_6 36$

(b) $\log_{10} 10\,000$

(c) $\log_2 \frac{1}{16}$

(d) $\log_5 \frac{1}{125}$

(e) $\log_{25} 5$

(f) $\log_8 2$

(g) $\log_{\frac{1}{2}}\left(\frac{1}{4}\right)$

(h) $\log_{\frac{1}{2}} 2$

(i) $\log_{\frac{1}{4}} 2$

9. Find the value of the following:

(a) $\log_5 12.5 + \log_5 10$

(b) $2\log_7 9 - \log_7 81$

(c) $\log_7 98 - \log_7 30 + \log_7 15$

(d) $3\log_2 4 + 2\log_2 5 - \log_2 100$

10. Solve the following equations:

(a) $2\log_5 x = \log_5(2x + 3)$

(b) $3\log_2 x = \log_2(3x - 2)$

(c) $\log_3(x^2 + 2) = 1 + \log_3(x + 2)$

(d) $\log_4(x^2 + 8x - 1) = 2 + \log_4(x - 1)$

(e) $\log_2(2x^2 + 3x + 5) = 3 + \log_2(x + 1)$

(f) $\log_4(x + 17) = 2\log_4(x - 3)$

(g) $\log_2(x^2 - x + 2) = 1 + 2\log_2 x$

(h) $\log_5 x = 1 - \log_5(x - 4)$

11. If $\log_2 x^3 + \log_2 x = 8$, find the value of x.

12. Find y if $\log_3 y = 2\log_3 7$.

13. If $\log_5 p - \log_5 4 = 2$, find the value of p.

14. Given that $\log_x 8 + \log_x 4 = 5$, find the number of x.

15. If $2\log_a 2 + \log_a 10 - 3\log_a 3 = 3 + \log_a 5$, find the value of a.

16. Given that $\log_3 x = a$ and $\log_3 y = b$, express the following in terms of a and b:

(a) $x^2 y^3$

(b) $3x\sqrt{y}$

(c) $\frac{9\sqrt{x}}{y^2}$

17. Given that $\log_3 x = p$ and $\log_9 y = q$, express the following as powers of 3:

(a) $x^3 y$

(b) $\frac{x}{\sqrt{y}}$

18. Given that $\log_2 x = a$ and $\log_4 y = b$, express $x^2 y$ and $\frac{x^3}{y}$ as powers of 2.
Given also that $x^2 y = 32$ and that $\frac{x^3}{y} = \frac{1}{8}$, find the values of a and b.

19. Solve the following simultaneous equations:

(a) $\log_3(x + y) = 2$
$\log_2 y - \log_2(2x - 1) = 1$

(b) $\log_{10} x + 2\log_{10} y = 3$
$2\log_5 x + \log_5 y = 3$

7.3 Change of Base of Logarithms

If $\quad x = \log_b a$,

then $b^x = a$.

Taking logarithms to base c on both sides,

$\log_c b^x = \log_c a$

$x \log_c b = \log_c a$

$$x = \frac{\log_c a}{\log_c b}$$

$\therefore \quad \log_b a = \dfrac{\log_c a}{\log_c b}$. (a, b and c are positive number; $b \neq 1$, $c \neq 1$)

Special case:

If $c = a$,

$$\log_b a = \frac{\log_a a}{\log_a b}$$

$\therefore \quad \log_b a = \dfrac{1}{\log_a b}$. (because $\log_a a = 1$)

▶ ## Example 11

If $\log_3 x = m$, express the following in terms of m:

(a) $\log_x 3$ **(b)** $\log_x 9$ **(c)** $\log_{27} 3x$

▶ ## Solution . . .

(a) $\log_x 3 = \dfrac{1}{\log_3 x}$

$\qquad\qquad = \dfrac{1}{m}$

(b) $\log_x 9 = \dfrac{\log_3 9}{\log_3 x}$

$\qquad\qquad = \dfrac{\log_3 3^2}{\log_3 x}$

$\qquad\qquad = \dfrac{2 \log_3 3}{\log_3 x}$

$\qquad\qquad = \dfrac{2}{m}$

(c) $\log_{27} 3x = \dfrac{\log_3 3x}{\log_3 27}$

$\qquad\qquad = \dfrac{\log_3 3 + \log_3 x}{\log_3 3^3}$

$\qquad\qquad = \dfrac{\log_3 3 + \log_3 x}{\log_3 3^3}$

$\qquad\qquad = \dfrac{1 + m}{3}$

▶ **Example 12**

Find the value of $\log_2 9 \cdot \log_3 5 \cdot \log_5 8$.

▶ **Solution**

$\log_2 9 \cdot \log_3 5 \cdot \log_5 8 = \dfrac{\log_2 9}{\log_2 2} \times \dfrac{\log_2 5}{\log_2 3} \times \dfrac{\log_2 8}{\log_2 5}$ (change to any base: 2, 3 or 5)

$\qquad\qquad\qquad\quad = \dfrac{\log_2 3^2}{\log_2 2} \times \dfrac{\log_2 5}{\log_2 3} \times \dfrac{\log_2 2^3}{\log_2 5}$

$\qquad\qquad\qquad\quad = \dfrac{2\log_2 3}{\log_2 2} \times \dfrac{\log_2 5}{\log_2 3} \times \dfrac{3\log_2 2}{\log_2 5}$

$\qquad\qquad\qquad\quad = 2 \times 3$

$\qquad\qquad\qquad\quad = 6$

▶ **Example 13**

Find the value of $\log_8 16$.

▶ **Solution . . .**

$\log_8 16 = \dfrac{\log_2 16}{\log_2 8}$ (change to base 2 because 16 and 8 are powers of 2)

$\qquad\quad = \dfrac{\log_2 2^4}{\log_2 2^3}$

$\qquad\quad = \dfrac{4\log_2 2}{3\log_2 2}$

$\qquad\quad = \dfrac{4}{3}$

▶ **Example 14**

Solve the equation $\log_9(x + 8) = \log_3(x + 6)$.

▶ **Solution . . .**

$\log_9(x + 8) = \log_3(x + 6)$

$\dfrac{\log_3(x+8)}{\log_3 9} = \log_3(x + 6)$

$\dfrac{\log_3(x+8)}{2} = \log_3(x + 6)$ $(\log_3 9 = \log_3 3^2 = 2\log_3 3 = 2)$

$\log_3(x + 8) = 2\log_3(x + 6)$

$\log_3(x + 8) = \log_3(x + 6)^2$

$\therefore \quad x + 8 = (x + 6)^2$

$\qquad x + 8 = x^2 + 12x + 36$

$x^2 + 11x + 28 = 0$

$(x + 4)(x + 7) = 0$

$x = -4$ or -7

If $x = -7$, $\log_3(x + 6) = \log_3(-1)$ which is undefined.
Therefore the only solution is $x = -4$.

▶ **Example 15**

Using the substitution $y = \log_8 x$ or otherwise, solve the equation
$3 \log_8 x = 2 \log_x 8 + 5$.

▶ **Solution . . .**

$3 \log_8 x = 2 \log_x 8 + 5$

$3 \log_8 x = \dfrac{2}{\log_8 x} + 5$

Substituting $y = \log_8 x$,

$$3y = \dfrac{2}{y} + 5$$
$$3y^2 = 2 + 5y$$
$$3y^2 - 5y - 2 = 0$$
$$(y - 2)(3y + 1) = 0$$

$y = 2$ or $y = -\dfrac{1}{3}$

$\log_8 x = 2$ $\qquad$ $\log_8 x = -\dfrac{1}{3}$

$x = 8^2$ $\qquad\qquad$ $x = 8^{-\frac{1}{3}}$

$= 64$ $\qquad\qquad\quad$ $= \dfrac{1}{2}$

Exercise 7C $\left(\textit{Answers on page 499}\right)$

1. If $\log_{2^r} x = m$, express the following in terms of m:
   (a) $\log_x 2$ $\qquad$ (b) $\log_x 8$ $\qquad$ (c) $\log_{2x} 4$
   (d) $\log_{16} x^3$ $\qquad$ (e) $\log_8 32x$ $\qquad$ (f) $\log_{4x} 8\sqrt{x}$

2. If $\log_6 3 = t$, express the following in terms of t:
   (a) $\log_3 6$ $\qquad$ (b) $\log_{27} 36$ $\qquad$ (c) $\log_{36} 9$
   (d) $\log_3 18$ $\qquad$ (e) $\log_9 2$ $\qquad$ (f) $\log_3 0.5$

3. If $\log_3 2 = p$ and $\log_3 5 = q$, express the following in terms of p and q:
   (a) $\log_{10} 3$ $\qquad$ (b) $\log_2 10$ $\qquad$ (c) $\log_5 30$
   (d) $\log_{15} 6$ $\qquad$ (e) $\log_6 2.5$ $\qquad$ (f) $\log_{0.4} 90$

4. Find the value of the following:
   (a) $\log_5 3 \cdot \log_{11} 5 \cdot \log_3 11$
   (b) $\log_2 25 \cdot \log_3 8 \cdot \log_5 9$
   (c) $\log_7 27 \cdot \log_2 5 \cdot \log_3 49 \cdot \log_5 4$
   (d) $\log_8 9 \cdot \log_5 4 \cdot \log_9\left(\dfrac{1}{5}\right)$

5. Given that a, b, c and d are positive numbers, and $b \neq 1$, $c \neq 1$, $d \neq 1$, show that $\log_b a \cdot \log_c b \cdot \log_d c = \log_d a$.

6. Find the value of
    (a) $\log_4 8$,
    (b) $\log_{27} 9$,
    (c) $\log_8\left(\dfrac{1}{4}\right)$,
    (d) $\log_{25} 0.2$.

7. Solve the following equations:
    (a) $\log_2 x = \log_4(4x + 5)$
    (b) $\log_9(x + 10) = \log_3(2x - 1)$
    (c) $\log_5(3x + 4) = 2\log_{25}(1 - 3x)$
    (d) $\log_4 \sqrt{1 + 2x} = \log_{16}(5x - 2)$

8. Solve the following equations:
    (a) $\log_2 x = 9\log_x 2$
    (b) $9\log_8 x = 25\log_x 8$
    (c) $2\log_4 x + 3\log_x 4 = 7$
    (d) $2\log_9 x = 5 - 2\log_x 9$

9. If $\log_{\sqrt{2}} y = 2 + \log_2 x^2$, express y in terms of x.

10. If $\log_5 8 \times \log_2 x = 3$, find the value of x.

11. Solve the simultaneous equations
    $$\log_2 x + \log_2 y = 1,$$
    $$\log_2(x + 1) = \log_4 9y.$$

7.4 Common and Natural Logarithms

7.4.1 *Common Logarithms*

Logarithms to base 10 are called **common logarithms**. These are written as **lg** x, which is an abbreviation for $\log_{10} x$. The values of common logarithms can be readily obtained from tables of common logarithms or by using the $\boxed{\log}$ key on a calculator.

For example, $\quad$ lg $46.87 = 1.67$
$$\text{lg } 0.025 = -1.60$$

Note that the common logarithm of a number smaller than 1 is a negative value.

Logarithms of other bases may be evaluated by converting them to common logarithms using the change-of-base formula.

▶ **Example 16**

Find the value of $\log_2 7$.

Solution . . .

$$\log_2 7 = \frac{\lg 7}{\lg 2}$$
$$= 2.81 \text{ (correct to 3 sig. fig.)}$$

Equations of the form $\lg x = a$ can be solved by first converting them into index form $x = 10^a$ and then using the $\boxed{10^x}$ key on a calculator to find the value of x.

▶ **Example 17**

Find the value of x if
(a) $\lg x = 0.715$, **(b)** $\lg (2x - 1) = -1.6$.

▶ **Solution . . .**

(a) $\lg x = 0.715$
$\quad x = 10^{0.715}$
$\quad\quad = 5.19$

(b) $\lg (2x - 1) = -1.6$
$\quad 2x - 1 = 10^{-1.6}$
$\quad 2x - 1 = 0.025\ 1$
$\quad\quad\quad x = 0.513$

▶ **Example 18**

If $\log_x 6 = 1.5$, find the value of x.

▶ **Solution . . .**

$$\log_x 6 = 1.5$$
$$\frac{\lg 6}{\lg x} = 1.5$$
$$\lg x = \frac{\lg 6}{1.5}$$
$$= 0.519$$
$$x = 10^{0.519}$$
$$= 3.30 \text{ (correct to 3 sig. fig.)}$$

7.4.2   Natural Logarithms

There is another system of logarithms, which is used in calculus. The base of these logarithms is a certain number **e**, where e $\approx$ 2.718.

How does the number **e** originate?

This comes from asking what happens to the value of $\left(1+\dfrac{1}{t}\right)^t$ as $t \to \infty$,

i.e. what is the value of (if any) of the limit, $\displaystyle\lim_{t\to\infty}\left(1+\dfrac{1}{t}\right)^t$?

We are not able to prove what this limit is. However, the following set of values obtained from a calculator will suggest an answer.

t	$\left(1+\dfrac{1}{t}\right)^t$
100	$(1.01)^{100}$ = 2.7048
1000	$(1.001)^{1000}$ = 2.7169
10 000	$(1.0001)^{10\,000}$ = 2.718 15
100 000	$(1.000\,01)^{100\,000}$ = 2.718 27
1 000 000	$(1.000\,001)^{1\,000\,000}$ = 2.718 28
10 000 000	$(1.000\,000\,1)^{10\,000\,000}$ = 2.718 28

As t increases, it appears that $\left(1+\dfrac{1}{t}\right)^t$ tends to a value which is approximately 2.718 28. This is true and we denote this limit by the letter **e**. Like π, e is an irrational number. Logarithms to base e are called **natural** or **Napierian logarithms**, in honour of the Scottish mathematician John Napier. Natural logarithms, $\log_e x$, are written as **ln x**.

The values of natural logarithms can be obtained from tables of natural logarithms or by using the $\boxed{\text{ln}}$ key on a calculator.

For example,   ln 36.5 = 3.60
                 ln 1.32 = 0.278
                 ln 0.052 = −2.96

Logarithms of other bases may also be evaluated by converting them to natural logarithms using the change-of-base formula.

▶ **Example 19**

Find the value of $\log_3 5$.

▶ **Solution . . .**

$\log_3 5 = \dfrac{\ln 5}{\ln 3}$

$\quad\;\; = 1.46$ (correct to 3 sig. fig.)

▶ **Example 20**

Find the value of x if
(a) $\ln x = 0.432$,   (b) $\ln (x + 1) = -0.3$.

Verification
An alternative method to determine the value of $\log_3 5$ (example 19) is to convert it to a common logarithm. Verify this.

▶ **Solution . . .**

(a) $\ln x = 0.432$
$$x = e^{0.432}$$
$$= 1.54$$

(b) $\ln (x + 1) = -0.3$
$$x + 1 = e^{-0.3}$$
$$x + 1 = 0.741$$
$$x = -0.259$$

Exercise 7D (*Answers on page 499*)

1. Find the values of the following, giving your answers correct to 3 significant figures.

(a) $\lg 60.3 + \lg 0.603$ (b) $2 \lg 0.075 - 3 \lg 0.75$

(c) $(\lg 12)(\lg 1.2)$ (d) $\dfrac{\lg 216}{\lg 2.16}$

(e) $5(\lg 2)^2$ (f) $\lg (\lg 30)$

2. Find the values of the following:

(a) $\log_2 3$ (b) $\log_3 0.5$ (c) $\log_{100} 48$

(d) $\log_{\frac{1}{4}} \dfrac{3}{8}$ (e) $\log_7 \sqrt{8}$ (f) $\log_{\sqrt{2}} 9$

3. Find the value of x if

(a) $\lg x = 0.463$,   (b) $\lg x = 2.32$,

(c) $\lg x = -1.8$,   (d) $\lg (x + 1) = 0.06$,

(e) $\lg (2x - 3) = -0.06$,   (f) $\lg (5 - 2x) = 1.5$.

4. Find the value of x if

(a) $\lg_x 3 = 17$,   (b) $\lg_x 12 = 5$,

(c) $\lg_x 6 = -1.2$,   (d) $\lg_x 8 = 0.03$.

5. Find the values of

(a) $\ln 6.1 + \ln 0.28$,   (b) $\dfrac{\ln 3}{\ln 6}$,

(c) $(\ln 5)^2$,   (d) $\ln (\ln 2)$.

6. Find the values of

(a) $\log_7 5$,   (b) $\log_4 0.3$,   (c) $\log_{0.4} 2$,

(d) $\log_{1.5}\left(\dfrac{1}{2}\right)$,   (e) $\log_{\sqrt{2}} 6$,   (f) $\log_{\frac{5}{3}} \sqrt{3}$.

7. Find the value of x if

(a) $\ln x = 0.508$,   (b) $\ln x = -1.7$

(c) $\ln (x - 2) = 2.35$,   (d) $\ln (2x + 1) = -0.5$

8. Solve the following equations:

(a) $2 \lg 5 + \lg (x + 1) = 1 + \lg (2x + 7)$ (C)

(b) $\lg (1 - 2x) - 2 \lg x = 1 - \lg (2 - 5x)$ (C)

7.5 Solving Equations of the form $a^x = b$

▶ **Example 21**

Solve the equations

(a) $3^x = 8$, (b) $2^{x+1} = 5^{2x-1}$.

▶ **Solution . . .**

(a)
$$3^x = 8$$
$$\lg 3^x = \lg 8$$
$$x \lg 3 = \lg 8$$
$$x = \frac{\lg 8}{\lg 3}$$
$$= 1.89 \quad \text{(correct to 3 sig. fig.)}$$

(b)
$$2^{x+1} = 5^{2x-1}$$
$$\lg 2^{x+1} = \lg 5^{2x-1}$$
$$(x+1) \lg 2 = (2x-1) \lg 5$$
$$x \lg 2 + \lg 2 = 2x \lg 5 - \lg 5$$
$$2x \lg 5 - x \lg 2 = \lg 2 + \lg 5$$
$$x(2 \lg 5 - \lg 2) = \lg 2 + \lg 5$$
$$x = \frac{\lg 2 + \lg 5}{2 \lg 5 - \lg 2}$$
$$= 0.912 \quad \text{(correct to 3 sig. fig.)}$$

▶ **Example 22**

A sum of \$5 000 is invested at a compound interest of 2% per year. The amount of money, \$$m$, after t years is given by the formula $m = 5\,000(1.02)^t$. Find

(a) the value of m when $t = 8$,
(b) the value of t when $m = 10\,000$.

▶ **Solution . . .**

(a) Given $m = 5\,000(1.02)^t$,
  when $t = 8$, $m = 5\,000(1.02)^8$
  $= 5\,858.30$

(b) When $m = 10\,000$,
$$10\,000 = 5\,000(1.02)^t$$
$$2 = 1.02^t$$
$$\lg 2 = \lg 1.02^t$$
$$\lg 2 = t \lg 1.02$$
$$t = \frac{\lg 2}{\lg 1.02}$$
$$= 35$$

▶ **Example 23**

Given that $y = ax^b + 3$ where $a > 0$, and that $y = 8$ when $x = 2$, and $y = 48$ when $x = 8$, find the values of a and b.

▶ **Solution . . .**

Given $y = ax^b + 3$,
substitute $x = 2$, $y = 8$,
$$8 = a(2)^b + 3$$
$$a(2)^b = 5 \quad \text{...........(1)}$$

Substitute $x = 8$, $y = 48$,
$$48 = a(8)^b + 3$$
$$a(8)^b = 45$$
$$a(2)^{3b} = 45 \quad \text{.........(2)}$$

$$\frac{(2)}{(1)} : \quad \frac{a(2)^{3b}}{a(2)^b} = \frac{45}{5}$$
$$2^{2b} = 9$$
$$(2^b)^2 = 3^2$$
$$2^b = 3$$
$$\lg 2^b = \lg 3$$
$$b \lg 2 = \lg 3$$
$$b = \frac{\lg 3}{\lg 2}$$
$$= 1.58$$
Substituting $2^b = 3$ into (1),
$$a(3) = 5$$
$$a = 1.67$$
$$\therefore \quad a = 1.67, b = 1.58.$$

Exercise 7E *(Answers on page 499)*

1. Solve the following equations, giving your answers correct to 3 significant figures:

   (a) $3^x = 5$ (b) $2^x = 1.5$ (c) $0.6^x = 0.4$
   (d) $2^{x-1} = 7$ (e) $6^{2x+1} = 8$ (f) $e^{x+1} = 9$
   (g) $5^{1-x} = e^x$ (h) $2^x = 3^{x-2}$ (i) $3^{2-x} = 5^{2x+1}$
   (j) $5^{3x+2} = 7^{6x-1}$

2. Given that $P = 50(0.75)^n$, find
   (a) the value of P when $n = 4$,
   (b) the value of n when $P = 10$.

3. A liquid cools from its original temperature of 90 °C to a temperature T °C in x minutes. Given that $T = 90(0.98)^x$, find the value of
   (a) T when $x = 10$,
   (b) x when $T = 27$.   (C)

4. The mass, m grams, of a radioactive substance present at time t days after first being observed, is given by the formula $m = 24e^{-0.02t}$.
Find
   (a) the value of m when $t = 30$,
   (b) the value of t when the mass is half of its value at $t = 0$. (C)

5. An object is heated in an open oven until it reaches a temperature of $X\,°C$. It is then allowed to cool. Its temperature, $\theta\,°C$, after it has been left to cool for t minutes, is given by the equation

$$\theta = 18 + 62\,e^{-\frac{t}{8}}.$$

Find
   (a) the value of X,
   (b) the value of θ when $t = 16$,
   (c) the value of t when $\theta = 48$.
State the value which θ approaches as t becomes very large. (C)

6. The population of a city at the beginning of the year 1950 was 1 500 000. The population was increasing at a rate of 5%. After n years, the new population was $1\,500\,000\,(1.05)^t$. Find
   (a) the population at the beginning of 1960,
   (b) the year in which the population first reached 10 000 000.

7. A sum of money $\$P$ is invested at a compound interest of $r\%$ per year. The amount of money, $\$m$, after t years, is given by the formula

$$m = P\left(1 + \frac{r}{100}\right)^t.$$

   (a) What is the resulting amount of money when \$2 000 is invested at 8% per year for a period of 12 years?
   (b) In which year would \$3 000 invested at 5% per year amount first to more than \$6 000?
   (c) What is the initial sum of money invested if the amount of money after 20 years at a compound interest of 10% per year is \$100 912?

8. Given that $y = ax^b - 2$ and that $y = 6$ when $x = 2$, and $y = 22$ when $x = 4$, find the values of a and b.

9. Given that $y = ax^n + 3$, that $y = 4.4$ when $x = 10$, and $y = 12.8$ when $x = 100$, find the values of n and a. (C)

7.6 Graphs of Logarithmic Functions

▶ Example 24

Draw the graph of $y = \lg x$ for $0 < x \le 10$.
From the graph
(a) estimate the value of $\lg 4$,
(b) find the approximate value of x if $\lg x = 0.75$,
(c) find the point where the curve cuts the x-axis.

► **Solution ...**

A table of values of x and $y = \lg x$ is constructed

x	0.1	0.5	1	5	10
y	−1.0	−0.301	0	0.699	1

The graph of $y = \lg x$ is then plotted.

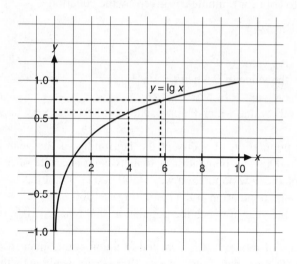

From the graph, we found that
(a) $\lg 4 = 0.60$,
(b) when $\lg x = 0.75$, $x = 5.6$,
(c) the curve cuts the x-axis at $(1,0)$.

From the graph of $y = \lg x$ in Example 24, we notice the following:
(i) $\lg x < 0$ for $0 < x < 1$
(ii) $\lg x \rightarrow -\infty$ as $x \rightarrow 0$
(iii) $\lg x = 0$ when $x = 1$
(iv) $\lg x > 0$ for $x > 1$ and $\lg x$ increases as x increases.

In general, a curve of the form $y = \lg f(x)$ is defined for $f(x) > 0$ and the curve cuts the x-axis at the point given by $f(x) = 1$.

► **Example 25**

Sketch the following graphs:
(a) $y = \lg (x - 2)$
(b) $y = \ln (x + 1)$

► **Solution ...**

(a) The curve $y = \lg (x - 2)$ is defined for $x - 2 > 0$, i.e. $x > 2$.
The curve cuts the x-axis at the point where
$$x - 2 = 1$$
$$x = 3.$$

Activity

IT and analytical skills

Use Graphmatica courseware to plot the following sets of graphs:

(a) $y = \lg x$, $y = \lg (x + 2)$, $y = \lg (x - 2)$
(b) $y = \lg x$, $y = \lg x + 2$, $y = \lg x - 2$

Observe how the graph of $y = \lg x$ is 'moved' or 'translated'.

The graph of $y = \lg(x - 2)$ is plotted below:

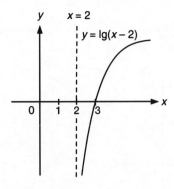

(b) The curve $y = \ln(x + 1)$ is defined for $x + 1 > 0$, i.e. $x > -1$.
The curve cuts the x-axis at the point where
$$x + 1 = 1$$
$$x = 0.$$
The graph of $y = \ln(x + 1)$ is plotted below:

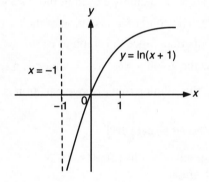

▶ **Example 26**

Draw the graph of $y = \ln(x + 2)$ for $0 \le x \le 4$, taking values of x at unit intervals. By drawing an appropriate straight line, obtain an approximate solution to the equation
$$2 \ln(x + 2) + x = 4.$$

▶ **Solution . . .**

A table of values of x and $y = \ln(x + 2)$ is constructed.

x	0	1	2	3	4
y	0.69	1.10	1.39	1.61	1.79

The graph of $y = \ln (x + 2)$ is shown below:

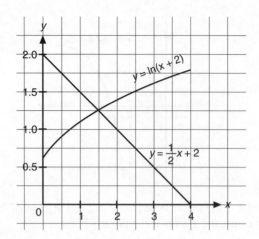

Given $2 \ln (x + 2) + x = 4$,
$$\ln (x + 2) = -\frac{1}{2} x + 2.$$
So to solve the above equation we need to plot two graphs: $y = \ln (x + 2)$ and $y = -\frac{1}{2} x + 2$. The point of intersection of the two graphs will give the solution to the equation. Since the graph of $y = \ln (x + 2)$ has been plotted, we need to draw the graph $y = -\frac{1}{2} x + 2$, which is a straight line.

From the graph, the solution to the above equation is 1.50.

Exercise 7F (Answers on page 499)

1. Draw the graph of $y = \ln x$ for $0 < x \leq 6$.
    From your graph,
    (a) estimate the values of ln 3 and ln 4.4,
    (b) find approximate values of x if
         (i) $\ln x = 1$,   (ii) $\ln x = 0.5$,
    (c) find the point where the curve cuts the x-axis.

2. On your graph in question 1, draw the graph of $y = \ln (x - 1)$ for $1 < x \leq 6$. Compare the two graphs.

3. Sketch the following graphs:
    (a) $y = \lg (x - 1)$ (b) $y = \ln (2x - 1)$
    (c) $y = \lg (x + 2)$ (d) $y = 2 \ln (2x + 1)$

4. Using graph paper, draw the curve $y \ln (x + 1)$ for $0 \leq x \leq 4$, taking values of x at unit intervals. By drawing an appropriate straight line, obtain an approximate value for the positive root of the equation $x - 2 \ln (x + 1) = 0$.   (C)

5. Draw the graph of $y = \ln(x - 1)$ for $1.5 \leq x \leq 3$, taking intervals of 0.5. Express $(x - 1)^2 = e^{3 - x}$ in the form $\ln (x - 1) = ax + b$.
    By drawing an appropriate straight line, obtain an approximate solution to the equation $(x - 1)^2 = e^{3 - x}$.

6. **(a)** Sketch the graph of $y = \lg (x + 1)$ for $x > 1$.
   (b) Express $(x + 1)^2 = 10^{6-2x}$ in the form $\lg x = ax + b$.
   (c) Insert on your sketch the additional graph required to obtain a graphical solution to $(x + 1)^2 = 10^{6-2x}$.

7. Sketch the graph of $y = \ln x$ for $x > 0$. Express $xe^x = 7.39$ in the form $\ln x = ax + b$ and state the value of a and of b.
   Insert on your sketch the additional graph required to obtain a graphical solution to the equation $xe^x = 7.39$.   (C)

7.7   Exponential Functions

The expression a^x where a is a positive constant and x is a variable is called an **exponential function**. Expressions such as 2^x, 3^{2x-1}, 5^{1-x} and $\left(\dfrac{1}{2}\right)^x$ are some examples of exponential functions.

7.7.1   *Graphs of Exponential Functions*

▶ **Example 27**

Draw the graph of $y = 2^x$ for $-3 \le x \le 3$.
From the graph,
(a) estimate the value of $2^{1.2}$,
(b) find the approximate value of x if $2^x = 7$,
(c) find the point where the curve cuts the y-axis.

▶ **Solution . . .**

A table of values of x and $y = 2^x$ is constructed.

x	-3	-2	-1	0	1	2	3
y	0.125	0.25	0.5	1	2	4	8

The graph of $y = 2^x$ is plotted.

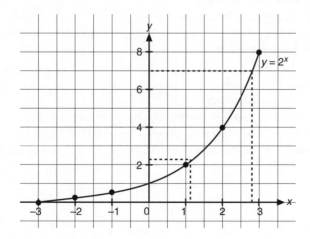

Verification and IT skills

Use Graphamatica courseware to plot the following pairs of graphs:

(a) $y = 2^x$ and $y = 2^{-x}$
(b) $y = 2^x$ and $y = -(2^x)$
(c) $y = 2^{1-x}$ and $y = 2^{x-1}$

Are the pairs of graphs reflections of each other? If so, what is the line of reflection?

From the graph, we found that
(a) $2^{1.2} \approx 2.4$,
(b) when $2^x = 7$, $x \approx 2.8$,
(c) the curve cuts the y-axis at the point $(0,1)$.

From the graph of $y = 2^x$ in Example 27, we notice the following:
(i) $2^x > 0$ for all values of x
(ii) 2^x increases as x increases
(iii) $2^x \to 0$ as $x \to -\infty$
(iv) $2^x = 1$ when $x = 0$.

▶ **Example 28**

Copy the graph of $y = 2^x$ from Example 27. On the same axes, draw the graph of $y = 2^{-x}$ for $-3 \leq x \leq 3$.
What is the relationship between the graph of $y = 2^x$ and that of $y = 2^{-x}$?

▶ **Solution . . .**

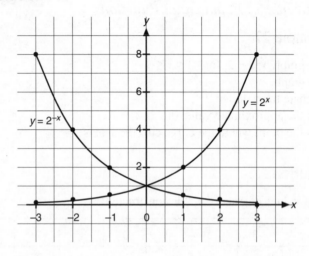

The graphs of $y = 2^x$ and $y = 2^{-x}$ are reflections of each other in the y-axis.
From the graph of $y = 2^{-x}$ in Example 28, we notice the following:
(i) $2^{-x} > 0$ for all values of x
(ii) 2^{-x} decreases as x increases
(iii) $2^{-x} \to 0$ as $x \to \infty$
(iv) $2^{-x} = 1$ when $x = 0$.

In general,
(i) $a^{px+q} > 0$ for all values of x,
(ii) $a^{px+q} \to 0$ as $x \to -\infty$ (for $p > 0$) or $x \to \infty$ (for $p < 0$),
(iii) the curve $y = a^{px+q}$ cuts the y-axis when $x = 0$ and $y = a^q$,
(iv) the shape of the curve is of one form $\diagup$ if $p > 0$ and of the form $\diagdown$ if $p < 0$.

▶ **Example 29**

Sketch the following graphs:

(a) $y = 5^{2x+1}$ (b) $y = \left(\dfrac{1}{2}\right)^x$

▶ **Solution . . .**

(a) The curve of $y = 5^{2x+1}$ cuts the y-axis when $x = 0$ and $y = 5$, i.e. at the point (0,5).

The shape of the curve is $\diagup$ as 2 (coefficient of x) is positive.

The graph of $y = 5^{2x+1}$ is plotted below:

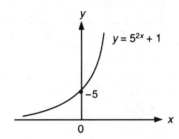

(b) $\left(\dfrac{1}{2}\right)^x = 2^{-x}$

The curve cuts the y-axis when $x = 0$ and $y = 2^0 = 1$.

The shape of the curve is $\diagdown$ as the coefficient of x is -1.

The graph of $y = \left(\dfrac{1}{2}\right)^x$ is plotted below:

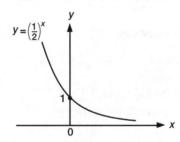

▶ **Example 30**

Draw the graph of $y = xe^{-x}$ for $0 \le x \le 2$ at intervals of 0.5.
By drawing an appropriate straight line, obtain an approximate solution to the equation $10x + xe^x = 2e^x$.

▶ **Solution . . .**

A table of values of x and $y = xe^{-x}$ is constructed.

x	0	0.5	1	1.5	2
y	0	0.303	0.368	0.335	0.271

The graph of $y = xe^{-x}$ is plotted below.

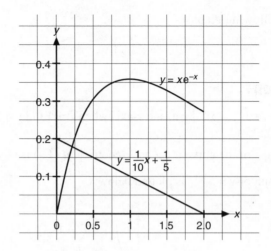

When $10x + xe^x = 2e^x$

$$10x = -xe^x + 2e^x$$

$$10x = (-x + 2)e^x$$

$$\frac{x}{e^x} = \frac{-x+2}{10}$$

$$xe^{-x} = -\frac{1}{10}x + \frac{1}{5}$$

We need to draw two graphs, i.e. $y = xe^{-x}$ and $y = -\frac{1}{10}x + \frac{1}{5}$, so as to solve the above equation graphically. Since the graph of $y = xe^{-x}$ has been plotted, we only need to plot the graph of $y = -\frac{1}{10}x + \frac{1}{5}$ which is a straight line.

From the graph, the solution of the above equation is 0.2.

Exercise 7G (Answers on page 499)

1. Draw the graph of $y = 3^x$ for $-2 \leq x \leq 2$.
   From your graph,
   (a) estimate the values of $3^{0.8}$ and $3^{1.4}$,
   (b) find the approximate values of x if
       (i) $3^x = 7$,   (ii) $3^x = 0.4$,
   (c) find the coordinates of the point where the graph cuts the y-axis.

2. On your graph in question 1, draw the curve $y = 4^x$ for $-2 \leq x \leq 1.5$.
   Compare the two graphs.

3. Draw the graph of $y = e^x$, where e = 2.718, for $-1 \leq x \leq 2.5$.
   From your graph,
   (a) estimate the values of $e^{0.8}$ and $e^{-0.3}$,
   (b) find the approximate values of x if
       (i) $e^x = 2$,   (ii) $e^x = 8$,
   (c) find the point of intersection between the curve $y = e^x$ and the y-axis.

4. Draw the graphs of $y = 4^x$ and $y = 4^x$ for the same domain $-2 \le x \le 2$. What is the relationship between the two graphs?

5. Sketch the following graphs:
   (a) $y = 8^x$ **(b)** $y = 3^{2x-1}$ **(c)** $y = 2e^{x+1}$
   (d) $y = 2^x + 3$ **(e)** $y = 5^{-x}$ **(f)** $y = \left(\frac{1}{3}\right)^x$
   (g) $y = \frac{1}{2}e^{1-2x}$ **(h)** $y = 3^{-x} + 2$

6. Draw the graph of $y = e^{-x}$ for $-2 \le x \le 2$, taking intervals of 1 unit. By drawing an appropriate straight line, obtain an approximate solution to the equation $5xe^x + 3e^x = 1$.

7. Draw the graph of $y = e^x - 2e^{-x}$ for values of x at intervals of 0.5 from $x = 0$ to $x = 2$.
   Use your graph to solve the equation $e^{2x} - 3e^x - 2 = 0$.

8. Sketch the graph of $y = e^{-x}$.
   Insert on your sketch the additional graph required to obtain a graphical solution to the equation $(x-1)e^x = 1$.

9. Sketch the graph of $y = e^{1-x}$.
   Insert on your sketch the additional graph required to obtain a graphical solution to the equation $1 - \ln x = x$.

Summary

1. **Definition of logarithms**
   $$y = a^x \quad \leftrightarrow \quad \log_a y = x$$

2. **Laws of logarithms**
   $$\log_a PQ = \log_a P + \log_a Q$$
   $$\log_a \frac{P}{Q} = \log_a P - \log_a Q$$
   $$\log_a P^n = n \log_a P$$

3. $\log_a 1 = 0$ and $\log_a a = 1$

4. **Change of base of logarithms**
   $$\log_b a = \frac{\log_c a}{\log_c b}$$
   $$\log_b a = \frac{1}{\log_a b} \quad \text{(when } c = a\text{)}$$

5. Common logarithms, $\log_{10} x$, are written as $\lg x$.
   Natural logarithms, $\log_e x$, are written as $\ln x$.

6. Equations of the form $a^x = b$ can be solved by taking the logarithms of each side.

7. Graphs of logarithmic functions

log f(x) is defined for f(x) > 0.

The curve $y = \log f(x)$ cuts the x-axis at the point f(x) = 1.

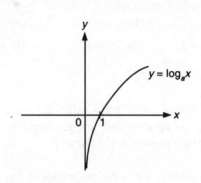

8. Graphs of exponential functions

$a^{px+q} > 0$ for all values of x

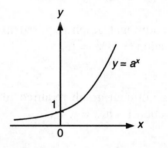 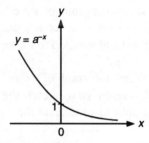

Revision Exercise 7 (Answers on page 499)

1. Find the value of x if
   (a) $\log_3 81 = x$,   (b) $\log_8 x = 2$,   (c) $\log_x 8 = 2$.

2. Find the value of x if
   (a) $\log_3(x - 3) + \log_3(x + 3) = 3$,
   (b) $\log_2(x^2 + 5x - 2) = \log_2(x^2 + 3x - 6) + \log_4 9$.

3. Solve the equations
   (a) $1.6^{3.7} = x$,   (b) $3.5^x = 7$,   (c) $x^{1.2} = 8$.

4. Solve the equations
   (a) $\lg(2x) - 3\lg 2 = \frac{1}{2}\lg(x - 3)$,   (C)

   (b) $1 + 2\lg(x + 1) = \lg(2x + 1) + \lg(5x + 8)$.   (C)

5. Solve the following simultaneous equations:
   (a) $\log_2 x - \log_4 y = 4$
       $\log_2(x - 2y) = 5$

   (b) $3^{x+y} = 27$
       $\log_4 x - 1 = \log_2 y$

(c) $\log_2(x - 14y) = 3$
$\lg x - \lg (y + 1) = 1$

(d) $2^x 4^y = 128$
$\ln (4x - y) = \ln 2 + \ln 5$ (C)

6. **(a)** Given that $\log_p 7 + \log_p k = 0$, find k.
    (b) Given that $4 \log_q 3 + 2 \log_q 2 - \log_q 144 = 2$, find q.
    (c) Given that $\log_3 2 = 0.631$ and that $\log_3 5 = 1.465$, evaluate $\log_3 1.2$
        without using tables or a calculator.   (C)

7. **(a)** Find the value of x if $e^{2x} = e^x + 6$.
    (b) If $y = px^q + 2$, $y = 14$ when $x = 2$, and $y = 194$ when $x = 8$, find
        the values of p and q.
    (c) Given that $\log_a(xy^3) = u$ and $\log_a\left(\dfrac{y^2}{x}\right) = v$, express $\log_a(xy)$ in
        terms of u and v.

8. If $\log_4 x = p$, show that $\log_2 x = 2p$.
Hence find
    (a) the value of k if $\log_4 k = 2 + \log_2 k$,
    (b) the value of n if $\log_2 n + \log_4 n = 9$.

9. If $T = T_0 e^{-0.5t}$, show that $t = 2 \ln\left(\dfrac{T_0}{T}\right)$.

10. Find the least integral value of x if
    (a) $1.8^{x-1} > 47$,   **(b)** $0.75^x < 0.15$.

11. \$2 000 is invested at 5% per year compound interest. After how many years will it have amounted to \$3 500?

12. Inflation in a certain country is 15% per year. If this rate continues unchanged, after how many years would the cost of living double?

13. If $\log_3 2 = a$ and $\log_3 13 = b$, express $\log_{78} 52$ in terms of a and b.

14. Solve the inequality $\log_2(\log_3 x) > 0$.

15. Given that $\log_8(p + 2) + \log_8 q = r - \dfrac{1}{3}$ and that $\log_2(p - 2) - \log_2 q = 2r + 1$, show that $p^2 = 32^r + 4$. If $r = 1$, find the possible values of p and q.

16. Draw the graph of $y = 2^x$ for $0 \le x \le 3$, taking values of x at intervals of 0.5. By adding a suitable straight line to your graph, find an approximate solution to the equation $2^{x+1} + x = 4$.

17. Sketch the graphs of $y = \lg x$ and $y = \lg 10x$. State the coordinates of the points where each curve meets the x-axis.

18. Sketch the graph of the function f : $x \longmapsto 3e^{2x}$ for real values of x, showing on your diagram the coordinates of any points of intersection with the axes.

State the range of f. Obtain an expression for f^{-1} in terms of x.   (C)

19. (a) Draw the graph of $y = 2^x$ for $0 \le x \le 2$, taking scales of 2 cm for 1 unit on each axis. And the line $y = x$ and hence draw the graph of $y = \log_2 x$ for $1 \le x < 4$.

    (b) Calculate the value of $\log_2 6$.

    (c) Express $x2^x = 6$ in the form $\log_2 x = px + q$, stating the values of p and q.

    (d) What is the equation of the straight line that must be added to the graph to find the solution to the equation $x2^x = 6$?

    (e) Draw this line and hence solve the equation approximately.

Maths Booster

1. If $m = \log_6 3$ and $n = \log_6 5$, express $\log_2 45$ in terms of m and n.

2. Given $\log_a x = 6$, $\log_b x = 8$ and $\log_{abc} x = 3$, find the value of $\log_c x$.

Chapter 8
Straight Line Graphs

We often come across straight line graphs when we want to represent relationships between one variable and another.

Straight line graphs come under the study of coordinate geometry which is also called cartesian geometry. Because of its usefulness, it is important for us to understand graphs of this type and how they can be used to solve problems.

8.1 Interpreting Equations of Straight Line Graphs in the form $y = mx + c$

In science, when two variables x and y are thought to be related, a set of measurements is made. The results can be used to find the mathematical law connecting x and y, if there is one.

Usually the results are plotted as a graph. If this is a straight line graph, the relationship is easily deduced as it will be of the form $y = mx + c$, where m is the gradient of the straight line and c is the y-intercept.

▶ ### Example 1

When values of x and y are plotted, a straight line is produced as shown in Fig. 8.1. This line passes through (0,2) and (6,4).
Find the relationship between x and y.

▶ ### Solution . . .

Since it is a straight line graph, the relationship between x and y will be of the form $y = mx + c$,

where gradient, $m = \dfrac{4-2}{6-0} = \dfrac{1}{3}$

and y-intercept, $c = 2$.

Hence the relationship between x and y is $y = \dfrac{1}{3}x + 2$.

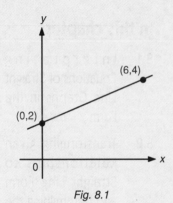

Fig. 8.1

▶ ### Example 2

Fig. 8.2(a) shows part of a straight line graph obtained by plotting y against x. This straight line passes through A(6,1) and B(2,5). Find the relationship between x and y.

▶ ### Solution . . .

From the graph, gradient $m = \dfrac{5-1}{2-6} = -1$. To find the y-intercept, c, the line AB is extended to meet the y-axis at C(0,c) (Fig.8.2(b)).

The gradient is $\dfrac{5-c}{2-0} = -1$
$$c = 7$$

Hence the relationship between x and y is $y = -x + 7$.

However, if the graph of y against x is not a straight line, the relationship between x and y will not be so simple.

To find the relationship, the values of X and Y are plotted where X and Y are expressions in x and/or y. If a straight line graph is obtained, the relationship will be of the form $Y = mX + c$ where m is the gradient of the straight line and c is the Y-intercept.

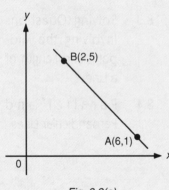

Fig. 8.2(a)

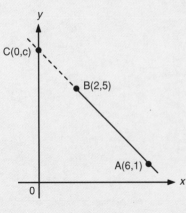

Fig. 8.2(b)

▶ **Example 3**

Variables x and y are related in such a way that when $\dfrac{y}{\sqrt{x}}$ is plotted against x^2, a straight line is produced as shown in Fig. 8.3(a). This line passes through the points $P(4,3)$ and $Q\left(1,1\dfrac{1}{2}\right)$. Find y in terms of x.

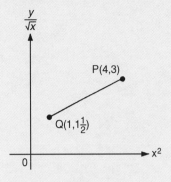

Fig. 8.3(a)

▶ **Solution . . .**

Since it is a straight line graph, the equation of the straight line will be of the form $Y = mX + c$,

where $Y = \dfrac{y}{\sqrt{x}}$

$\qquad X = x^2$

$\qquad m = \dfrac{3 - 1\frac{1}{2}}{4 - 1} = \dfrac{1}{2}$

The Y-intercept, c, can be obtained by extending the line PQ to meet the Y-axis at $R(0,c)$, as shown in Fig. 8.3(b).

The gradient is $\dfrac{1\frac{1}{2} - c}{1 - 0} = \dfrac{1}{2}$

$\qquad\qquad \therefore \quad c = 1$

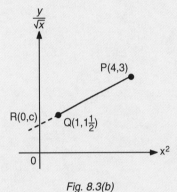

Fig. 8.3(b)

Hence the equation of the straight line is $\dfrac{y}{\sqrt{x}} = \dfrac{1}{2}x^2 + 1$,

$$\therefore \quad y = \dfrac{1}{2}x^{\frac{5}{2}} + x^{\frac{1}{2}}.$$

▶ **Example 4**

Fig. 8.4 shows part of a straight line graph obtained by plotting $\lg y$ against $\lg x$, together with coordinates of two of the points on the line.

Find
(a) $\lg y$ in terms of $\lg x$,
(b) y in terms of x,
(c) the value of x when $y = 500$.

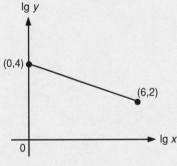

Fig. 8.4

▶ **Solution . . .**

(a) From the graph, we obtain
$\qquad Y = \lg y$
$\qquad X = \lg x$

$\qquad m = \dfrac{4 - 2}{0 - 6} = -\dfrac{1}{3}$

$\qquad c = 4$

$\qquad \therefore \quad \lg y = -\dfrac{1}{3}\lg x + 4.$

(b) From (a), $\lg y = -\dfrac{1}{3}\lg x + 4$

$$\lg y + \frac{1}{3}\lg x = 4$$

$$\lg yx^{\frac{1}{3}} = 4$$

$$yx^{\frac{1}{3}} = 10^4$$

$$y = 10^4 x^{-\frac{1}{3}}.$$

(c) When $y = 500$,

$$500 = 10^4 x^{-\frac{1}{3}}$$

$$x^{\frac{1}{3}} = \frac{10^4}{500} = 20$$

$$x = 20^3 = 8000.$$

▶ **Example 5**

The table shows the experimental values of two variables x and y.

x	1	2	3	4	5
y	5.0	12.2	23.2	38.0	56.7

Using the vertical axis for $\dfrac{y}{\sqrt{x}}$ and the horizontal axis for $x\sqrt{x}$, plot $\dfrac{y}{\sqrt{x}}$ against $x\sqrt{x}$ and obtain a straight line graph.

Make use of your graph to

(a) express y in terms of x,

(b) estimate the value of x when $2y = 35\sqrt{x}$.

▶ **Solution . . .**

A table of the values of $\dfrac{y}{\sqrt{x}}$ and $x\sqrt{x}$ is constructed.

$\dfrac{y}{\sqrt{x}}$	5.0	8.6	13.4	19.0	25.4
$x\sqrt{x}$	1.0	2.8	5.2	8.0	11.2

A graph of $\dfrac{y}{\sqrt{x}}$ against $x\sqrt{x}$ is then plotted.

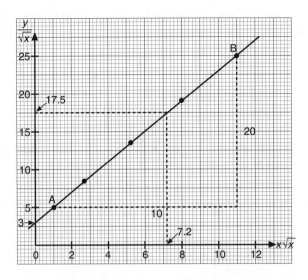

Note:

We see that the points lie very nearly in a straight line. Any inaccuracies can reasonably be assumed to be due to experimental errors. We draw the line which fits the points as well as we can judge. There may be some differences of opinion over the position of the line, so our results will be approximate.

(a) Since it is a straight line graph, the equation of the line will be of the form $Y = mX + c$,

where Y is $\dfrac{y}{\sqrt{x}}$, X is $x\sqrt{x}$, m is the gradient of the graph, and c is the $\dfrac{y}{\sqrt{x}}$-intercept.

To find the gradient, we take two well-spaced points such as A and B on the line. It helps to make the x-step between these two points a convenient number.

From the graph, the gradient is

$$m = \frac{20}{10} = 2,$$

the $\dfrac{y}{\sqrt{x}}$-intercept, $c = 3$

Hence the equation of the straight line is $\dfrac{y}{\sqrt{x}} = 2\,x\sqrt{x} + 3$

$$y = 2x^2 + 3\sqrt{x}.$$

(b) If $2y = 35\sqrt{x}$,

$$\frac{y}{\sqrt{x}} = 17.5.$$

From the graph, $x\sqrt{x} = 7.2$

$$x^{\frac{3}{2}} = 7.2$$

$$x = 7.2^{\frac{2}{3}}$$

$$= 3.73.$$

Exercise 8A (Answers on page 500)

1. Each of the following shows part of a straight line graph obtained by plotting y against x. In each case, find the relationship between x and y.

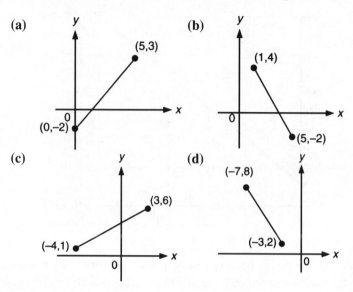

(a)

(b)

(c)

(d)

2. Each of the following shows part of a straight line graph obtained by plotting the values of the variables indicated. In each case, express y in terms of x.

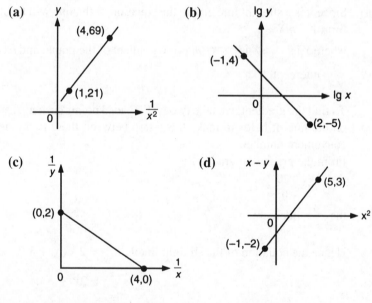

(a)

(b)

(c)

(d)

3. Variables x and y are related in such a way that when $x - y$ is plotted against xy, a straight line is produced as shown in the diagram. This line passes through the points $(1,2)$ and $(5,4)$. Find y in terms of x.   (C)

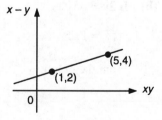

4.

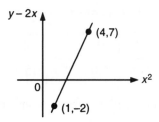

The variables x and y are related in such a way that when $y - 2x$ is plotted against x^2, a straight line is obtained passing through $(1,-2)$ and $(4,7)$.

Find

(a) y in terms of x,

(b)   the values of x when $y = 11$.   (C)

5.   Fig. 8.5 shows part of a straight line graph obtained by plotting $\lg y$ against x. This straight line passes through the point $(3,2)$ and $(7,4)$.

Find

(a) $\lg y$ in terms of x,

(b) y in terms of x,

(c)   the value of x when $y = \dfrac{1}{10}$.

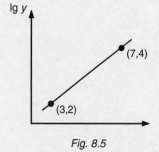

Fig. 8.5

6.   The variables x and y are related in such a way that when y is plotted against $\dfrac{1}{x}$, a straight line is obtained which passes through $(2,3)$ and $(3,2)$. Express y in terms of x.

7.   The variables x and y are related in such a way that when $\dfrac{y}{x}$ is plotted against x^2, a straight line is obtained which passes through $(4,-1)$ and $(16,5)$. Express y in terms of x.   (C)

8.   The variables x and y are related in such a way that when $x + y$ is plotted against x^2, a straight line is obtained passing through $(1,-1)$ and $(5,2)$. Find

(a)   the values of x when $x + y = 5$,

(b) y as a function of x,

(c)   the values of x when $y = 0$.   (C)

9.   The table shows the experimental values of two variables x and y.

x	1	2	3	4	5
y	6.5	6.01	6.06	6.25	6.48

Using the vertical axis for $y\sqrt{x}$ and the horizontal axis for x, plot $y\sqrt{x}$ against x and obtain a straight line graph. Make use of your graph to

(a)   express y in terms of x,

(b)   estimate the value of x when $y = \dfrac{10}{\sqrt{x}}$.

10. The table shows the experimental values of two variables x and y.

x	1	2	3	4	5
y	1.9	5.0	9.3	15.2	22.0

Using the data given, plot $\dfrac{y}{x}$ against x and obtain a straight line graph.

Make use of your graph to
(a) express y in terms of x,
(b) find the value of x when $y = 3x$.

11. The table shows the experimental values of two variables x and y.

x	1.0	1.2	1.4	1.6	1.8
y	79.0	56.0	36.5	18.4	0.9

Using the data given, plot xy against x^3 and obtain a straight line graph. Male use of your graph to

(a) express y in terms of x,
(b) estimate the value of x when $y = \dfrac{60}{x}$. (C)

8.2 Transforming given Relationships to Straight Line Form and Determining the Unknown Constants

So far we have dealt with relationships between x and y in the form $Y = mX + c$.

However, there are relationships which are not explicitly given in this form. For example, $xy = \dfrac{a}{x} + bx$ and $y = ax^b$.

We can determine the unknown constants a and b as follows:

1. Convert the relationships to a straight line form $Y = mX + c$.

2. Plot Y against X to obtain a straight line graph.

3. The unknown constants a and b can then be determined from the gradient of the straight line, m, and the Y-intercept, c.

▶ **Example 6**

Convert each of the following relationships to straight line form.

State what functions of x and/or y should be plotted to obtain a straight line graph.

State also the gradient and intercept of the straight line in terms of a and b.

(a) $y = ax + \dfrac{b}{x}$ **(b)** $\dfrac{a}{x} + \dfrac{b}{y} = 1$

(c) $y = \dfrac{a}{x - b}$ **(d)** $y = ax^b$

▶ Solution . . .

(a)
$$y = ax + \frac{b}{x}$$

Multiplying by x: $xy = ax^2 + b$

Thus a straight line graph is obtained when xy is plotted against x^2. The gradient is a and the xy-intercept is b.

(b)
$$\frac{a}{x} + \frac{b}{y} = 1$$

$$\frac{b}{y} = -\frac{a}{x} + 1$$

Dividing by b: $\dfrac{1}{y} = -\dfrac{a}{b}\left(\dfrac{1}{x}\right) + \dfrac{1}{b}$

Thus, a straight line graph is obtained when $\dfrac{1}{y}$ is plotted against $\dfrac{1}{x}$. The gradient is $-\dfrac{a}{b}$ and the $\dfrac{1}{y}$-intercept is $\dfrac{1}{b}$.

(c) $\quad y = \dfrac{a}{x - b}$

$$\frac{1}{y} = \frac{x - b}{a}$$

$$\frac{1}{y} = \frac{1}{a}(x) - \frac{b}{a}$$

Thus, a straight line graph is obtained when $\dfrac{1}{y}$ is plotted against x. The gradient is $\dfrac{1}{a}$ and the $\dfrac{1}{y}$-intercept is $-\dfrac{b}{a}$.

(d) $\quad y = ax^b$

$\lg y = \lg ax^b$

$\lg y = \lg a + \lg x^b$

$\lg y = \lg a + b\lg x$

$\lg y = b\lg x + \lg a$

Thus, a straight line is obtained when $\lg y$ is plotted against $\lg x$. The gradient is b and the $\lg y$-intercept is $\lg a$.

▶ Example 7

The table below shows the experimental values of two variables x and y.

x	1.5	2.8	3.0	4.2	5.0	6.5
y	80	35	33	18	8	5

It is known that x and y are related by an equation $y = ab^{-x}$, where a and b are constants.

(a) Express the equation in a form suitable for drawing a straight line graph.

(b) Draw the graph and use it to determine the value of a and of b.

(c) One reading of y is inaccurate. Find a more accurate value of y.

▶ **Solution . . .**

(a)
$$y = ab^{-x}$$
$$\lg y = \lg ab^{-x}$$
$$\lg y = \lg a - x\lg b$$
$$\lg y = (-\lg b)x + \lg a,$$
where $Y = \lg y$ and $X = x$, $m = -\lg b$ and $c = \lg a$.

(b) A table of the values of x and $\lg y$ is constructed.

x	1.5	2.8	3.0	4.2	5.0	6.5
$\lg y$	1.90	1.54	1.52	1.26	0.90	0.70

A graph of $\lg y$ against x is then plotted.

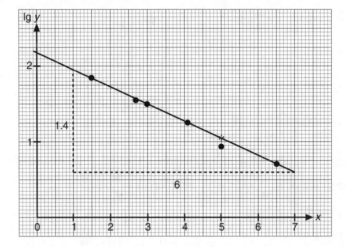

From the graph,

the gradient, $m = -\dfrac{1.4}{6} = -0.233$,

the $\lg y$-intercept, $c = 2.2$.

Hence
$$-\lg b = -0.233$$
$$\lg b = 0.233$$
$$b = 10^{0.233}$$
$$= 1.71$$

and
$$\lg a = 2.2$$
$$a = 10^{2.2}$$
$$= 158.$$

Note:
The line drawn is the one which best fits the points. However, there may be some differences in opinion as to the position of the line. Hence, a slight difference in results is allowed.

(c) The reading of y is inaccurate when $x = 5.0$. A more accurate reading of y can be obtained from the graph by taking a point on the line where $x = 5.0$ (marked * on the graph).

From the graph, when $x = 5.0$,

$$\lg y = 1.05$$
$$\therefore \quad y = 10^{1.05}$$
$$= 11.2$$

▶ **Example 8**

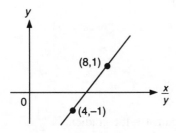

The variables x and y are related by the equation $ay^2 + by = x$, where a and b are constants. Part of the straight line graph obtained by plotting y against $\dfrac{x}{y}$ is shown in the diagram. Find the value of a and of b.

▶ **Solution ...**

From the given equation,
$$ay^2 + by = x$$
$$ay^2 = x - by$$
$$y^2 = \frac{x}{a} - \frac{by}{a}$$

Dividing both sides by y: $y = \dfrac{1}{a}\left(\dfrac{x}{y}\right) - \dfrac{b}{a}$,

where $Y = y$, $X = \dfrac{x}{y}$, $m = \dfrac{1}{a}$, $c = -\dfrac{b}{a}$.

From the graph, $m = \dfrac{1-(-1)}{8-4} = \dfrac{1}{2}$

Hence, $\qquad \dfrac{1}{a} = \dfrac{1}{2}$
$$a = 2.$$

Extending the line to meet the y-axis at $(0,c)$ (Fig. 8.6), the gradient is

$$\frac{-1-c}{4-0} = \frac{1}{2}$$
$$c = -3.$$

Hence, $\qquad -\dfrac{b}{a} = -3$
$$b = 3a$$
$$= 3 \times 2$$
$$= 6$$
$$\therefore \quad a = 2, b = 6.$$

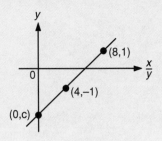

Fig. 8.6

▶ Example 9

The variables x and y are related by the equation $xy = 2px - qy$. The straight line graph, obtained by plotting values of $\frac{x}{y}$ against values of x, has a gradient of 2 and passes through the point $(1,8)$. Calculate the values of p and of q.

▶ Solution ...

$$xy = 2px - qy$$

$$x = 2p\frac{x}{y} - q$$

$$2p\frac{x}{y} = x + q$$

$$\frac{x}{y} = \frac{1}{2p}x + \frac{q}{2p}$$

When $\frac{x}{y}$ is plotted against x, the gradient is $\frac{1}{2p}$.

Hence, $\quad \frac{1}{2p} = 2$

$$p = 0.25$$

Substituting $x = 1$, $\frac{x}{y} = 8$ and $\frac{1}{2p} = 2$ into the equation,

$$\frac{x}{y} = \frac{1}{2p}x + \frac{q}{2p}$$

$$8 = 2(1) + \frac{q}{2p}$$

$$\frac{q}{2p} = 6$$

$$\frac{q}{2(0.25)} = 6$$

$$q = 3$$

$$\therefore \quad p = 0.25, q = 3.$$

Exercise 8B (Answers on page 500)

1. Convert each of the following relationships to straight line form. State what functions of x and/or y should be plotted to obtain a straight line graph. State also the gradient and intercept of the straight line in terms of a and b.

(a) $y = ax + bx^2$

(b) $y = a\sqrt{x} + \frac{b}{\sqrt{x}}$

(c) $xy = ax + \frac{b}{x}$

(d) $ay = x - \frac{b}{x}$

(e) $ay + bx^2 = x$

(f) $y = \frac{x+a}{x-b}$

(g) $y = \frac{a^x}{b}$

(h) $y = a(x+3)^b$

2. The following results were obtained experimentally for two variables x and y:

x	1	2	3	4	5
y	42	120	430	920	2 600

It is believed that x and y are related by the equation $y = ab^x$ where a and b are constants.

(a) Express the equation in a form suitable for drawing a straight line graph.

(b) Draw the graph and use it to determine the value of a and of b.

(c) One quantity of y is inaccurate. Find a more accurate value of y.

3. The following set of values for two variables x and y was obtained in an experiment:

x	3	8	15	30	60
y	50	225	580	1 640	4 650

It is believed that xy are related by the equation $y = ax^b$ where a and b are constants.

(a) Express the equation in a form suitable for drawing a straight line graph.

(b) Draw this graph and use it to estimate the value of a and of b.

(c) From the graph, find the value of x when $y = 1\ 000$.

4. Two variables x and y are known to be connected by the formula $\dfrac{a}{y} + \dfrac{b}{x^2} = 1$ where a and b are constants. The following table shows some values obtained by experiment:

x	3.5	4.0	5.0	6.5	10
y	0.66	0.86	1.22	1.61	2.78

Draw a suitable straight line graph to represent the above data and use it to estimate the value of a and of b.

5. The table shows the experimental values of two variables x and y.

x	0.5	1.5	2.5	3.5	4.5	5.5
y	3.3	2.4	1.8	1.5	1.3	1.1

It is known that x and y are related by the equation $y = \dfrac{a}{x+b}$ where a and b are constants.

(a) Plot xy against y and obtain a straight line graph.

(b) Use your graph to estimate the value of a and of b.

(c) Obtain the value of the gradient of the straight line obtained when $\dfrac{1}{y}$ is plotted against x.   (C)

6. The table shows the experimental values of two variables x and y.

x	1	2	3	4	5
y	3.8	11.2	20.5	33.2	50.6

It is known that x and y are related by the equation $y = ax + bx^2$. Draw a suitable straight line graph to represent the above data and use it to estimate

(a) the value of a and of b,

(b) the value of x when $y = 5x$. (C)

7.

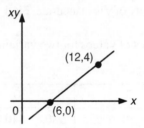

The variables x and y are related by the equation $by = \dfrac{a}{x} + x$, where a and b are constants. Part of the straight line graph obtained by plotting xy against x^2 is shown in the diagram. Find the value of a and of b.

8.

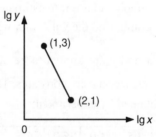

The diagram shows part of a straight line graph drawn to represent the equation $y = Ax^n$. Find the value of A and of n. (C)

9.

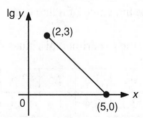

The diagram shows part of a straight line graph drawn to represent the equation $y = Ab^x$. Find the value of A and of b.

10.

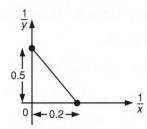

The diagram shows part of a straight line graph drawn to represent the equation $px + qy = xy$ where p and q are constants. Find the value of p and of q.

11.

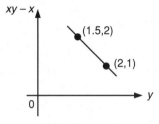

The equation $y = \dfrac{x+c}{x+d}$, where c and d are constants, can be represented by a straight line when $xy - x$ is plotted against y as shown in the diagram. Find the value of c and of d. **(C)**

12. The variables x and y are connected by the equation $by = ax^2 + x$, where a and b are constants. When $\dfrac{y}{x}$ is plotted against x, a straight line is obtained. This line has a gradient of 2.3 and $\dfrac{y}{x}$-intercept of 0.5. Calculate the value of a and of b.

13. The variables x and y are related by the equation $\dfrac{y}{p} + \dfrac{y^2}{q} = 1$, where p and q are positive constants. When the graph of y^2 against x is drawn, a straight line is obtained. Given that the intercept on the y^2-axis is 6 and that the gradient of the line is -3, calculate the value of p and of q.

14. The variables x and y are related by the equation $ax^2 - by^2 = x$. The straight line graph, obtained by plotting values of $\dfrac{y^2}{x}$ against values of x, has a gradient of $\dfrac{4}{9}$ and passes through the point $(18,4)$. Calculate the value of a and of b.

15. The variables x and y are connected by an equation of the form $y = ab^x$, where a and b are constants. When $\lg x$ is plotted against x, a straight line is obtained which passes through $(0,2)$ and $(2,3)$. Find the values of a and of b. **(C)**

8.3 Solving Questions involving the Midpoint and Length of a Line

8.3.1 Distance between Two Points

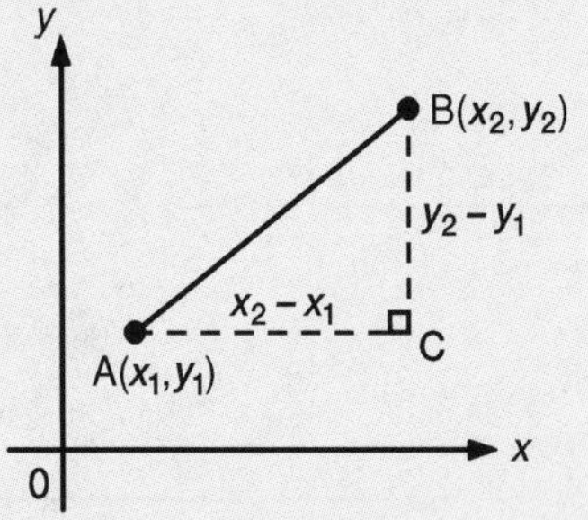

Consider any two points $A(x_1, y_1)$ and $B(x_2, y_2)$ (Fig. 8.7).

If we draw AC parallel to the x-axis and CB parallel to the y-axis, then we obtain the right-angled triangle ACB.

Fig. 8.7

In the right-angled triangle ACB, we have

$$AC = x_2 - x_1,$$
$$BC = y_2 - y_1.$$

Using Pythagoras' theorem:

$$
\begin{aligned}
AB^2 &= AC^2 + BC^2 \\
&= (x_2 - x_1)^2 + (y_2 - y_1)^2 \\
AB &= \sqrt{(x_2 - x_1)^2 + (y_2 - y_1)^2}
\end{aligned}
$$

So the general formula for the distance between any two points $A(x_1, y_1)$ and $B(x_2, y_2)$ is:

$$AB = \sqrt{(x_2 - x_1)^2 + (y_2 - y_1)^2}$$

▶ **Example 10**

Show that $A(1,5)$, $B(8,10)$ and $C(-6,0)$ are the vertices of an isosceles triangle.

▶ **Solution . . .**

$AB = \sqrt{(8-1)^2 + (10-5)^2} = \sqrt{74}$

$BC = \sqrt{(-6-8)^2 + (0-10)^2} = \sqrt{296}$

$AC = \sqrt{(-6-1)^2 + (0-5)^2} = \sqrt{74}$

As $AB = AC$, hence ABC is an isosceles triangle.

▶ **Example 11**

Given $A(h,-4)$ and $B(7,2)$. If the length of AB is 10 units, find the possible values of h.

► **Solution . . .**

Given AB = 10

$$\sqrt{(7-h)^2 + [2-(-4)]^2} = 10$$
$$\sqrt{49 - 14h + h^2 + 36} = 10$$
$$\sqrt{85 - 14h + h^2} = 10$$
$$85 - 14h + h^2 = 10$$
$$h^2 - 14h - 15 = 0$$
$$(h + 1)(h - 15) = 0$$
$$\therefore \quad h = -1 \text{ or } 15$$

8.3.2 *Midpoint of Two Points*

Consider any two points $A(x_1, y_1)$ and $B(x_2, y_2)$ (Fig. 8.8). Let the midpoint of AB be $M(x_m, y_m)$.

ME and AC are drawn parallel to the *x*-axis while MD and BC are drawn parallel to the *y*-axis.

Note that the two triangles BME and BAC are similar. Since M is the midpoint of AB, D and E are also midpoints of AC and BC respectively.

Then

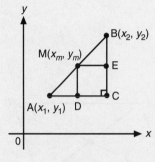

Fig. 8.8

$$AD = DC$$
$$x_m - x_1 = x_2 - x_m$$
$$2x_m = x_1 + x_2$$
$$x_m = \left(\frac{x_1 + x_2}{2}\right)$$

and

$$BE = EC$$
$$y_2 - y_m = y_m - y_1$$
$$2y_m = y_1 + y_2$$
$$y_m = \left(\frac{y_1 + y_2}{2}\right)$$

$\therefore$ The coordinates of the midpoints of $A(x_1, y_1)$ and $B(x_2, y_2)$ are

$$\left(\frac{x_1 + x_2}{2}, \frac{y_1 + y_2}{2}\right).$$

The coordinates of the midpoint are the **average** of the two *x*-coordinates and two *y*-coordinates of the points.

► **Example 12**

If M(–2,1) is the midpoint of AB, where A is (–3,2), find the coordinates of B.

► **Solution . . .**

Let (h,k) be the coordinates of B.

Midpoint of AB = $\left(\dfrac{-3+h}{2}, \dfrac{2+k}{2}\right)$

Hence $\left(\dfrac{-3+h}{2}, \dfrac{2+k}{2}\right) = (-2,1)$

Thus $\dfrac{-3+h}{2} = -2$ and $\dfrac{2+k}{2} = 1$

$\quad\quad\quad h = -1$ and $\quad\quad k = 0$

Therefore the coordinates of B are (–1,0).

8.3.3 *Midpoint of the Diagonals of a Parallelogram*

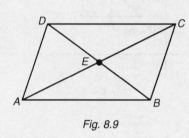

Fig. 8.9

In a parallogram ABCD (Fig. 8.9), the diagonals AC and BD bisect each other at E, i.e. midpoint of AC = point E and midpoint of BD = point E.

Hence, midpoint of AC = midpoint of BD.

As rhombuses, rectangles and squares are parallelograms, the diagonals of a rhombus, a rectangle or a square bisect each other too, i.e. the diagonals have a common midpoint.

► **Example 13**

A(–2,3), B(1,6), C(3,2) and D are the four vertices of a parallelogram. Find the coordinates of D.

► **Solution . . .**

Let the coordinates of D be (h,k).
Since ABCD is a parallelogram,
midpoint of AC = mid-point of BD

$\left(\dfrac{-2+3}{2}, \dfrac{3+2}{2}\right) = \left(\dfrac{1+h}{2}, \dfrac{6+k}{2}\right)$

Thus $\dfrac{-2+3}{2} = \dfrac{1+h}{2}$ and $\dfrac{3+2}{2} = \dfrac{6+k}{2}$

$\quad\quad\quad h = 0 \quad$ and $\quad\quad k = -1$

Therefore the coordinates of D are (0,–1).

Exercise 8C (*Answers on page 500*)

1. In each of the following triangles ABC,
   - (i) find the length of each side of the triangle,
   - (ii) determine whether $\triangle$ABC is a right-angled triangle, an isosceles triangle or neither of the above.
   - (a) A(–1,2), B(2,2), C(2,6)
   - (b) A(–2,5), B(4,4), C(5,–2)
   - (c) A(2,2), B(0,–4), C(–4,3)

2. A circle has its centre at (1,2). One point on its circumference is (–3,–1). What is the radius of the circle?

3. Show that A(–11,2) and B(–5,–10) are equidistant from the origin.

4. Given A(–3,k) and B(9,–1), if the length of AB is 13 units, find the possible values of k.

5. Given P(2,p), Q(0,–1) and R(1,4), find the possible values of p if the length of PQ is twice that of QR.

6. Calculate the distance of the point A(5,8) from M, the midpoint of the line joining the points B(–1,10) and C(3,2).   (C)

7. The vertices of a triangle are A(–4,–2), B(4,2) and C(2,6).
   - (a) Is the triangle right-angled?
   - (b) If a circle is drawn round this triangle touching two of its vertices, what are the coordinates of the centre of the circle?
   - (c) Hence find the radius of this circle.

8. Circle C_1 has centre (3,4) and radius 2 units.
   Circle C_2 has centre (–1,7) and radius 3 units.
   Find the distance between the two centres and hence show that the circles touch each other.

9. Find the coordinates of the midpoint of the following pairs of points:
   - (a) (0,4) and (3,–2)
   - (b) (–4,–2) and (–2,6)
   - (c) (p,2p) and (3p,–4p)
   - (d) (a + 2b,b – a) and (a – 2b,3a + b)

10. A(1,5) and B(7,–9) are two points. AB is divided into four equal parts at C, D and E. Find the coordinates of C, D and E.

11. The midpoint of PQ is (2,3). If the coordinates of P are (–1,4), find the coordinates of Q.

12. The points A and B are (a,–4) and (–3,b) respectively. If the midpoint of AB is (–2,3), find the values of a and b.

13. A(2,–6), B(7,4), C(–4,2) and D are the four vertices of a parallelogram. Find the coordinates of D.

14. ABCD is a parallelogram. A is the point (2,5), B is the point (8,8) and the diagonals intersect at $\left(3\frac{1}{2}, 2\frac{1}{2}\right)$. What are the coordinates of C and D?

15. The points (4,–2), (b,2), (–1,3) and (a,–1) in that order form a parallelogram. Show that $a + b = 3$.

16. ABCD is a quadrilateral where A is (1,7), B is (4,3), C is (–1,–3) and D is (–4,5). Is ABCD a parallelogram?
If not, state new coordinates for B so that ABCD will be a parallelogram.

8.4 Parallel and Perpendicular Lines

8.4.1 Parallel Lines

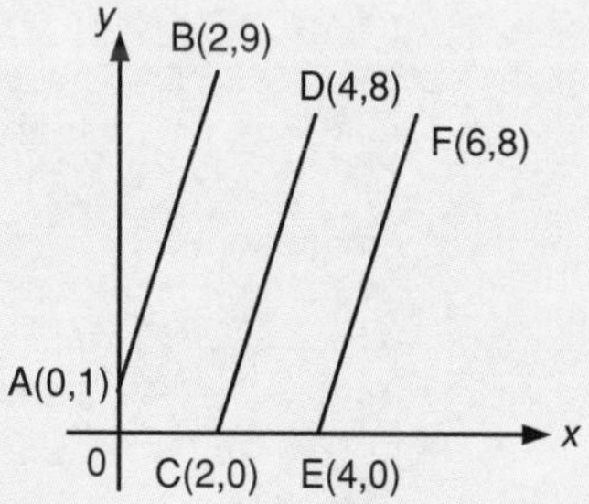

Fig. 8.10 shows three parallel lines AB, CD and EF. Find the gradients of the lines. What can you induce from the results?

Fig. 8.10

Gradient of AB = $\dfrac{9-1}{2-0} = 4$

Gradient of CD = $\dfrac{8-0}{4-2} = 4$

Gradient of EF = $\dfrac{8-0}{6-4} = 4$

Hence, the gradients of AB, CD and EF are equal.

> **Parallel lines** have equal gradients.
> Lines with **equal gradients** are parallel.

▶ **Example 14**

A(5,–2), B(2,10), C(–1,2) and D(0,2) are four points.
(a) Which of the lines AB, BC, CD and DA are parallel?
(b) What type of quadrilateral is ABCD?

▶ **Solution ...**

(a) Gradient of AB = $\dfrac{10-(-2)}{2-5} = -4$

Gradient of BC = $\dfrac{2-10}{-1-2} = \dfrac{8}{3}$

Gradient of CD = $\dfrac{-2-2}{0-(-1)} = -4$

Gradient of DA = $\dfrac{-2-(-2)}{0-5} = 0$

From the above, we notice that the gradient of AB equals the gradient of CD. Hence, AB is parallel to CD.

(b) As it has two parallel lines, ABCD is a trapezium.

8.4.2 Perpendicular Lines

▶ **Example 15**

(i)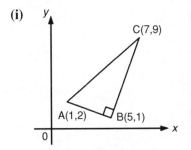

(ii)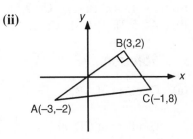

For each of the right-angled triangles ABC above, calculate
(a) the gradient of AB,
(b) the gradient of BC,
(c) the products of the two gradients.
Tabulate your results.
What conclusion can you draw from these results?

▶ **Solution ...**

Part	Gradient of AB m_1	Gradient of BC m_2	Products of gradients $m_1 \times m_2$
(i)	$-\dfrac{1}{4}$	4	-1
(ii)	$\dfrac{2}{3}$	$-\dfrac{3}{2}$	-1

We can conclude that the product of the gradients of two perpendicular lines is equal to -1.

In general, if m_1 and m_2 are the gradients of two perpendicular lines, then

$$m_1 m_2 = -1$$

or $\qquad m_1 = -\dfrac{1}{m_2} \qquad (m_1 \neq 0, m_2 \neq 0).$

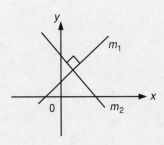

Conversely, if m_1 and m_2 are the gradients of two lines, and $m_1 m_2 = -1$, then the lines are perpendicular.

▶ Example 16

In each of the following cases, determine whether the lines AB and CD are perpendicular:

(a) A(−1,−4), B(1,6), C(−2,4), D(3,3)

(b) A(−5,2), B(6,4), C(−1,−6), D(1,5)

▶ Solution . . .

(a) Gradient of AB, $m_{AB} = \dfrac{6-(-4)}{1-(-1)} = 5$

Gradient of CD, $m_{CD} = \dfrac{3-4}{3-(-2)} = -\dfrac{1}{5}$

$$m_{AB} \times m_{CD} = (5)\left(-\dfrac{1}{5}\right) = -1$$

Hence AB and CD are perpendicular.

(b) Gradient of AB, $m_{AB} = \dfrac{4-2}{6-(-5)} = \dfrac{2}{11}$

Gradient of CD, $m_{CD} = \dfrac{5-(-6)}{1-(-1)} = \dfrac{11}{2}$

$$m_{AB} \times m_{CD} = \left(\dfrac{2}{11}\right)\left(\dfrac{11}{2}\right) = 1$$

Since $m_{AB} \times m_{CD} \neq -1$,

hence AB and CD are not perpendicular.

▶ Example 17

Four points have coordinates A(−k,1), B(2,7), P(−1,2k) and Q(5,1). Find the value of k if the lines AB and PQ are perpendicular to each other.

▶ Solution . . .

Gradient of AB, $m_{AB} = \dfrac{7-1}{2-(-k)} = \dfrac{6}{2+k}$

Gradient of PQ, $m_{PQ} = \dfrac{1-2k}{5-(-1)} = \dfrac{1-2k}{6}$

Since AB and PQ are perpendicular,

$$m_{AB} \times m_{PQ} = -1$$

$$\left(\dfrac{6}{2+k}\right)\left(\dfrac{1-2k}{6}\right) = -1$$

$$\dfrac{1-2k}{2+k} = -1$$

$$1 - 2k = -2 - k$$

$$k = 3.$$

▶ Example 18

Find the gradient of the line which is perpendicular to PQ where P is (−2,6) and Q is (4,−4).

► Solution . . .

Gradient of PQ, $m_{PQ} = \dfrac{-4-6}{4-(-2)} = -\dfrac{5}{3}$

Gradient of the line which is perpendicular to PQ

$$\text{is} -\dfrac{1}{m_{PQ}} = -\dfrac{1}{(-\frac{5}{3})}$$

$$= \dfrac{3}{5}.$$

► Example 19

Find the equations of the lines through the point (1,2) which are **(a)** parallel and **(b)** perpendicular to the line $2x - 3y = 4$.

► Solution . . .

(a) $2x - 3y = 4$

$$y = \dfrac{2}{3}x - 4$$

Thus the gradient of the line $2x - 3y = 4$ is $\dfrac{2}{3}$. So the gradient of any parallel line is also $\dfrac{2}{3}$.

Hence the equation of the parallel line is

$$y - 2 = \dfrac{2}{3}(x - 1)$$
$$2x - 3y = -4$$

(b) As the gradient of any perpendicular line is $-\dfrac{3}{2}$, the equation of the perpendicular line is

$$y - 2 = -\dfrac{3}{2}(x - 1)$$
$$3x + 2y = 7.$$

► Example 20

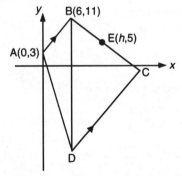

The diagram shows a trapezium ABCD in which AB is parallel to DC. The coordinates of A and B are (0,3) and (6,11) respectively. D is a point that makes BD parallel to the y-axis. E(h,5) is a point on BC such that AB = BE and h is positive. E is also the midpoint of BC. Find

(a) the value of h,
(b) the coordinates of C,
(c) the equation of DC,
(d) the coordinates of D.

Show that the angle ABC = 90°.

▶ **Solution ...**

(a) Given that AB = BE,

$$\sqrt{(6-0)^2+(11-3)^2} = \sqrt{(h-6)^2+(5-11)^2}$$

$$\sqrt{100} = \sqrt{h^2-12h+72}$$

$$h^2-12h-28=0$$

$$(h-14)(h+2)=0$$

$$h=14 \text{ or } h=-2$$

As h is positive, hence $h=14$.

(b) Let the coordinates of C be (p,q).
Given that mid-point of BC = E,

$$\left(\frac{p+6}{2},\frac{q+11}{2}\right)=(14,5)$$

$$\frac{p+6}{2}=14 \qquad \text{and} \qquad \frac{q+11}{2}=5$$

$$p=22 \qquad \text{and} \qquad q=-1$$

Hence the coordinates of C are $(22,-1)$.

(c) Gradient of AB = $\dfrac{11-3}{6-0}=\dfrac{4}{3}$

As AB is parallel to DC,
gradient of DC = gradient of AB

$$=\frac{4}{3}.$$

Equation of DC is

$$y-(-1)=\frac{4}{3}(x-22)$$

$$4x-3y=91$$

(d) To find the coordinates of D, the point of intersection of lines BD and DC, we first solve the equations simultaneously.

Equation of BD : $\qquad x=6$ ....(1)

Equation of DC : $4x-3y=91$ .... (2)

Substituting (1) into (2):

$$4(6)-3y=91$$

$$y=-22\frac{1}{3}$$

Hence the coordinates of D are $\left(6,-22\frac{1}{3}\right)$.

Gradient of AB, $m_{AB}=\dfrac{4}{3}$

Gradient of BC, $m_{BC}=\dfrac{-1-11}{22-6}=-\dfrac{3}{4}$

$$m_{AB}\times m_{BC}=\frac{4}{3}\times\left(-\frac{3}{4}\right)$$

$$=-1$$

i.e. AB and BC are perpendicular.
Hence $\angle ABC=90°$.

Exercise 8D (Answers on page 500)

1. In each of the following cases, determine whether the lines AB and CD are parallel.
   (a) A(–1,3), B(4,5), C(–4,–3), D(1,–1)
   (b) A(2,5), B(6,6), C(–2,–7), D(0,1)

2. A(2,1), B(3,4), C(–1,2) and D(–2,–1) are four points.
   (a) Which of the lines AB, BC, CD and DA are parallel?
   (b) What type of quadrilateral is ABCD?

3. A(4,2), B(2,–1), C(3,–1) and D(7,k) are four points. If AB is parallel to CD, find the value of k.

4. Fig. 8.11 shows a trapezium PQRS where P is (–4,3), Q is (0,15), R(3, t) and S is (–4,–2). Find the value of t.

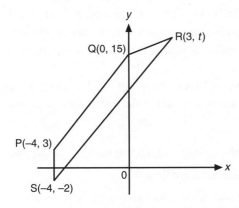

Fig. 8.11

5. In each of the following cases, determine whether the lines AB and CD are perpendicular:
   (a) A(1,2), B(5,–4), C(–4,–2), D(–1,0)
   (b) A(3,2), B(6,4), C(5,0), D(1,–6))

6. Is the triangle formed by the points A(–3,2), B(0,4) and C(4,–2) right-angled?

7. In each of the following cases, AB and PQ are perpendicular. Find the value of k.
   (a) A(2,–3), B(k,7), P(6,k), Q(1,8)
   (b) A(–k,2k), B(2k,k + 4), P(3k – 1,1), Q(k – 1,13)

8. The points A(k + 1,1), B(3,5) and C(4,k) form a right-angled triangle. If $\angle$ABC = 90º, find the value of k.

9. Find the gradient of the line which is perpendicular to PQ where
   (a) P is (3,–2) and Q is (0,4),
   (b) P is (–3,–3) and Q is (2,4).

10. The vertices of triangle ABC are A(–2,–4), B(2,–1) and C(5,–5).
    (a) Show that the triangle is right-angled.
    (b) Find the gradient of the altitude through B.

11. CD is the perpendicular bisector of the line joining A(2,3) and B(5,7).
    (a) State
        (i) the coordinates of the point where CD intersects AB,
        (ii) the gradient of CD.
    (b) If the point (p,q) lies on CD, find a relationship between p and q.

12. (a) Show that the point (7,1) lies on the perpendicular bisector of the line joining (2,4) and (4,6).
    (b) The point $(a,4)$ also lies on this bisector. Find the value of a.

13. Find the equation of the line which is
    (a) parallel to $2x + y = 3$ and passes through (0,1),
    (b) parallel to $3x – y = 5$ and passes through (–2,–1),
    (c) perpendicular to $2x + y = 0$ and passes through (–1,–2),
    (d) perpendicular to $4x + 3y = 1$ and passes through (0,–2).

14. A line is drawn through the point (–1,2) parallel to the line $y + 5x = 2$. Find its equation and that of the perpendicular line through the same point.

15. (a) Find the equation of the line through (–3,–1) and perpendicular to a line with gradient $-\frac{1}{3}$.
    (b) P(0,9) and Q(6,0) are two points. A line is drawn from the origin perpendicular to PQ. Find the equation of this perpendicular line.
    (c) From the point (2,5), a perpendicular is drawn to the line joining (–1,–4) and (5,2). Find the equation of this perpendicular.

16. Find the equation of the perpendicular bisector of the line joining A(–3,3) and B(1,–5).

17. A(3,1) and B(0,6) are two points. BC is perpendicular to AB and meets the x-axis at C. Find
    (a) the equation of BC,
    (b) the coordinate of C,
    (c) the area of triangle ABC.

18. The diagram shows a triangle ABC, where A is (6,9), B(–2,3) and C is $(h,–5)$.
    Given that AB = BC, and that h is positive,
    (a) find the value of h,
    (b) show that angle ABC = 90°.

The midpoint of AB is M. The line through M, parallel to BC, meets AC at the point P and the *x*-axis at the point Q.

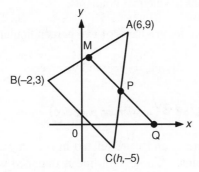

Find

(c) the coordinates of M, P and Q,

(d) the ratio MP:PQ. (C)

19.

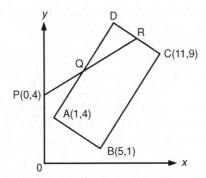

ABCD is a rectangle where A is (1,4), B(5,1) and C is (11,9). The midpoint of AD is Q. The point P is (0,4) and PQ produced meets CD at R.

Calculate

(a) the coordinates of D and of Q,

(b) the equation of PR and of CD,

(c) the coordinates of R,

(d) the length of QD and of DR,

(e) the area of triangle QDR. (C)

Summary

1. X and Y are expressions in x and/or y. When Y is plotted against X and a straight line graph is obtained, the equation of the straight line can be written in the form

$$Y = mX + c$$

where m is the gradient of the straight line, and c is the Y-intercept.

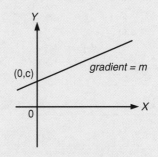

Fig. 8.12

2. Given $A(x_1, y_1)$ and $B(x_2, y_2)$, then $AB = \sqrt{(x_2 - x_1)^2 + (y_2 - y_1)^2}$.

3. Midpoint of (x_1,y_1) and (x_2,y_2) is $(\dfrac{x_1 + x_2}{2}, \dfrac{y_1 + y_2}{2})$.

4. Parallel lines have equal gradients.

5. If m_1 and m_2 are gradients of two perpendicular lines, then

$$m_1 m_2 = -1 \quad \text{and vice versa.}$$

Revision Exercise 8 (Answers on page 500)

1. The variables x and y are related in such a way that when $y - x$ is plotted against x^2, a straight line is obtained which passes through $(2,-3)$ and $(8,0)$. Express y in terms of x and sketch the graph of y against x.

2. The variables x and y are related in such a way that when $\dfrac{1}{y}$ is plotted against x, a straight line is obtained which has a gradient of $-\dfrac{1}{4}$ and passes through $(1,1)$. Express y in terms of x.

   When y is plotted against xy, a straight line graph is obtained. Find the gradient of the line.

3. Express the equation $y^2 = ax^{3b}$ in a form suitable for drawing a straight line graph. State the variables to be plotted on each axis and explain how the constants a and b can be obtained from the graph.

4. The variables x and y are related by the equation $y^2 = px^q$. When the graph of lg y against lg x is drawn, the resulting straight line has a gradient of -2 and an intercept of 0.5 on the axis of lg y. Calculate the value of p and of q. (C)

5. The table shows the experimental values of the two variables x and y.

x	5	10	15	20	25
y	319	113	40	14	5

   It is known that x and y are related by the equation $y = A10^{-kx}$ where A and k are constants.
   Using graph paper, plot lg y against x for the above data and use your graph to estimate the value of A and of b.

6. The quantities p and v are related by the equation $pv^n = a$ where a and n are constants. The following values of p and v were found:

p	0.9	2.7	5.4	8.7
v	5	2.4	1.5	1.1

   Convert the equation to linear form and draw the straight line graph. Using the graph, estimate the value of a and of n.

7. The variables x and y are related by the equation $ay = (\sqrt{x} - 1)^b$, where a and b are constants. Some values of x and y were found and are shown in the following table:

x	4	6	9	12	16
y	0.25	0.32	0.41	0.47	0.54

By drawing a suitable straight line graph, estimate the values of a and b.

8. The table shows the experimental values of the two variables x and y.

x	1	2	2.5	3
y	2.12	2.86	3.44	4.18

It is known that x and y are related by the equation $ay^2 - bx^3 = 1$. By plotting y^2 against x^3, obtain a straight line to represent the above data.

Use your graph to estimate the value of a and of b.

By drawing a suitable straight line, find the value of x and of y which satisfy the following simultaneous equations:

$$ay^2 - bx^3 = 1$$
$$y^2 - x^3 = 1 \qquad\qquad\text{(C)}$$

9. The coordinates of A and C are $(-6,-3)$ and $(-1,1)$ respectively.
   (a) If C is the midpoint of AB, find the coordinates of B.
   (b) BF is divided into three equal parts at D and E. If the coordinates of E are $(6,-1)$, find the coordinates of D and F.

10. The points A$(-1,4)$, B$(4,10)$, C$(6,-5)$ and D$(-2,-8)$ form a quadrilateral ABCD. P, Q, R and S are the midpoints of the sides AB, BC, CD and DA respectively. Prove that PQRS is a parallelogram.

11. The points A$(-1,10)$ and C$(3,2)$ are opposite corners of a rhombus ABCD. The point B lies on the x-axis and E is the midpoint of AC. Find the coordinates of the points, E, B and D. (C)

12. Find the gradient of a line perpendicular to the longest side of the triangle formed by A$(-3,4)$, B$(5,2)$ and C$(0,-3)$.

13. A$(-1,-2)$, B$(b,1)$ and C$(6,-3)$ are three points and AB is perpendicular to BC.
    (a) State, in terms of b, the gradients of AB and BC.
    (b) Hence show that $(b + 1)(b - 6) = -12$.
    (c) Now find the two possible values of b.

14. A semicircle with centre O (the origin) and radius 5 units, meets the x-axis at A and B, and the positive y-axis at C.
  (a) State the coordinates of A, B and C.
  (b) If a point (x,y) lies on the semicircle, show that $x^2 + y^2 = 25$.
  (c) Verify that the point P(−3,4) lies on the semicircle and show by using gradients that $\angle APB = 90°$.

15. A(−1,2) and C(3,4) are opposite vertices of a rhombus ABCD. Find
  (a) the coordinates of the point where the diagonals intersect,
  (b) the gradient of AC,
  (c) the equation of the diagonal BD.

16. The side BC of a triangle ABC lies on the line $2x - 3y = 4$. A is the point (2,3). Find the equation of the altitude through A.

17. A line through (3,1) has gradient $m\left(> \dfrac{1}{3}\right)$. It meets the x-axis at A and the y-axis at B. From A and B, perpendiculars to the line are drawn to meet the y-axis at C and the x-axis at D respectively. Show that the gradient of CD is $\dfrac{1}{m^3}$.

18. A(x_1,y_1), B(x_2,y_2), C(x_3,y_3) and D(x_4,y_4) are the vertices of a parallelolgram ABCD.
  (a) Show that $x_1 + x_3 = x_2 + x_4$ and $y_1 + y_3 = y_2 + y_4$.
  (b) If ABCD is a rhombus, show that
  $(x_1 - x_3)(x_2 - x_4) + (y_1 - y_3)(y_2 - y_4) = 0$.
  (c) However if ABCD is a rectangle, show that
  $x_1x_3 + y_1y_3 = x_2x_4 + y_2y_4$.

19. A is the point (−1,6). Lines are drawn through A with gradients 3 and −2, meeting the x-axis at B and C respectively. BD is perpendicular to AB and CD is perpendicular to AC.
  Calculate
  (a) the coordinates of B and of C,
  (b) the equation of BD and of CD,
  (c) the coordinates of D,
  (d) the ratio BD:CD.

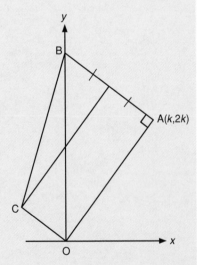

Fig. 8.13

20. Fig. 8.13 shows the quadrilateral OABC. The coordinates of A are $(k,2k)$ where $k > 0$, and the length of OA is $\sqrt{80}$ units.
  (a) Calculate the value of k.
  (b) If AB is perpendicular to OA and B lies on the y-axis, find the equation of AB and the coordinates of B.
  (c) If the point C lies on the line through O, parallel to $y + 3x = 5$ and is also on the perpendicular bisector of AB,
    (i) calculate the coordinates of C,
    (ii) find the ratio OA:AB. (C)

Chapter 9

Circular Measure

The practical unit of measurement for angles is degree (°) which is $\frac{1}{360}$ of a complete revolution. The number 360 comes from Babylonian times but it is an arbitrary choice. There is another system of measurement called **circular** or **radian** measure which is more suitable for further mathematics, particularly in Calculus. This system does not depend on the choice of any particular number.

9.1 Radian Measure

9.1.1 Definition of Radian

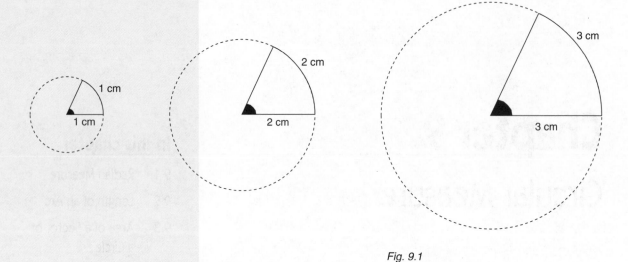

Fig. 9.1

Fig. 9.1 shows three circles of radii 1 cm, 2 cm and 3 cm having arc lengths of 1 cm, 2 cm and 3 cm respectively.

> **One radian is the angle made by an arc of length equal to the radius.**

In general, if the arc length is θ times the radius, the angle subtended is θ radian, i.e. angle subtended at centre = $\dfrac{\text{arc length}}{\text{radius}}$ (Fig. 9.2),

i.e. $\boxed{\theta = \dfrac{s}{r}}$.

▶ **Example 1**

Find the angle subtended by an arc at the centre.

(a)

(b)

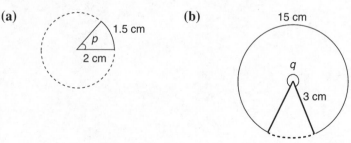

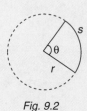

Fig. 9.2

▶ **Solution . . .**

(a) $p = \dfrac{1.5}{2} = 0.75$ rad

(b) $q = \dfrac{15}{3} = 5$ rad

9.1.2 Relationship between Radians and Degrees

In Fig. 9.3,
when arc length AB = r, $\angle$AOB = 1 rad;
when arc length AB = $2r$, $\angle$AOB = 2 rad;
when arc length AB = $2\pi r$, $\angle$AOB = 2π rad.

As the circumference of a circle of radius r has length $2\pi r$ and subtends an angle of $360°$ at the centre, therefore:

$$2\pi \text{ rad} = 360°$$

$$\boxed{\pi \text{ rad} = 180°}$$

$$1 \text{ rad} = \frac{180}{\pi} \approx 57.3°$$

$$1° = \frac{\pi}{180} \approx 0.017\,45 \text{ rad}$$

These values cannot be found exactly as π is an irrational number.

To convert radian measure to degree measure, we multiply the radian measure by a factor of $\dfrac{180}{\pi}$.

Conversely, to convert degree measure to radian measure, we multiply the degree measure by a factor of $\dfrac{\pi}{180}$.

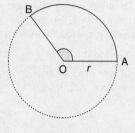

Fig. 9.3

▶ **Example 2**

Convert the following radians to degree measure:

(a) $\dfrac{5\pi}{6}$ rad

(b) 0.8 rad

▶ **Solution . . .**

(a) $\dfrac{5\pi}{6}$ rad $= \dfrac{5\pi}{6} \times \dfrac{180°}{\pi} = 150°$

(b) 0.8 rad $= 0.8 \times \dfrac{180}{\pi} = 45.8°$

▶ **Example 3**

(a) Convert $135°$ to radian measure.
(b) Convert $36°$ to radian measure as a multiple of π.

▶ **Solution . . .**

(a) $135° = 135 \times \dfrac{\pi}{180} = 2.36$ rad

(b) $36° = 36 \times \dfrac{\pi}{180} = \dfrac{\pi}{5}$ rad

Note that when an angle is shown without units, it is assumed to be in radians. Hence sin 0.8 rad is sometimes written as sin 0.8. We can use a calculator to find the values of trigonometrical functions in radians by setting the mode to 'radian'.

▶ **Example 4**

Find the value of

(a) sin 0.4,   (b) cos 2.2,   (c) $\tan \dfrac{5}{3}\pi.$

▶ **Solution . . .**

(a) $\sin 0.4 = 0.389$

(b) $\cos 2.2 = -0.589$

(c) $\tan \dfrac{5}{3}\pi = -1.732$

Exercise 9A (*Answers on page 501*)

1. Find the angle subtended by an arc at the centre.

(a)   4 cm
     5 cm

(b) 9.6 cm 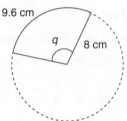 q 8 cm

(c) 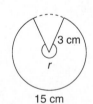 3 cm
     r
     15 cm

2. Covert the following radians to degree measure:

(a) $\dfrac{\pi}{3}$ rad   (b) $\dfrac{2}{3}\pi$ rad   (c) 4π rad

(d) $1\dfrac{5}{6}$ rad   (e) 0.8 rad   (f) 1.25 rad

(g) 4 rad   (h) 12.5 rad

3. Convert the following degrees to radian measure:

(a) 38°   (b) 142°   (c) 60.5°   (d) 605°

4. Convert the following to radian measure as a multiple of π:

    (a) 135°   **(b)** 540°   **(c)** 200°   **(d)** $22\frac{1}{2}°$

5. Find the values of the following:

    (a) $\sin 2$ **(b)** $\cos 0.25$ **(c)** $\tan 1.6$

    (d) $\sin 2\frac{1}{2}$ **(e)** $\cos \dfrac{\pi}{6}$ **(f)** $\cos \dfrac{3}{4}\pi$

    (g) $\tan \dfrac{\pi}{4}$ **(h)** $\sin \dfrac{\pi}{2}$

6. Find the value of $\theta - \sin \theta$ if $\theta = 0.75$ rad.

9.2 Length of an Arc

From the definition of radian (Fig. 9.4), we have

$$\theta = \frac{s}{r}$$

$$\boxed{s = r\theta}$$ where θ is in radians.

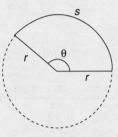

Fig. 9.4

▶ **Example 5**

In each of the following cases, find the arc length, s:

(a) 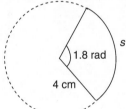   **(b)**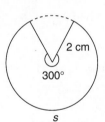

▶ **Solution . . .**

(a) $s = r\theta = 4 \times 1.8 = 7.2$ cm

(b) $300° = 300 \times \dfrac{\pi}{180} = 5.236$ rad

       $s = r\theta = 2 \times 5.236 = 10.47$ cm

▶ **Example 6**

Fig. 9.5 shows the sector AOB of radius 8 cm and a perimeter of 21 cm. Find the angle AOB in radians.

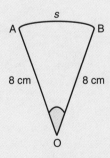

Fig. 9.5

▶ **Solution . . .**

Given   perimeter of sector = 21 cm

              $8 + 8 + s = 21$

                 $s = 5$ cm

From the formula $s = r\theta$

$$\theta = \frac{s}{r}$$

$$= \frac{5}{8}$$

$$= 0.625 \text{ rad}$$

$$\therefore \quad \angle AOB = 0.625 \text{ rad}.$$

▶ **Example 7**

Fig. 9.6 shows a sector OACB of a circle centre O and radius 5 cm. If the length of the chord AB is 8 cm, find

(a) θ in radians,

(b) the length of the arc ACB.

▶ **Solution ...**

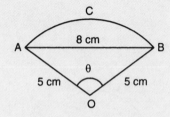

Fig. 9.6

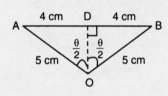

Fig. 9.7

(a) As $\triangle OAB$ is an isosceles triangle (Fig. 9.7), the perpendicular OD bisects $\angle AOB$ and the line AB.

So AD = DB = 4 cm,

and $\angle AOD = \angle DOB = \dfrac{\theta}{2}$ rad.

Hence $\sin \dfrac{\theta}{2} = \dfrac{4}{5}$

$$\frac{\theta}{2} = 0.927 \text{ rad}$$

$$\theta = 1.85 \text{ rad}$$

(b) Length of the arc $= 5 \times 1.85$

$$= 9.25 \text{ cm}$$

Exercise 9B (*Answers on page 501*)

1. In each of the following cases, find the arc length, *s*.

   (a)   (b)   (c)

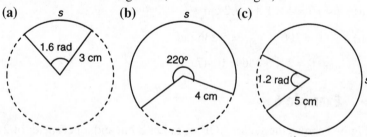

2. The length of an arc in a circle of radius 5 cm is 6 cm. Find the angle subtended at the centre.

3. The angle subtended at the centre of a circle by an arc of length 2π cm is $60°$. Find the radius of the circle.

4. A sector of a circle of radius 4 cm has an angle of 1.2 radians. Find the perimeter of the sector.

5. The perimeter of a sector of a circle of radius 6 cm is 15 cm. Find the angle of the sector.

6. A sector of a circle has radius r cm and angle θ radians. Find the value of θ correct to 3 significant figures if the perimeter of the sector equals half the circumference of the circle.

7. Fig. 9.8 shows a semicircle of centre O. Given the length of the arc AB is 4π cm and angle BOC is $\frac{2}{3}\pi$ radians, find
    (a) the radius of the circle,
    (b) the length of the arc BC.

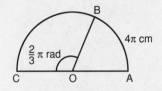

Fig. 9.8

8. A wheel of radius 0.6 m rotates on its axis at a rate of 4.5 radians per second. Calculate the speed at which a point on its rim is moving.

9. In Fig. 9.9, the chord AC of a circle centre O and radius 10 cm is 14 cm. Find
    (a) the angle subtended at the centre of the circle by the chord,
    (b) the length of the arc ABC.

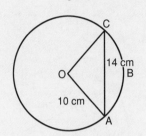

Fig. 9.9

10. Fig. 9.10 shows the cross-section of a tunnel, which is part of a circle of radius 5 m. The width of the floor AB is 8 m.
    Calculate
    (a) the angle subtended at the centre of the circle by the chord AB,
    (b) the length of the arc ACB.

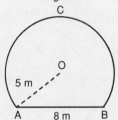

Fig. 9.10

11. In Fig. 9.11, AXB is an arc of a circle centre O and radius 10 cm with $\angle AOB = 0.8$ radians. AYB is an arc of a circle centre P and radius 5 cm with $\angle APB = \theta$.
    Calculate
    (a) the length of the chord AB,
    (b) the value of θ in radians,
    (c) the difference in length between the arcs AYB and AXB.   (C)

9.3 Area of a Sector of a Circle

In the Fig. 9.12, AOB is a sector of angle θ radians in a circle with centre O and radius r.

The area of the sector, A, is proportional to the angle θ subtended at the centre of the circle,

i.e. $\dfrac{\text{area of sector AOB}}{\text{area of circle}} = \dfrac{\text{angle subtended by the arc AB at O}}{\text{angle subtended by the circle at O}}$

$$\frac{A}{\pi r^2} = \frac{\theta}{2\pi}$$

$$A = \frac{1}{2}r^2\theta$$

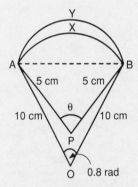

Fig. 9.11

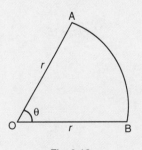

Fig. 9.12

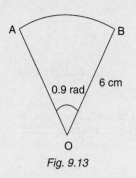

Fig. 9.13

▶ Example 8

Fig. 9.13 shows a sector of radius 6 cm and $\angle AOB = 0.9$ rad. Find the area of the sector.

▶ Solution ...

$$A = \frac{1}{2}r^2\theta$$

$$= \frac{1}{2}(6)^2(0.9)$$

$$= 16.2 \text{ cm}^2$$

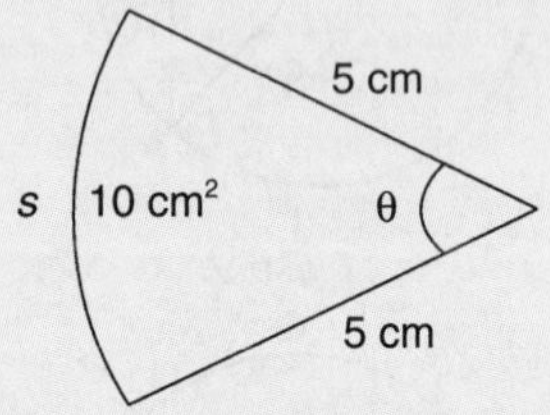

▶ Example 9

Fig. 9.14 shows a sector of radius 5 cm and area of 10 cm². Find the perimeter of the sector.

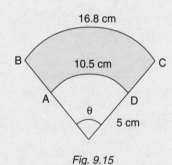

Fig. 9.14

▶ Solution ...

Given area of sector $= 10 \text{ cm}^2$

$$\frac{1}{2}r^2\theta = 10$$

$$\frac{1}{2}(5)^2\theta = 10$$

$$\theta = 0.8 \text{ rad}$$

Arc length $s = r\theta$

$$= 5 \times 0.8$$

$$= 4 \text{ cm}$$

$\therefore$ Perimeter of sector $= 5 + 5 + 4$

$$= 14 \text{ cm}$$

▶ Example 10

In Fig. 9.15, AD and BC are arcs of concentric circles of centre O. The lengths of the arcs AD and BC are 10.5 cm and 16.8 cm respectively, and OD = 5 cm. Calculate the area of the shaded region ABCD.

Fig. 9.15

▶ Solution ...

Given length of arc AD $= 10.5$ cm

$$5\theta = 10.5$$

$$\theta = 2.1 \text{ rad}$$

Given length of arc BC $= 16.8$ cm

$$OC \times 2.1 = 16.8 \text{ cm}$$

$$OC = 8 \text{ cm}$$

Area of sector OBC $= \frac{1}{2} \times 8^2 \times 2.1$

$$= 67.2 \text{ cm}^2$$

Area of sector OAD = $\frac{1}{2} \times 5^2 \times 2.1$

$\qquad\qquad\qquad = 26.25 \text{ cm}^2$

∴ Area of shaded region ABCD

= Area of sector OBC – Area of sector OAD

= 67.2 – 26.25

= 40.95 cm^2

▶ **Example 11**

Fig. 9.16 shows a sector of a circle, centre O, radius 6 cm and $\angle AOB = \frac{3}{5}\pi$ radians. Find the area of the shaded region.

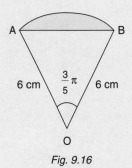

Fig. 9.16

▶ **Solution . . .**

Area of sector AOB = $\frac{1}{2} r^2 \theta$

$\qquad\qquad\qquad = \frac{1}{2} (6)^2 \left(\frac{3}{5}\pi \right)$

$\qquad\qquad\qquad = 33.93 \text{ cm}^2$

Area of $\triangle AOB = \frac{1}{2} \times OA \times OB \times \sin \angle AOB$

$\qquad\qquad\qquad = \frac{1}{2} \times 6 \times 6 \times \sin \frac{3}{5}\pi$

$\qquad\qquad\qquad = 17.12 \text{ cm}^2$

Area of shaded region = Area of sector AOB – Area of $\triangle$ AOB

$\qquad\qquad\qquad = 33.93 - 17.12$

$\qquad\qquad\qquad = 16.81 \text{ cm}^2$

▶ **Example 12**

The diagram shows a semicircle OABC of centre O and radius 5 cm. BN is perpendicular to OA.

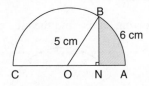

Given that the length of arc AB is 6 cm, find

(a) angle AOB in radians and

(b) the area of the shaded region.

(c) Express the area of the shaded region as a percentage of the area of the semicircle.

► **Solution . . .**

(a) Given length of arc $AB = 6$ cm

$$5\theta = 6$$
$$\theta = 1.2 \text{ rad}$$
$$\therefore \quad \angle AOB = 1.2 \text{ rad}$$

(b) In $\triangle OAB$, $\quad \dfrac{ON}{5} = \cos 1.2$ rad

$$ON = 5 \times \cos 1.2 \text{ rad}$$
$$= 1.81 \text{ cm}$$

Area of $\triangle OBN = \dfrac{1}{2} \times OB \times ON \times \sin \angle AOB$

$$= \dfrac{1}{2} \times 5 \times 1.81 \times \sin 1.2 \text{ rad}$$
$$= 4.22 \text{ cm}^2$$

Area of sector $OAB = \dfrac{1}{2} \times 5^2 \times 1.2$

$$= 15 \text{ cm}^2$$

$\therefore$ Area of shaded region = Area of sector OAB – area of $\triangle OBN$
$$= 15 - 4.22$$
$$= 10.78 \text{ cm}^2$$

(c) Area of semicircle $= \dfrac{1}{2} \times \pi \times 5^2$

$$= 39.28 \text{ cm}^2$$

Area of shaded region as a percentage of area of semicircle

$$= \frac{\text{area of shaded region}}{\text{area of semicircle}} \times 100\%$$

$$= \frac{10.78}{39.28} \times 100\%$$

$$= 27.4\%$$

Exercise 9C (*Answers on page 501*)

1. In each of the following cases, find the area of the sector:

(a) (b) (c)

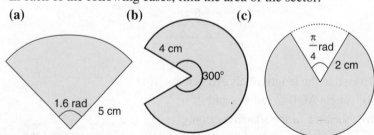

2. The area of a sector of a circle is 9 cm^2. If the radius is 6 cm, find the angle of the sector.

3. A sector of a circle has an angle of 2.25 rad and an area of 112.5 cm^2. Find the radius of the circle.

4. If the area of a sector is 6.4 cm^2 and its angle is 0.8 radians, calculate the perimeter of the sector.

5. The area of a sector of a circle is 15 cm^2 and the length of its arc is 3 cm. Calculate
  (a) the radius of the sector,
  (b) the angle of the sector.

6. The perimeter of a sector is 128 cm and its area is 960 cm^2. Find the possible values of the radius of the sector and its angle.

7. The diagram shows the action of a windscreen wiper of a car. It rotates about O and travels from AB to A′B′ and back. Calculate
  (a) the area AA′B′B swept clear,
  (b) the perimeter of this area.

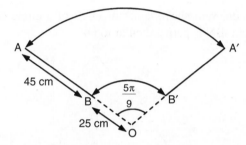

8. In a circle centre O, AOB and COD are two concentric sectors as shown in the figure. The lengths of the arcs AB and DC are 2.8 cm and 2 cm respectively, and AD = 2 cm.
  Calculate
  (a) the length of OC.
  (b) ∠AOB in radians,
  (c) the area of ABCD.

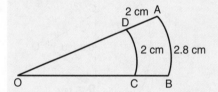

9. In the figure below, O is the centre of the circle containing the sector OAB. DC is a parallel arc and BC = 3 cm.

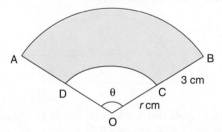

If OC = r cm and ∠AOB = θ rad, show that
  (a) the shaded area = $\dfrac{\theta}{2}(6r + 9)$ cm^2,
  (b) the perimeter of the shaded area equals $6 + \theta(2r + 3)$ cm.
  (c) Given that the shaded area is three-quarters of the area of the sector OAB, find the value of r.
  (d) If, however, the total perimeter of the shaded area equals the total perimeter of the sector OAB, find the value of θ.

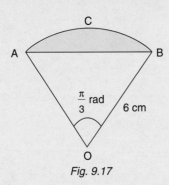

Fig. 9.17

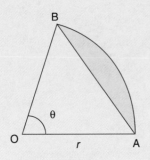

Fig. 9.18

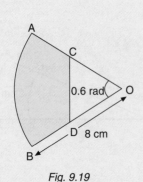

Fig. 9.19

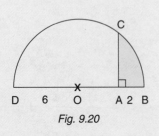

Fig. 9.20

10. Fig. 9.17 shows a sector of a circle of centre O and radius 6 cm. If angle AOB = $\frac{\pi}{3}$ radians, find

(a) the area of sector OACB,

(b) the area of triangle OAB,

(c) the area of the shaded region.

11. Fig. 9.18 shows a sector of a circle, centre O, radius r units and $\angle AOB = \theta$ radians. Show that the area of the segment which is shaded is $\frac{1}{2} r^2(\theta - \sin \theta)$ units^2.

12. In Fig. 9.19, OAB is a sector of a circle centre O and radius 8 cm. The mid-points of OA and OB are C and D respectively. CD is a straight line. Given that $\angle AOB = 0.6$ radians, calculate the area of the shaded region.

13. The diagram shows a sector OAB of a circle centre O and radius 10 cm. BN is perpendicular to OA.

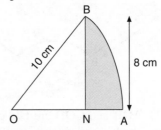

Given that BN = 8 cm, calculate

(a) angle BON in radians,

(b) the area of the shaded region.

14. In the figure below, ADB is a semicircle with centre O and radius 20 cm. DC is perpendicular to AB where C is the mid-point of OB. Calculate

(a) $\angle DOC$ in radians,

(b) the area of the shaded region.

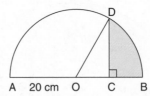

15. In Fig. 9.20, DOBC is a semicircle, centre O and radius 6 cm. CA is perpendicular to DOB where AB is 2 cm.
Calculate

(a) the length of CA,

(b) $\angle COA$ in radians, and

(c) the perimeter of the shaded region.

(d) Express the area of the shaded region as a percentage of the area of the semicircle.

16. In the figure below, the chord AB, of length 8 cm, is parallel to the diameter DOC of the semicircle with centre O and radius 5 cm. Calculate

(a) ∠AOB in radians,

(b) the area of the segment ABE,

(c) what fraction the area of the segment ABE is of the area of the semicircle.

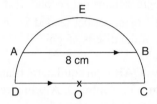

Summary

1. 1 radian is the angle subtended by an arc of the length equal to the radius.

2. π rad = 180°

3. Length of an arc AB is $s = r\theta$.

4. Area of a sector OAB is $A = \frac{1}{2}r^2\theta$, where θ is in radians.

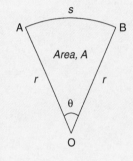

Revision Exercise 9 (*Answers on page 501*)

1. In Fig. 9.21, the area of a sector OAB of a circle, centre O and radius 12 cm, is 150 cm². Find

(a) the angle of the sector in radians,

(b) the length of arc AB.

If the sector is folded up to form a cone, what is the radius of the cone?

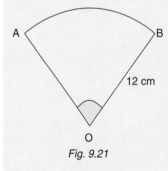

Fig. 9.21

2. A piece of wire, 10 cm long, is formed into the shape of a sector of a circle of radius r cm and angle θ radians.

(a) Show that $\theta = \dfrac{10 - 2r}{r}$.

(b) Show also that the area A cm² of the sector is given by $A = 5r - r^2$.

(c) If $4 \leq A \leq 6$ and $\theta \leq 3$, find the limits within which r must lie.

3. In the figure below, O is the centre of the sector OAB. CD is another arc, with centre O and radius r cm. DB = 2 cm. If the area of ABDC is one-third the area of the sector OCD, find the value of r.

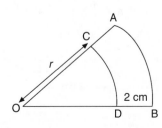

4. OBD is a sector of a circle with centre O and radius 6 cm. $\angle BOD = \dfrac{2\pi}{5}$. A is a point on OB where OA = 2 cm and C is a point on OD such that OC = 4 cm. Find the area of the region bounded by BA, AC, CD and the arc BD.

5. A disc is rotating at $33\dfrac{1}{3}$ revolutions per minute.
    (a) At what rate, in radians per second, is it rotating?
    (b) At what speed, in metres per second, is a point on the rim moving, if the radius of the disc is 15 cm?

6. In the figure below, OAB is an equilateral triangle of side 10 cm. The arc ADB is drawn with centre O. A semicircle is drawn on AB as diameter. Find the area of the shaded region.

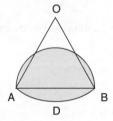

7. A cylindrical barrel floats in water. The diameter of the barrel is 120 cm and its highest point P is 80 cm above the water level AB.
    (a) Calculate $\angle AOB$ in radians, where O is the centre of the circular face.
    (b) What fraction of the volume of the barrel is below the water line?

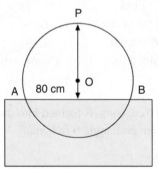

8. Two circle have centres A and B, and radii 5 cm and 12 cm respectively. Calculate the area of the shaded region.

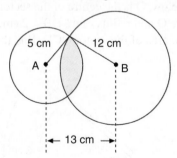

9. ABCD is a square of side 4 cm. Equal arcs AE and EB are drawn with radius 4 cm and centres B and A respectively.

Calculate the area of the shaded region.

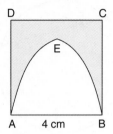

10. In Fig. 9.22, sector OAB has centre O, radius 6 cm and $\angle AOB = \frac{\pi}{3}$ radians. OC is the bisector of $\angle AOB$ and P is the midpoint of OC. An arc DE of a circle is drawn with centre P to meet OA and OB at D and E respectively.

   (a) Find the size of $\angle OPD$.

   (b) Calculate the area of the shaded region.

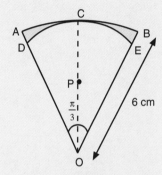

Fig. 9.22

11. A sector of a circle with radius r has a total perimeter of 12 cm. If its area is A cm^2, show that $A = 6r - r^2$. Hence find the value of r for which the value of A is at its maximum and the corresponding value of the angle of the sector in radians.

12. In Fig. 9.23, ABCD is a rhombus of side x and $\angle A = \theta$ radians. Arcs, each of radius $\frac{x}{3}$, are drawn with centres A, B, C and D. If the shaded area is half the area of the rhombus, show that $\sin \theta = \frac{2\pi}{9}$ and find the two possible values of θ.

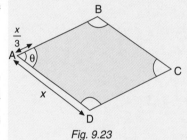

Fig. 9.23

13. A, B and C are three points in that order on the circumference of a circle radius 5 cm. The chords AB and BC have lengths 8 cm and 4 cm respectively. Find the ratio of the areas of the minor segments on AB and BC.

1.

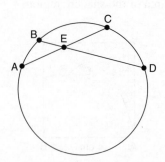

A, B, C and D are four points on a circle such that AC and BD intersects at E and ∠CED = 30°. If the radius of the circle is 3 cm, find the sum of the length of arcs AB and CD.

2. A wheel of radius 20 cm rolls without slipping on level ground. A point P on the rim is in the position P_1 at the start. When the centre of the wheel has moved through 50 cm, P is now in the position P_2. Calculate the angle (in radians) through which the wheel has turned.

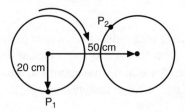

1. (a) The polynomial $2x^3 + x^2 + ax + b$ has $(x - 2)$ as a factor and leaves a remainder of -4 when it is divided by $(x - 1)$. Find the value of a and of b and hence factorize the polynomial.
    (b) Find the value of k for which $x^2 + (k - 1)x + k^2 - 16$ is exactly divisible by $x - 3$ but not divisible by $x + 4$.   (C)

2. (a) Solve the equation $2x^3 - 9x^2 + 12x - 4 = 0$.
    (b) If the remainder when f(x) is divided by $x - 2$ is 3, what is the remainder when f($x + 1$) is divided by $x - 1$?

3. (a) Without using tables or a calculator, find the value of $\log_2 24 - \log_2 6 + \log_4 64 - 2 \log_2 4$.
    (b) Sketch the curve $y = 1 + e^x$.

4. (a) Find x if $(1.2)^x = (2.1)^{2x-1}$.
    (b) Solve the equation $\log_5 x + \log_5 (6x - 5) = 2$.

5. (a) Solve the equation $3^{2x+2} - 10(3^x) + 1 = 0$.
    (b) On the same axes, draw the graphs of $y = \ln(1 + x)$ and $y = \dfrac{1}{x}$ for $\dfrac{1}{2} \le x \le 4$. From your graph, find approximately
         (i) the solution of the equation $x \ln(1 + x) = 1$,
         (ii) the value of $e^{\frac{1}{2}}$.

6. The perimeter of a sector of a circle is 8 cm and its area is 4 cm^2. Find (a) the angle of the sector, (b) the length of its arc.

7. Figure R3.1 shows two sectors OABC and ODE with centre O. It is given that angle AOB = 0.8 rad, OC = 10 cm, and the lengths of the arcs AB and BC are equal. The areas of the sectors OABC and ODE are also equal.
    Find (a) the length of the arc DE, (b) the area of the shaded region.

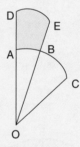

Fig. R3.1

8. Figure R3.2 shows part of a straight line graph obtained by plotting lg y against lg x. Given that the length of AB is 10 units,
    (a) find the coordinates of A,
    (b) obtain an expression for y in terms of x,
    (c) calculate the value of y when $x = 256$.

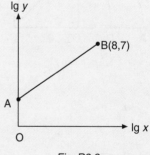

Fig. R3.2

9. The values of x and y in the table below are believed to fit the equation $y = ax^n$.

x	1.5	1.7	1.9	2.1	2.3
y	8.6	10.4	12.3	14.3	16.4

By drawing a suitable straight line graph, estimate the values of a and n to 2 significant figures.

10. (a) When $\ln y$ is plotted against x for a certain function, a straight line is obtained passing through the points $(1,3)$ and $(3,-1)$. Express y in terms of x.

(b) A production line assembling computers is to be run down. Production started at 500 per week but this is reduced by 15% each week. When production first reaches 100 or fewer computers in a week, the line will be shut down at the end of that week. For how many weeks will it be operated?

(c) Solve the equation $x^3 + 12 = x^2 + 8x$.

Revision Paper 4 (Answers on page 512)

1. Given that $2x^3 + ax^2 + bx + 6$ has factors $(2x - 1)$ and $(x + 2)$, find the value of a and of b. With these values, find the remaining factor.

2. Solve the equation $8x^3 - 2x^2 - 5x - 1 = 0$. Hence find the values of θ, between $0°$ and $180°$, which satisfy the equation
$8\tan^2\theta - 2\tan\theta - 5 = \cot\theta$.   (C)

3. (a) Given that $1 - \log_{10}y = 2\log_{10}x$, express y in terms of x.

(b) Solve the equation $\log_{\sqrt{x}} 27 = \log_{\sqrt{x}} 3 - 2$.

4. Solve the equations
(a) $3^{x-1} = 2^{x+1}$,   **(b)** $e^{2x} - e^x - 6 = 0$.

5. Using graph paper, draw the curve $y = \ln(x + 2)$ for $-1 \le x \le 3$, taking values of x at unit intervals.
By drawing the appropriate straight line, obtain an approximate value of the solution of the equation $\sqrt{x+2} = e^{1-x}$.   (C)

6. Given that $\log_a 5 = 0.774$. Without using tables or calculators,
(a) find the values of $\log_a 125a^2$.
(b) solve the equation $\sqrt{5} \times a^{n+1} = 5$.

7. The variables x and y are related by the equation $p\sqrt{x} + qy^2 = 1$. When a graph of y^2 against $\sqrt{x}$ is drawn, a straight line is obtained which passes through the point $(2,3)$.
(a) Given that the gradient of this line is $\dfrac{5}{3}$, calculate the values of p and q.
(b) Given also that this line passes through $(4,k)$, find the value of k.

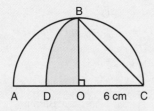

Fig. R4.1

8. In Fig. R4.1, OABC is a semicircle, centre O and radius 6 cm. BO is perpendicular to AC. Given that BD is an arc of a circle, centre C, find, in terms of π,
(a) the length of the arc BD,   **(b)** the area of the shaded region.

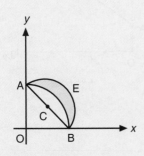

Fig. R4.2

9. In Fig. R4.2, AEB is a semicircle, centre C and ADB is an arc of a circle, centre O. The equation of the line AB is $x + y = 6$. Find, in terms of π,
(a) the length of the arc ADB,
(b) the area of the shaded region.

Chapter 10
Trigonometry

Use your graphic calculator to find out the shapes of the following graphs for the domain $0° \leq x \leq 360°$:

(1) $y = \sin x$
(2) $y = \cos x$
(3) $y = \tan x$

Now explore and compare the graphs of

(4) $y = \sin 2x$
(5) $y = \sin 3x$

with respect to the graph of $y = \sin x$ in the same domain.

The above activities will come in handy later in the chapter.

10.1   Trigonometric Function for a General Angle

You have already been introduced to the trigonometric functions sine, cosine and tangent of an acute angle θ as ratios of the sides of a right-angled triangle.

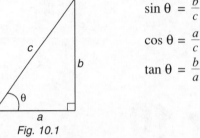

$$\sin \theta = \frac{b}{c}$$

$$\cos \theta = \frac{a}{c}$$

$$\tan \theta = \frac{b}{a}$$

Fig. 10.1

We now extend the definition for sine, cosine and tangent to cover a general angle.

Consider an arm OR of unit length (Fig. 10.2) that rotates about O (the origin in the Cartesian coordinate axes) in an anticlockwise direction, and makes an angle θ with the positive *x*-axis. The complete revolution is divided by the *x*-axis and *y*-axis into 4 quadrants. Let the coordinates of R be (*x,y*).

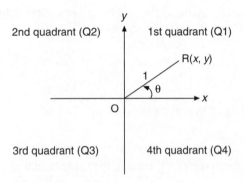

Fig. 10.2

We now revise our definitions as follows:

$$\sin \theta = \frac{y\text{ - coordinate of R}}{1}$$

$$\cos \theta = \frac{x\text{ - coordinate of R}}{1}$$

$$\tan \theta = \frac{y\text{ - coordinate of R}}{x\text{ - coordinate of R}}$$

You will see that for θ in the first quadrant, the revised definitions fit in nicely with the previous definitions for an acute angle using the right-angled triangle.

By drawing the right-angled triangle OPR,

we note that $\sin \theta = \dfrac{y}{1}$

$\cos \theta = \dfrac{x}{1}$

$\tan \theta = \dfrac{y}{x}$

These results are identical to those of the revised definitions.

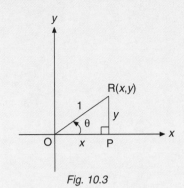

Fig. 10.3

10.2 Signs of Trigonometric Functions

In the first quadrant (Fig. 10.4), both the x-coordinate and the y-coordinate are positive.

Hence,

$$\sin \theta = \frac{y}{1} = \frac{\text{positive}}{1} = \text{positive}$$

$$\cos \theta = \frac{x}{1} = \frac{\text{positive}}{1} = \text{positive}$$

$$\tan \theta = \frac{y}{x} = \frac{\text{positive}}{\text{positive}} = \text{positive}$$

We observe that ALL the three functions have positive values when θ is in the first quadrant.

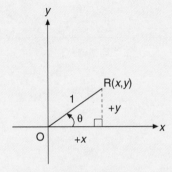

Fig. 10.4

In the second quadrant (Fig. 10.5), the x-coordinate is negative while the y-coordinate is positive.

Hence,

$$\sin \theta = \frac{y}{1} = \frac{\text{positive}}{1} = \text{positive}$$

$$\cos \theta = \frac{-x}{1} = \frac{\text{negative}}{1} = \text{negative}$$

$$\tan \theta = \frac{y}{-x} = \frac{\text{positive}}{\text{negative}} = \text{negative}$$

We observe that only the *sine* value is positive while the values of both cosine and tangent are negative when θ is in the second quadrant.

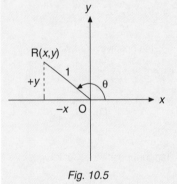

Fig. 10.5

In the third quadrant (Fig. 10.6), both the x-coordinate and y-coordinate are negative.

Hence,

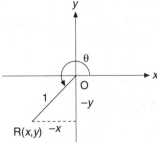

Fig. 10.6

$$\sin \theta = \frac{-y}{1} = \frac{\text{negative}}{1} = \text{negative}$$

$$\cos \theta = \frac{-x}{1} = \frac{\text{negative}}{1} = \text{negative}$$

$$\tan \theta = \frac{-y}{1} = \frac{\text{negative}}{\text{negative}} = \text{positive}$$

We observe that only the *tangent* value is positive while the values of both sine and cosine are negative when θ is in the third quadrant.

In the fourth quadrant (Fig. 10.7) the *x*-coordinate is positive while the *y*-coordinate is negative.

Hence,

$$\sin \theta = \frac{-y}{1} = \frac{\text{negative}}{1} = \text{negative}$$

$$\cos \theta = \frac{x}{1} = \frac{\text{positive}}{1} = \text{positive}$$

$$\tan \theta = \frac{-y}{x} = \frac{\text{negative}}{\text{positive}} = \text{negative}$$

We observe that only the *cosine* value is positive while the values of both sine and tangent are negative when θ is in the fourth quadrant.

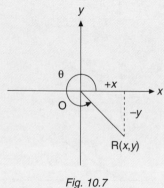

Fig. 10.7

We now summarise the above results as follows:

For θ in Q_1 (first quadrant), **A**ll sin θ, cos θ and tan θ are positive.

For θ in Q_2, only **S**in θ is positive.

For θ in Q_3, only **T**an θ is positive.

For θ in Q_4, only **C**os θ is positive.

Note:

The sentence 'All Science Teachers are Crazy' will help you remember the positive ratios.

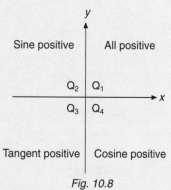

Fig. 10.8

10.3 Note on Special Angles 30°, 45°, 60°

As these angles are often used, it will be useful for future work to have their trigonometrical ratios in fractional form.

Special angle: 45°

In Fig. 10.9(a), ABC is an isosceles right-angled triangle with AB = BC = 1. Hence AC = $\sqrt{2}$, and $\angle A = \angle C = 45°$.

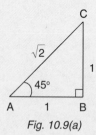

Fig. 10.9(a)

Then
$$\sin 45° = \frac{1}{\sqrt{2}} = \cos 45°$$
$$\tan 45° = 1$$

Special angles: 30°, 60°

In Fig. 10.9(b), ABC is an equilateral triangle with side 2. CD is the perpendicular bisector of AB, so AD = 1 and CD = $\sqrt{3}$.
∠A = 60° and ∠ACD = 30°.

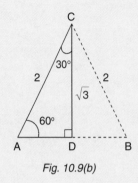

Fig. 10.9(b)

Then

$$\sin 60° = \cos 30° = \frac{\sqrt{3}}{2}$$
$$\sin 30° = \cos 60° = \frac{1}{2}$$
$$\tan 60° = \sqrt{3}, \tan 30° = \frac{1}{\sqrt{3}}$$

10.4 Negative Angles

In the discussion in section 10.1, the angle θ is the angle of rotation of the arm OR in an anticlockwise direction from the positive *x*-axis. If the arm OR rotates in a clockwise direction (see Fig. 10.10), it will describe a **negative** angle, –θ.

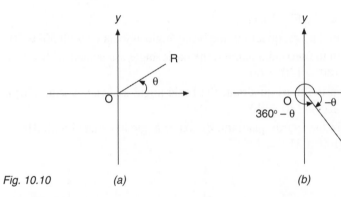

Fig. 10.10   (a)   (b)

We note that the position of the arm OR describing angle –θ is the same as that describing angle 360° – θ (or 2π – θ in radians).

Hence, to find the value of a trigonometric function of a negative angle –θ, we can find the corresponding value of the positive angle 360° – θ.

Thus,
$$\sin(-30°) = \sin(360° - 30°)$$
$$= \sin 330°$$
$$\cos(-120°) = \cos(360° - 120°)$$
$$= \cos 240°$$
$$\tan(-200°) = \tan(360° - 200°)$$
$$= \tan 160°$$
$$\tan(-\frac{\pi}{3}) = \tan(2\pi - \frac{\pi}{3})$$
$$= \tan(\frac{5\pi}{3})$$
and so on.

In general,

$$\sin(-\theta) = (-\sin\theta)$$
$$\cos(-\theta) = \cos\theta$$
$$\tan(-\theta) = -\tan\theta$$

10.5 Basic Angles

The basic angle is the acute angle between an arm OR and the *x*-axis. In Fig. 10.11, α_1, α_2, α_3 and α_4 are basic angles in the four quadrants.

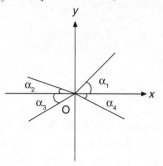

Fig. 10.11

For example (see Fig. 10.12),

(a) in the first quadrant, the basic angle associated with 30° is 30°;

(b) in the second quadrant, the basic angle associated with 120° is $180° - 120° = 60°$;

(c) in the third quadrant, the basic angle associated with 220° is $220° - 180° = 40°$;

and (d) in the fourth quadrant, the basic angle associated with 310° is $360° - 310° = 50°$.

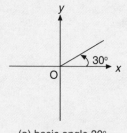 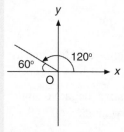 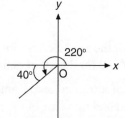 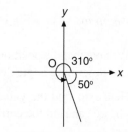

(a) basic angle 30° (b) basic angle 60° (c) basic angle 40° (d) basic angle 50°

Fig. 10.12

10.6 Trigonometric Ratio of a General Angle θ, in terms of its associated Basic Angle α

In the first quadrant (Fig. 10.13), the arm OR = 1 unit, where R is (a,b) with $a > 0$ and $b > 0$. The basic angle $\alpha = \theta$.

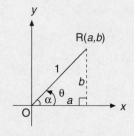

Fig. 10.13

We have:

$$\sin \theta = \frac{b}{1} = \sin \alpha$$

$$\cos \theta = \frac{a}{1} = \cos \alpha$$

$$\tan \theta = \frac{b}{a} = \tan \alpha$$

In the second quadrant (Fig. 10.14), the basic angle $\alpha = 180° - \theta$, and R is $(-a,b)$.

We have:

$$\sin \theta = \frac{b}{1} = \sin \alpha$$

$$\cos \theta = \frac{-a}{1} = -\cos \alpha$$

$$\tan \theta = \frac{b}{-a} = -\tan \alpha$$

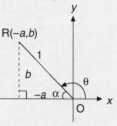

Fig. 10.14

In the third quadrant (Fig. 10.15), the basic angle $\alpha = \theta - 180°$, and R is $(-a,-b)$.

We have:

$$\sin \theta = \frac{-b}{1} = -\sin \alpha$$

$$\cos \theta = \frac{-a}{1} = -\cos \alpha$$

$$\tan \theta = \frac{-b}{-a} = \frac{b}{a} = \tan \alpha$$

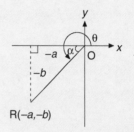

Fig. 10.15

In the fourth quadrant (Fig. 10.16), the basic angle $\alpha = 360° - \theta$, and R is $(a, -b)$.

We have:

$$\sin \theta = \frac{-b}{1} = -\sin \alpha$$

$$\cos \theta = \frac{a}{1} = \cos \alpha$$

$$\tan \theta = \frac{-b}{a} = -\tan \alpha$$

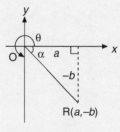

Fig. 10.16

In summary, the trigonometric ratio of a general angle θ can be obtained from the corresponding trigonometric ratio of the basic angle α, with its sign determined by the rule discussed in section 10.2.

▶ **Example 1**

Express the following trigonometric ratios in terms of basic angles and find their values:

(a) $\sin 160°$ **(b)** $\cos 256°$ **(c)** $\tan 330°$

▶ **Solution . . .**

(a) Basic angle associated with $160° = 180° - 160°$
$$= 20°$$
$\sin 160° = \sin 20°$ ($160°$ is in Q_2, where sine is positive)
$$= 0.3420$$

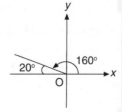

(b) Basic angle associated with $256° = 256° - 180°$
$$= 76°$$
$\cos 256° = -\cos 76°$ ($256°$ is in Q_3, where cosine is negative)
$$= -0.2756$$

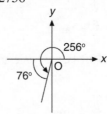

(c) Basic angle associated with $330° = 360° - 330$
$$= 30°$$
$\tan 330° = -\tan 30°$ ($330°$ is in Q_4, where tangent is negative)
$$= -\frac{1}{\sqrt{3}} \text{ (if exact value is required)}$$
or -0.5774 (from calculator)

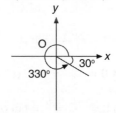

Note:
The actual values of $\sin \theta$, $\cos \theta$ and $\tan \theta$ can be found directly using a calculator, given θ. (Verify the above cases.) However, the concept of basic angles is important when we wish to solve trigonometric equations as we shall see in the next section.

10.7   Basic Trigonometric Equations

A basic trigonometric equation is an equation which involves one trigonometric function, such as $\sin \theta = 0.5$, $\cos \theta = -0.4415$ or $\tan \theta = 1.725$.

A basic equation in θ usually has two solutions for the range $0° \leq \theta \leq 360°$. Unless their values are exact, angles in degrees are to be given to one decimal place in the answers while retaining 2 decimal places in the working stage.

To solve a basic equation, such as $\sin \theta = k$:

Step 1:   Find the basic angle α for which $\sin \alpha = |k|$
            (i.e. take the absolute or positive value of k).

Step 2:   Find the quadrants in which θ will lie by considering the sign of k.

Step 3:   Determine the corresponding angles for those quadrants.

Steps involved in solving basic equations $\cos \theta = k$ or $\tan \theta = k$ are similar.

▶ **Example 2**

Solve   **(a)** $\sin \theta = 0.57$,

        (b) $\sin \theta = -0.38$ for $0° \leq \theta \leq 360°$.

▶ **Solution . . .**

(a)   Basic angle α is given by

       $\sin \alpha = 0.57$

         $\alpha = 34.75°$

θ will lie in Q_1 and Q_2 (because $\sin \theta$ is positive).

Hence, $\theta = 34.75°$ (for Q_1)   or $180° - 34.75°$ (for Q_2)

                                        $= 145.25°$

The solutions are $34.8°$ and $145.3°$.

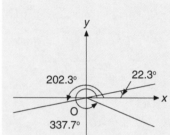

(b)   Basic angle α is given by

       $\sin \alpha = +0.38$ (taking positive value as $|-0.38| = +0.38$)

         $\alpha = 22.33°$

θ will lie in Q_3 and Q_4 (because $\sin \theta$ is negative).

Hence, $\theta = 180° + 22.33°$ (for Q_3)   or $360° - 22.33°$ (for Q_4)

          $= 202.33°$ $= 337.67°$

The solutions are $202.3°$ and 337.7^0.

▶ **Example 3**

Solve   **(a)** $\cos \theta = -0.381\,4$,

        (b) $\tan \theta = 1.25$ for $0° \leq \theta \leq 360°$.

▶ **Solution . . .**

(a)   Basic angle α is given by

$\cos \alpha = +0.381\,4$

   $\alpha = 67.58°$

θ will lie in Q_2 and Q_3 (because $\cos \theta$ is negative).

Hence, $\theta = 180° - 67.58°$ (for Q_2) or $180^0 + 67.58°$ (for Q_3)

       $= 112.4°$ $= 247.6°$ (to 1 decimal place)

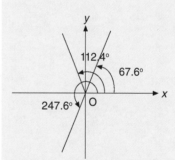

(b)   Basic angle α is given by

$\tan \theta = 1.25$

$\theta = 51.34°$

θ will lie in Q_1 and Q_3 (because $\tan \theta$ is positive).

Hence $\theta = 51.34°$ (for Q_1)   or $180° + 51.34°$ (for Q_3)

       $= 51.3°$ $= 231.3°$ (to 1 decimal place)

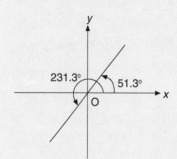

With sufficient practice, most of the work can be done mentally and the written work can be reduced to a couple of lines. For example, part (a) can be presented briefly as follows:

$$\cos \theta = -0.3814$$

$$\theta = 180° - 67.58° \qquad \text{or} \qquad 180° + 67.58°$$
$$= 112.4° \qquad \qquad \qquad = 247.6° \text{ (to 1 decimal place)}$$

We will use the shortened presentation in subsequent examples.

Most trigonometric equations can be reduced to one or more basic equations and therefore can be solved in the same way, as we shall see in the next few examples.

▶ **Example 4**

Solve the equation $3\cos^2\theta + 2\cos\theta = 0$ for $0° \le \theta \le 360°$.

▶ **Solution . . .**

$$3\cos^2\theta + 2\cos\theta = 0 \quad [\text{Note: } \cos^2\theta = (\cos\theta)^2]$$

By factorising, $\quad \cos\theta(3\cos\theta + 2) = 0$,
which separates into 2 basic equations:

$$\cos\theta = 0 \quad \text{or} \quad 3\cos\theta + 2 = 0$$

$$\text{i.e. } \cos\theta = \frac{-2}{3}$$
$$= -0.6667.$$

For $\cos\theta = 0$, $\theta = 90°$ or $270°$.
For $\cos\theta = -0.666\,7$, ($\alpha = 48.19$, $\theta \in Q_2$ and Q_3)

$$\theta = 180° - 48.19° \qquad \text{or} \qquad 180° + 44.19°$$
$$= 131.81° \qquad \qquad \qquad = 224.19°$$

Hence, the solutions are $90°$, $131.8°$, $224.2°$ and $270°$.

Note:

Do not divide the original equation by a factor containing the unknown angle (in this case, $\cos\theta$), as doing so would mean omitting an equation (in this case, $\cos\theta = 0$) and consequently missing some solutions.

▶ **Example 5**

For $0° \le \theta \le 360°$, solve $6\cos^2\theta + \cos\theta = 1$.

▶ **Solution . . .**

This is a quadratic equation in $\cos\theta$:

$$6\cos^2\theta + \cos\theta - 1 = 0$$

and so $\quad (3\cos\theta - 1)(2\cos\theta + 1) = 0$,
which separates into $\cos\theta = 0.3333$ and $\cos\theta = -0.5$.

Verify that the solutions are $\theta = 70.5°$, $120°$, $240°$ and $289.5°$.

▶ **Example 6**

Solve the equation $\sin(\theta - 30°) = 0.4$ for $0° \le \theta \le 360°$.

▶ **Solution . . .**

Write $\phi = \theta - 30°$.
Then $\sin \phi = 0.4$.
Solve for ϕ.
Verify that $\phi = 23.6°$ and $156.4°$.
Then $\theta = 53.6°$ and $186.4°$.

10.8 Other Trigonometric Functions

There are three other functions which are the reciprocals of the sine, cosine and tangent. They are

cosecant: $\text{cosec}\,\theta = \dfrac{1}{\sin\theta}$

secant: $\sec\theta = \dfrac{1}{\cos\theta}$

cotangent: $\cot\theta = \dfrac{1}{\tan\theta}$

▶ **Example 7**

Solve **(a)** $\text{cosec}\,\theta = -1.58$, **(b)** $4\cot\theta = \tan\theta$, for $0° \le \theta \le 360°$.

▶ **Solution . . .**

(a) Replace $\text{cosec}\,\theta$ by $\dfrac{1}{\sin\theta}$.

$\dfrac{1}{\sin\theta} = -1.58$ so $\sin\theta = -\dfrac{1}{1.58} = -0.632\,9$

Now verify that $\theta = 219.3°$ or $320.7°$.

(b) Replace $\cot\theta$ by $\dfrac{1}{\tan\theta}$.

Then $\dfrac{4}{\tan\theta} = \tan\theta$, i.e., $\tan^2\theta = 4$.

So $\tan\theta = \pm 2$ (**Note:** Don't forget the negative root.)
Verify that the solutions of these equations are $63.4°$, $116.6°$, $243.4°$ and $296.6°$.

Exercise 10A (Answers on page 501)

1. Solve the following equations for $0° \le \theta \le 360°$:

(a) $\sin\theta = \dfrac{1}{3}$	**(b)** $\cos\theta = 0.762$	**(c)** $\tan\theta = 1.15$
(d) $\cos\theta = -0.35$	**(e)** $\sin\theta = -0.25$	**(f)** $\tan\theta = -0.81$
(g) $\sin\theta = -0.117\,8$	**(h)** $\sin\theta = -0.65$	**(i)** $\cos\theta = 0.23$
(j) $\tan\theta = -1.5$	**(k)** $\text{cosec}\,\theta = 1.75$	**(l)** $\cos\theta = -0.14$
(m) $\sec\theta = -1.15$	**(n)** $\cot\theta = 0.54$	**(o)** $\sec\theta = 2.07$

2. Find all the angles between 0° and 180° which satisfy the equations
   (a) $\sin x = 0.45$,   **(b)** $\cos y = -0.63$,   **(c)** $\tan \theta = 2.15$.

3. Solve the following equations for $0° \leq \theta \leq 360°$:
   (a) $5 \sin^2 \theta = 2 \sin \theta$ **(b)** $9 \tan \theta = \cot \theta$
   (c) $3 \tan^2 \theta + 5 \tan \theta = 2$ **(d)** $4 \cos^2 \theta + 3 \cos \theta = 0$
   (e) $5 \sin^2 \theta = 2$ **(f)** $6 \sin^2 \theta + 7 \sin \theta + 2 = 0$
   (g) $\cos(\theta + 20°) = -0.74$ **(h)** $\tan(\theta - 50°) = -1.7$
   (i) $3 \sin^2 \theta = \sin \theta$ **(j)** $4 \sec^2 \theta = 5$
   (k) $\cos^2 \theta = 0.6$ **(l)** $6 \sin^2 \theta = 2 + \sin \theta$
   (m) $2 \sec^2 \theta = 3 - 5 \sec \theta$ **(n)** $\sec(\theta - 50°) = 2.15$
   (o) $\sin(\theta + 60°) = -0.75$

4. Find θ for $0° \leq \theta \leq 360°$ if $3 \cos^2 \theta - 2 = 0$.

5. If $5 \tan \theta + 2 = 0$, find θ in the range $0° \leq \theta \leq 360°$.

6. Solve the equation $5 \cos \theta - 3 \sec \theta = 0$ for $0° \leq \theta \leq 360°$.

7. Solve the equations
   (a) $\sin(-\theta) = 0.35$,   **(b)** $\sin(-\theta) = -0.27$,
   (c) $\cos(-\theta) = -0.64$,   **(d)** $\tan(-\theta) = 1.34$,
   for $0° \leq \theta \leq 360°$.

10.9 Graphs of Trigonometric Functions

10.9.1 *sin θ and cos θ*

Complete the following table of values of $\sin \theta$ and $\cos \theta$, taking a domain of 0° to 360° at 30° steps:

θ	0°	30°	60°	90°	120°	150°	180°	...	270°	...	360°
sin θ	0	0.5		1			0		-1		0
cos θ	1		0.5	0			-1				1

Plot these values on graph paper using scales of say 1 cm ≡ 30° on the θ-axis and 2 cm ≡ 1 unit on the function axis (Fig. 10.17).

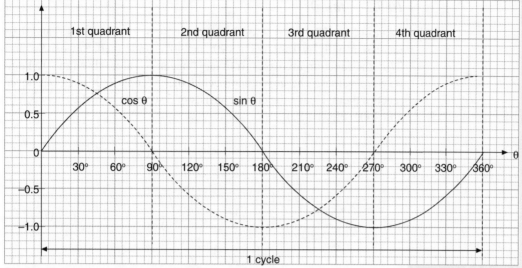

Fig. 10.17

The graph shows **one cycle** of each function.

You can verify the shapes of the graphs using your graphic calculators. The sine curve has a maximum of 1 when $\theta = 90°$ and a minimum of -1 when $\theta = 270°$. The cosine curve is identical to the sine curve but is shifted $90°$ to the left. This difference is called the **phase difference** between the two functions.

For angles greater than $360°$ or less than $0°$ the curves repeat themselves in successive cycles (Fig. 10.18). Functions which repeat themselves like this are called **periodic** functions. The sine and cosine functions each have a **period** of $360°$ (or 2π). Hence

$$\sin(\theta + n360°) = \sin\theta \qquad \text{or} \qquad \cos(\theta + 2n\pi) = \cos\theta$$

where n is any integer. This means that we can add or subtract $360°$ from any solution of $\sin\theta = k$ or $\cos\theta = k$ and obtain other solutions outside the domain $0° \leq \theta \leq 360°$.

For example, if the solutions of $\sin\theta = 0.5$ for $0° \leq \theta \leq 360°$ are $30°$ and $150°$, then $30° + 360° = 390°$ and $150° - 360° = -210°$ are also solutions of the equation. These solutions are marked by dots on the graph of $\sin\theta$ in Fig. 10.18.

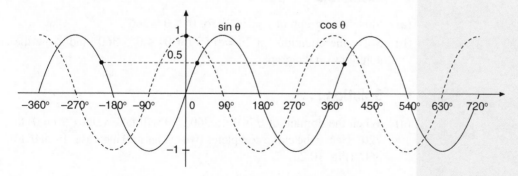

Fig. 10.18

10.9.2 tan θ

Values of tan θ begin at 0 for θ = 0°, increase to 1 when θ = 45° and then increase rapidly as θ approaches 90°. tan 90° is undefined. Beween 90° and 270°, the function increases from large negative values through 0 to large positive values. The curve approaches the 90° and 270° axes but never reaches them. Hence the curve consists of 3 separate branches between 0° and 360° (Fig. 10.19).

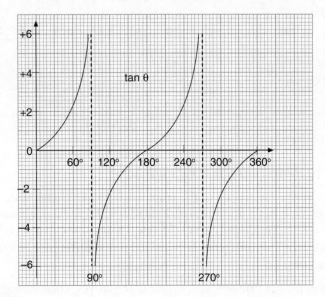

Fig. 10.19

tan θ is also a periodic function but with a period of 180°. Hence tan(θ + nπ) or tan(θ + n180°) = tan θ where n is an integer.

10.10 Multiple Angle Functions and their Graphs

Functions such as sin 2θ and cos 3θ are multiple angle functions as 2θ and 3θ are multiples of θ.

▶ Example 8

(a) Sketch the graph of y = sin 2θ for 0° ≤ θ ≤ 360°.

(b) Solve the equation sin 2θ = 0.55 for 0° ≤ θ ≤ 360° and show the solutions on the graph.

▶ Solution . . .

(a) When the domain of θ is 0° to 360°, 2θ will take values from 0° to 720°. Hence the curve completes **two** cycles as θ increases from 0° to 360° (Fig. 10.20).

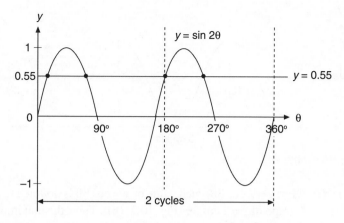

Fig. 10.20

(b) For convenience, write $2\theta = \phi$ so $\sin \phi = 0.55$.

ϕ lies in Q_1 and Q_2 so $\phi = 33.37°$ or $180° - \phi = 33.37°$.

Hence $\phi = 33.37°$ or $146.63°$.

But ϕ takes values from $0°$ to $720°$, so we add $360°$ to each of these to obtain further solutions.

Then $\phi = 2\theta = 33.37°$ or $146.63°$ or $393.37°$ or $506.63°$.

Hence $\quad \theta = 16.7°$ or $73.3°$ or $196.7°$ or $253.3°$.

So we obtain 4 solutions, 2 for each cycle. These solutions are marked on the graph.

Note that all the solutions for 2θ must be obtained first before dividing by 2 to obtain the values of θ, which are then corrected to 1 decimal place.

You may verify the shape and solutions using your graphic calculator. You should also do this for subsequent examples.

▶ **Example 9**

(a) Sketch the graph of $y = \cos 3\theta$ for $0° \le \theta \le 360°$.

(b) Using the graph of $y = \cos 3\theta$, sketch the following graphs in the same domain:

(i) $\quad y = 2 \cos 3\theta$

(ii) $\quad y = 2 \cos 3\theta + 1$

(iii) $\quad y = 2 \cos 3\theta - 2$

▶ **Solution . . .**

(a) When the domain of θ is $0°$ to $360°$, 3θ will take values from $0°$ to $1080°$.

Hence, the curve completes **three** cycles as θ increases from $0°$ to $360°$ (Fig. 10.21(a)).

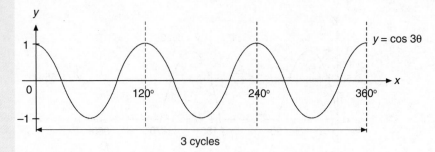

Fig. 10.21(a)

(b) (i) For $y = 2 \cos 3\theta$, each value of $y = \cos 3\theta$ is doubled to give the graph of $y = 2 \cos 3\theta$ (Fig. 10.21(b)). Thus, the maximum value of y is 2 and the minimum value of y is –2.

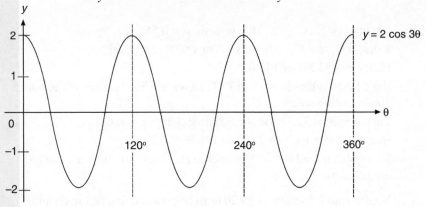

Fig. 10.21(b)

(ii) The graph of $y = 2 \cos 3\theta + 1$ is obtained by shifting **up** the graph of $y = 2 \cos 3\theta$ by 1 unit (Fig. 10.21(c)).

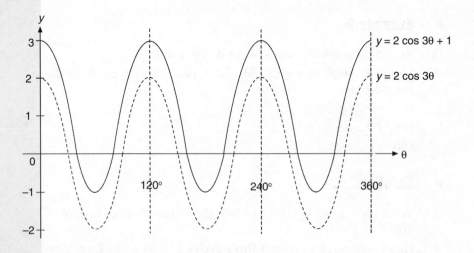

Fig. 10.21(c)

(iii) Similarly, the graph of $y = 2 \cos 3\theta - 2$ is obtained by shifting **down** the graph of $y = 2 \cos 3\theta$ by 2 units (Fig. 10.21(d)).

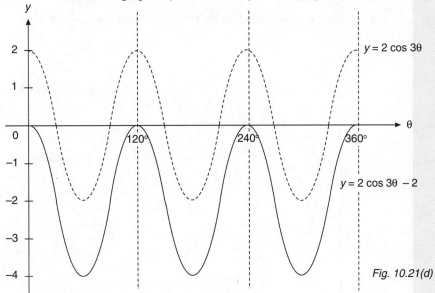

Fig. 10.21(d)

▶ **Example 10**

For $0° \leq \theta \leq 360°$, sketch separate graphs of

(a) $y = 2 \sin \theta$,

(b) $y = |\, 2 \sin \theta \,|$,

(c) $y = 1 + |\, \cos 2\theta \,|$,

(d) $y = 1 - |\, \cos 2\theta \,|$.

▶ **Solution**

(a) First sketch $y = \sin \theta$ (Fig. 10.22).

For $y = 2 \sin \theta$, each value of $y = \sin \theta$ is doubled to give the graph of $y = 2 \sin \theta$.

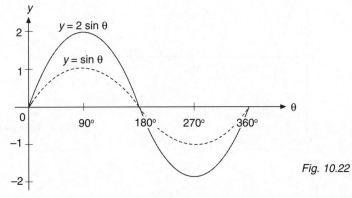

Fig. 10.22

(b) As we did earlier, we reflect the negative part of $y = 2 \sin \theta$ in the θ-axis to obtain $y = |\, 2 \sin \theta \,|$ (Fig. 10.23).

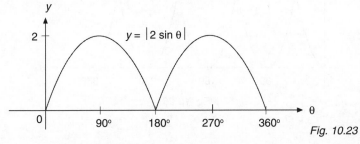

Fig. 10.23

(c) First sketch $y = \cos 2\theta$ (Fig. 10.24) which has two cycles. Now reflect the negative part in the θ-axis to obtain $y = |\cos 2\theta|$.

This curve is now shifted up by 1 unit to obtain $y = 1 + |\cos 2\theta|$.

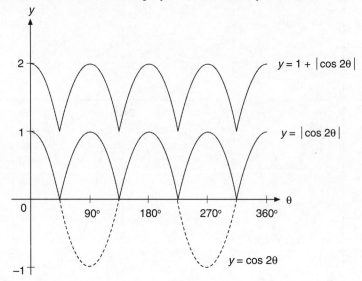

Fig. 10.24

(d) Start by sketching $y = |\cos 2\theta|$ as in part (c) (Fig. 10.25).

Then obtain $y = -|\cos 2\theta|$ by reflection of the whole curve in the θ-axis.

This is shifted up by 1 unit to obtain $y = 1 - |\cos 2\theta|$ (Fig. 10.26).

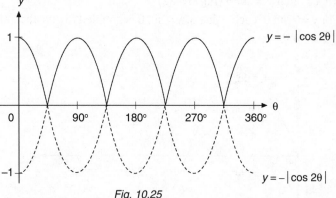

Fig. 10.25

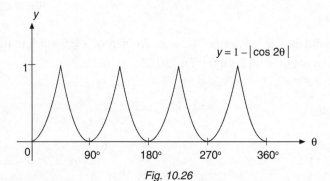

Fig. 10.26

▶ **Example 11**

Sketch on the same diagram, the graphs of $y = |2 \sin x|$ and $y = \dfrac{x}{\pi}$ for $0 \leq x \leq 2\pi$. Hence state the number of solutions of the equations $|2\pi \sin x| = x$, and $2\pi \sin x = x$ for $0 \leq x \leq 2\pi$.

▶ **Solution . . .**

We have to work in radians here as $y = \dfrac{x}{\pi}$ is a linear equation.

($y = \dfrac{x}{180^o}$ is not meaningful.)

The graph of $y = 2 \sin x$ is drawn and then $y = |2 \sin x|$ (Fig. 10.27).

To draw the line $y = \dfrac{x}{\pi}$ we take the points $x = 0$, $y = 0$ and $x = 2\pi$, $y = 2$.

The equation $|2\pi \sin x| = x$ is the same as $|2 \sin x| = \dfrac{x}{\pi}$ as π is positive. The solutions will occur at the intersections of the curve and the line, giving 4 solutions at the points marked O, A, B and C.

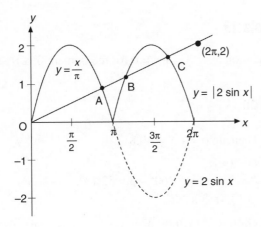

Fig. 10.27

The equation $2\pi \sin x = x$ is the same as $2 \sin x = \dfrac{x}{\pi}$. Thus, we look for the intersections of the original curve $y = 2 \sin x$ with the line, which reduces the number of solutions to 2 (points O and A).

▶ **Example 12**

Sketch on the same diagram the graphs of $y = |2 \cos x|$ and $3y = x$ for the domain $0 \leq x \leq 2\pi$. Hence state the number of solutions in this domain of the equation $6 |\cos x| = x$.

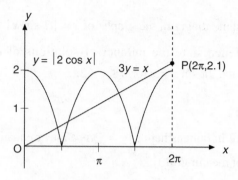

Fig. 10.28

Fig. 10.28 shows the graphs. The graph of $3y = x$, i.e., $y = \frac{x}{3}$ is the line OP, where O is the origin and P is the point $(2\pi, \frac{x}{3} \approx 2.1)$. There are 3 solutions to the equation $|2 \cos x| = \frac{x}{3}$, i.e., $6|\cos x| = x$.

► **Example 13**

Solve the equation $5 \sin \frac{3\theta}{4} + 4 = 0$ for the domain $0° \le \theta \le 360°$.

► **Solution ...**

Let $\frac{3\theta}{4} = \phi$. Then $\sin \phi = -\frac{4}{5} = -0.8$.
ϕ lies in Q_3 and Q_4.
Then $\phi - 180° = 53.13°$ and $360° - \phi = 53.13°$.
Hence $\phi = 233.13°$ or $306.87°$.

If the domain of θ is $0°$ to $360°$, then $\phi = \frac{3\theta}{4}$ takes values from $0°$ to $270°$.

Hence the only solution is $\phi = 233.13°$, i.e., $\theta = \frac{4}{3} \times 233.13° = 310.8°$.
($\phi = 306.87°$ would give $\theta = 409.2°$.)

► **Example 14**

Solve $\cos(2\theta + 60°) = -0.15$ for $0° \le \theta \le 360°$.

► **Solution ...**

Let $\phi = 2\theta + 60°$. Then $\cos \phi = -0.15$ giving $\phi = 98.63°$ and $261.37°$.
However if the domain of θ is $0°$ to $360°$, then the domain of ϕ is $60°$ to $780°$.
So we must add $360°$ to each of the above values.
Therefore $\phi = 2\theta + 60° = 98.63°$ or $261.37°$ or $458.63°$ or $621.37°$
and hence $\theta = 19.3°$ or $100.7°$ or $199.3°$ or $280.7°$.

Exercise 10B (Answers on page 502)

1. Sketch the graphs of **(a)** $y = \sin 3\theta$, **(b)** $y = \cos 2\theta$ for $0° \leq \theta \leq 360°$. What is the period of each of these functions?

2. Sketch the graphs of **(a)** $y = \tan 2\theta$, **(b)** $y = \tan 3\theta$ for $0° \leq \theta \leq 360°$.

3. On the same diagram, sketch the graphs of $y = \sin 2\theta$ and $y = \cos \theta$ for $0° \leq \theta \leq 360°$. How many solutions of the equation $\sin 2\theta = \cos \theta$ are there in this domain?

4. By sketching the graph of $y = \sin 2\theta$ for $0° \leq \theta \leq 360°$, find how many solutions the equation $\sin 2\theta = k$ will have in this interval, where $0 < k < 1$. How many solutions will the equation $|\sin 2\theta| = k$ have in the same interval?

5. Sketch the graphs of $y = |\cos \theta|$ and $y = |\cos \theta| - 1$ for $0° \leq \theta \leq 360°$.

6. On the same diagram, sketch the graphs of $y = |\sin \theta|$ and $y = |\cos \theta|$ for $0° \leq \theta \leq 360°$. How many solutions will the equation $|\sin \theta| = |\cos \theta|$ have in this interval?

7. Sketch the graphs of $y = 1 + 2 \sin \theta$ and $y = |1 + 2 \sin \theta|$ for $0° \leq \theta \leq 360°$. On another diagram, sketch the graph of $y = 1 + |2 \sin \theta|$.

8. On the same diagram, for $0° \leq \theta \leq 360°$, sketch the graphs of $y = 2 \cos \theta$ and $y = |2 \cos \theta|$. Now add the graph of $y = 1 - |2 \cos \theta|$.

9. On the same diagram, sketch the graphs of $y = |2 \cos x|$ and $y = \dfrac{x}{2\pi}$ for $0 \leq x \leq 2\pi$. Hence state the number of solutions of the equations $|4\pi \cos x| = x$ and $4\pi \cos x = x$ for $0 \leq x \leq 2\pi$.

10. Sketch the graph of $y = |\tan x|$ for $0° \leq \theta \leq 360°$.

11. Sketch on the same diagram the graphs of $y = |\cos 2x|$ and $2y = x$ for the domain $0 \leq x \leq \pi$. Hence state the number of solutions in this domain of the equation $|2 \cos 2x| = x$.

12. For $0 \leq x \leq 2\pi$, sketch the graphs of $y = |\cos x|$ and $y = \sin 2x$ on the same axes. State the number of solutions of the equation $\sin 2x = |\cos x|$ in this interval.

13. Sketch the graphs of $y = |\sin 3x|$ and $2\pi y = x$ for $0 < x \leq 2\pi$. How many solutions do the equations $2\pi \sin 3x = x$ and $|2\pi \sin 3x| = x$ have in this interval?

14. On the same diagram, sketch the graphs of $y = |\sin x - 1|$ and $y = 2 \cos x$ for $0 \le x \le 2\pi$. Hence find the number of solutions of the equation $2 \cos x = |\sin x - 1|$ in this interval.

15. Solve, for $0° \le \theta \le 360°$, the following equations:

(a) $\sin 2\theta = 0.67$ **(b)** $\cos 3\theta = 0.58$

(c) $\tan \dfrac{\theta}{2} = 1.5$ **(d)** $\sin \dfrac{\theta}{3} = 0.17$

(e) $3 \cos 2\theta = 2$ **(f)** $\sec \dfrac{\theta}{2} = -1.7$

(g) $\sin \dfrac{\theta}{3} = -0.28$ **(h)** $3 \tan 2\theta + 1 = 0$

(i) $3 \sin \dfrac{2\theta}{3} = 2$ **(j)** $4 \cos \dfrac{3\theta}{2} + 3 = 0$

(k) $2 \operatorname{cosec} 2\theta + 3 = 0$ **(l)** $\cot \dfrac{\theta}{2} = 1.35$

(m) $\cos \dfrac{3\theta}{3} = \dfrac{3}{4}$ **(n)** $\tan 2\theta = -1$

(o) $3 \sin^2 2\theta + 2 \sin 2\theta = 1$ **(p)** $2 \cos^2 \dfrac{\theta}{2} = \cos \dfrac{\theta}{2}$

(q) $\sin 2\theta = -0.76$ **(r)** $\sec \dfrac{\theta}{2} = 1.88$

(s) $\cos 2\theta = -0.65$ **(t)** $\tan \dfrac{2\theta}{3} + 2 = 0$

(u) $5 \sin \dfrac{4\theta}{5} + 3 = 0$ **(v)** $2 \operatorname{cosec} \dfrac{\theta}{2} = 3$

16. For $0° \le \theta \le 360°$, solve the following:

(a) $\sin(\dfrac{\theta}{3} + 20°) = 0.47$ **(b)** $\tan(2\theta - 60°) = 1.55$

(c) $\cos(\dfrac{\theta}{2}) = 0.75$ **(d)** $\sin(2\theta + 80°) = -0.54$

(e) $\sec^2(\dfrac{\theta}{3} - 50°) = 1.2$

10.11 Identities

We have defined earlier, for an angle θ, $\sin \theta = y$, $\cos \theta = x$ and $\tan \theta = \dfrac{y}{x}$ where (x, y) were the coordinates of R and OR = 1 unit (Fig. 10.29).

Then $\tan \theta \equiv \dfrac{\sin \theta}{\cos \theta}$.

This is an **identity** which is true for all values of θ. So we use the symbol '≡' meaning 'identical to' or 'equivalent to'. In any expression, $\tan \theta$ could be replaced by $\dfrac{\sin \theta}{\cos \theta}$ or vice-versa.

As $\cot \theta = \dfrac{1}{\tan \theta}$, then $\cot \theta \equiv \dfrac{\cos \theta}{\sin \theta}$.

From Fig. 10.29, $x^2 + y^2 = 1$ for all values of x and y.

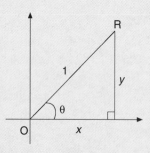

Fig. 10.29

Hence, $\sin^2 \theta + \cos \theta^2 \equiv 1$

[Note: $\sin^2 \theta$ means $(\sin \theta)^2$]

and $\sin^2 \theta \equiv 1 - \cos^2 \theta$

and $\cos^2 \theta \equiv 1 - \sin^2 \theta$.

Taking the identity $\sin^2 \theta + \cos^2 \theta \equiv 1$, divide both sides by $\cos^2 \theta$:

then $\dfrac{\sin^2 \theta}{\cos^2 \theta} + 1 \equiv \dfrac{1}{\sin^2 \theta}$

i.e. $\tan^2 \theta + 1 \equiv \sec^2 \theta$.

Dividing both sides of the identity $\sin^2 \theta + \cos^2 \theta \equiv 1$ by $\sin^2 \theta$,

then $1 + \dfrac{\cos^2 \theta}{\sin^2 \theta} \equiv \dfrac{1}{\sin^2 \theta}$

i.e. $1 + \cot^2 \theta \equiv \operatorname{cosec}^2 \theta$.

Summarising:

$$\tan \theta \equiv \frac{\sin \theta}{\cos \theta} \qquad \cot \theta \equiv \frac{\cos \theta}{\sin \theta}$$
$$\sin^2 \theta + \cos^2 \theta \equiv 1$$
$$\sin^2 \theta \equiv 1 - \cos^2 \theta \qquad \cos^2 \theta \equiv 1 - \sin^2 \theta$$
$$\tan^2 \theta + 1 \equiv \sec^2 \theta \qquad \cot^2 \theta + 1 \equiv \operatorname{cosec}^2 \theta$$

These identities are used to transform trigonometric expressions into another form.

▶ **Example 15**

Prove that $\cot \theta + \tan \theta \equiv \operatorname{cosec} \theta \sec \theta$.

▶ **Solution . . .**

We take one side and convert it to the expression on the other side. It is usually easier to start with the side which is more complicated or which involves sums of functions. This gives more scope for manipulation.

Taking the left-hand side (LHS):

$$\cot \theta + \tan \theta \equiv \frac{\cos \theta}{\sin \theta} + \frac{\sin \theta}{\cos \theta}$$
$$\equiv \frac{\cos^2 \theta + \sin^2 \theta}{\sin \theta \cos \theta}$$
$$\equiv \frac{1}{\sin \theta \cos \theta}$$
$$\equiv \frac{1}{\sin \theta} \times \frac{1}{\cos \theta}$$
$$\equiv \operatorname{cosec} \theta \sec \theta$$

If we start with the RHS, then

$$\frac{1}{\sin \theta} \times \frac{1}{\cos \theta} \equiv \frac{1}{\sin \theta \cos \theta}$$

but it is not obvious that we should now replace 1 by $\sin^2 \theta + \cos^2 \theta$. Do this and then divide the numerator by $\sin \theta \cos \theta$ to complete the proof.

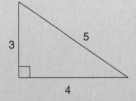
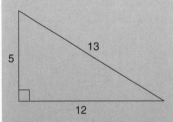

▶ **Example 16**

Show that $\dfrac{1}{1 + \sin \theta} + \dfrac{1}{1 - \sin \theta} \equiv 2 \sec^2 \theta$.

▶ **Solution . . .**

We take the more complicated LHS.

Then $\dfrac{1}{1 + \sin \theta} + \dfrac{1}{1 - \sin \theta} \equiv \dfrac{1 - \sin \theta + 1 + \sin \theta}{(1 + \sin \theta)(1 - \sin \theta)}$

$$\equiv \dfrac{2}{1 - \sin^2 \theta}$$

$$\equiv \dfrac{2}{\cos^2 \theta} \equiv 2 \sec^2 \theta$$

▶ **Example 17**

Prove that $\tan^2 \theta \equiv \sin^2 \theta (1 + \tan^2 \theta)$.

▶ **Solution . . .**

$\text{RHS} \equiv \sin^2 \theta \left(1 + \dfrac{\sin^2 \theta}{\cos^2 \theta} \right)$

$$\equiv \sin^2 \theta \left(\dfrac{\cos^2 \theta + \sin^2 \theta}{\cos^2 \theta} \right)$$

$$\equiv \sin^2 \theta \left(\dfrac{1}{\cos^2 \theta} \right) \equiv \tan^2 \theta$$

Exercise 10C

Prove the following identities:

1. $\sin \theta \cot \theta \equiv \cos \theta$ 2. $(1 + \tan^2 \theta)\cos^2 \theta \equiv 1$

3. $(1 + \tan^2 \theta)(1 - \sin^2 \theta) \equiv 1$ 4. $\cos^2 \theta - \sin^2 \theta \equiv 1 - 2 \sin^2 \theta$

5. $\sec \theta - \cos \theta \equiv \sin \theta \tan \theta$ 6. $\cot^2 \theta (1 - \cos^2 \theta) \equiv \cos^2 \theta$

7. $\dfrac{1}{\cos^2 \theta} - \dfrac{1}{\cot^2 \theta} \equiv 1$ 8. $\dfrac{\cot \theta}{\tan \theta} + 1 \equiv \csc^2 \theta$

9. $\tan^2 \theta - \sin^2 \theta \equiv \sin^4 \theta \sec^2 \theta$

10. $(\sin \theta + \cos \theta)(\tan \theta + \cot \theta) \equiv \sec \theta + \csc \theta$

11. $\sin^4 \theta - \cos^4 \theta \equiv 1 - 2 \cos^2 \theta$

12. $(\cos \theta + \sin \theta)^2 + (\cos \theta - \sin \theta)^2 \equiv 2$

13. $\dfrac{1 - \tan^2 \theta}{\cot^2 \theta - 1} \equiv \tan^2 \theta$

14. $\sec \theta + \tan \theta \equiv \dfrac{1}{\sec \theta - \tan \theta}$

15. $\sec^4 \theta - \sec^2 \theta \equiv \tan^2 \theta + \tan^4 \theta$

16. $(\csc \theta - \cot \theta)^2 \equiv \dfrac{1 - \cos \theta}{1 + \cos \theta}$

10.12 Equations with More Than One Function

Other types of trigonometrical equations can be solved using the identities we have just learnt. Some methods of solution are now shown. The object is to reduce the equation to one function.

▶ **Example 18**

Solve the equation $3 \cos \theta + 2 \sin \theta = 0$ for $0° \le \theta \le 360°$.

▶ **Solution . . .**

The equation contains two functions but if we divide throughout by $\cos \theta$, this will be reduced to one function.

Then $3 + 2 \dfrac{\sin \theta}{\cos \theta} = 0$ or $\tan \theta = -1.5$.

Now solve this basic equation.

Verify that the solutions are 123.7° and 303.7°.

▶ **Example 19**

Solve the equation $2 \sin \theta = \tan \theta$ for $0° \le \theta \le 360°$. Illustrate the solutions graphically.

▶ **Solution . . .**

Rewrite the equation as $2 \sin \theta = \dfrac{\sin \theta}{\cos \theta}$

i.e. $2 \sin \theta \cos \theta - \sin \theta = 0$

or $\sin \theta (2 \cos \theta - 1) = 0$.

This can be separated into two basic equations $\sin \theta = 0$ and $2 \cos \theta - 1 = 0$,

i.e. $\cos \theta = 0.5$.

The solutions of $\sin \theta = 0$ are 0°, 180° and 360°.

The solutions of $\cos \theta = 0.5$ are 60° and 300°.

Hence, the solutions are 0°, 60°, 180°, 300° and 360°.

The graphs of $y = 2 \sin \theta$ and $y = \tan \theta$ are shown in Fig. 10.30 with the positions of the solutions marked.

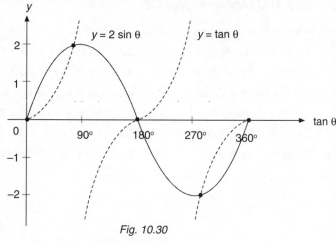

Fig. 10.30

▶ **Example 20**

Solve $3 \sin \theta + 5 \cot \theta = \operatorname{cosec} \theta$ for $0° \le \theta \le 360°$.

▶ **Solution . . .**

This involves three functions. Reduce this to two by replacing $\cot \theta$ and $\operatorname{cosec} \theta$.

Then $3 \sin \theta + 5 \dfrac{\cos \theta}{\sin \theta} = \dfrac{1}{\sin \theta}$.

Removing the fractions: $3 \sin^2 \theta + 5 \cos \theta = 1$

We can now reduce the equation to one function by replacing $\sin^2 \theta$ by $1 - \cos^2 \theta$.

Then $3(1 - \cos^2 \theta) + 5 \cos \theta = 1$ or $3 \cos^2 \theta - 5 \cos \theta - 2 = 0$.

This is a quadratic equation in $\cos \theta$ and gives $(3 \cos \theta + 1)(\cos \theta - 2) = 0$.

We now have two basic equations:

$\cos \theta = -\dfrac{1}{3}$ which gives $\theta = 109.47°$ or $250.53°$,

and $\cos \theta = 2$ which has no solution.

Hence, the solutions are $\theta = 109.5°$ and $250.5°$.

▶ **Example 21**

Solve the equation $4 \operatorname{cosec}^2 \theta - 7 = 4 \cot \theta$ for $0° \le \theta \le 180°$.

▶ **Solution . . .**

If we replace $\operatorname{cosec}^2 \theta$ by $1 + \cot^2 \theta$, we shall have an equation in $\cot \theta$ only.

Then $4(1 + \cot^2 \theta) - 7 = 4 \cot \theta$, i.e., $4 \cot^2 \theta - 4 \cot \theta - 3 = 0$.

This is a quadratic equation in $\cot \theta$ and gives $(2 \cot \theta - 3)(2 \cot \theta + 1) = 0$ leading to the basic equations $\cot \theta = 1.5$ and $\cot \theta = -0.5$.

Hence $\tan \theta = 0.6667$ and $\tan \theta = -2$.

Now solve these but note that the domain is $0°$ to $180°$.

The solutions are therefore $\theta = 33.7°$ and $116.6°$.

Exercise 10D (*Answers on page 502*)

Solve the following equations for $0° \le \theta \le 360°$:

1.	$8 \cot \theta = 3 \sin \theta$	**2.**	$\sin \theta + 4 \cos^2 \theta = 1$
3.	$8 \sin \theta = 3 \cos^2 \theta$	**4.**	$2 \sec^2 \theta = 3 - \tan^2 \theta$
5.	$\cot \theta + \tan \theta = 2 \sec \theta$	**6.**	$\tan \theta + 3 \cot \theta = 4$
7.	$\cot^2 \theta + 3 \operatorname{cosec}^2 \theta = 5$	**8.**	$3(\sec \theta - \tan \theta) = 2 \cos \theta$
9.	$2 \cot^2 \theta + 11 = 9 \operatorname{cosec} \theta$	**10.**	$3 \sin^2 \theta = 1 + \cos \theta$
11.	$5 \cos \theta - \sec \theta = 4$	**12.**	$3 \cot 2\theta + 2 \sin 2\theta = 0$

Summary

1. If θ is any angle, $\sin \theta = y$, $\cos \theta = x$ and $\tan \theta = \dfrac{y}{x}$ where (x, y) are the coordinates of R and OR = 1 (Fig. 10.31).

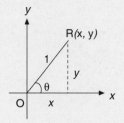

Fig. 10.31

SIN +	ALL+
$\sin \theta = \sin \alpha$	$\sin \theta = \sin \alpha$
$\cos \theta = -\cos \alpha$	$\cos \theta = \cos \alpha$
$\tan \theta = -\tan \alpha$	$\tan \theta = \tan \alpha$
(Q_2)	(Q_1)
(Q_3)	(Q_4)
$\sin \theta = -\sin \alpha$	$\sin \theta = -\sin \alpha$
$\cos \theta = -\cos \alpha$	$\cos \theta = \cos \alpha$
$\tan \theta = \tan \alpha$	$\tan \theta = -\tan \alpha$
TAN+	COS+

where α is the basic angle corresponding to θ.

2. To solve a basic equation such as $\sin \theta = k$:
   (a) Find the basic angle α (in the 1st quadrant) such that $\sin \alpha = |k|$.
   (b) Find the quadrants in which θ will lie.
   (c) Determine the corresponding angles in these quadrants and solve for θ. A basic equation will usually have 2 solutions in the interval $0°$ to $360°$.

3. $\operatorname{cosec} \theta = \dfrac{1}{\sin \theta}, \qquad \sec \theta = \dfrac{1}{\cos \theta}, \qquad \cot \theta = \dfrac{1}{\tan \theta}.$

4. Graphs of sin, cos, tan (Fig. 10.32)

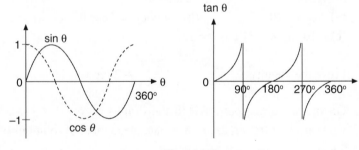

Fig. 10.32

sin and cos have a period of $360°$:

$\sin(n360° + \theta) = \sin \theta$, $\cos(n360° + \theta) = \cos \theta$, where n is an integer.

tan has a period of $180°$:

$\tan(n180° + \theta) = \tan \theta$.

5. For equations with a multiple angle $k\theta$, solve for $k\theta$ first and then derive the values of θ.

6. Identities

$$\tan \theta = \frac{\sin \theta}{\cos \theta} \qquad \cot \theta = \frac{\cos \theta}{\sin \theta}$$

$$\sin^2 \theta + \cos^2 \theta = 1$$

$$\sin^2 \theta \equiv 1 - \cos^2 \theta \qquad \cos^2 \theta \equiv 1 - \sin^2 \theta$$

$$\tan^2 \theta + 1 \equiv \sec^2 \theta \qquad \cot^2 \theta + 1 \equiv \text{cosec}^2 \theta$$

To solve the equations with more than one function, use the above identities to reduce them to one function.

Revision Exercise 10 (Answers on page 502)

1. Find all the angles between 0° and 360° which satisfy the equations
   (a) $\cot 2x = -\frac{1}{2}$,   (b) $2 \sin y = 3 \cos y$.

2. Sketch on the same diagram, for $0 \le x \le 2\pi$, the graph of $y = 2 \cos x - 1$ and the graph of $y = \sin 2x$. Hence state the number of solutions in this interval of the equation $2 \cos x - 1 = \sin 2x$. (C)

3. Sketch the graph of (a) $y = |\cos x|$, (b) $y = |\cos x| - 1$ and (c) $y = 1 - |\cos x|$ for values of x between 0 and 2π.

4. Prove the identity $\sec x - \cos x \equiv \sin x \tan x$.

5. Find all the angles between 0° and 180° which satisfy the equations
   (a) $\cos \frac{2}{3} x = \frac{2}{3}$,   (b) $3 \cot y - 4 \cos y = 0$,
   (c) $3 \sec^2 z = 7 + 4 \tan z$.   (C)

6. Solve for $0° \le \theta \le 360°$, the equations
   (a) $\text{cosec } 2\theta = 3$ (b) $4 \cot \theta = 5 \cos \theta$,
   (c) $10 \sin^2 \theta + 31 \cos \theta = 13$.   (C)

7. Prove the identity $\dfrac{1 + \sin x}{\cos x} + \dfrac{\cos x}{1 + \sin x} \equiv 2 \sec x$.   (C)

8. On the same diagram, sketch the graphs of $y = 1 + \cos x$ and $y = |\sin x|$ for $0 \le x \le 2\pi$. Hence state the number of solutions of the equation $1 + \cos x = |\sin x|$ in this interval.

9. Find all the angles between 0° and 180° which satisfy the equations
   (a) $\tan(x + 70°) = 1$,
   (b) $8 \sin y + 3 \cos y = 0$,
   (c) $3 \sin^2 \theta + 5 \sin \theta \cos \theta - 2 \cos^2 \theta = 0$.

10. Sketch on the same diagram, the graphs of $y = |\,2\cos x\,|$ and $y = \dfrac{4x}{3\pi}$ for $0 \le x \le 2\pi$.

State, for the range $0 \le x \le 2\pi$, the number of solutions of

(a) $|\,3\pi \cos x\,| = 2x,$ (b) $3\pi \cos x = 2x.$

11. State the range of $y = 2 - |\cos x|$ for the domain $0 \le x \le \dfrac{3\pi}{2}$.

12. On the same diagram, sketch the graphs of $y = \sin 2x$ and $y = \sin \dfrac{x}{2}$ for $0 \le x \le 2\pi$.

Hence state the number of solutions of the equation $\sin 2x = \sin \dfrac{x}{2}$ in that interval.

What would be the number of solutions of $|\sin 2x| = \sin \dfrac{x}{2}$?

13. For the domain $0° \le \theta \le 360°$, solve

(a) $\sin \theta + \cos \theta \cot \theta = 2,$

(b) $6 \cot^2 \theta = 1 + 4 \,\mathrm{cosec}^2\, \theta.$

14. Solve the equation $\sin \theta = 4 \sin^3 \theta$ for $0° \le \theta \le 360°$.

15. Solve, for $0° \le \theta \le 360°$, the equations

(a) $8 \sin^2 \theta = \mathrm{cosec}\, \theta,$

(b) $4 \cos^2 \theta = 9 - 2 \sec^2 \theta.$

16. Sketch the graphs of $y = |\,2\sin x\,|$ and $y = |\,\dfrac{x}{\pi} - 1\,|$ for $0 \le x \le 2\pi$.

How many solutions are there of the equation $|\,2\pi \sin x\,| = |\,x - \pi\,|$ in this interval?

17. A segment ACB in a circle is cut off by the chord AB where $\angle AOB = \theta$ radians (O is the centre.). If the area of this segment is $\dfrac{1}{4}$ of the area of the circle, show that $\theta - \sin \theta = \dfrac{\pi}{2}$.

Draw the graphs of $y = \sin \theta$ and $y = \theta - \dfrac{\pi}{2}$ for $0 \le \theta \le \pi$, taking scales of 4 cm for $\dfrac{\pi}{2}$ on the x-axis and 4 cm per unit on the y-axis. (Take $\pi = 3.14$). Hence find an approximate solution of the equation $\theta - \sin \theta = \dfrac{\pi}{2}$.

18. In Fig. 10.33, ACB is a semicircle of radius r, centre O and $\angle ABC = \theta°$.

(a) Using the identity $2 \sin \theta \cos \theta = \sin 2\theta$, show that the area of the shaded region is $r^2(\dfrac{\pi}{2} - \sin 2\theta)$.

(b) State, in terms of r, the maximum and minimum possible values of this area and the corresponding values of θ.

(c) Find the values of θ for which the area of the shaded region equals $\dfrac{1}{2}$ the area of the semicircle.

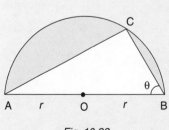

Fig. 10.33

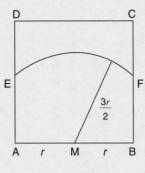

Fig. 10.34

19. A goat is tied to one end of a rope of length $\frac{3r}{2}$, the other end being fixed to the midpoint M of the side AB of a square field ABCD of side $2r$ (Fig. 10.34).
    (a) Find, in radians, ∠EMF.
    (b) Find in terms of r the area ABFE.
    (c) Calculate what percentage of the area of the field the goat can cover.

20. In Fig. 10.35, OA and OB are two radii of a circle O where angle BOA = θ radians. The tangent to the circle at A meets OB produced at C. If the area of the sector OAB is twice the area of the shaded region, show that $2 \tan θ = 3θ$. By drawing the graphs $y = \tan θ$ and $y = \frac{3θ}{2}$ for a suitable domain, or otherwise, find the approximate value of θ. (Otherwise, a solution could be found by trial and error using a calculator in radian mode. Test values of θ to make $\tan θ - 1.5θ$ reasonably small.)

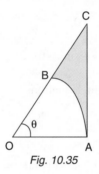

Fig. 10.35

Maths Booster

A and B are 2 km apart on a straight road. A helicopter H hovers above the road between A and B.

Another helicopter K hovers vertically above B. From helicopter H, the angle of depression of K is $θ°$ and the angle of depression of A is $90° − θ°$. Given that AH = 2000 m and KH = 1000 m, find the altitudes of the helicopters.

Chapter 11

Combinations and Permutations

Suppose each student in your class is to shake the hand of every other student in the class. Can you find the total number of handshakes? Discuss a plan where you can find the answer systematically. Later in the chapter, you will learn a quick way of finding the answer.

11.1 Combinations

Suppose your school organises an inter-class chess tournament and each class is to send in 2 contestants. In your class, there are 4 good chess players: Alan, Bob, Charlie and Dick. If the students are asked to vote for 2 of the 4 players to represent the class, how many different ways can 2 players be selected?

Let the letters A, B, C and D represent the players Alan, Bob, Charlie and Dick respectively. Then the 2 players can be chosen in the following ways:

A and B, A and C, A and D,
B and C, B and D, C and D.

[Check to confirm that there is no other way of making a choice and note that there is no difference in choosing 'A and B' and choosing 'B and A'.]

So we see there are 6 different ways of choosing 2 players out of 4 to represent the class. Another way of saying this is that for 4 players, 6 **selections** or **combinations** of 2 players can be made.

11.2 Permutations

Now, suppose that in the example in Section 11.1, the rules of the chess tournament require that each class names its 'First Player' and 'Second Player'. In this situation, Alan as the 'First Player' and Bob as the 'Second Player' would be different from Bob as the 'First Player' and Alan as the 'Second Player'. In other words, the order AB and BA makes a difference. So the possible ways of entering the 'First Player' and the 'Second Player' respectively are as follows:

AB, AC, AD, BC, BD, CD,
BA, CA, DA, CB, DB, DC.

For each of the combinations in the previous section, we now have 2 ways of choosing the 2 players when the order is taken into account, resulting in a total of 12 different ways. We call each of these ways an **arrangement** or a **permutation**. Thus, from 4 players, 12 arrangements or permutations of 2 players can be made.

11.3 Definitions of Combination and Permutation

From the discussion in the preceding sections, we now give the formal definitions of the terms 'combination' and 'permutation'.

A **combination** (or selection) of a given number of articles is a set of articles chosen from those given, where the order of the articles in the set is *not* taken into consideration.

A **permutation** (or arrangement) of a given number of articles is a set of articles chosen from those given, where the order of the articles in the set is taken into consideration:

Thus given 2 articles A and B, we can have 2 permutations (AB and BA) but only one combination (A and B).

▶ Example 1

Given 4 letters a, b, c and d, find

(a) the number of different combinations of 3 of the letters,

(b) the number of permutations of 3 of the letters.

▶ Solution . . .

(a) We list the different combinations of 3 letters as follows:

abc, abd, acd, bcd

Hence, there are 4 combinations.

(b) Consider the combination abc.
We can arrange them in the following ways:

abc, acb,
bac, bca,
cab, cba.

That is, there are 6 permutations.

So, for each combination in (a), there are 6 permutations. Thus there are altogether $4 \times 6 = 24$ permutations.

11.4   The Product Principle

If there are 2 bus services a and b plying between station X and station Y, and 3 bus services c, d and e plying between station Y and station Z, how many different ways can a passenger travel from station X to station Z via station Y?

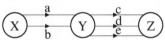

Listing the different bus services the passenger can travel, we have:

ac, ad, ae,
bc, bd, be.

So there are 6 different combinations. We can reason it this way:

There are 2 ways the passenger can go from X to Y. For each of these ways, there are 3 ways he can go from Y to Z. Hence the total number of ways he can go from X to Z via Y is $2 \times 3 = 6$.

This is the basic idea in the **Product Principle** which can be summarised below.

> **The Product Principle**: If one process can be done in p ways and a second process can be done in q ways, then the number of different ways in which both processes can be done is $p \times q$.

▶ Example 2

There are 10 girls in a class of 40 students. How many ways are there of selecting a male and a female representative from the class?

▶ Solution . . .

There are 10 ways of choosing a female representative from 10 girls.

As there are 30 boys in the class, so there are 30 ways of choosing a male representative.

Hence the number of ways of selecting a male and a female representative is $10 \times 30 = 300$.

▶ Example 3

In how many ways can a vowel and a consonant be chosen from the letters of the word 'combine'?

▶ Solution . . .

There are 3 vowels (o, i and e); so a vowel can be chosen in 3 ways.

There are 4 consonants (c, m, b and n), so a consonant can be chosen in 4 ways.

Hence the number of ways a vowel and a consonant can be chosen is $3 \times 4 = 12$.

11.4.1 Extension of the Product Principle for More Than 2 Processes

If one process can be done in p ways, a second process in q ways, a third process in r ways and so on, then the number of ways in which all the processes can be done is $p \times q \times r \times \ldots$.

▶ Example 4

There are 2 routes from town A to town B,

        3 routes from town B to town C,

     and 4 routes from town C to town D.

How many different ways are there of travelling from town A to town D via town B and town C?

▶ Solution . . .

Number of ways to travel from town A to town B = 2

Number of ways to travel from town B to town C = 3

Number of ways to travel from town C to town D = 4

Hence, the total number of ways of travelling from town A to town D via town B and town C is $2 \times 3 \times 4 = 24$.

▶ Example 5

Three prizes comprising an apple, an orange and a pear are to be given away to a group of 10 children playing some games. In how many ways can this be done if

(a)   a child may not receive more than 1 prize,

(b)   a child may receive more than 1 prize?

▶ **Solution . . .**

(a) The apple may be given to any of the 10 children, so there are 10 ways to give it away.

The orange may be given to any of the remaining 9 children (since the first child who receives the apple is no longer eligible for the orange), so there are 9 ways of doing so.

Similarly, the pear may be given to any of the remaining 8 children, so there are 8 ways to give it away.

Hence, the number of ways of giving the 3 prizes is $10 \times 9 \times 8 = 720$.

(b) The apple may be given to any of the 10 children, so there are 10 ways to give it away.

The orange may also be given to any of the 10 children (since the first child who receives the apple is still eligible for the orange), so there are 10 ways of doing so.

Similarly, the pear may be given to any of the 10 children, so there are 10 ways to give it away.

Hence, the number of ways of giving the 3 prizes is
$10 \times 10 \times 10 = 1000$.

▶ **Example 6**

How many 5-digit natural numbers are there?

▶ **Solution . . .**

The 1st digit may be any of the digits 1, 2, 3, . . . 9 (i.e. except 0). Thus the first digit can be chosen in 9 ways.

The 2nd digit may be any of the ten digits (including 0). Thus the 2nd digit can be chosen in 10 ways.

Similarly, each of the 3 remaining digits can be chosen in 10 ways.

Hence, the number of 5-digit numbers is $9 \times 10^4 = 90\,000$.

The information above may be represented diagrammatically by boxes as follows:

Digit:	1st	2nd	3rd	4th	5th

Number of ways: 9   10   10   10   10
Total number of ways is $9 \times 10^4 = 90\,000$

▶ **Example 7**

How many different sums of money can be formed by using some or all of the following coins: 1 five-cent coin, 3 twenty-cent coins and 5 fifty-cent coins?

▶ **Solution . . .**

The five-cent coin can either be used or left out, so there are 2 ways of handling it.

One, two, three or none of the twenty-cent coins may be used, so there are 4 ways of handling these coins.

Similarly, one, two, three, four, five or none of the fifty-cent coins may be used, so there are 6 ways of handling these coins.

Hence the total number of ways of grouping the coins is $2 \times 4 \times 6 = 48$. However, one of these ways involves leaving out all coins and this has to be excluded.

Hence there are $48 - 1 = 47$ different sums of money.

Exercise 11A (*Answers on page 502*)

1. Given the letters A, B, C, D and E,
   (a) list the different selections of 2 letters, and state the number of different selections,
   (b) list the different arrangements of 2 letters, and state the number of different permutations.

2. 5 ships ply between port A and port B, and 8 ships ply between port B and port C.
   (a) How many ways can a man travel from port A to port C via port B?
   (b) How many ways can another man travel from port A to port B and return to port A by a different ship?
   (c) How many ways can a third man travel from port A to port C via port B and return to port A, also via port B, if he takes a different ship for each section of his journey?

3. In how many ways can a vowel and a consonant be chosen from the word 'SINGAPORE'?

4. In how many ways can a boy and a girl be chosen from a class of 20 boys and 18 girls?

5. In a class, there are 30 Chinese, 7 Malays and 3 Indians. A committee of three, comprising a Chinese, a Malay and an Indian, is to be formed. In how many ways can this be done?

6. 8 chairs are arranged in a row. In how many ways can three students be seated?

7. 7 S-League soccer matches are to be played this week. Each match may end in one of the three ways for a team: a win, a loss or a draw. In how many different ways can the results for the matches turn out?

8. In the lottery game of 4-digits, punters arrange 4 digits from the digits 0 to 9. How many ways can this be done?

9. There are 5 envelopes of different colours and 5 different letters. Find the number of ways in which the letters can be put into the envelopes with one in each.

10. 3 tourists arrive at a place where there are 6 hotels to choose from. In how many ways can they choose their hotels so that each is at a different one?

11.5 Arranging *n* Unlike Things Taken All Together

Suppose we want to seat 7 boys in a row of 7 chairs. How many ways can this be done?

The first chair can be occupied by any of the 7 boys, i.e. in 7 ways. After the first chair is occupied, the second chair can be occupied by any of the remaining 6 boys, i.e. in 6 ways.

Using the same reasoning, the third chair can be occupied in 5 ways and so on. Hence the total number of ways (using the product principle) is $7 \times 6 \times 5 \times 4 \times 3 \times 2 \times 1 = 5040$.

The product of a number *n* and all the positive numbers less than *n* is called **factorial *n*** and is written as ***n*!**.

That is, $n! = n \times (n-1) \times (n-2) \ldots 3 \times 2 \times 1$.

Thus $7 \times 6 \times 5 \times 4 \times 3 \times 2 \times 1$ can be written as $7!$.

[The factorial key ($n!$) is available in most calculators. Check that your calculator has this key and verify that $7! = 5040$.]

Going back to the earlier discussion, if we use this notation, the number of ways of seating the 7 boys in the 7 chairs is $7!$. Another way of saying this is that the number of arrangements or permutations of the 7 boys is $7!$. In generalising, we have the following result:

> The number of permutations (or arrangements) of *n* unlike things taken all together is ***n*!**.

▶ **Example 8**

There are 8 parking lots. In how many ways can 8 cars be parked in the lots?

▶ **Solution . . .**

Number of ways of parking the 8 cars in the 8 lots = $8! = 40\,320$.

▶ **Example 9**

Using the digits 1, 2, 3, 4, 5 and 6, how many 6-digit numbers can be formed?

▶ **Solution . . .**

Number of 6-digit numbers
= number of permutations of 6 digits taken all together
= $6! = 720$

11.6 Arranging *n* Unlike Things Taken *r* at a Time

Suppose in the previous section, we have 7 boys but only a row of 4 chairs. How many ways are there of seating 4 of the 7 boys on the 4 chairs?

In this case, the first chair can be occupied by any of the 7 boys, i.e. in 7 ways. After the first chair is occupied, the second chair can be occupied by any of the remaining 6 boys, i.e. in 6 ways. Similarly, the third and fourth chairs can be occupied in 5 and 4 ways respectively. Hence, the total number of ways = $7 \times 6 \times 5 \times 4 = 840$.

We can also express this in factorial notation as follows:

$$\text{Total number of ways} = \frac{7 \times 6 \times 5 \times 4 \times 3 \times 2 \times 1}{3 \times 2 \times 1}$$

$$= \frac{7!}{3!}$$

$$= \frac{7!}{(7-4)!} = 840$$

In generalising, we have the following result:

> The number of permutations (or arrangements) of *n* unlike things taken *r* at a time is $n \times (n-1) \times (n-2) \times ... \times (n-r+1) = \dfrac{n!}{(n-r)!}$.

The notation for the number of permutations of *n* things taken *r* at a time is $_n\mathbf{P}_r$.

Hence, $_n P_r = \dfrac{n!}{(n-r)!}$.

Thus the number of ways of seating 4 of the 7 boys in 4 chairs is $_7 P_4$. [The permutation key ($_n P_r$) is available in most calculators. Check that your calculator has this key and verify that $_7 P_4 = 840$.]

In the special case when $r = n$, we have $_n P_n = \dfrac{n!}{0!}$. However, from section 11.5, the number of permutations of *n* things taken *n* (i.e. all) at a time is $n!$. To be compatible, we define $0! = 1$. So $_n P_n = n!$.

▶ Example 10

Using the digits 1, 2, 3, 4, 5 and 6, how many 4-digit numbers can be formed if repetition is not allowed?

▶ Solution . . .

Number of 4-digit numbers that can be formed
= number of permutations of 6 digits taken 4 at a time
= $_6 P_4 = 360$

▶ Example 11

(a) 10 different books are to be arranged on a book shelf. How many possible arrangements are there?

(b) If the shelf has space for only 8 books, how many ways are there of arranging 8 of the books on the shelf?

▶ **Solution . . .**

(a) Number of arrangements of 10 different books
= 10! = 3 628 800

(b) There are 10 different books.
Number of ways of arranging 8 books on the shelf
= $_{10}P_8$ = 1 814 400

▶ **Example 12**

Find the number of ways of arranging the letters in the word 'algebra' such that it begins and ends with an 'a'.

▶ **Solution . . .**

Since the two 'a's are fixed in the first and last positions (there is only one way of arranging this), the remaining 5 letters, l, g, e, b and r, can be arranged in the five positions between the two 'a's in 5! ways, i.e. 120 ways.

Exercise 11B *(Answers on page 502)*

1. Without using a calculator, find the value of

    (a) 5!,   **(b)** $\dfrac{10!}{7!}$,   **(c)** $_8P_3$,   **(d)** $\dfrac{_{10}P_4}{_8P_2}$.

2. Find the value of n if
    (a) $_nP_2 = 72$,   **(b)** $_nP_3 = 120$.

3. 4 playing cards, ace of spade, ace of heart, ace of diamond and ace of club, are to be arranged in a row. How many ways can this be done?

4. 6 girls are to stand in a straight line. How many possible arrangements are there?

5. Find the number of ways of arranging the letters a, b, c, d, e, f and g, taken 4 at a time.

6. Given 10 different letters, find the number of permutations of 3 letters.

7. Using the digits 1, 2, 3, 4, 5 and 6, find (without repetition)

   (a) the number of 6-digit numbers that can be formed,

   (b) the number of 5-digit numbers that can be formed.

8. In how many ways can 10 girls be arranged in a line if the shortest girl must be at the front of the line and the tallest must be at the back?

9. In how many ways can 5 girls and 4 boys be arranged in a line if no two persons of the same sex can be next to each other?

10. In how many ways can the letters of the word 'eleven' be arranged such that the vowels occupy alternate positions?

11.7 Selecting *r* Things from *n* Different Things

We recall that a selection or combination of a given number of things is a set of things chosen from those given, where the order of the things in the set is not taken into consideration.

Suppose we are given the set of letters A, B, C, D, E, F and G (7 letters) and we wish to make a selection of 4 letters from it. How many ways can this be done?

Let us assume there are x possible selections. Now, for each selection of 4 letters (e.g. ABCD) there are 4! permutations of the 4 letters (see section 11.5). Hence, the total number of permutations $= x(4!)$. However, we have learned that the total number of permutations of 7 things taken 4 at a time is $_7P_4$.

$$\therefore \qquad x(4!) = {_7}P_4$$

$$\text{or} \qquad x(4!) = \frac{7!}{(7-4)!}$$

$$\text{i.e.} \qquad x = \frac{7!}{(7-4)!\,4!}$$

$$= 35$$

So there are 35 selections of 4 letters from the set of 7 letters.

In generalising, we have the following result:

> The number of combinations (or selections) of n unlike things taken r at a time is $\dfrac{n!}{(n-r)!\,r!}$.

The notation for the number of combinations of n things taken r at a time is $_nC_r$.

Hence, $_nC_r = \dfrac{n!}{(n-r)!\,r!} = \dfrac{n(n-1)(n-2)...(n-r+1)}{r!}$

Another notation used instead of $_nC_r$ is $\binom{n}{r}$. We shall be using the $_nC_r$ notation in this chapter and the $\binom{n}{r}$ notation in the next chapter. Students are expected to be familiar with both notations.

Thus, the number of combinations of 4 letters from the set of 7 is

$$_7C_4 = \frac{7 \cdot 6 \cdot 5}{3 \cdot 2 \cdot 1} = 35.$$

[The combination key ($_nC_r$) is available in most calculators. Check that your calculator has this key and verify that $_7C_4 = 35$.]

In the special case when $r = n$, we have $_nC_n = \dfrac{n!}{0!n!}$

$$= 1 \text{ (as } 0! = 1)$$

This is logical as there is only 1 way of selecting n things from n things, that is, the selection of all the n things.

Let us now return to the notation $_nC_r = \dfrac{n!}{(n-r)!r!}$.

Rearranging it, we have $\qquad r! \, _nC_r = \dfrac{n!}{(n-r)!}$,

but $\dfrac{n!}{(n-r)!}$ is $_nP_r$ (see section 11.6).

Hence, $r!_nC_r = {}_nP_r$.

Also, starting from the notation $_nC_r = \dfrac{n!}{(n-r)!r!}$, if we replace r by $n-r$, we

obtain $_nC_{n-r} = \dfrac{n!}{[n-(n-r)]!(n-r)!}$

$$= \frac{n!}{r!(n-r)!} \text{ which is the same as } _nC_r.$$

Hence, $_nC_r = {}_nC_{n-r}$.

This result is useful in numerical work especially if the use of a calculator is disallowed. For example, it is troublesome to write

$$_{100}C_{97} = \frac{100 \cdot 99 \cdot 98 \dots 6 \cdot 5 \cdot 4}{97 \cdot 96 \cdot 95 \dots 3 \cdot 2 \cdot 1}$$

but easier to use $_{100}C_{97} = {}_{100}C_3$

$$= \frac{100 \cdot 99 \cdot 98}{3 \cdot 2 \cdot 1}$$

$$= 161\ 700$$

▶ **Example 13**

In how many ways can a committee of 3 be chosen from a group of 10 students?

▶ **Solution . . .**

Number of ways of choosing a committee of 3 from 10 students

$= {}_{10}C_3$

$= \dfrac{10 \cdot 9 \cdot 8}{3 \cdot 2 \cdot 1}$ (or use a calculator to obtain the value of $_{10}C_3$)

$= 120$

▶ Example 14

Find the number of combinations of 30 things taken 27 at a time.

▶ Solution . . .

Number of combinations of 30 things taken 27 at a time

$= {}_{30}C_{27}$

$= {}_{30}C_3$

$= \dfrac{30 \cdot 29 \cdot 28}{3 \cdot 2 \cdot 1}$

$= 4\ 060$

▶ Example 15

3 boys and 2 girls are to be chosen to represent a class of 30 boys and 10 girls. In how many ways can this be done?

▶ Solution . . .

The 3 boys can be chosen from 30 in ${}_{30}C_3$ ways.

The 2 girls can be chosen from 10 in ${}_{10}C_2$ ways.

Number of ways of choosing 3 boys and 2 girls from the class

$= {}_{30}C_3 \times {}_{10}C_2$

$= 4\ 060 \times 25$

$= 101\ 500$

▶ Example 16

A committee of 4 which must have members of both sexes is to be chosen from 5 boys and 6 girls. In how many ways can this be done?

▶ Solution . . .

To have members of both sexes in the committee, the committee can comprise 3 boys and 1 girl, 2 boys and 2 girls, or 1 boy and 3 girls.

Number of ways of choosing a committee of 3 boys and 1 girl

$= {}_5C_3 \times {}_6C_1$

$= 10 \times 6$

$= 60$

Number of ways of choosing a committee of 2 boys and 2 girls

$= {}_5C_2 \times {}_6C_2$

$= 10 \times 15$

$= 150$

Number of ways of choosing a committee of 1 boy and 3 girls

$= {}_5C_1 \times {}_6C_3$

$= 5 \times 20$

$= 100$

Hence, the total number of ways of choosing the committee of 4
= 60 + 150 + 100
= 310

Exercise 11C (*Answers on page 502*)

1. Without using a calculator, find the value of

   (a) $_8C_4$,   **(b)** $_{50}C_{48}$,   **(c)** $\dfrac{_{20}C_6}{_{20}C_5}$.

2. Find the value of n if
   (a) $_nC_2 = 21$,   **(b)** $_nC_3 = 20$,   **(c)** $_nC_{13} = {}_nC_7$.

3. In how many ways can 4 books be selected from 9 books?

4. How many selections of 4 cards can be made from an ordinary pack of 52 playing cards?

5. How many selections of 20 letters can be made from the alphabet of 26 letters?

6. How many combinations of 2 vowels and 3 consonants can be made from the word 'SINGAPORE'?

7. Given the digits 1, 2, 3, 4, 5, 6, 7, 8 and 9, how many selections of 2 odd and 2 even digits can be made?

8. A committee of 4 men and 3 women are to be formed from 10 men and 8 women. In how many ways can this be done?

9. An advisory council consisting of 1 Indian, 2 Malays and 3 Chinese are to be formed from 3 Indians, 6 Malays and 10 Chinese. In how many ways can the council be formed?

10. A committee of 5 members is to be formed from 8 men and 6 women. In how many ways can this be done if both sexes must be represented in the committee? In how many of these committees is there a majority of men?

Summary

1. 3 notations:
   (a) $n! = n \cdot (n-1) \cdot (n-2) \ldots 3 \cdot 2 \cdot 1$

   (b) $_nP_r = \dfrac{n!}{(n-r)!}$

   $= n \cdot (n-1) \cdot (n-2) \ldots (n-r+1)$

   (c) $_nC_r = \dfrac{n!}{(n-r)!\,r!}$

   $= \dfrac{n(n-1)(n-2)\ldots(n-r+1)}{r!}$

2. 2 relationships:
   (a) $r!\,_nC_r = {_nP_r}$
   (b) $_nC_r = {_nC_{n-r}}$

3. **Product Principle:** If one process can be done in p ways, and a second process can be done in q ways, then the total number of different ways in which both processes can be done is $p \times q$.

   Extension: If one process can be done in p ways, a second process can be done in q ways, a third process can be done in r ways and so on, then the number of ways in which all the processes can be done is $p \times q \times r \times \ldots$.

4. The number of permutations (or arrangements) of n unlike things taken all together is $_nP_n = n!$

5. The number of permutations (or arrangements) of n unlike things taken r at a time is $_nP_r$.

6. The number of combinations (or selections) of n unlike things taken r at a time is $_nC_r$.

Revision Exercise 11 (Answers on page 503)

1. In how many ways can 4 playing cards be selected from an ordinary pack of 52 if one of the cards must be an ace?

2. In how many ways can the letters of the word 'equation' be arranged? In how many ways can a consonant and 2 vowels be chosen from the word?

3. Find the number of ways of arranging 5 boys and 6 girls in a line if no two persons of the same sex are next to each other.

4. In how many ways can the letters of the word 'permutation' be arranged such that it begins and ends with a 't'? In addition, if no two vowels are to be next to each other, how many arrangements can there be?

5. If there are 12 points, no 3 of which are collinear, find the greatest number of triangles that can be drawn with these points as vertices.

6. In a mathematics examination, there are 2 papers of 10 questions each. In the first paper, candidates are required to answer any 6 questions, and in the second paper, any 5 questions. In how many different ways can a candidate choose the 11 questions?

7. Find how many numbers between 4000 and 5000 can be formed using only the digits 1, 2, 3, 4 and 5, no digit being repeated.

8. 3 boys and 2 girls are to stand in a straight line. Find how many different arrangements there are if
   (a) no two persons of the same sex are to stand next to each other,
   (b) the first and last person in the line are both girls.

9. A delegation of 4 students is to be chosen from a group of 5 boys and 6 girls. Find the number of such delegations that contain at least a boy and a girl.

10. 8 teams participate in a soccer tournament.
    (a) If each team has to play against every other team, what is the total number of matches?
    (b) In this case, in how many different ways can the results of the matches turn out?

Maths Booster

There are 4 different letters addressed to 4 people whose addresses are written on four envelopes. How many ways are there of putting the letters in the envelopes such that
(a) 3 of the letters are in the wrong envelopes and 1 is in the correct envelope,
(b) 1 of the letters is in the wrong envelope and 3 are in the correct envelopes?

Chapter 12
Binomial Expansions

Around 300 BC, Euclid discovered that $(a + b)^2 = a^2 + 2ab + b^2$.

Then Omar Khayyan developed the expansions for $(a + b)^4$, $(a + b)^5$ and $(a + b)^6$ around AD1100.

The array of coefficients seen in a series of binomial expressions is associated with Pascal (1623 – 1662), although the use of this array was discovered even earlier.

Sir Isaac Newton later (about 1676) extended the idea of the Binomial Theorem and applied it to the many difficult problems.

Today the Binomial Theorem is useful in many branches of mathematics.

12.1 Pascal's Triangle

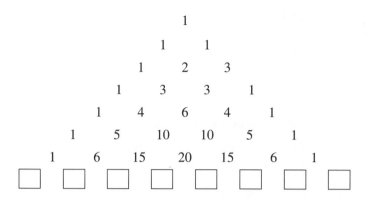

Look at patterns
1. Refer to the Pascal's Triangle given on this page. Complete the bottom row by filling in the boxes with the appropriate numbers.
2. Make a copy of Pascal's Triangle for binomial coefficients up to a power of 10 to keep for reference.

Study the above triangular array of numbers carefully. Note that the first and last numbers are 1's and each of the other numbers is the sum of the two numbers immediately above it.

Observe also that the numbers in each row are symmetrically arranged. Using the above method, you can construct the triangular array of numbers one row at a time. This triangular array of numbers is called **Pascal's Triangle**.

MATHS BULLETIN

Pascal's Triangle is named after the French mathematician, Blaise Pascal. Pascal was born on the 19th of June, 1623, in Clermont (now Clermont- Ferrand), Paris. He was the third child and the only son in the family. His mother died when he was only three years old.

Pascal and his family moved to Paris in 1632. His father had an unorthodox view about education and taught his son himself. He decided that young Pascal was not to study mathematics till the age of 15. All texts on mathematics were removed from their house. Being curious at the age of 12, Pascal started to work on geometry on his own. He made a discovery that the sum of the angles of a triangle is two right angles.

When he was 16, he presented a paper containing a number of projective geometry theorems. In 1640, he started working on a device to help his father who was working as a tax collector. This device could do simple calculations like addition and subtraction. In the later part of his life, Pascal continued to make further discoveries and contributed to the field of mathematics and science.

1. Discuss the factors that could have helped Pascal in his discoveries and inventions.

2. 'Great minds think alike!' There is certainly some truth to that phrase. Find out from the Internet two other persons in history who had studied or described a triangular pattern of numbers similar to Pascal's.

12.2 Binomial Expansion

'Bi' means '2', and 'nomial' means 'term' in Latin.

A **binomial expression** is one that contains two terms such as $(x + 2y)$, $(3 + 4a)$ and $(2a - b)$.

If we square the binomial $(a + b)$, i.e.

$$(a + b)^2 = (a + b)(a + b)$$
$$= a^2 + 2ab + b^2,$$

the result is called an **expansion** of $(a + b)^2$.

We now expand $(a + b)^3$ and $(a + b)^4$ as follows:

$$(a + b)^3 = (a + b)(a + b)^2$$
$$= (a + b)(a^2 + 2ab + b^2)$$
$$= a^3 + 2a^2b + ab^2 + a^2b + 2ab^2 + b^3$$
$$= a^3 + 3a^2b + 3ab^2 + b^3$$
$$(a + b)^4 = (a + b)(a + b)^3$$
$$= (a + b)(a^3 + 3a^2b + 3ab^2 + b^3)$$
$$= a^4 + 3a^3b + 3a^2b^2 + ab^3 + a^3b + 3a^2b^2 + 3ab^3 + b^4$$
$$= a^4 + 4a^3b + 6a^2b^2 + 4ab^3 + b^4$$

In this way, we can expand $(a + b)^n$ for any positive integral value of n. However, this gets more and more tedious for bigger values of n.

Let us explore another way of expanding $(a + b)^n$ by first looking at the coefficients of the terms. These are the numbers accompanying the terms in a and b. For example, the coefficient of a^3b in $4a^3b$ is 4. The coefficients of terms in binomial expansions are called **binomial coefficients**. The binomial coefficients of $(a + b)^4$ are 1, 4, 6, 4, 1. If we arrange the binomial coefficients of $(a + b)^n$ in increasing powers of n, we have:

Expansion of			Coefficients			
$(a + b)^1$				1	1	
$(a + b)^2$			1	2	1	
$(a + b)^3$		1	3	3	1	
$(a + b)^4$	1	4	6	4	1	

Does the pattern of numbers look familiar? Compare this to the Pascal's Triangle in section 12.1. Indeed, this is part of Pascal's Triangle. We therefore have a convenient way of expanding binomial expressions using the binomial coefficients in Pascal's Triangle. For example, the binomial coefficients of $(a + b)^5$ are 1, 5, 10, 10, 5, 1. So $(a + b)^5 = a^5 + 5a^4b + 10a^3b^2 + 10a^2b^3 + 5ab^4 + b^5$.

Observation

From the binomial expansion of $(a + b)^5$ as shown,

(a) what do you observe about the powers of a and the powers of b,

(b) what do you observe about the sum of the powers of a and b in each term,

(c) what do you observe about the number of terms compared to the power of the binomial,

(d) what can you say about the symmetry of the binomial coefficients?

▶ ## Example 1

Expand

(a) $(a + b)^6$,

(b) $(x + y)^8$.

▶ ## Solution . . .

(a) From Pascal's Triangle, the binomial coefficients of $(a + b)^6$ are

$$1, 6, 15, 20, 15, 6, 1.$$

$$(a + b)^6 = 1a^6 + 6a^5b + 15a^4b^2 + 20a^3b^3 + 15a^2b^4 + 6ab^5 + 1b^6$$

Note:

(1) $1a^6$ and $1b^6$ can be written as a^6 and b^6 respectively, omitting 1.

(2)   The powers of a decrease from 6 to 0 while the powers of b increase from 0 to 6.

(3)   The sum of the powers of the variables in each term is always 6.

(b) From Pascal's Triangle, the binomial coefficients are

$$1, 8, 28, 56, 70, 56, 28, 8, 1.$$

Here, a is replaced by x and b by y respectively.

$$(x + y)^8 = x^8 + 8x^7y + 28x^6y^2 + 56x^5y^3 + 70x^4y^4 + 56x^3y^5 + 28x^2y^6 \\ + 8xy^7 + y^8$$

▶ ## Example 2

Expand

(a) $(1 + 2x)^4$,   **(b)** $(2x - 1)^4$.

▶ ## Solution . . .

The binomial coefficients for $(a + b)^4$ are 1, 4, 6, 4, 1.

(a) Here, $a = 1$ and $b = 2x$.

$$(1 + 2x)^4 = (1)^4 + 4(1)^3(2x) + 6(1)^2(2x)^2 + 4(1)^1(2x)^3 + (2x)^4$$
$$= 1 + 8x + 24x^2 + 32x^3 + 16x^4$$

Note:

(1)   The resulting coefficients are different from the original binomial coefficients.

(2)   Powers of 1, eg. $(1)^4$ and $(1)^3$, may be written simply as 1 if it stands by itself, or omitted if it is part of a term.

(3) The powers of x are in ascending order.

(b) Here, $a = 2x$ and $b = -1$.

$$(2x - 1)^4 = (2x)^4 + 4(2x)^3(-1) + 6(2x)^2(-1)^2 + 4(2x)(-1)^3 + (-1)^4$$
$$= 16x^4 - 32x^3 + 24x^2 - 8x + 1$$

Note:

(1) The powers of x are in descending order.

(2) The signs of the terms alternate between positive and negative as even powers of -1 give a value of 1 while odd powers of -1 give a value of -1.

▶ **Example 3**

Expand and simplify $\left(2 + \dfrac{x}{2}\right)^6$. Hence, write down the expansion of $\left(2 - \dfrac{x}{2}\right)^6$.

▶ **Solution . . .**

The binomial coefficients are 1, 6, 15, 20, 15, 6, 1.

Here, $a = 2$ and $b = \dfrac{x}{2}$.

$$\left(2 + \frac{x}{2}\right)^6 = 2^6 + 6(2)^5\left(\frac{x}{2}\right) + 15(2)^4\left(\frac{x}{2}\right)^2 + 20(2)^3\left(\frac{x}{2}\right)^3 + 15(2)^2\left(\frac{x}{2}\right)^4 +$$
$$6(2)\left(\frac{x}{2}\right)^5 + \left(\frac{x}{2}\right)^6$$

$$= 64 + 96x + 60x^2 + 20x^3 + \frac{15}{4}x^4 + \frac{3}{8}x^5 + \frac{x^6}{64}.$$

Replacing $\left(\dfrac{x}{2}\right)$ by $\left(-\dfrac{x}{2}\right)$ and noting that even powers of $\left(-\dfrac{x}{2}\right)$ give a positive value and odd powers of $\left(-\dfrac{x}{2}\right)$ give a negative value, then

$$\left(2 - \frac{x}{2}\right)^6 = 64 - 96x + 60x^2 - 20x^3 + \frac{15}{4}x^4 - \frac{3}{8}x^5 + \frac{x^6}{64}.$$

▶ **Example 4**

(a) Write down the expansions of $(x + 1)^3$ and $(x - 1)^3$.

(b) Hence, simplify $(x + 1)^3 - (x - 1)^3$.

(c) Use your result to find the exact value of $(\sqrt{3} + 1)^3 - (\sqrt{3} - 1)^3$.

▶ **Solution . . .**

(a) $(x + 1)^3 = x^3 + 3x^2 + 3x + 1$ . . . . . (1)
$(x - 1)^3 = x^3 - 3x^2 + 3x - 1$ . . . . . (2)

(b) $(1) - (2)$: $(x + 1)^3 - (x - 1)^3 = 6x^2 + 2$

(c) Putting $x = \sqrt{3}$ in part (b),

$$(\sqrt{3} + 1)^3 - (\sqrt{3} - 1)^3 = 6(\sqrt{3})^2 + 2$$
$$= 18 + 2$$
$$= 20$$

▶ Example 5

(a) Write down the first four terms of the expression of $(1 + x)^8$ in ascending powers of x.

(b) Use these terms to find an approximate value of $(1.01)^8$.

▶ Solution . . .

(a) $(1 + x)^8 = 1 + 8x + 28x^2 + 56x^3$ (first four terms)

(b) $(1.01)^8 = (1 + 0.01)^8$

$\approx 1 + 8(0.01) + 28(0.01)^2 + 56(0.01)^3$

$= 1 + 0.08 + 0.002\ 8 + 0.000\ 056$

$= 1.082\ 856$

Compare this approximate value to the exact value of $1.082\ 856\ 706$ found using the calculator.

▶ Example 6

(a) Expand $(1 + y)^4$ in ascending powers of y.

(b) Hence, find the expansion of $(1 + x + x^2)^4$ as far as the term in x^3.

▶ Solution . . .

(a) $(1 + y)^4 = 1 + 4y + 6y^2 + 4y^3 + y^4$

(b) Replacing y by $(x + x^2)$, we get:

$(1 + x + x^2)^4 = 1 + 4(x + x^2) + 6(x + x^2)^2 + 4(x + x^2)^3 + (x + x^2)^4$

$= 1 + 4x + 4x^2 + 6(x^2 + 2x^3 + \ldots) + 4(x^3 + \ldots) + \ldots$

(where terms higher than x^3 are left out)

$= 1 + 4x + 4x^2 + 6x^2 + 12x^3 + 4x^3 + \ldots$

$= 1 + 4x + 10x^2 + 16x^3$ (up to the term in x^3)

▶ Example 7

(a) Find, in ascending powers of x, the expansions of $(1 - 2x)^3$ and $(2 + x)^4$.

(b) Hence find the first four terms of the expansion of $(1 - 2x)^3(2 + x)^4$.

▶ Solution . . .

(a) $(1 - 2x)^3 = 1 + 3(-2x) + 3(-2x)^2 + (-2x)^3$

$$= 1 - 6x + 12x^2 - 8x^3$$

$(2 + x)^4 = 2^4 + 4(2^3)(x) + 6(2^2)(x^2) + 4(2)(x^3) + 4x^4$

$$= 16 + 32x + 24x^2 + 8x^3 + x^4$$

(b) $(1 - 2x)^3(2 + x)^4 = (1 - 6x + 12x^2 - 8x^3)(16 + 32x + 24x^2 + 8x^3 + x^4)$

The first four terms will go up to the power of x^3. So we multiply the terms in the first bracket by 16, 32x, 24x^2 and 8x^3 and leave out any terms higher than x^3.

Multiplying by 16	$16 - 96x + 192x^2 - 128x^3$
Multiplying by 32x	$32x - 192x^2 + 384x^3$
Multiplying by 24x^2	$24x^2 - 144x^3$
Multiplying by 8x^3	$8x^3$
Adding	$16 - 64x + 24x^2 + 120x^3$

▶ Example 8

(a) Find the terms in x^3 and x^4 in the expansion of $\left(3 - \frac{x}{3}\right)^6$ in ascending powers of x.

(b) Hence find the coefficient of x^4 in the expansion of $\left(1 - \frac{x}{2}\right)\left(3 - \frac{x}{3}\right)^6$.

▶ Solution . . .

(a) $\left(3 - \frac{x}{3}\right)^6 = 3^6 + 6(3^5)\left(-\frac{x}{3}\right) + 15(3^4)\left(-\frac{x}{3}\right)^2 + 20(3^3)\left(-\frac{x}{3}\right)^3 +$

$$15(3^2)\left(-\frac{x}{3}\right)^4 \ldots$$

So the x^3 term is $-20x^3$ and the x^4 term is $+\frac{5x^4}{3}$.

(b) Then $\left(1 - \frac{x}{2}\right)\left(3 - \frac{x}{3}\right)^6 = \left(1 - \frac{x}{2}\right)\left(\ldots - 20x^3 + \frac{5x^4}{3} \ldots\right)$

The term in x^4 is found by multiplying the relevant terms as shown, and is $10x^4 + \frac{5x^4}{3}$ giving a coefficient of $\frac{35}{3}$.

▶ Example 9

Write down and simplify the first three terms in the expansions (in ascending powers of x) of **(a)** $\left(1 - \frac{3x^2}{2}\right)^5$ and **(b)** $(2 + x)^5$. Hence find the coefficient of x^2 in the expansion of $\left(2 - 2x - \frac{3x^2}{2}\right)^5$.

▶ Solution . . .

(a) $\left(1 - \frac{3x}{2}\right)^5 = 1 + 5\left(-\frac{3x}{2}\right) + 10\left(-\frac{3x}{2}\right)^2 \ldots = 1 - \frac{15x}{2} + \frac{45x^2}{2} \ldots$

(b) $(2 + x)^5 = 2^5 + 5(2^4)(x) + 10(2^3)(x^2) \ldots = 32 + 80x + 80x^2 \ldots$

We notice that $\left(2 - 2x - \dfrac{3x^2}{2}\right)^5$ is the product of (a) and (b),

i.e. $\left[\left(1 - \dfrac{3x}{2}\right)(2 + x)\right]^5$

$$= \left[1 - \frac{15x}{2} + \frac{45x^2}{2} \ldots\right]\left[32 + 80x + 80x^2 \ldots\right]$$

The term in x^2 is the sum of the products linked together as shown, so the coefficient of x^2 is $80 - \left(\dfrac{15}{2} \times 80\right) + \left(\dfrac{45}{2} \times 32\right) = 200$.

▶ **Example 10**

(a) Find the first three terms in the expansion of $(1 - 3x)^5$ in ascending powers of x.

(b) If the first three terms in the expansion of $(p + qx)(1 - 3x)^5$ are $3 + rx + 300x^2$, state the value of p and find the values of q and r.

▶ **Solution . . .**

(a) The first three terms of $(1 - 3x)^5$ are $1 + 5(-3x) + 10(-3x)^2$
$$= 1 - 15x + 90x^2.$$

(b) The first three terms of $(p + qx)(1 - 3x)^5$ will come from
$(p + qx)(1 - 15x + 90x^2)$.

The first term is p, so $p = 3$.

The term in x is $qx - 15px$, so $q - 15p = r$. $\qquad$ . . . . . (1)

The term in x^2 is $90px^2 - 15qx^2$, so $90p - 15q = 300$. $\quad$ . . . . . (2)

From (2), $270 - 15q = 300$, so $q = -2$.

From (1), $r = -2 - 45 = -47$.

Exercise 12A *(Answers on page 503)*

1. Find, in descending powers of x, the expansions of:
   (a) $(x - 2)^4$ $\qquad\qquad$ **(b)** $(2x - 3)^3$

   (c) $(2x + 1)^5$ $\qquad\qquad$ **(d)** $\left(x - \dfrac{1}{2}\right)^5$

   (e) $\left(x + \dfrac{1}{x}\right)^6$ $\qquad\qquad$ **(f)** $\left(\dfrac{x}{4} - 2\right)^4$

2. Expand the following in ascending powers of x:
   (a) $(1 - 2x)^5$ $\qquad\qquad$ **(b)** $(2 - 3x)^4$

   (c) $\left(2 - \dfrac{x}{2}\right)^6$ $\qquad\qquad$ **(d)** $(1 - x^2)^3$

3. Find, in ascending powers of x, the first four terms in the expansion of:

 (a) $(2-x)^5$ (b) $(1-2x)^7$

 (c) $(1-\frac{x}{2})^8$ (d) $\left(4-\frac{x}{2}\right)^5$

4. Find the expansions of (a) $(3x-2y)^4$, (b) $\left(x-\frac{1}{x}\right)^5$.

5. Expand $(a+b)^5$. If $a=\frac{3}{4}$ and $b=\frac{1}{4}$, find the value (as a fraction) of the fourth term of the expansion.

6. Write down the first four terms of the expansion of $(1-x)^6$ in ascending powers of x.
 Using these terms, find an approximate value of $(0.99)^6$.

7. (a) Write down the expansions of $(1+x)^3$ and $(1-x)^3$.
 (b) Hence simplify $(1+x)^3+(1-x)^3$. Use your result to find the exact value of $(1+\sqrt{2})^3+(1-\sqrt{2})^3$.

8. By using the expansions of $(2+x)^4$ and $(2-x)^4$, find the exact value of $(2+\sqrt{3})^4+(2-\sqrt{3})^4$.

9. (a) Write down the expansions of $(1+x)^4$ and $(1-x)^4$.
 (b) Hence simplify the expression $(1+x)^4-(1-x)^4$. Use your result to find the value of $1.01^4-0.99^4$.

10. (a) Obtain the expansions of $\left(x+\frac{1}{x}\right)^5$ and $\left(x-\frac{1}{x}\right)^5$.

 (b) Hence simplify $\left(x+\frac{1}{x}\right)^5-\left(x-\frac{1}{x}\right)^5$.

 (c) Choosing a suitable value of x, find the value of $2.5^5-1.5^5$.

11. Write down the expansion of $(1-x)^4$. Use your result to find the expansion of $\left(1-x+\frac{x^2}{2}\right)^4$ in ascending powers of x as far as the term in x^2.

12. Use the expansion of $(1+x)^3$ to find the first three terms in the expansion of $\left(1+\frac{x}{2}-x^2\right)^3$ in ascending powers of x.

13. Find, in ascending powers of x, the first three terms in the expansions of (a) $(2-x)^4$ and (b) $\left(3-\frac{x}{2}\right)^4$. Hence find the coefficients of x and x^2 in the expansion of $\left(6-4x+\frac{x^2}{2}\right)^4$.

14. **(a)** Write down the expansion of $(1 + x)^5$ in ascending powers of x as far as the term in x^3.
   (b) Hence find the first four terms in the expansion of $(1 + x - x^2)^5$.

15. Expand, in ascending powers of x, **(a)** $(1 + 2x)^4$ and **(b)** $(1 - x)^3$. Hence find the first three terms in the expansion of $(1 + 2x)^4(1 - x)^3$.

16. Write down the expansions of $(1 + 2x)^3$ and $\left(2 - \frac{x}{2}\right)^4$ in ascending powers of x. Hence find the coefficient of the term in x^2 in the expansion of $(1 + 2x)^3\left(2 - \frac{x}{2}\right)^4$.

17. Find the coefficient of x^3 in the expansion of $(1 - 2x)^3\left(1 + \frac{3x}{2}\right)^4$.

18. Expand each of the binomials $(1 + x)^5$ and $(2 - x)^5$ as far as the term in x^3. Hence find the coefficient of x^3 in the expansion of $(2 + x - x^2)^5$.

19. **(a)** Expand $(1 + ax)^3$ and $(b + x)^4$ in ascending powers of x.
   (b) If the first two terms in the expansion of $(1 + ax)^3(b + x)^4$ are $16 - 64x$, state the value of b and find the value of a.

20. **(a)** State the expansions of **(i)** $(1 + ax)^3$ and **(ii)** $(1 + bx)^4$ in ascending powers of x.
   (b) If the second and third terms in the expansion of $(1 + ax)^3 (1 + bx)^4$ are $5x$ and $3x^2$ respectively, find the values of a and b.

12.3 Binomial Theorem

Although Pascal's Triangle is useful for binomial expansions, it is not always practical to use it. For example, during examination conditions, you will not have access to Pascal's Triangle and it may take too much time to construct one.

In addition it will be very tedious to extend Pascal's Triangle when the value of the power n is large, eg. $n = 20$. It is not practical to use Pascal's Triangle in problems where n is an unknown. To overcome these difficulties, we use the **Binomial Theorem** as follows:

$$(a + b)^n = a^n + \binom{n}{1}a^{n-1}b + \binom{n}{2}a^{n-2}b^2 + \ldots + \binom{n}{r}a^{n-r}b^r + \ldots + b^n$$

The proof of the Binomial Theorem is beyond the scope of the syllabus.

We note that there are $(n + 1)$ terms in the expansion of $(a + b)^n$.

The coefficients are:　　1　　$\binom{n}{1}$　$\binom{n}{2}$　$\ldots$　$\binom{n}{r}$　$\ldots$　1

The terms are:　　　　T_1　T_2　T_3　$\ldots$　T_{r+1}　$\ldots$　T_{n+1}

where T_r represents the rth term.

The first and last coefficients are always 1 when n is a positive integer (which will always be the case in our work). Thus, the binomial coefficients in the expansion of $(a + b)^6$ are:

$$1 \quad \binom{6}{1} \quad \binom{6}{2} \quad \binom{6}{3} \quad \binom{6}{4} \quad \binom{6}{5} \quad 1$$

$$1 \quad 6 \quad 15 \quad 20 \quad 15 \quad 6 \quad 1$$

The expansion of $(a + b)^6$ is then $a^6 + 6a^5b + 15a^4b^2 + 20a^3b^3 + 15a^2b^4 + 6ab^5 + b^6$.

It is useful to bear in mind that in the general term $T_{r+1} = \binom{n}{r}a^{n-r}b^r$, the coefficient is $\binom{n}{r}$, the power of b is r and the power of a is $n - r$ (or the sum of the powers of a and b is n).

Although the value of $\binom{n}{r}$ can be obtained from the calculator when numerical values of n and r are known, we still need the general term in problems with algebraic terms.

▶ **Example 11**

Use the Binomial Theorem to find, in ascending powers of x, the first four terms in the expansion of

(a) $(2 + x)^8$,

(b) $(1 - 2x)^{12}$.

Compare and Verify
Compare the binomial coefficients in the expansion of $(a + b)^6$ as shown to the corresponding coefficient in Pascal's Triangle.
Verify that they are identical.

▶ **Solution . . .**

(a) Here, $a = 2$, $b = x$ and $n = 8$.

$$(2 + x)^8 = 2^8 + \binom{8}{1}2^7x + \binom{8}{2}2^6x^2 + \binom{8}{3}2^5x^3 + \dots$$

$$= 2^8 + 8(2^7)x + 28(2^6)x^2 + 56(2^5)x^3 + \dots$$

$$= 256 + 1024x + 1792x^2 + 1792x^3 \text{ (first four terms)}$$

(b) Here, $a = 1$, $b = -2x$ and $n = 12$.

$$(1 - 2x)^{12} = 1 + \binom{12}{1}(-2x) + \binom{12}{2}(-2x)^2 + \binom{12}{3}(-2x)^3 + \dots$$

$$= 1 + 12(-2x) + 66(4x^2) + 220(-8x^3) + \dots$$

$$= 1 - 24x + 264x^2 - 1760x^3 \text{ (first four terms)}$$

▶ **Example 12**

Find the 5th and 6th terms in the expansion of $\left(2x - \frac{1}{2}\right)^{10}$ in descending powers of x.

► **Solution . . .**

Here, $a = 2x$, $b = -\frac{1}{2}$ and $n = 10$.

The $r + 1^{\text{th}}$ term is $\binom{n}{r}a^{n-r}b^r$.

Thus the 5th term, T_5, is obtained when $r = 4$.

$$T_5 = \binom{10}{4}(2x)^{10-4}\left(-\frac{1}{2}\right)^4$$
$$= 210(2x)^6\left(\frac{1}{2}\right)^4$$
$$= 840x^6$$

The 6th term, T_6, is obtained when $r = 5$.

$$T_6 = \binom{10}{5}(2x)^{10-5}\left(-\frac{1}{2}\right)^5$$
$$= 252(2x)^5\left(-\frac{1}{2}\right)^5$$
$$= -252x^5$$

► **Example 13**

In the expansion of $\left(\frac{1}{4} + 2x\right)^9$, find

(a) the term containing x^6,

(b) the coefficient of x^7.

► **Solution . . .**

Here, $a = \frac{1}{4}$, $b = 2x$ and $n = 9$.

(a) The term containing $x^6 = \binom{9}{6}\left(\frac{1}{4}\right)^3(2x)^6$

$$= 84\left(\frac{1}{2}\right)^6(2)^6x^6$$
$$= 84x^6$$

Alternatively, note that the term in x^6 is the 7th term and proceed to find T_7 as in Example 12.

(b) The term containing $x^7 = \binom{9}{7}\left(\frac{1}{4}\right)^2(2x)^7$

$$= 36\left(\frac{1}{2}\right)^4(2)^7x^7$$
$$= 216x^7$$

Hence, the coefficient of x^7 is 216.

► **Example 14**

In the expansion of $\left(2x - \frac{1}{x}\right)^{10}$, find

(a) the coefficient of x^6,

(b) the term independent of x.

▶ **Solution . . .**

From the Binomial Theorem, the $(r + 1)^{th}$ term is

$$\binom{10}{r}(2x)^{10-r}\left(-\frac{1}{x}\right)^r$$

$$= \binom{10}{r}(2^{10-r})x^{10-r}(-1)^r\left(\frac{1}{x}\right)^r$$

$$= \binom{10}{r}(2^{10-r})(-1)^r(x)^{10-r}(x)^{-r}$$

$$= \binom{10}{r}(2^{10-r})(-1)^r(x)^{10-2r}$$

(a) If this term is the term in x^6, then $x^{10-2r} = x^6$

$$10 - 2r = 6$$
$$2r = 4$$
$$r = 2$$

Hence, the term in x^6 is $\binom{10}{2}(2^8)(-1)^2x^6 = 45(2^8)x^6$

$$= 11\,520x^6$$

∴ the coefficient of x^6 is 11 520.

(b) For the term independent of x, the resulting power of x in the term must be zero.
Thus, $x^{10-2r} = x^0$

$$10 - 2r = 0$$
$$2r = 10$$
$$r = 5$$

So the 6th term is independent of x and this term is $\binom{10}{5}(2^5)(-1)^5x^0$

$$= -252(2^5)$$
$$= -8064$$

▶ **Example 15**

(a) Find, in ascending powers of x, the first three terms in the expansions of **(i)** $(1 + 2x)^8$, **(ii)** $(1 + mx)^6$.

(b) If the coefficient of x in the expansion of $(1 + 2x)^8(1 + mx)^6$ is 19, find **(i)** the value of m, **(ii)** the coefficient of x^2.

▶ **Solution . . .**

(a) **(i)** $(1 + 2x)^8 = 1 + \binom{8}{1}(2x) + \binom{8}{2}(2x)^2 + \ldots$

$$= 1 + 8(2x) + 28(4x^2) + \ldots$$
$$= 1 + 16x + 112x^2 \text{ (first three terms)}$$

(ii) $(1 + mx)^6 = 1 + \binom{6}{1}(mx) + \binom{6}{1}(mx)^2 + \ldots$

$$= 1 + 6(mx) + 15(m^2x^2) + \ldots$$
$$= 1 + 6mx + 15m^2x^2 \text{ (first three terms)}$$

(b) $(1 + 2x)^8(1 + mx)^6 = (1 + 16x + 12x^2)(1 + 6mx + 15m^2x^2) + \ldots$

(i) We require the term in x, so we pick out the terms (linked together above) whose products give x.

$\therefore$ term in $x = 1(6mx) + 16x(1)$

$\qquad\qquad = (6m + 16)x$

Hence, $6m + 16 = 19$,

$$\text{giving } m = \frac{1}{2}.$$

(ii) Substituting $m = \frac{1}{2}$,

$$(1 + 2x)^8\left(1 + \frac{1}{2}x\right)^6 = (1 + 16x + 112x^2)\left(1 + 3x + \frac{15}{4}x^2\right) + \ldots$$

We require the term in x^2, so we pick out the terms (linked together above) whose products give x^2.

$\therefore$ term in $x^2 = 1\left(\dfrac{15}{4}x^2\right) + 16x(3x) + 112x^2(1)$

$$= \frac{15}{4}x^2 + 48x^2 + 112x^2$$

$$= \frac{655}{4}x^2$$

Hence, the coefficient of x^2 is $\dfrac{655}{4}$.

▶ Example 16

Write down (without simplifying) the first three terms in the expansion of $(x + b)^n$ where n is a positive integer. If the coefficients of the second and third terms are –8 and 30 respectively, find the values of n and b.

▶ Solution . . .

$(x + b)^n = x^n + \binom{n}{1}x^{n-1}b + \binom{n}{2}x^{n-2}b^2$ (first three terms)

Hence the coefficients of the second and third terms are nb and $\dfrac{n(n-1)}{1 \times 2}b^2$ respectively.

Then $\qquad nb = -8 \qquad\qquad\qquad\qquad \ldots\ldots (1)$

and $\dfrac{n(n-1)}{2}b^2 = 30$, i.e. $n(n-1)b^2 = 60 \qquad \ldots\ldots (2)$

We solve these equations for n and b.

In (2), substituting $b = \dfrac{-8}{n}$,

$$n(n-1)\frac{64}{n^2} = 60 \qquad \text{or} \qquad \frac{n-1}{n} = \frac{60}{64}.$$

Then $64n - 64 = 60n$ from which we find $n = 16$.

From (1), $b = \dfrac{-8}{16} = -\dfrac{1}{2}$.

▶ **Example 17**

(a) Expand $(1-x)^{10}$ in ascending powers of x as far as the term in x^4.

(b) Use your expansion to find the value of $(0.98)^{10}$ correct to 5 decimal places.

▶ **Solution . . .**

(a) $(1-x)^{10} = 1 + \binom{10}{1}(-x) + \binom{10}{2}(-x)^2 + \binom{10}{3}(-x)^3 + \binom{10}{4}(-x)^4 + \ldots$

$\qquad = 1 - 10x + 45x^2 - 120x^3 + 210x^4$ (up to term in x^4)

(b) $(0.98)^{10} = (1 - 0.02)^{10}$ (so $x = 0.02$)

$\qquad \approx 1 - 10(0.02) + 45(0.02)^2 - 120(0.02)^3 + 210(0.02)^4$

$\qquad = 1 - 0.2 + 0.018 - 0.000\,96 + 0.000\,033\,6$

$\qquad = 0.817\,07$ (to 5 decimal places)

Note:

(1) As a check, observe that the next term $\binom{10}{5}(-x)^5$

$\qquad = -252(0.02)^5$

$\qquad = -0.000\,000\,806\,4$

would not affect the answer to 5 decimal places, thus ensuring that sufficient terms have been taken in (b) to ensure the required accuracy.

(2) Always check the value with that obtained by using a calculator to ensure that mistakes are not made in the working.

Exercise 12B *(Answers on page 503)*

1. Write down and simplify the first three terms of

    (a) $(1+x)^{10}$,

    (b) $\left(x - \dfrac{1}{2}\right)^{12}$,

    (c) $\left(x - \dfrac{1}{x}\right)^{9}$.

2. For the following expansions, find

    (a) the coefficient of the ninth term in $(2x - 1)^{12}$,

    (b) the coefficient of the fourth term in $(1 - 3x)^{10}$,

    (c) the coefficient of the fifth term in $\left(x - \dfrac{1}{x}\right)^{9}$.

3. **(a)** Find the coefficients of x^4 and x^5 in the expansion of $\left(2x - \dfrac{1}{2}\right)^{7}$.

    (b) Hence find the coefficient of x^5 in the expansion of

      $\left(\dfrac{x}{5} - 2\right)\left(2x - \dfrac{1}{2}\right)^{7}$.

4. Find the coefficients of x^3 and x^4 in the expansion of $\left(\frac{2}{3} - x\right)^6$.

    Hence find the coefficient of x^4 in the expansion of $(1 + 3x)\left(\frac{2}{3} - x\right)^6$.

5. Write down
    (a) the first four terms in the expansion of $(1 - 2x)^4$, and
    (b) the first three terms in the expansion of $(1 - x)^8$.
         If the sum of the terms in (a) equals the sum in (b) where $x \neq 0$,
         find the value of x.

6. The coefficient of the second term in the expansion of $(1 + 2x)^n$ in
    ascending powers of x is 40. Find the value of n.

7. If the first three terms in the expansion of $(1 + ax)^n$ in ascending
    powers of x are $1 + 6x + 16x^2$, find the values of n and a.

8. In the expansion of $(1 + px)^n$ in ascending powers of x, the second
    term is $18x$ and the third term is $135x^2$. Find the values of n and p.

9. If the ratio of the 5th to the 6th term in the expansion of $\left(a + \frac{1}{x}\right)^{11}$ is
    $5x : 1$, find the value of a.

10. In the expansion of $\left(2x - \frac{1}{x}\right)^8$, find
    (a) the term in x^2,
    (b) the term independent of x.

11. In the expansion of $\left(x - \frac{1}{2x}\right)^{12}$, find
    (a) the coefficient of x^2.
    (b) the term independent of x.

12. Write down the first three terms in the expansion of $(1 - x)^8$ in
    ascending powers of x. Use this expansion to find the value of $(0.999)^8$
    correct to 5 significant figures.

13. Expand $(1 - 2x)^{10}$ as far as the term in x^4.
    Hence find the value of 0.988^{10} correct to 5 decimal places.

14. Using the expansion of $\left(1 - \frac{x}{2}\right)^8$ and a suitable value of x, evaluate
    0.996^8 to 5 decimal places.

15. Find the first four terms in the expansion of $(1 + x + x^2)^{10}$ in ascending
    powers of x. Using this and a suitable value of x, find, as a fraction,
    an approximate value of $(1.11)^{10}$.

Summary

1. Pascal's Triangle can be used to obtain binomial coefficients in the expansion of $(a + b)^n$, where n is a positive integer:

$$
\begin{array}{llccccccc}
(a + b)^1 & & & & & 1 & & 1 & \\
(a + b)^2 & & & & 1 & & 2 & & 1 \\
(a + b)^3 & & & 1 & & 3 & & 3 & & 1 \\
(a + b)^4 & & 1 & & 4 & & 6 & & 4 & & 1 \\
(a + b)^5 & 1 & & 5 & & 10 & & 10 & & 5 & & 1
\end{array}
$$

and so on.

2. **Binomial Theorem**

$$(a + b)^n = a^n + \binom{n}{1}a^{n-1}b + \binom{n}{2}a^{n-2}b^2 + \ldots + \binom{n}{r}a^{n-r}b^r + \ldots + b^n,$$

where n is a positive integer.

Note:

In the expansion of $(a + b)^n$,

(1) there are $n + 1$ terms,

(2) the powers of a decrease from n to 0 while the powers of b increase from 0 to n,

(3) the sum of the powers of a and b is n,

(4) the $(r + 1)^{\text{th}}$ term, $\text{T}_{r+1} = \binom{n}{r}a^{n-r}b^r$.

Revision Exercise 12 (Answers on page 503)

1. Find, in ascending powers of x, the first four terms in the expansion of **(a)** $(1 - 3x)^5$, **(b)** $(1 + 5x)^7$. Hence find the coefficient of x^2 in the expansion of $(1 - 3x)^5(1 + 5x)^7$. (C)

2. Obtain the first three terms in the expansion of $\left(a + \dfrac{x}{b}\right)^6$ in ascending powers of x. If the first and third terms are 64 and $\dfrac{80x^2}{3}$ respectively, find the values of a and b, and the second term.

3. Find the first three terms in the expansion of $(1 - 2x)^5$ in ascending powers of x, simplifying the coefficients.
   Given that the first three terms in the expansion of $(a + bx)(1 - 2x)^5$ are $2 + cx + 10x^2$, state the value of a and hence find the value of b and of c. (C)

4. **(a)** Expand $(1 + 2x)^5$ and $(1 - 2x)^5$ in ascending powers of x.
   (b) Hence reduce $(1 + 2x)^5 - (1 - 2x)^5$ to its simplest form.
   (c) Using this result, evaluate $(1.002)^5 - (0.998)^5$.

5. The first three terms in the expansion of $\left(1 + \dfrac{x}{p}\right)^n$ in ascending powers of x are $1 + x + \dfrac{9x^2}{20}$. Find the values of n and p.

6. Write down and simplify the expansion of $(1 - p)^5$. Use this result to find the expansion of $(1 - x - x^2)^5$ in ascending powers of x as far as the term in x^3. Find the value of x which would enable you to estimate $(0.989\ 9)^5$ from this expansion. (C)

7. Find which term is independent of x in the expansion of $\left(x - \dfrac{1}{3x^2}\right)^{15}$.

8. Obtain and simplify
   (a) the first four terms in the expansion of $(2 + x^2)^6$ in ascending powers of x,
   (b) the coefficient of x^4 in the expansion of $(1 - x^2)(2 + x^2)^6$. (C)

9. In the expansion of $(1 - x)^{10}$, the sum of the first three terms is $\dfrac{4}{5}$ when a certain value of x is substituted. Find this value of x.

10. Evaluate the coefficients of x^5 and x^4 in the binomial expansion of $\left(\dfrac{x}{3} - 3\right)^7$. Hence evaluate the coefficient of x^5 in the expansion of $\left(\dfrac{x}{3} - 3\right)^7 (x + 6)$. (C)

11. If the first three terms in the expansion of $(1 + kx)^n$ in ascending powers of x are $1 - 6x + \dfrac{33x^2}{2}$ find the values of k and n.

12. Find, in ascending powers of x, the first three terms in the expansion of $(1 + ax)^6$. Given that the first two non-zero terms in the expansion of $(1 + bx)(1 + ax)^6$ are 1 and $\dfrac{-21x^2}{4}$, find the possible values of a and of b. (C)

13. Find the ratio of the 6th term to the 8th term in the expansion of $(2x + 3)^{11}$ when $x = 3$.

14. In the expansion of $(1 + px)(1 + qx)^4$ in ascending powers of x, the coefficient of the x term is -5 and there is no x^2 term. Find the value of p and of q.

15. If the fifth term in the expansion of $\left(x + \dfrac{1}{x}\right)^n$ is independent of x, find the value of n.

1. In the expansion of $\left(x^2 + \dfrac{2}{x^3}\right)^7$, find which term will have the form $\dfrac{A}{x}$ where A is an integer. Hence find the value of A.

2. The first three terms in the expansion of $(1 + x + ax^2)^n$ are $1 + 7x + 14x^2$. Find the values of n and a.

3. (a) Obtain the expansions of $(1 + x)^5$ and $(1 + x^2)^5$ in ascending powers of x.
   (b) Show that $(1 + x)(1 + x^2) = 1 + x + x^2 + x^3$.
   (c) Hence find the first four terms in the expansion of $(1 + x + x^2 + x^3)^5$ in ascending powers of x.

4. For what value of x is the fifth term of $(1 + 2x)^{10}$ equal to the sixth term of $(2 + x)^8$?

5. Show that (a) $\left(x - \dfrac{1}{x}\right)^3 = x^3 - \dfrac{1}{x^3} - 3\left(x - \dfrac{1}{x}\right)$, and

   (b) $\left(x - \dfrac{1}{x}\right)^5 = x^5 - \dfrac{1}{x^5} - 5\left(x^3 - \dfrac{1}{x^3}\right) + 10\left(x - \dfrac{1}{x}\right)$.

   Hence show that $x^5 - \dfrac{1}{x^5} = p^5 + 5p^3 + 5p$ where $p = x - \dfrac{1}{x}$.

Chapter 13

Vectors

Consider the following scenario:

You belong to the Singapore Marine Police. While on patrol one day, you spot a man suspected of smuggling. He is in a motorboat 3 km due north of your position. The motorboat is moving at 40 km h^{-1} due east. Your patrol boat has a maximum speed of 60 km h^{-1}. In what direction must you move in order to intercept your suspect? Discuss how the solution can be worked out.

We will deal with similar problems later in this chapter.

13.1 Scalars and Vectors

A **scalar** is a purely numerical quantity with a unit, such as $20 or a mass of 2 kg. No idea of *direction* is involved. A **vector** quantity, however, has a direction which must be stated, such as a velocity of 20 m s⁻¹ northeast (NE). A velocity of 20 m s⁻¹ southeast (SE) would be quite different.

To specify a vector, both its **magnitude** (e.g. 20 m s⁻¹) *and* its direction (e.g. NE) must be given.

Scalars are added and subtracted by the usual rules of arithmetic but to 'add' or 'subtract' vectors, we use a special rule – the **parallelogram law**, or **triangle law** which we will discuss in Section 13.8.

13.2 Representation of Vectors

A simple example of a vector is a **displacement**. Suppose a piece of board is moved, without rotation, across a flat surface (Fig. 13.8).

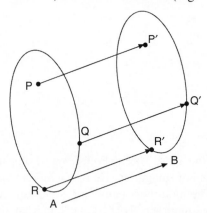

Fig. 13.1

Points on the board such as P, Q, and R are displaced through the same distance and in the same direction to points P′, Q′, and R′. So we can represent this vector by *any* line segment AB, where AB = PP′ = QQ′ = RR′, and AB // PP′ // QQ′ // RR′. The arrow head shows the sense of direction. AB is drawn to scale to give the correct magnitude of the displacement. We write such a vector as $\overrightarrow{AB}$.

13.3 Notation for Vectors

We state the endpoints of a vector by writing it as $\overrightarrow{AB}$, or use a single letter (Fig. 13.2). A vector could then be given as **a** (printed in **bold**). We write this as $\vec{a}$ or $\underset{\sim}{a}$. Always distinguish a vector **a** in this way from an algebraic quantity a.

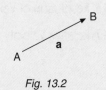

Fig. 13.2

13.4 Equality of Vectors

In Fig. 13.3, the line segments AB, CD and EF are parallel (in the same direction) and equal in length. Then these lines can each represent the same vector and $\overrightarrow{AB} = \overrightarrow{CD} = \overrightarrow{EF}$.

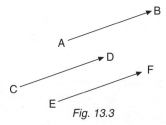

Fig. 13.3

Conversely, if $\overrightarrow{AB} = \overrightarrow{CD}$ (Fig. 13.4), then

(a) the line segments AB and CD are equal in length and

(b) AB // CD, (i.e. AB is the same direction as CD).

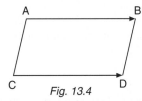

Fig. 13.4

It is important to remember that both parts (a) and (b) are implied by the statement $\overrightarrow{AB} = \overrightarrow{CD}$. The figure ABDC is therefore a parallelogram

13.5   Magnitude of a Vector

The magnitude or **modulus** of a vector $\overrightarrow{AB}$ is the length of the line segment representing the vector to the scale used. We denote this as $| \overrightarrow{AB} |$.

If AB in Fig 13.4 is drawn to a scale of 1 cm $\equiv$ 10 m s^{-1} for example, then $| \overrightarrow{AB} | = 30$ m s^{-1}. The magnitude of the vector **a** is written as $| \mathbf{a} |$ or as a.

Note this carefully: **a** is the vector but $| \mathbf{a} |$ or a is its magnitude.

13.6   Zero Vector or Null Vector

The vector which has no magnitude (and of course no direction) is the **zero** vector or null vector, written as $\underset{\sim}{0}$ or $\overrightarrow{0}$.

13.7   Scalar Multiple of a Vector

Given a vector **a** (Fig. 13.5), we can make multiples of this vector.

For example, $\overrightarrow{PQ} = 2\mathbf{a}$. $\overrightarrow{PQ}$ has the same direction as **a** but twice its magnitude.

$| \overrightarrow{PQ} | = 2 | \mathbf{a} | = 2a$.

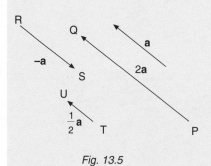

Fig. 13.5

$\vec{RS} = -\mathbf{a}$, i.e. it has the same magnitude as $\mathbf{a}$ but is in the reverse direction.

Note that $\vec{RS} = -\vec{SR}$.

$\vec{TU} = \frac{1}{2}\mathbf{a}$.

> If $\mathbf{a} = k\mathbf{b}$, where k is a scalar (a number) $\neq 0$, then the vectors $\mathbf{a}$ and $\mathbf{b}$ are parallel, and in the same direction if $k > 0$, but in opposite directions if $k < 0$. $|\mathbf{a}| = |k| \times |\mathbf{b}|$.

Conversely, if $\mathbf{a}$ and $\mathbf{b}$ are parallel, then $\mathbf{a} = k\mathbf{b}$. (k will be positive if $\mathbf{a}$ and $\mathbf{b}$ are in the same direction, negative if they are in opposite directions.)

Scalar multiples of a vector can be combined arithmetically. For example $2\mathbf{a} + 3\mathbf{a} = 5\mathbf{a}$, and $4(2\mathbf{a}) = 8\mathbf{a}$.

So $m\mathbf{a} + n\mathbf{a} = (m + n)\mathbf{a}$, and $m(n\mathbf{a}) = mn\mathbf{a}$ for all values of m and n.

▶ **Example 1**

Given the vector $\mathbf{p}$ (Fig. 13.6(a)), draw the vectors $3\mathbf{p}$, and $-\frac{1}{3}\mathbf{p}$.

▶ **Solution . . .**

The vectors are shown in Fig. 13.6(b). They are all parallel but the vector $-\frac{1}{3}\mathbf{p}$ is in the opposite direction to $\mathbf{p}$.

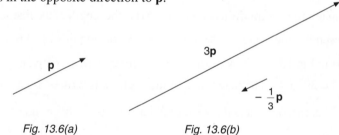

Fig. 13.6(a)   Fig. 13.6(b)

▶ **Example 2**

What type of quadrilateral is ABCD if

(a) $\vec{AB} = \vec{DC}$,   (b) $\vec{AB} = 3\vec{DC}$?

▶ **Solution . . .**

(a)   AB = DC and AB // DC. Then ABCD is a parallelogram (Fig. 13.7(a)).
       It follows therefore that $\vec{AD} = \vec{BC}$.

(b)   AB = 3DC and AB // DC. Then ABCD is a trapezium (Fig. 13.7(b)).

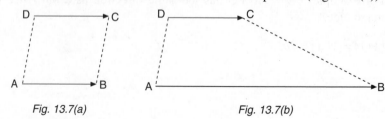

Fig. 13.7(a)   Fig. 13.7(b)

1. Copy Fig. 13.8 and draw the vectors **(a)** 2**p**, **(b)** –**p**, **(c)** $\frac{3}{4}$**p**.

    Fig. 13.8

2. In Fig. 13.9, state each of the vectors **p**, **q** and **r** in the form k**a**.

    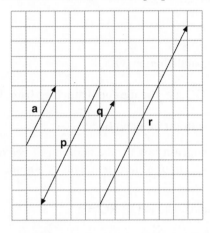

    Fig. 13.9

3. C and D are points on the line AB such that AC = CD = DB. If $\overrightarrow{AD}$ = **a**, state as scalar multiples of **a**,

    (a) $\overrightarrow{AB}$,   **(b)** $\overrightarrow{CB}$,   **(c)** $\overrightarrow{BD}$.

4. In Fig. 13.10, ABCDEF is a regular hexagon. Given that $\overrightarrow{AB}$ = **a**, $\overrightarrow{BC}$ = **b** and $\overrightarrow{CD}$ = **c**, state the following vectors as scalar multiples of **a**, **b** or **c**:

    (a) $\overrightarrow{DE}$ **(b)** $\overrightarrow{EF}$ **(c)** $\overrightarrow{FA}$ **(d)** $\overrightarrow{BE}$ **(e)** $\overrightarrow{AD}$

    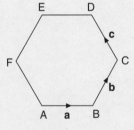

    Fig. 13.10

5. If AB = kBC ($k \neq 0$), what can be said about the points A, B and C?

6. A is the point (4,0) and B the point (0,3). State the value of $\left| \overrightarrow{AB} \right|$.

7. If P is (–2,–5) and Q is (3,7), find $\left| \overrightarrow{PQ} \right|$.

8. O is the origin, $\left| \overrightarrow{OR} \right|$ = 3 and the line OR makes an angle θ with the x-axis where sin θ = $\frac{2}{3}$. Find the possible coordinates of R.

13.8 Addition of Vectors

To 'add' two vectors **a** and **b**, i.e., to combine them into one vector, we place them so that they start from the same point O (Fig. 13.11).

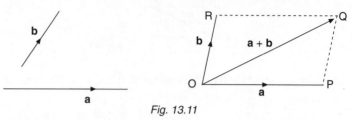

Fig. 13.11

Now complete the parallelogram OPQR.

We define $\mathbf{a} + \mathbf{b} = \overrightarrow{OQ}$, i.e. **the diagonal starting from O.**

$\overrightarrow{OQ}$ is called the **resultant** of **a** and **b**.

This is the **parallelogram law** for the addition of vectors. Note that we use the symbol '+', though here it means 'combined with' and not arithmetical addition.

As RQ is parallel and equal to OP, $\overrightarrow{RQ} = \mathbf{a}$.

Then $\overrightarrow{OR} + \overrightarrow{RQ} = \mathbf{b} + \mathbf{a} = \overrightarrow{OQ} = \mathbf{a} + \mathbf{b}$.

Hence $\mathbf{a} + \mathbf{b} = \mathbf{b} + \mathbf{a}$.

In practice, it is not necessary to draw the parallelogram. The vectors can be placed 'end-on'. PQ is equal and parallel to OR so $\overrightarrow{PQ} = \mathbf{b}$. We draw **a** and then **b** starting from the end of **a** (Fig. 13.12).

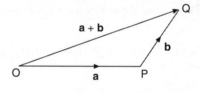

Fig. 13.12

The third side OQ of the triangle gives **a** + **b**. This is the **triangle law** for the addition of vectors.

More than two vectors can be combined in this way. For example, in Fig. 13.13, $\mathbf{a} + \mathbf{b} = \overrightarrow{OQ}$ and $\overrightarrow{OQ} + \mathbf{c} = \mathbf{a} + \mathbf{b} + \mathbf{c} = \overrightarrow{OR}$.

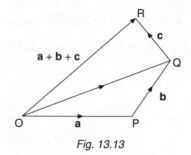

Fig. 13.13

13.9   Diagonals of a Parallelogram

In Fig. 13.14, $\overrightarrow{OP} = \mathbf{a}$, $\overrightarrow{OR} = \mathbf{b}$.

Then $\overrightarrow{OQ} = \mathbf{a} + \mathbf{b}$.

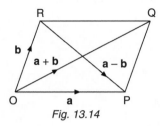

Fig. 13.14

$\overrightarrow{RP} = \overrightarrow{RQ} + \overrightarrow{QP} = \mathbf{a} + (-\mathbf{b}) = \mathbf{a} - \mathbf{b}$.

Also $\overrightarrow{PR} = -\overrightarrow{RP} = -(\mathbf{a} - \mathbf{b}) = \mathbf{b} - \mathbf{a}$.

These last two results are important and can be remembered as follows:

   $\mathbf{a} - \mathbf{b}$ is the vector from the endpoint of $\mathbf{b}$ to the endpoint of $\mathbf{a}$;

   $\mathbf{b} - \mathbf{a}$ is the vector from the endpoint of $\mathbf{a}$ to the endpoint of $\mathbf{b}$

where $\mathbf{a}$ and $\mathbf{b}$ start from the same point (Fig. 13.15).

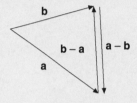

Fig. 13.15

▶   **Example 3**

The vectors $\mathbf{a}$ and $\mathbf{b}$ are given (Fig. 13.16(a)). Draw the vectors

(a) $2\mathbf{a} + \mathbf{b}$,   **(b)** $\mathbf{a} - \mathbf{b}$,   **(c)** $\mathbf{a} - 2\mathbf{b}$.

▶   **Solution . . .**

The vectors are shown in Fig. 13.16(b).

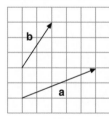

Fig. 13.16(a)

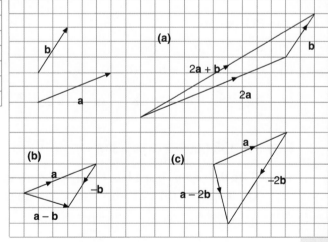

Fig. 13.16(b)

(a)   Draw $2\mathbf{a}$ followed by $\mathbf{b}$.

(b)   Draw $\mathbf{a}$ followed by $-\mathbf{b}$. Alternatively draw $\mathbf{a}$ and $\mathbf{b}$ from the same point and use the rule above (Fig. 13.15).

(c)   Draw $\mathbf{a}$ followed by $-2\mathbf{b}$.

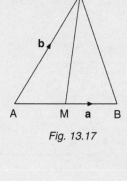

Fig. 13.17

▶ Example 4

In $\triangle ABC$, $\overrightarrow{AB} = \mathbf{a}$, $\overrightarrow{AC} = \mathbf{b}$ and M is the midpoint of AB (Fig. 13.17). State in terms of $\mathbf{a}$ and $\mathbf{b}$,

(a) $\overrightarrow{AM}$,   (b) $\overrightarrow{MC}$,   (c) $\overrightarrow{CM}$.

▶ Solution . . .

(a) $\overrightarrow{AM} = \frac{1}{2}\overrightarrow{AB} = \frac{1}{2}\mathbf{a}$

(b) $\overrightarrow{MC} = \overrightarrow{AC} - \overrightarrow{AM}$

$\quad\quad = \mathbf{b} - \frac{1}{2}\mathbf{a}$

(c) $\overrightarrow{CM} = -\overrightarrow{MC} = \frac{1}{2}\mathbf{a} - \mathbf{b}$

▶ Example 5

$\overrightarrow{OA}$, $\overrightarrow{OB}$ and $\overrightarrow{OC}$ are the vectors $\mathbf{a}$, $\mathbf{b}$ and $\mathbf{c}$ respectively. D is the midpoint of AB and E lies on BC where BE = 2BC (Fig. 13.18). State in terms of $\mathbf{a}$, $\mathbf{b}$ and $\mathbf{c}$,

(a) $\overrightarrow{AB}$, (b) $\overrightarrow{AD}$, (c) $\overrightarrow{OD}$, (d) $\overrightarrow{BC}$, (e) $\overrightarrow{BE}$, (f) $\overrightarrow{OE}$, (g) $\overrightarrow{DE}$.

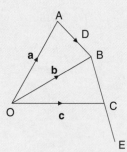

Fig. 13.18

▶ Solution . . .

(a) $\overrightarrow{AB} = \mathbf{b} - \mathbf{a}$

(b) $\overrightarrow{AD} = \frac{1}{2}(\mathbf{b} - \mathbf{a})$

(c) $\overrightarrow{OD} = \overrightarrow{OA} + \overrightarrow{AD} = \mathbf{a} + \frac{1}{2}(\mathbf{b} - \mathbf{a}) = \frac{1}{2}(\mathbf{a} + \mathbf{b})$

(d) $\overrightarrow{BC} = \mathbf{c} - \mathbf{b}$

(e) $\overrightarrow{BE} = 2(\mathbf{c} - \mathbf{b})$

(f) $\overrightarrow{OE} = \overrightarrow{OB} + \overrightarrow{BE} = \mathbf{b} + 2(\mathbf{c} - \mathbf{b}) = 2\mathbf{c} - \mathbf{b}$

(g) $\overrightarrow{DE} = \overrightarrow{OE} - \overrightarrow{OD} = 2\mathbf{c} - \mathbf{b} - \frac{1}{2}(\mathbf{a} + \mathbf{b}) = 2\mathbf{c} - \frac{\mathbf{a}}{2} - \frac{3\mathbf{b}}{2}$

Exercise 13B (Answers on page 504)

1.   Given the vectors $\mathbf{a}$ and $\mathbf{b}$ in Fig. 13.19, draw the vectors
      (a) $\mathbf{a} + 2\mathbf{b}$,   (b) $2\mathbf{a} - \mathbf{b}$,   (c) $3\mathbf{a} - 2\mathbf{b}$.

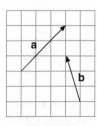

Fig. 13.19

2.   In △ABC, $\overrightarrow{AB}$ = **a** and $\overrightarrow{BC}$ = **b**. State in terms of **a** and **b**,
     (a) $\overrightarrow{AC}$,   (b) $\overrightarrow{CA}$.

3.   Given the vectors **a**, **b** and **c** in Fig. 13.20, draw
     (a) **a** + 2**b**,   (b) **a** + 2**b** + **c**,
     (c) **a** − **b** + **c**,   (d) $\frac{1}{2}$**a** + **b** − 2**c**.

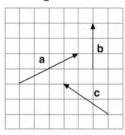

Fig. 13.20

4.   If | **a** | = | **b** | but **a** ≠ **b**, explain why **a** + **b** bisects the angle between **a** and **b** and is perpendicular to **a** − **b**.

5.   In △OAB, $\overrightarrow{OA}$ = **a**, $\overrightarrow{OB}$ = **b** and M is the midpoint of AB. State in terms of **a** and **b**,
     (a) $\overrightarrow{AB}$,   (b) $\overrightarrow{AM}$,   (c) $\overrightarrow{OM}$.

6.   In △OPQ, $\overrightarrow{OP}$ = **p**, $\overrightarrow{OQ}$ = **q**. R is the midpoint of OP and S lies on OQ such that OS = 3SQ. State in terms of **p** and **q**,
     (a) $\overrightarrow{OR}$,   (b) $\overrightarrow{PQ}$,   (c) $\overrightarrow{OS}$,   (d) $\overrightarrow{RS}$.

7.   In △OAB, $\overrightarrow{OA}$ = **a**, $\overrightarrow{OB}$ = **b**. BC is drawn parallel to OA (in the same direction) and BC = 2OA. State in terms of **a** and **b**,
     (a) $\overrightarrow{BC}$,   (b) $\overrightarrow{OC}$,   (c) $\overrightarrow{AC}$.

8.   OACB is a parallelogram with $\overrightarrow{OA}$ = **a** and $\overrightarrow{OB}$ = **b**. AC is extended to D where AC = 2CD. Find, in terms of **a** and **b**,
     (a) $\overrightarrow{AD}$,   (b) $\overrightarrow{OD}$,   (c) $\overrightarrow{BD}$.

9.   OAB is a triangle with $\overrightarrow{OA}$ = **a** and $\overrightarrow{OB}$ = **b**. M is the midpoint of OA and G lies on MB such that MG = $\frac{1}{2}$GB. State in terms of **a** and **b**,
     (a) $\overrightarrow{OM}$,   (b) $\overrightarrow{MB}$,   (c) $\overrightarrow{MG}$,   (d) $\overrightarrow{OG}$.

10. $\overrightarrow{OA}$ = **p** + **q**, $\overrightarrow{OB}$ = 2**p** − **q**, where **p** and **q** are two vectors and M is the midpoint of AB. Find in terms of **p** and **q**,
     (a) $\overrightarrow{AB}$,   (b) $\overrightarrow{AM}$,   (c) $\overrightarrow{OM}$.

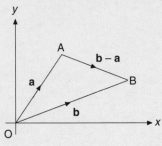

Fig. 13.21

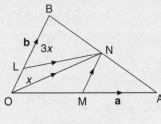

Fig. 13.22

13.10 Position Vectors

If O is the origin, then the vector $\overrightarrow{OA}$ is called the **position vector** of A. For example, if the position vector of A is **a**, and the position vector of B is **b**, then the vector $\overrightarrow{AB}$ can be expressed in terms of the position vectors **a** and **b**. Thus, $\overrightarrow{AB} = \overrightarrow{OB} - \overrightarrow{OA}$

$$= \mathbf{b} - \mathbf{a}$$

Similarly, the vector of $\overrightarrow{BA} = \overrightarrow{OA} - \overrightarrow{OB}$

$$= \mathbf{a} - \mathbf{b}$$

On the other hand, if the position vector of C is $2\mathbf{a} - 3\mathbf{b}$, then $\overrightarrow{OC} = 2\mathbf{a} - 3\mathbf{b}$.

▶ **Example 6**

The position vectors of the points A and B are **a** and **b** respectively. M is the midpoint of OA, N is the midpoint of AB and L is the point on OB such that OL:LB = 1:3.

(a) Find the position vectors of
    (i) L,
    (ii) M,
    (iii) N.

(b) Find in terms of **a** and **b**
    (i) $\overrightarrow{MN}$,
    (ii) $\overrightarrow{LN}$.

▶ **Solution . . .**

(a) **(i)** $\overrightarrow{OL} = \dfrac{1}{4}\overrightarrow{OB}$

$$= \dfrac{1}{4}\mathbf{b}$$

∴ position vector of L is $\dfrac{1}{4}\mathbf{b}$.

(ii) $\overrightarrow{OM} = \dfrac{1}{2}\overrightarrow{OA}$

$$= \dfrac{1}{2}\mathbf{a}$$

∴ position vector of M is $\dfrac{1}{2}\mathbf{a}$.

(iii) $\overrightarrow{AB} = \overrightarrow{OB} - \overrightarrow{OA}$

$$= \mathbf{b} - \mathbf{a}$$

$$\overrightarrow{AN} = \dfrac{1}{2}\overrightarrow{AB}$$

$$= \dfrac{1}{2}(\mathbf{b} - \mathbf{a})$$

$$= \dfrac{1}{2}\mathbf{b} - \dfrac{1}{2}\mathbf{a}$$

$$\overrightarrow{ON} = \overrightarrow{OA} + \overrightarrow{AN}$$

$$= \mathbf{a} + \left(\frac{1}{2}\mathbf{b} - \frac{1}{2}\mathbf{a}\right)$$

$$= \frac{1}{2}\mathbf{a} + \frac{1}{2}\mathbf{b}$$

$\therefore$ position vector of N is $\frac{1}{2}\mathbf{a} + \frac{1}{2}\mathbf{b}$.

(b) **(i)** $\overrightarrow{MN} = \overrightarrow{ON} - \overrightarrow{OM}$

$$= \left(\frac{1}{2}\mathbf{a} + \frac{1}{2}\mathbf{b}\right) - \frac{1}{2}\mathbf{a}$$

$$= \frac{1}{2}\mathbf{b}$$

(ii) $\overrightarrow{LN} = \overrightarrow{ON} - \overrightarrow{OL}$

$$= \left(\frac{1}{2}\mathbf{a} + \frac{1}{2}\mathbf{b}\right) - \frac{1}{4}\mathbf{b}$$

$$= \frac{1}{2}\mathbf{a} + \frac{1}{4}\mathbf{b}$$

13.11 Using Vectors

The following principles should be carefully noted:

(1) If $m\mathbf{a} + n\mathbf{b} = p\mathbf{a} + q\mathbf{b}$, then $m = p$ and $n = q$. (See Examples 7 and 10).

(2) If the points P, Q and R are collinear, then $\overrightarrow{PQ} = k\overrightarrow{QR}$ (and conversely) because $\overrightarrow{PQ}$ and $\overrightarrow{QR}$ are parallel but meet at Q. (See Examples 8 and 9). We could also use $\overrightarrow{PQ} = k\overrightarrow{PR}$.

(3) If the vectors $m\mathbf{a} + n\mathbf{b}$ and $p\mathbf{a} + q\mathbf{b}$ are parallel, then $\dfrac{m}{p} = \dfrac{n}{q}$.

(See Example 11).

▶ **Example 7**

If $\mathbf{p} = 2\mathbf{a} - 3\mathbf{b}$ and $\mathbf{q} = \mathbf{a} + 2\mathbf{b}$, find numbers x and y such that $x\mathbf{p} + y\mathbf{q} = \mathbf{a} - 12\mathbf{b}$.

▶ **Solution . . .**

$x\mathbf{p} + y\mathbf{q} = x(2\mathbf{a} - 3\mathbf{b}) + y(\mathbf{a} + 2\mathbf{b}) = (2x + y)\mathbf{a} + (-3x + 2y)\mathbf{b}$

If $\qquad\qquad x\mathbf{p} + y\mathbf{q} = \mathbf{a} - 12\mathbf{b}$,

then $\qquad (2x + y)\mathbf{a} + (-3x + 2y)\mathbf{b} = \mathbf{a} - 12\mathbf{b}$.

According to principle (1) above, the multiples of $\mathbf{a}$ and the multiples of $\mathbf{b}$ on each side must be separately equal.

Hence $2x + y = 1$ and $-3x + 2y = -12$.

Solving these equations, $x = 2$, $y = -3$.

Checking this, $2(2\mathbf{a} - 3\mathbf{b}) - 3(\mathbf{a} + 2\mathbf{b}) = \mathbf{a} - 12\mathbf{b}$ as required.

▶ **Example 8**

The position vectors of P, Q and R are $\mathbf{a} - 2\mathbf{b}$, $2\mathbf{a} - 3\mathbf{b}$ and $\mu\mathbf{a} - 6\mathbf{b}$, where μ is a scalar constant. If the points P, Q and R are collinear, find

(a) the value of μ, and

(b) the ratio PQ:QR.

▶ **Solution . . .**

First we find $\overrightarrow{PQ}$ and $\overrightarrow{QR}$.

(a) $\overrightarrow{PQ} = \overrightarrow{OQ} - \overrightarrow{OP} = 2\mathbf{a} - 3\mathbf{b} - (\mathbf{a} - 2\mathbf{b}) = \mathbf{a} - \mathbf{b}$

$\overrightarrow{QR} = \overrightarrow{OR} - \overrightarrow{OQ} = \mu\mathbf{a} - 6\mathbf{b} - (2\mathbf{a} - 3\mathbf{b}) = (\mu - 2)\mathbf{a} - 3\mathbf{b}$

Now if P, Q and R are to be collinear, $\overrightarrow{PQ} = k\overrightarrow{QR}$, so the multiples of $\mathbf{a}$ and of $\mathbf{b}$ in the two vectors must be in the same ratio.

$\overrightarrow{PQ} = \mathbf{a} - \mathbf{b}$ and $\overrightarrow{QR} = (\mu - 2)\mathbf{a} - 3\mathbf{b}$

Comparing these, the multiple of $-\mathbf{b}$ in $\overrightarrow{QR}$ is 3, so the multiple of $\mathbf{a}$ must also be 3. Hence $\mu - 2 = 3$ or $\mu = 5$.

(b) When $\mu = 5$, $|\overrightarrow{PQ}| = |\mathbf{a} - \mathbf{b}|$ and $|\overrightarrow{QR}| = |3(\mathbf{a} - \mathbf{b})|$ which gives the ratio PQ:QR as 1:3.

▶ **Example 9**

$\overrightarrow{OP} = 3\mathbf{a} + \mathbf{b}$, $\overrightarrow{OQ} = \mu(\mathbf{a} - \mathbf{b})$ and $\overrightarrow{OR} = 4\mathbf{a} + 4\mathbf{b}$.

Given that P, Q and R are collinear, find the value of μ and the ratio PQ:QR.

▶ **Solution . . .**

$\overrightarrow{PQ} = \overrightarrow{OQ} - \overrightarrow{OP} = \mu\mathbf{a} - \mu\mathbf{b} - 3\mathbf{a} - \mathbf{b} = (\mu - 3)\mathbf{a} - (\mu + 1)\mathbf{b}$

$\overrightarrow{QR} = \overrightarrow{OR} - \overrightarrow{OQ} = 4\mathbf{a} + 4\mathbf{b} - \mu\mathbf{a} + \mu\mathbf{b} = (4 - \mu)\mathbf{a} + (\mu + 4)\mathbf{b}$

The relation between these vectors is not as straightforward as it was in Example 8. We shall have to find an equation for μ. If P, Q and R are collinear, $\overrightarrow{PQ} = k\overrightarrow{QR}$ so the multiples of $\mathbf{a}$ and of $\mathbf{b}$ in the two vectors must be in the same ratio.

Then $\dfrac{\mu - 3}{4 - \mu} = -\dfrac{\mu + 1}{\mu + 4}$ which leads to $\mu^2 + \mu - 12 = \mu^2 - 3\mu - 4$ giving $\mu = 2$.

Hence $\overrightarrow{PQ} = -\mathbf{a} - 3\mathbf{b}$ and $\overrightarrow{QR} = 2\mathbf{a} + 6\mathbf{b} = -2(-\mathbf{a} - 3\mathbf{b})$.

The ratio PQ:QR = 1:−2 which means that QR is twice as long as PQ but in the *opposite direction* as shown in Fig. 13.23.

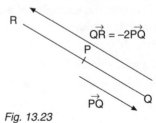

Fig. 13.23

▶ **Example 10**

In Fig. 13.24, $\vec{OA} = \mathbf{a}$ and $\vec{OB} = \mathbf{b}$. C lies on OA where $OC = \frac{2}{3}OA$, D is the midpoint of AB, and BC and OD intersect at M.

(a) By taking $\vec{OM} = p\vec{OD}$ and $\vec{BM} = q\vec{BC}$, where p and q are numbers, find two vector expressions for $\vec{OM}$.

Hence find

(b) the values of p and q,

(c) the ratios OM:MD and BM:MC.

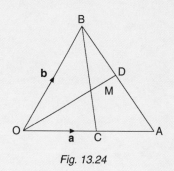

Fig. 13.24

▶ **Solution . . .**

(a) First find $\vec{OM}$ as part of $\vec{OD}$. To obtain $\vec{OD}$, we find $\vec{AD}$.

$\vec{AB} = \mathbf{b} - \mathbf{a}$ so $\vec{AD} = \frac{1}{2}(\mathbf{b} - \mathbf{a})$.

Then $\vec{OD} = \vec{OA} + \vec{AD} = \mathbf{a} + \frac{1}{2}(\mathbf{b} - \mathbf{a}) = \frac{1}{2}(\mathbf{a} + \mathbf{b})$

So $\vec{OM} = p\vec{OD} = \frac{p}{2}(\mathbf{a} + \mathbf{b}) = \frac{p}{2}\mathbf{a} + \frac{p}{2}\mathbf{b}$ . . . . .(1)

Now to find another expression for $\vec{OM}$, we use $\vec{OB} + \vec{BM}$.

First find $\vec{BM}$ as part of $\vec{BC}$.

$\vec{BC} = \vec{OC} - \vec{OB} = \frac{2}{3}\mathbf{a} - \mathbf{b}$ so $\vec{BM} = q\left(\frac{2}{3}\mathbf{a} - \mathbf{b}\right)$

Then $\vec{OM} = \vec{OB} + \vec{BM} = \mathbf{b} + q\left(\frac{2}{3}\mathbf{a} - \mathbf{b}\right) = \frac{2q}{3}\mathbf{a} + (1 - q)\mathbf{b}$ . . . . . (2)

(b) As (1) and (2) are expressions for the *same* vector, then by principle (1), the multiples of **a** and of **b** for both expressions are equal.

So $\frac{p}{2} = \frac{2q}{3}$ and $\frac{p}{2} = 1 - q$. We solve these equations.

$\frac{2q}{3} = 1 - q$ giving $q = \frac{3}{5}$ and hence $p = \frac{4}{5}$.

(c) $OM = \frac{4}{5}OD$ so OM:MD = 4:1 and $BM = \frac{3}{5}BC$ so BM:MC = 3:2.

13.12 Ratio Theorem (Optional)

This theorem is not necessary for this syllabus but may be useful. It gives a direct way of finding the position vector of a point dividing a line in a given ratio. In Fig. 13.25, $\vec{OA} = \mathbf{a}$, $\vec{OB} = \mathbf{b}$ and R divides AB in the ratio p:q. We wish to find $\vec{OR}$.

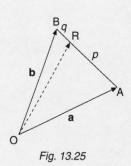

Fig. 13.25

$\vec{OR} = \vec{OA} + \vec{AR} = \mathbf{a} + \frac{p}{p+q}\vec{AB} = \mathbf{a} + \frac{p}{p+q}(\mathbf{b} - \mathbf{a}) = \frac{q\mathbf{a} + p\mathbf{b}}{q + p}$

This is known as the **ratio theorem** for vectors. Note carefully that q multiplies **a** (on the other side of OR) and p multiplies **b**.

For example, if R was the midpoint of AB, then $p = q = 1$.

So $\vec{OR} = \frac{\mathbf{a} + \mathbf{b}}{2}$. If $\vec{AR} = \frac{1}{3}\vec{AB}$, then $p = 1$, $q = 2$ and $\vec{OR} = \frac{2\mathbf{a} + \mathbf{b}}{3}$.

Similarly, if $\vec{AR} = \frac{3}{5}\vec{AB}$ where the position vectors of A and B are $3\mathbf{a} - 2\mathbf{b}$ and $-\mathbf{a} + 5\mathbf{b}$, then $p = 3$, $q = 2$ and the position vector of R will be

$$\frac{2(3\mathbf{a} - 2\mathbf{b}) + 3(-\mathbf{a} + 5\mathbf{b})}{5} = \frac{3\mathbf{a} + 11\mathbf{b}}{5}.$$

Note that care must be taken when R divides $\vec{AB}$ **externally**, i.e. R lies outside AB. One value of p or q must be taken as negative (Fig. 13.26).

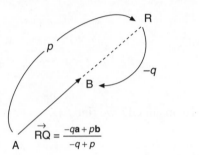

Fig. 13.26

▶ Example 11

In Fig. 13.27, the position vectors of the points A, B and C are $2\mathbf{a} - \mathbf{b}$, $4\mathbf{a} + 5\mathbf{b}$ and $-\mathbf{a} + 4\mathbf{b}$ respectively. L and N are the midpoints of AB and AC respectively. M is a point such that $\vec{LM} = \frac{1}{3}\vec{LC}$.

(a) Find the position vectors of L, M and N.

(b) Show that B, M and N are collinear and state the ratio BM:MN.

(c) P is a point on BN produced such that BP = pBN. If PC is parallel to AM, find the value of p.

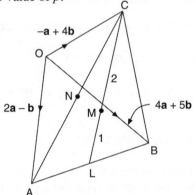

Fig. 13.27

▶ Solution . . .

(a) The position vector of L is $\dfrac{(2\mathbf{a} - \mathbf{b}) + (4\mathbf{a} + 5\mathbf{b})}{2} = 3\mathbf{a} + 2\mathbf{b}$.

As $LM = \frac{1}{3}LC$, LM:MC = 1:2.

The position vector of M is $\dfrac{2(3\mathbf{a} + 2\mathbf{b}) + 1(-\mathbf{a} + 4\mathbf{b})}{2 + 1} = \dfrac{5\mathbf{a} + 8\mathbf{b}}{3}$.

The position vector of N is $\dfrac{(2\mathbf{a} - \mathbf{b}) + (-\mathbf{a} + 4\mathbf{b})}{2} = \dfrac{\mathbf{a} + 3\mathbf{b}}{2}$.

(b) We find $\overrightarrow{BM}$ and $\overrightarrow{MN}$.

$$\overrightarrow{BM} = \overrightarrow{OM} - \overrightarrow{OB} = \frac{5\mathbf{a}+8\mathbf{b}}{3} - (4\mathbf{a}+5\mathbf{b}) = \frac{-7\mathbf{a}-7\mathbf{b}}{3} = -\frac{7}{3}(\mathbf{a}+\mathbf{b})$$

$$\overrightarrow{MN} = \overrightarrow{ON} - \overrightarrow{OM} = \frac{\mathbf{a}+3\mathbf{b}}{2} - \frac{5\mathbf{a}+8\mathbf{b}}{3} = \frac{-7\mathbf{a}-7\mathbf{b}}{6} = -\frac{7}{6}(\mathbf{a}+\mathbf{b})$$

Then B, M and N are collinear as $\overrightarrow{BM}$ is a multiple of $\overrightarrow{MN}$.

$$BM:MN = -\frac{7}{3} : -\frac{7}{6} = 2:1.$$

(c) $\overrightarrow{BP} + \overrightarrow{PC} = \overrightarrow{BC}$

so $p\overrightarrow{BN} + \overrightarrow{PC} = (-\mathbf{a}+4\mathbf{b}) - (4\mathbf{a}+5\mathbf{b})$

i.e. $p\left[\dfrac{\mathbf{a}+3\mathbf{b}}{2} - (4\mathbf{a}+5\mathbf{b})\right] + \overrightarrow{PC} = -5\mathbf{a}-\mathbf{b}$

so $p\left(\dfrac{-7\mathbf{a}-7\mathbf{b}}{2}\right) + \overrightarrow{PC} = -5\mathbf{a}-\mathbf{b}$

giving $\overrightarrow{PC} = \left(\dfrac{7p-10}{2}\right)\mathbf{a} + \left(\dfrac{7p-2}{2}\right)\mathbf{b}$

$\overrightarrow{AM} = \dfrac{5\mathbf{a}+8\mathbf{b}}{3} - (2\mathbf{a}-\mathbf{b}) = \dfrac{-\mathbf{a}+11\mathbf{b}}{3} = -\dfrac{1}{3}\mathbf{a} + \dfrac{11}{3}\mathbf{b}$

If these are parallel, the multiples of $\mathbf{a}$ and $\mathbf{b}$ must be in the same ratio.

Hence $\dfrac{\frac{7p-10}{2}}{-\frac{1}{3}} = \dfrac{\frac{7p-2}{2}}{\frac{11}{3}}$, i.e. $\dfrac{7p-10}{-1} = \dfrac{7p-2}{11}$

which simplifies to $77p - 110 = -7p + 2$ or $p = \dfrac{4}{3}$.

Exercise 13C (*Answers on page 504*)

1. Given that $\mathbf{p} = 3\mathbf{a} - \mathbf{b}$ and $\mathbf{q} = 2\mathbf{a} - 3\mathbf{b}$, find the numbers x and y such that $x\mathbf{p} + y\mathbf{q} = \mathbf{a} + 9\mathbf{b}$.

2. If $\mathbf{a} = 3\mathbf{r} + 2\mathbf{s}$, $\mathbf{b} = -2\mathbf{r} + 3\mathbf{s}$ and $\mathbf{c} = 12\mathbf{r} - 5\mathbf{s}$, find the numbers p and q such that $p\mathbf{a} + q\mathbf{b} = \mathbf{c}$.

3. Given that $\mathbf{p} = 2\mathbf{r} + 3\mathbf{s}$ and $\mathbf{q} = \mathbf{r} - \mathbf{s}$, find the numbers x and y such that $x\mathbf{p} + y\mathbf{q} = -4\mathbf{r} - 11\mathbf{s}$.

4. If $\mathbf{p} = 2\mathbf{a} - 5\mathbf{b}$, $\mathbf{q} = \mathbf{a} + 2\mathbf{b}$ and $\mathbf{r} = \mathbf{a} - 16\mathbf{b}$, find the numbers x and y such that $x\mathbf{p} + y\mathbf{q} = \mathbf{r}$.

5. If $\overrightarrow{OP} = 2\mathbf{a} + 5\mathbf{b}$, $\overrightarrow{OQ} = 5\mathbf{a} - \mathbf{b}$ and $\overrightarrow{OR} = 11\mathbf{a} + 7\mathbf{b}$, show that P, Q and R are collinear and state the ratio PQ:QR.

6. The position vectors P, Q and R are $\mathbf{a} - 2\mathbf{b}$, $2\mathbf{b}$ and $-4\mathbf{a} + k\mathbf{b}$ respectively. If P, Q and R are collinear, find the value of k. What is the ratio PQ:OR?

7. Given that $\overrightarrow{OP} = \mathbf{a} + \mathbf{b}$, $\overrightarrow{OQ} = k\mathbf{a}$ and $\overrightarrow{OR} = 7\mathbf{a} - 2\mathbf{b}$, find the value of k if Q lies on PR.

8. The position vectors of P, Q and R are $2\mathbf{a} - \mathbf{b}$, $\mu(\mathbf{a} - \mathbf{b})$ and $\mathbf{a} + \mathbf{b}$ respectively. Find the value of μ if PQR is a straight line. State the ratio PQ:QR.

9. (a) The position vectors of L, M and N are $\mathbf{p} + 2\mathbf{q}$, $m(\mathbf{p} + \mathbf{q})$ and $\mathbf{p} - \mathbf{q}$ respectively. Find the value of m for which LMN is a straight line, and state the ratio LM:MN.

   (b) The position vectors of A, B and C are $\mathbf{a} + 2\mu\mathbf{b}$, $\mu\mathbf{a} - \mathbf{b}$ and $2\mathbf{a} - 3\mathbf{b}$ respectively. If AB is parallel to OC, where O is the origin, find the value of μ.

10. The position vectors of A and B are $-\mathbf{a} - 2\mathbf{b}$ and $3\mathbf{a} + 4\mathbf{b}$ respectively. Using the ratio theorem or otherwise, find the position vector P where

    (a) $\overrightarrow{AP} = 2\overrightarrow{PB}$,   (b) $\overrightarrow{AP} = \frac{1}{3}\overrightarrow{AB}$,   (c) $4\overrightarrow{AP} = 3\overrightarrow{AB}$.

    (d) P lies on AB extended and AP = 3BP,

    (e) P lies on BA extended and AP = 2BA.

11. $\overrightarrow{OA} = 2\mathbf{a} - 4\mathbf{b}$ and $\overrightarrow{OB} = 4\mathbf{a} + 6\mathbf{a}$, where O is the origin. P and Q are the midpoints of OA and AB respectively.

    (a) State the position vectors of P and Q.

    (b) G lies on BP such that BG = 2GP. Find the position vector of G.

    (c) Show that O, G and Q are collinear and state the ratio OG:GQ.

    (d) R lies on OA where $\overrightarrow{OR} = p\overrightarrow{OA}$. If BR is parallel to GA, find the value of p.

12. P and Q divide the sides BC and AC respectively of $\triangle ABC$ in the ratio 2:1. If $\overrightarrow{AB} = \mathbf{a}$ and $\overrightarrow{AC} = \mathbf{b}$, find (a) $\overrightarrow{QP}$ and (b) show that QP is parallel to AB and one-third its length.

13. OABC is a parallelogram with $\overrightarrow{OA} = \mathbf{a}$ and $\overrightarrow{OC} = \mathbf{c}$. D lies on OB where OD:DB = 1:4. AD meets OC at E. By taking $\overrightarrow{OE} = p\overrightarrow{OC}$ and $\overrightarrow{AD} = q\overrightarrow{AE}$, show that $\frac{1}{5}(\mathbf{a} + \mathbf{c}) = (1 - q)\mathbf{a} + pq\mathbf{c}$.
    Hence find the values of p and q and the ratios OE:EC and AD:DE.

14. OABC is a parallelogram in which $\overrightarrow{OA} = \mathbf{a}$ and $\overrightarrow{OC} = \mathbf{b}$. M is the midpoint of AB and MC meets OB at X.

    (a) By taking $\overrightarrow{MX} = p\overrightarrow{MC}$ and $\overrightarrow{OX} = q\overrightarrow{OB}$, express $\overrightarrow{OX}$ in terms of (i) p, $\mathbf{a}$ and $\mathbf{b}$, (ii) q, $\mathbf{a}$ and $\mathbf{b}$.

    (b) Hence evaluate p and q and state the ratios OX:XB and CX:XM.

15. C lies on the side OA of $\triangle OAB$ where OC:CA = 2:1. D lies on the side OB where OD:DB = 1:2. AD meets BC at T.

    (a) Taking $\overrightarrow{OA} = \mathbf{a}$, $\overrightarrow{OB} = \mathbf{b}$, $\overrightarrow{AT} = p\overrightarrow{AD}$ and $\overrightarrow{CT} = q\overrightarrow{CB}$, find two expressions for $\overrightarrow{OT}$.

    Hence find

    (b) the values of p and q,

    (c) the ratios CT:TB and AT:TD.

16. C and D divide OA and OB respectively in the ratio 1:3. E divides CB in the ratio 1:4. Taking $\overrightarrow{OA} = \mathbf{a}$ and $\overrightarrow{OB} = \mathbf{b}$, use vector methods to prove DEA is a straight line and find the ratio DE:EA.

17. In $\triangle OAB$, C divides OA in the ratio 2:3 and D divides AB in the ratio 1:2 . OD meets CB at E.

    (a) Taking $\overrightarrow{OA} = \mathbf{a}$, $\overrightarrow{OB} = \mathbf{b}$, $\overrightarrow{OE} = p\overrightarrow{OD}$ and $\overrightarrow{CE} = q\overrightarrow{CB}$, obtain two expressions for $\overrightarrow{OE}$.

    (b) Hence find the values of p and q.

    (c) State the ratios OE:ED and CE:EB.

18. The position vectors of A and B are $\mathbf{a}$ and $\mathbf{b}$ respectively relative to an origin O. C is the midpoint of AB and D divides OB in the ratio 2:1. AD and OC meet at P.

    (a) Taking $\overrightarrow{OP} = p\overrightarrow{OC}$ and $\overrightarrow{AP} = q\overrightarrow{AD}$, express $\overrightarrow{OP}$ in two different forms.

    Hence find

    (b) the values of p and q,

    (c) the ratio OP:PC.

    (d) Q lies on BA produced where $\overrightarrow{AQ} = k\overrightarrow{BA}$. State the position vector of Q. If OQ is parallel to DC, find the value of k.

19. OABC is a parallelogram with $\overrightarrow{OA} = \mathbf{a}$ and $\overrightarrow{OC} = \mathbf{c}$. $\overrightarrow{OB}$ is extended to D where $\overrightarrow{OB} = \overrightarrow{BD}$ and $\overrightarrow{OA}$ is extended to E where $\overrightarrow{AE} = \frac{1}{2}\overrightarrow{OA}$. CE and AD meet at X.

    (a) Taking $\overrightarrow{AX} = p\overrightarrow{AD}$ and $\overrightarrow{CX} = q\overrightarrow{CE}$, find two expressions for $\overrightarrow{OX}$.

    (b) Hence find the values of p and q and the ratios AX:XD and CX:XE.

    (c) F lies on AD and BF is parallel to CE. Taking $\overrightarrow{AF} = r\overrightarrow{AD}$, find the value of r.

    (d) Hence state the ratio BF:CE.

20. $\overrightarrow{OA} = \mathbf{a}$ and $\overrightarrow{OB} = \mathbf{b}$. OB is produced to C where $\overrightarrow{OB} = 2\overrightarrow{BC}$. D is the midpoint of AB. OD produced meets AC at E. Taking $\overrightarrow{OD} = p\overrightarrow{OE}$ and $\overrightarrow{AE} = q\overrightarrow{AC}$, derive two expressions for OD and hence find the values of p and q and the ratios OD:DE and AE:EC.

21. OABC is a parallelogram with $\overrightarrow{OA} = \mathbf{a}$ and $\overrightarrow{OC} = \mathbf{c}$. D lies on OC where OD:DC = 1:2 and E is the midpoint of CB. DB meets AE at T. Taking $\overrightarrow{DT} = p\overrightarrow{DB}$ and $\overrightarrow{AT} = q\overrightarrow{AE}$, form two vector expressions for OT and hence find the values of p and q.

22. The position vectors of A and B are $\mathbf{a}$ and $\mathbf{b}$ respectively, relative to O. C lies on OB where OC:CB = 1:3. AC is produced to D where $\overrightarrow{AD} = p\overrightarrow{AC}$. If DB is parallel to OA, find the value of p.

23. The position vectors of the points A, B and C are $7\mathbf{a} - 2\mathbf{b}$, $\mathbf{a} + \mathbf{b}$ and $\mathbf{a} - 2\mathbf{b}$ respectively. L is the point where $\overrightarrow{AL} = \frac{1}{3}\overrightarrow{AB}$. M is the midpoint of BC and N is the point such that $\overrightarrow{CN} = 2\overrightarrow{CA}$. Find the position vectors of L, M and N and show that these points are collinear. State the ratio ML:LN.

24. A, B and C have position vectors $\mathbf{a} - \mathbf{b}$, $3\mathbf{a} + 2\mathbf{b}$ and $4\mathbf{a} - 3\mathbf{b}$ respectively. P lies on AB where AP:AB = 2:3, Q lies on BC where BQ:BC = 3:4 and R lies on AC extended so that AC = CR. Find the position vectors of P, Q and R and show that P, Q and R are collinear. State the ratio PQ:QR.

13.13 Components of a Vector

Suppose $\overrightarrow{AB} = \mathbf{a}$ and $\overrightarrow{BC} = \mathbf{b}$ (Fig. 13.28).

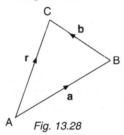

Fig. 13.28

The resultant of $\mathbf{a}$ and $\mathbf{b}$ is $\overrightarrow{AC} = \mathbf{r} = \mathbf{a} + \mathbf{b}$. The vectors $\mathbf{a}$ and $\mathbf{b}$ are called the **components** of $\mathbf{r}$. The components of a vector $\mathbf{r}$ are *any* two vectors whose resultant is $\mathbf{r}$. A vector can therefore be resolved into two components in an infinite number of ways. However if we take the components parallel to the x- and y-axes (Fig. 13.29), they will be unique and perpendicular.

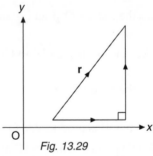

Fig. 13.29

We now define two standard unit vectors $\mathbf{i}$ and $\mathbf{j}$ called the **unit coordinate** (or **base**) **vectors** (Fig. 13.30).

$\mathbf{i}$ is a vector in the direction of the positive x-axis and $|\mathbf{i}| = 1$;

$\mathbf{j}$ is a vector in the direction of the positive y-axis and $|\mathbf{j}| = 1$.

The perpendicular components of any vector can now be expressed in terms of $\mathbf{i}$ and $\mathbf{j}$ in a standard form. For example, suppose the vector $\overrightarrow{AC} = \mathbf{r}$ has components of magnitude 3 and 4 parallel to the axes (Fig. 13.31). The horizontal component $\overrightarrow{AD} = 3\mathbf{i}$ and the vertical component $\overrightarrow{DC} = 4\mathbf{j}$.

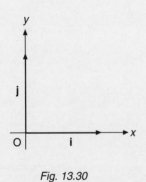

Fig. 13.30

Hence the vector $\mathbf{r} = \overrightarrow{AD} + \overrightarrow{DC} = 3\mathbf{i} + 4\mathbf{j}$.

$\mathbf{r}$ is now expressed in terms of the base vectors $\mathbf{i}$ and $\mathbf{j}$.

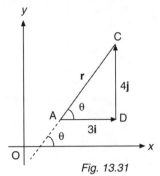

Fig. 13.31

$\mathbf{r}$ can also be written as $\begin{pmatrix} 3 \\ 4 \end{pmatrix}$, i.e. in **column vector** form. [Do not confuse this with coordinates (3,4)]. For example, $2\mathbf{i} - 3\mathbf{j}$ can be written as $\begin{pmatrix} 2 \\ -3 \end{pmatrix}$, $\mathbf{i} = \begin{pmatrix} 1 \\ 0 \end{pmatrix}$ and $\mathbf{j} = \begin{pmatrix} 0 \\ 1 \end{pmatrix}$.

Given $\mathbf{r}$ in terms of $\mathbf{i}$ and $\mathbf{j}$, we can find $|\mathbf{r}|$ and the angle θ it makes with the positive x-axis.

From $\triangle ADC$ (Fig. 13.31), $AC^2 = AD^2 + DC^2$, so $|\mathbf{r}^2| = 3^2 + 4^2 = 25$ and $|\mathbf{r}| = \sqrt{25} = 5$.

$\tan \theta = \dfrac{4}{3}$ giving $\theta = 53.13°$.

Note:
To find θ for a given vector, draw a diagram to locate the correct quadrant as $\tan \theta = \dfrac{b}{a}$ will give two values for $0° \leq \theta \leq 360°$.

In general, for a vector $\mathbf{r}$ with perpendicular components of magnitude a and b (Fig. 13.32):

$\mathbf{r} = a\mathbf{i} + b\mathbf{j} = \begin{pmatrix} a \\ b \end{pmatrix}$

$|\mathbf{r}| = |a\mathbf{i} + b\mathbf{j}| = \sqrt{a^2 + b^2}$

$\tan \theta = \dfrac{b}{a}$

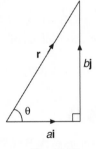

Fig. 13.32

▶ Example 12

The position vector of A is $-2\mathbf{i} + 3\mathbf{j}$.

(a) State the coordinates of A.

(b) Find $|\overrightarrow{OA}|$ and the angle the vector OA makes with the x-axis.

► **Solution ...**

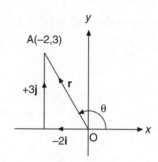

Fig. 13.33

(a) The coordinates of A are (–2,3) (Fig. 13.33).

(b) $|\overrightarrow{OA}| = |-2\mathbf{i} + 3\mathbf{j}| = \sqrt{(-2)^2 + 3^3} = \sqrt{13} \approx 3.6$

$\tan \theta = \dfrac{3}{-2}$ giving $\theta = 123.7°$ (2nd quadrant, Fig. 13.33)

► ## Example 13

(a) $\overrightarrow{OC}$ has the same direction as $\begin{pmatrix} -3 \\ 4 \end{pmatrix}$ and $|\overrightarrow{OC}| = 30$. Express $\overrightarrow{OC}$ as a column vector.

(b) The position vectors of A and B are $\begin{pmatrix} -2 \\ 3 \end{pmatrix}$ and $\begin{pmatrix} -1 \\ 2 \end{pmatrix}$ respectively. Find **(i)** $\overrightarrow{AB}$, **(ii)** the equation of AB.

► **Solution ...**

(a) $\overrightarrow{OC}$ must be a scalar multiple of $\begin{pmatrix} -3 \\ 4 \end{pmatrix}$ so $\overrightarrow{OC} = \begin{pmatrix} -3k \\ 4k \end{pmatrix}$ where $k > 0$.

$|\overrightarrow{OC}|^2 = 9k^2 + 16k^2 = 25k^2$ so $|\overrightarrow{OC}| = 5k = 30$ and $k = 6$. Hence $\overrightarrow{OC} = \begin{pmatrix} -18 \\ 24 \end{pmatrix}$.

(b) **(i)** $\overrightarrow{AB} = \overrightarrow{OB} - \overrightarrow{OA} = \mathbf{i} - 2\mathbf{j} - (-2\mathbf{i} + 3\mathbf{j}) = 3\mathbf{i} - 5\mathbf{j}$.

(ii) The coordinates of A and B are (–2,3) and (1,–2).

Hence the equation of AB is $\dfrac{y - 3}{-2 - 3} = \dfrac{x + 2}{1 + 2}$, i.e. $5x + 3y = -1$.

► ## Example 14

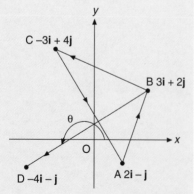

Fig. 13.34

The position vectors of A, B and C are $2\mathbf{i} - \mathbf{j}$, $3\mathbf{i} + 2\mathbf{j}$ and $-3\mathbf{i} + 4\mathbf{j}$ respectively (Fig. 13.34).

(a) Find $|\overrightarrow{AB}|$, $|\overrightarrow{BC}|$ and $|\overrightarrow{AC}|$ and show that $\triangle ABC$ is right angled.

(b) If the position vector of D is $-4\mathbf{i} - \mathbf{j}$, find the angle BD makes with the x-axis.

▶ **Solution . . .**

(a) $\overrightarrow{AB} = 3\mathbf{i} + 2\mathbf{j} - (2\mathbf{i} - \mathbf{j}) = \mathbf{i} + 3\mathbf{j}; \ |\overrightarrow{AB}| = \sqrt{10}$

$\overrightarrow{BC} = -3\mathbf{i} + 4\mathbf{j} - (3\mathbf{i} + 2\mathbf{j}) = -6\mathbf{i} + 2\mathbf{j}; \ |\overrightarrow{BC}| = \sqrt{40}$

$\overrightarrow{CA} = 2\mathbf{i} - \mathbf{j} - (-3\mathbf{i} + 4\mathbf{j}) = 5\mathbf{i} - 5\mathbf{j}; \ |\overrightarrow{CA}| = \sqrt{50}$

As $|\overrightarrow{CA}|^2 = |\overrightarrow{AB}|^2 + |\overrightarrow{BC}|^2$, the triangle is right angled.

(b) $\overrightarrow{BD} = -4\mathbf{i} - \mathbf{j} - (3\mathbf{i} + 2\mathbf{j}) = -7\mathbf{i} - 3\mathbf{j}$

$\tan\theta = \dfrac{-3}{-7}$ giving $\theta = 203.2°$ (3rd quadrant).

13.14 Unit Vectors

The magnitude of a vector $\mathbf{a} = 3\mathbf{i} + 4\mathbf{j}$ is $\left|3\mathbf{i} + 4\mathbf{j}\right| = 5$, so the vector is 5 units long. Hence the vector $\dfrac{3\mathbf{i} + 4\mathbf{j}}{5}$ is one unit long and is in the **same** direction as **a**. This is the **unit vector** in the direction of **a** (Fig. 13.35). It is written as $\hat{\mathbf{a}}$ (read 'vector a cap').

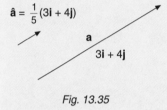

Fig. 13.35

If $\mathbf{r} = a\mathbf{i} + b\mathbf{j}$, then $\hat{\mathbf{r}} = \dfrac{a\mathbf{i} + b\mathbf{j}}{\sqrt{a^2 + b^2}}$.

For example, if $\mathbf{a} = 2\mathbf{i} - \mathbf{j}$ then $\hat{\mathbf{a}} = \dfrac{2\mathbf{i} - \mathbf{j}}{\sqrt{5}}$.

Again, if $\overrightarrow{OA} = \begin{pmatrix} 2 \\ 3 \end{pmatrix}$, the unit vector parallel to $\overrightarrow{AO}$ would be $\dfrac{-2\mathbf{i} - 3\mathbf{j}}{\sqrt{13}}$.

Exercise 13D (Answers on page 504)

1. On graph paper, mark the positions of the points with position vectors $\mathbf{i} + \mathbf{j}, -2\mathbf{i} - \mathbf{j}, 3\mathbf{i} + 2\mathbf{j}, -3\mathbf{j}$.

2. A, B and C are points with position vectors $2\mathbf{i} - 3\mathbf{j}, \mathbf{i} + 2\mathbf{j}$ and $4\mathbf{i} - \mathbf{j}$ respectively. Find in terms of **i** and **j**, the vectors $\overrightarrow{AB}, \overrightarrow{BC}$ and $\overrightarrow{CA}$.

3. The position vectors of A and B are $3\mathbf{i} + \mathbf{j}$ and $2\mathbf{i} + 3\mathbf{j}$ respectively. Points C and D have position vectors given by $\overrightarrow{OC} = \overrightarrow{AO}$ and $\overrightarrow{CD} = \overrightarrow{AB}$.
   - **(a)** Find the position vectors of C and D in terms of **i** and **j** and show the positions of the four points on a diagram.
   - **(b)** Express $\overrightarrow{DB}$ in terms of **i** and **j**.
   - **(c)** Find $|\overrightarrow{DB}|$ and the angle $\overrightarrow{DB}$ makes with the x-axis.

4. Find the magnitude and the angle made with the x-axis of the vectors
   - **(a)** $\begin{pmatrix} -1 \\ 2 \end{pmatrix}$,
   - **(b)** $\begin{pmatrix} 3 \\ -3 \end{pmatrix}$,
   - **(c)** $2\mathbf{i} + 3\mathbf{j}$,
   - **(d)** $-4\mathbf{i} - 2\mathbf{j}$.

5. **(a)** The coordinates of A are $(-3,2)$ and the position vector of B is $2\mathbf{i} + 4\mathbf{j}$. Find the vector $\overrightarrow{BA}$.

(b) The vector $\overrightarrow{OA}$ has magnitude 25 units and is in the same direction as $\begin{pmatrix} 3 \\ -4 \end{pmatrix}$. The vector $\overrightarrow{OB}$ has magnitude 6.5 units and is opposite in direction to $\begin{pmatrix} 5 \\ 12 \end{pmatrix}$. State the vectors $\overrightarrow{AO}$ and $\overrightarrow{AB}$ in column vector form.

6. The point with position vector $3\mathbf{i} - 2\mathbf{j}$ is displaced by a vector $\begin{pmatrix} 4 \\ 2 \end{pmatrix}$. Find its new position vector.

7. If the coordinates of A are $(2,4)$ and $\overrightarrow{AB} = \mathbf{i} + 2\mathbf{j}$, find the position vector of B.

8. **(a)** If $\mathbf{a} = 6\mathbf{i} - 8\mathbf{j}$ and $\mathbf{b} = \mathbf{i} + 3\mathbf{j}$, find $\hat{\mathbf{a}}$ and $\hat{\mathbf{b}}$.

(b) $\overrightarrow{OA} = \begin{pmatrix} 3 \\ -4 \end{pmatrix}$ and $\overrightarrow{OB} = \begin{pmatrix} 7 \\ -7 \end{pmatrix}$. Find the unit vectors parallel to $\overrightarrow{AO}$ and $\overrightarrow{BA}$.

9. In this question, take $\mathbf{a} = 3\mathbf{i} + \mathbf{j}$, $\mathbf{b} = -\mathbf{i} + 2\mathbf{j}$, $\mathbf{c} = 3\mathbf{i}$. Find

(a) $\hat{\mathbf{a}}$, **(b)** $\hat{\mathbf{b}}$.

Express in terms of $\mathbf{i}$ and $\mathbf{j}$,

(c) $\mathbf{a} + 2\mathbf{b}$, **(d)** $2\mathbf{c} - 3\mathbf{b}$, **(e)** $\mathbf{a} + \mathbf{b} - 2\mathbf{c}$.

Find

(f) $|\mathbf{a} + 2\mathbf{b}|$, **(g)** $|2\mathbf{c} - 3\mathbf{b}|$, **(h)** $|\mathbf{a} + \mathbf{b} - 2\mathbf{c}|$.

10. The position vectors of A, B, C and D are $\mathbf{i} + 3\mathbf{j}$, $2\mathbf{i} - \mathbf{j}$, $-\mathbf{i} - 4\mathbf{j}$ and $3\mathbf{i} + 2\mathbf{j}$ respectively. Find in terms of $\mathbf{i}$ and $\mathbf{j}$ the vectors

(a) $\overrightarrow{AB}$, **(b)** $\overrightarrow{BD}$, **(c)** $\overrightarrow{CA}$, **(d)** $\overrightarrow{AD}$.

11. The position vectors of A and B are $2\mathbf{i} + 3\mathbf{j}$ and $3\mathbf{i} - 8\mathbf{j}$ respectively. D is the midpoint of AB and E divides OD in the ratio 2:3. Find the coordinates of E.

12. P and Q have position vectors $5\mathbf{i} + 2\mathbf{j}$ and $\mathbf{i} - 4\mathbf{j}$ respectively. If $\overrightarrow{OP} = 3\overrightarrow{OQ} + 2\overrightarrow{OR}$, find the position vector of R.

13. A, B and C have coordinates $(1,2)$, $(2,5)$ and $(0,-4)$ respectively. If $\overrightarrow{AB} = \overrightarrow{CD}$, find the position vector of D.

14. The position vectors of A and B are $3\mathbf{i} + \mathbf{j}$ and $-4\mathbf{i} + 2\mathbf{j}$ respectively. Find the position vector of C if $\overrightarrow{AB} = \overrightarrow{BC}$.

15. Points A and B have position vectors $2\mathbf{i} - \mathbf{j}$ and $\mathbf{i} + 3\mathbf{j}$ respectively.

(a) Given that $\overrightarrow{OC} = \overrightarrow{AB}$ and $\overrightarrow{AD} = \overrightarrow{CB}$, find the position vectors of C and D.

(b) Show the positions of the four points on a diagram.

(c) Find $|\overrightarrow{CD}|$ and the angle $\overrightarrow{CD}$ makes with the x-axis.

16. The position vectors of A and B are $4\mathbf{i} + 5\mathbf{j}$ and $\mathbf{i} - 2\mathbf{j}$ respectively. Find the position vector of C if $3\overrightarrow{OA} = 2\overrightarrow{OB} + \overrightarrow{OC}$.

17. The coordinates of A and B are (2,3) and (–2,5) respectively. Find the position vector of C if $2\overrightarrow{OA} = 2\overrightarrow{OB} + \overrightarrow{OC}$.

18. Show that the points with position vectors $4\mathbf{i} + 5\mathbf{j}$, $3\mathbf{i} + 3\mathbf{j}$ and $-3\mathbf{j}$ are collinear.

19. What is the gradient of the line joining the points with position vectors $2\mathbf{i} + \mathbf{j}$ and $\mathbf{i} + 3\mathbf{j}$?

20. Show that the triangle whose vertices have position vectors $2\mathbf{i} + 4\mathbf{j}$, $5\mathbf{i} + 2\mathbf{j}$ and $3\mathbf{i} + 5\mathbf{j}$ is isosceles.

21. **(a)** The velocity $\mathbf{v}$ m s^{-1} of a body is given by the vector $\mathbf{v} = \mathbf{i} + 3\mathbf{j}$. Find the speed of the body and the angle its path makes with the x-axis.

    (b) If its position vector at the start was $\mathbf{i} + \mathbf{j}$, what is its position vector **(i)** after 1 sec, **(ii)** after 3 secs, **(iii)** after t secs?

    (c) After what time will it reach the position given by $7\mathbf{i} + 19\mathbf{j}$?

22. A body is moving with velocity $\mathbf{v}$ m s^{-1} where $\mathbf{v} = 2\mathbf{i} - 3\mathbf{j}$. If it started from the position $\mathbf{i} + 4\mathbf{j}$, what is its position after 3 seconds? How long will it take to reach the position $11(\mathbf{i} - \mathbf{j})$?

23. The position vector $\mathbf{r}$ of a point on a straight line is given by $\mathbf{r} = \mathbf{i} + \mathbf{j} + t(2\mathbf{i} - \mathbf{j})$ where t is a number.

    (a) What is its position vector when $t = 2$?

    (b) Find the position vector of another point on the line by taking any other value of t.

    (c) Hence find the gradient and the equation of the line.

24. Find the gradient and equation of the line given by $\mathbf{r} = \mathbf{i} - \mathbf{j} + k(\mathbf{i} - \mathbf{j})$ where k is a number.

25. The position vector $\mathbf{r}$ of a point is given by $\mathbf{r} = 2\mathbf{i} - \mathbf{j} + t(\mathbf{i} + 2\mathbf{j})$, where t is a number. What is its position vector when

    (a) $t = -1$,   **(b)** $t = 3$?

    (c) What is the value of t when its position vector is $7\mathbf{i} + 9\mathbf{j}$?

26. If the vectors $m\mathbf{i} - 2\mathbf{j}$ and $4\mathbf{i} - 6\mathbf{j}$ are parallel, state the value of m.

27. The position vectors of A and B are $3\mathbf{i} - 2\mathbf{j}$ and $t\mathbf{i} + \mathbf{j}$ respectively. Find the value of t if OAB is a straight line.

28. OABC is a parallelogram where O is the origin. The position vectors of A and B are $4\mathbf{i} + 6\mathbf{j}$ and $6\mathbf{i} + 8\mathbf{j}$ respectively. D is the midpoint of CB and E is the midpoint of AB. OD meets CE at F.

    (a) State the position vectors of C, D and E.

    (b) By taking $\overrightarrow{OF} = m\overrightarrow{OD}$ and $\overrightarrow{CF} = n\overrightarrow{CE}$, find the values of m and n and the ratio OF:FD.

29. **(a)** State the condition for the lines $y = m_1 x + c_1$ and $y = m_2 x + c_2$ to be perpendicular.

(b) The points A, B, C and D have position vectors $\mathbf{i} + \mathbf{j}$, $3\mathbf{i} - 2\mathbf{j}$, $-3\mathbf{i} - 3\mathbf{j}$ and $-\mathbf{j}$ respectively. Find the gradient of AB and CD and show that these lines are perpendicular.

30. The points A, B, C and D have position vectors $\mathbf{i}$, $2\mathbf{i} + 3\mathbf{j}$, $2\mathbf{i} + \mathbf{j}$ and $5\mathbf{i}$ respectively. Show that AB and CD are perpendicular.

31. P, Q, R and S have position vectors $\mathbf{i} + 2\mathbf{j}$, $3\mathbf{i} - \mathbf{j}$, $-\mathbf{i} - \mathbf{j}$ and $k\mathbf{i} + \mathbf{j}$ respectively, where k is a number.
(a) Find the gradients of PQ and RS.
(b) For what value of k will the lines PQ and RS be perpendicular?

32. If $\mathbf{a} = 3\mathbf{i} + 4\mathbf{j}$ and $|\mathbf{b}| = 2$, what are the greatest and smallest values of $|\mathbf{a} + \mathbf{b}|$?

13.15 Composition of Velocities

We now apply what we have learned about vectors to velocity, which is a vector.

A moving body can have two (or more) velocities at the same time. A simple example of a body having two velocities is the case of a man rowing a boat on a river. Suppose the man is on the river bank at A (Fig. 13.36) and attempts to row in a direction perpendicular to the bank to head for B on the opposite bank. If there is a current, the boat will not move along AB at a right angle to the bank but will move along the path AC at an angle θ to AB. Thus the resultant path of the boat is determined by two velocities: one as a result of the man's rowing in the direction AB, and the other as result of the current of the river downstream.

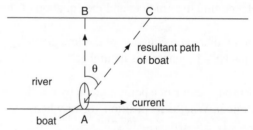

Fig. 13.36

As velocities are vectors, they obey the laws of vector algebra. The vector sum of the velocities is the **resultant velocity**. If a body has 2 velocities $\mathbf{a}$ and $\mathbf{b}$ as shown in Fig. 13.37, then the resultant velocity $\mathbf{c} = \mathbf{a} + \mathbf{b}$.

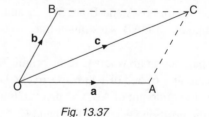

Fig. 13.37

c is represented by the diagonal of the parallelogram OACB. The velocities **a** and **b** are the **components** of the resultant velocity **c**. Hence a body that has velocities **a** and **b** will move as though it has the single velocity **c**.

Let us consider another case of a man rowing a boat on a river. Suppose he rows the boat at a velocity **a** and the river is flowing at velocity **b**. Then the resultant velocity of the boat is **c** = **a** + **b** (Fig. 13.38). Hence the actual path of the boat will be along OC.

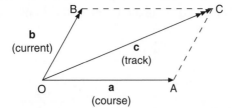

Fig. 13.38

This path is called the **track** of the boat and the actual speed along the track is called the **ground speed**. The direction of **a** is the **course** (which is the direction the boat would have moved if there were no current). In diagrams, it is helpful to mark vectors with different numbers of arrows. Thus in Fig. 13.38, we use the following notations:

course vector marked with 1 arrow ⟶

current vector marked with 2 arrows ⟶▸▸

track vector marked with 3 arrows ⟶▸▸▸

Then we have:

course vector + current vector = track vector
⟶   ⟶▸▸   ⟶▸▸▸
(1 arrow)   (2 arrows)   (3 arrows)

The track vector is the resultant of the other two vectors.

Another practical example is the case of an aircraft flying in a wind. The aircraft has a velocity **a** through the air (Fig. 13.39). Its direction is the course (as in the case of the boat) and its speed along the course is the **airspeed**. The aircraft is also affected by the wind with velocity **b**. As a result, the actual velocity **c** is the resultant of the velocity of the aircraft and that of the wind. As in the case of the boat, the actual path is called the **track** and the speed along the track is the **ground speed**. The same arrow notations are used, with current velocity replaced by the wind velocity. It should be noted, however, that a current is described as moving *towards* a certain direction whereas a wind is described as coming *from* a certain direction. So a current in the direction NE is moving in the direction 045° whereas a NE wind is actually moving in the direction 225°.

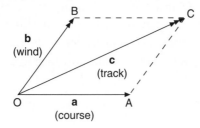

Fig. 13.39

13.16 Resolution of Velocities

Just as we can combine component velocities to obtain a resultant velocity, we can also resolve ('split') a velocity into its components. Particularly useful is the resolution of a velocity into 2 perpendicular components, usually in the directions of the *x*- and *y*-axes. In practical problems, it is convenient to resolve along the east and north directions respectively (in place of the *x*- and *y*-axes). In Fig. 13.40 the velocity **r** is resolved into its components **p** and **q** along the *x*- and *y*-directions respectively.

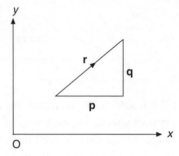

Fig. 13.40

We can also use **unit coordinate vectors i** and **j**, where **i** is the unit vector along the *x*-axis and **j** the unit vector along the *y*-axis. Thus we can represent **r** as $p\mathbf{i} + q\mathbf{j}$ where p and q are the magnitudes of **p** and **q** respectively (Fig. 13.41). So $\mathbf{r} = p\mathbf{i} + q\mathbf{j}$.

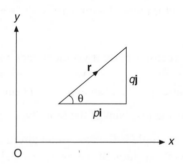

Fig. 13.41

Note that the magnitude of **r** is $r = \sqrt{p^2 + q^2}$. Also, if **r** makes an angle θ with the *x*-axis, then we have

$$p = r \cos \theta, \quad q = r \sin \theta$$

and $\tan \theta = \dfrac{q}{p}$.

▶ **Example 15**

A river is flowing at 0.9 m s^{-1}. A man sets out, at right angles to the banks, to row across. He can row at 1.2 m s^{-1} in still water.

(a) What is the actual velocity across the river?

(b) If the river is 600 m wide, how long does he take to cross the river?

Solution ...

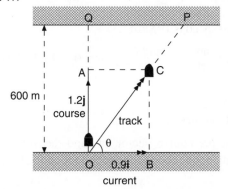

Fig. 13.42

(a) Relative to the water, the boat will move at 1.2 m s^{-1} perpendicular to the banks (Fig. 13.42); but the water, moving at 0.9 m s^{-1}, simultaneously carries the boat along parallel to the banks. The boat therefore moves crabwise across pointing at right angles to the bank. The resultant of the course vector ($\overrightarrow{OA}$) and the current vector ($\overrightarrow{OB}$) is the track vector ($\overrightarrow{OC}$). Hence the path of the boat is along OC.

The actual velocity of the boat is represented by the resultant (track) vector and it has magnitude $\sqrt{0.9^2 + 1.2^2} = 1.5$ m s^{-1} at an angle θ to the bank where $\tan \theta = \dfrac{1.2}{0.9} = \dfrac{4}{3}$ ($\theta \approx 53°$).

(b) The boat moves along the track OC and will reach the opposite bank at P.

The time taken $= \dfrac{\text{distance of OP}}{\text{speed along the track}}$

$= \dfrac{750}{1.5}$ (using similar triangles, $\dfrac{OP}{1.5} = \dfrac{600}{1.2}$)

$= 500$ s or 8 min 20 s

(**Note:** The time taken can also be found more simply by considering the course component of velocity, thus time taken

$= \dfrac{\text{distance of OQ}}{\text{speed along the course}} = \dfrac{600}{1.2} = 500$ s.)

► Example 16

An aeroplane has an airspeed of 200 km h^{-1} and flies on a course of N30° E. A wind is blowing steadily at 50 km h^{-1} from the NW. Find the track and ground speed.

► Solution ...

(1) By trigonometry

In Fig. 13.43, $\overrightarrow{OC}$ is the course vector (1 arrow), $\overrightarrow{OW}$ the wind vector (2 arrows). $\overrightarrow{OC} + \overrightarrow{OW} = \overrightarrow{OT}$, the track vector (3 arrows) which has speed v and $\angle COT = \theta$.

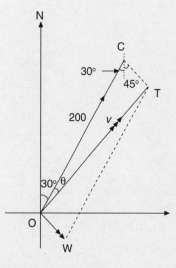

Fig. 13.43

From $\triangle$OCT, using the cosine rule, $v^2 = 200^2 + 50^2 - 2 \times 200 \times 50 \times \cos 75°$ giving $v \approx 193$.

Hence the ground speed is 193 km^{-1}.

By the sine rule, $\dfrac{\sin\theta}{50} = \dfrac{\sin 75°}{193}$ giving $\theta \approx 14.5°$. Hence the track is N44.5°E.

(2) Using unit vectors

Here we resolve the course vector $\overrightarrow{OC}$ and the wind vector $\overrightarrow{OW}$ into components along perpendicular directions OC and OD respectively (Fig. 13.44).

If **i** and **j** are unit vectors along $\overrightarrow{OC}$ and $\overrightarrow{OD}$ respectively,

then $\overrightarrow{OC} = 200\mathbf{i}$

and $\overrightarrow{OW} = -(50 \sin 15°)\mathbf{i} + (50 \cos 15°)\mathbf{j}$
$= -12.94\mathbf{i} + 48.30\mathbf{j}.$

Now $\overrightarrow{OT} = \overrightarrow{OC} + \overrightarrow{OW}$
$= 200\mathbf{i} - 12.94\mathbf{i} + 48.30\mathbf{j}$
$= 187.1\mathbf{i} + 48.30\mathbf{j}$

Therefore $v = |\overrightarrow{OT}| \approx 193$

Hence the ground speed is 193 km h^{-1}.

Also $\tan\theta = \dfrac{48.30}{187.1}$
$\theta \approx 14.5°$

Hence the track is N44.5°E.

The drawing method can only be used if the question specifically allows it.
To be satisfactory, drawings must be made carefully.

Draw a north line ON as in Fig. 13.43. Now select a suitable scale — as large as possible to ensure reasonably accurate results, say 1 cm for 10 km h⁻¹.

From O, draw OC 20 cm long with ∠NOC = 30°.
Draw OW 5 cm long with ∠NOW = 135°.

Complete the parallelogram OWTC.

Measure OT and ∠NOT to obtain the results and compare with the calculated values obtained in the example.

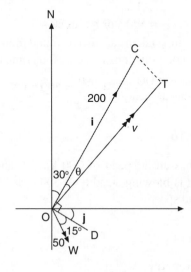

Fig. 13.44

► **Example 17**

A helicopter leaves an airfield A for another airfield B 500 km away on a bearing of 140°. There is a steady wind of 30 km h^{-1} from the NE. The helicopter has an airspeed of 150 km h^{-1}.

(a) Find the course the pilot must take and the time taken for him to reach B.

(b) What course should be taken for the return journey, if the wind continues as before?

► **Solution . . .**

(a) **(1)** **By trigonometry**
The facts are shown in Fig. 13.45 ; v is the ground speed.

From $\triangle AWT$, using the sine rule,

$\dfrac{\sin\theta}{30} = \dfrac{\sin 85°}{150}$ giving $\theta \approx 11.5°$.

Hence the course to take is 128.5°.
$\angle AWT = 180° - (85° + 11.5°) = 83.5°$
Using the sine rule again,

$\dfrac{v}{\sin 83.5°} = \dfrac{150}{\sin 85°}$ giving $v \approx 149.6$.

Hence the time taken $= \dfrac{500}{149.6} \approx 3.34\text{ h} \approx 3\text{ h }21\text{ min}$

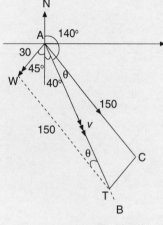

Fig. 13.45

(2) **Using unit vectors**
Take **i** along the track $\overrightarrow{AT}$ and **j** along $\overrightarrow{AU}$ (Fig. 13.46).
$\overrightarrow{AT} = v\mathbf{i}$ (no **j** component)
$\overrightarrow{AC} = (150\cos\theta)\mathbf{i} - (150\sin\theta)\mathbf{j}$
$\overrightarrow{AW} = (30\cos 85°)\mathbf{i} + (30\sin 85°)\mathbf{j}$
$\overrightarrow{AT} = \overrightarrow{AC} + \overrightarrow{AW}$

Therefore $v\mathbf{i} = (150\cos\theta + 30\cos 85°)\mathbf{i} + (30\sin 85° - 150\sin\theta)\mathbf{j}$
Equating the **j** components,
  $0 = 30\sin 85° - 150\sin\theta$, giving $\theta \approx 11.5°$ as before.
Equating the **i** components,
  $v = 150\cos\theta + 30\cos 85°$, giving $v \approx 149.6$,
and the time taken can be obtained as before.

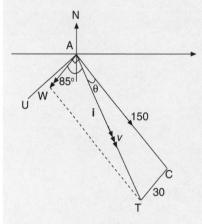

Fig. 13.46

(b) By trigonometry

The starting point is now airfield B (Fig. 13.47). $\overrightarrow{BW}$ is the wind vector, $\overrightarrow{BC}$ is the course vector (airspeed 150) and $\overrightarrow{BT}$ is the track vector.

From $\triangle BCT$, using the sine rule,

$$\frac{\sin\phi}{30} = \frac{\sin 95^\circ}{150} \text{ giving } \phi \approx 11.5^\circ.$$

Hence the course for the return journey should be 331.5°.

Verify that this can also be solved using unit vectors as in (a).

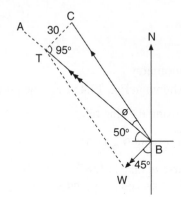

Fig. 13.47

Exercise 13E (*Answers on page 504*)

1. Find the resultants (giving both magnitude and direction) of the following velocities by trigonometry or using unit vectors:
   (a) 5 km h^{-1} due north and 3 km h^{-1} due east.
   (b) 8 m s^{-1} north-east and 5 m s^{-1} north-west.
   (c) 10 m s^{-1} north 60° east and 4 m s^{-1} east.
   (d) 40 km h^{-1} on a bearing 050° and 40 km h^{-1} on a bearing 110°.

2. A steamship is sailing due north at 20 km h^{-1}. There is a wind of 15 km h^{-1} from the west. Find the direction in which the smoke from the funnel is drifting.

3. A ship is travelling at 10 m s^{-1}. A ball is rolled across the deck (at right angles to the motion of the ship) at 4 m s^{-1}. Find the actual velocity of the ball relative to the ground.

4. An aeroplane pilot sets a course due north. The airspeed is 150 km h^{-1}. There is a wind of 40 km h^{-1} from the west. Find the track and ground speed of the plane.

5. A man sets out to swim across a river 0.4 km wide at right angles to its parallel banks. He can swim at a steady speed of 2 km h^{-1} in still water but there is a current flowing at 1 km h^{-1}. Find
   (a) his track and ground speed across the river,
   (b) how far downstream he is carried when he lands.

6. An aeroplane has an airspeed of 200 km h^{-1} and is headed on a course of 330°. There is a wind of 50 km h^{-1} from a bearing of 210°. Find the track and ground speed of the plane.

7. A river flows at 3 km h^{-1} and its parallel banks are 400 m apart. A man wishes to cross the river in a motor boat which can make 5 km h^{-1} in still water to reach the point directly opposite. Find the direction in which he must steer and the time taken to cross the river.

8. An aeroplane pilot wishes to fly from an airfield P to another airfield Q, 300 km due east. The airspeed is 200 km h^{-1}. There is a steady wind of 40 km h^{-1} from the north-east. Find

(a) the course he must take,

(b) the actual ground speed,

(c) the time taken to reach Q,

(d) the course required for the return journey, the wind being the same,

(e) the time taken over the return journey.

9. An aeroplane, flying at a steady airspeed of 200 km h^{-1}, flies in a straight line from A to B, where B is due east of A and then returns along the same route. There is a constant wind of 60 km h^{-1} blowing from the north-east throughout the double flight. Find the ground speed of the aeroplane on both trips.

10. A motorboat, capable of travelling at 40 km h^{-1} is to be sailed from point A to a point B where B lies 25 km on a bearing 070° from A. There is a steady current of 10 km h^{-1} running due S. Find the course to be taken and the time required for the journey.

11. An aeroplane starts from A intending to fly to B, 300 km due N of A and the pilot sets a course due N. Due to a wind from the west, the aeroplane reaches a point 30 km due E of B after flying for $1\frac{1}{2}$ hours. Calculate

(a) the speed of the wind,

(b) the airspeed of the aeroplane.

Find also

(c) the course that should have been taken to reach B directly, and

(d) the time, to the nearest minute, that the flight would then have taken.

12. A stretch of river 300 m wide has straight parallel banks and the speed of the current is 4 m s^{-1}. A man starts to cross the river in a boat from a point A on one bank. The boat can sail at 5 m s^{-1} in calm water. If he takes a course making an angle of 60° upstream with the bank, find

(a) the distance where he lands from the point directly opposite A,

(b) the time taken to cross the river.

13. An aeroplane can fly 300 km h⁻¹ in still air and there is a wind blowing from the direction 060° at a constant rate of 40 km h⁻¹.

(a) What course should the pilot take to reach an airfield 200 km due N of his starting point?

(b) If he takes this course, how long will the flight last?

(c) What course should be taken for the return flight (the wind being as before) and how long will this flight last?

14. The speed of a helicopter in still air is v km h⁻¹. The pilot leaves A and flies on a course 067°. There is a wind of 50 km h⁻¹ blowing from the direction 020°. After 45 minutes, the helicopter is above a point B which is due E of A. Find

(a) the value of v to the nearest km h⁻¹,

(b) the distance AB.

13.17 Relative Velocity

Consider two aeroplanes A and B flying at the same height. A is flying at 200 km h⁻¹ due N and B at 400 km h⁻¹ on a course 030°. These are their velocities **relative to the ground** and are their **true** velocities. To the pilot of A, however, B will seem to have a different velocity from 400 km h⁻¹ because he himself is moving. We call this apparent velocity, the **velocity of B relative to A** and we write this as $\overrightarrow{BvA}$. Similarly B will see A moving with the velocity of A relative to B or $\overrightarrow{AvB}$.

In general, suppose **a** represents the velocity of A and **b** the velocity of B (Fig. 13.48),

then $\overrightarrow{OA} = \mathbf{a}$ and $\overrightarrow{OB} = \mathbf{b}$.

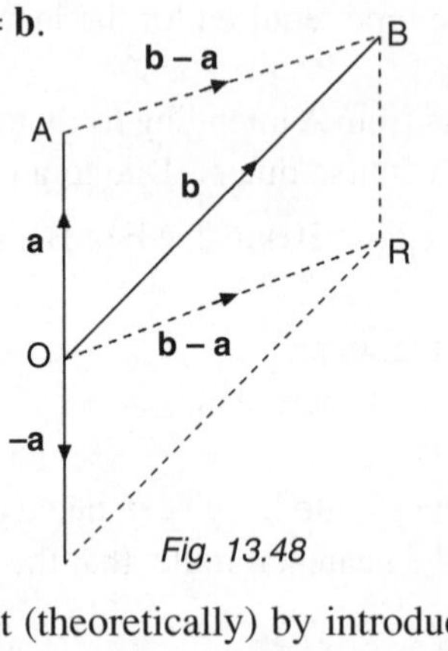

Fig. 13.48

Let us reduce A to rest (theoretically) by introducing a velocity −**a**. A is now not moving. In order to preserve their relative positions, we must also give B the same velocity −**a**. B now has 2 velocities, **b** and −**a** and the resultant of these is $\overrightarrow{OR}$. $\overrightarrow{OR}$ represents the velocity of B as seen from A (as A is not moving). But $\overrightarrow{OR} = \overrightarrow{AB} = \mathbf{b} - \mathbf{a}$. Hence the velocity of B relative to A is $\mathbf{b} - \mathbf{a}$ or $\overrightarrow{BvA} = \mathbf{b} - \mathbf{a}$. Similarly, $\overrightarrow{AvB} = \mathbf{a} - \mathbf{b}$.

We can now find BvA for the two aeroplanes. From Fig. 13.49,

$$| \overrightarrow{BvA} |^2 = 200^2 + 400^2 - 2 \times 200 \times 400 \times \cos 30°$$

giving $| \overrightarrow{BvA} | = 248$.

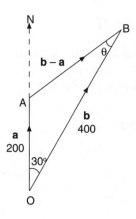

Fig. 13.49

Also $\dfrac{\sin\theta}{200} = \dfrac{\sin 30^\circ}{248}$ giving $\theta \approx 23.8^\circ$.

Therefore $\angle NAB \approx 30^\circ + 23.8^\circ = 53.8^\circ$.

Hence the velocity of B relative to A is 248 km h^{-1} in the direction N53.8°E.

Note:

Problems on relative velocity may also be solved by drawing if the rubric of the question does not forbid it (see Example 20).

[We can also work with the unit vectors as follows:

Taking **i** along $\overrightarrow{OE}$ and **j** along $\overrightarrow{ON}$ (Fig. 13.50)

$$\mathbf{a} = 200\mathbf{j}$$

and $\mathbf{b} = (400 \sin 30^\circ)\mathbf{i} + (400 \cos 30^\circ)\mathbf{j}$

$$= 200\mathbf{i} + (200\sqrt{3})\mathbf{j}$$

So $\overrightarrow{BvA} = \mathbf{b} - \mathbf{a}$

$$= 200\mathbf{i} + (200\sqrt{3} - 200)\mathbf{j}$$

$$= 200\mathbf{i} + 146.4\mathbf{j}$$

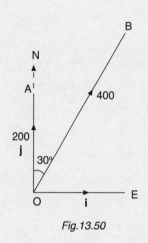

Fig. 13.50

Hence $|\overrightarrow{BvA}|^2 = 200^2 + 146.4^2$ (Fig. 13.51)

giving $|\overrightarrow{BvA}|^2 \approx 248$

and $\tan\phi = \dfrac{200}{146.4}$ giving $\phi \approx 53.8^\circ$.

Hence $\overrightarrow{BvA}$ is 248 km h^{-1} in the direction N53.8°E as before.]

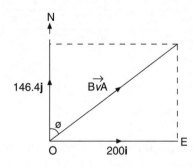

Fig. 13.51

Example 18

Rain is falling vertically at 5 km h^{-1}. A man is sitting by the window of a train travelling at 40 km h^{-1}. In what direction do the raindrops appear to cross the windows of the train?

Solution . . .

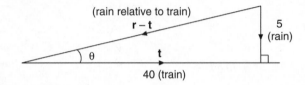

Fig. 13.52

The vectors are shown in Fig. 13.52.

The velocity of the rain relative to the train = $\mathbf{r} - \mathbf{t}$.

So $\tan \theta = \dfrac{5}{40}$ giving $\theta \approx 7.1°$.

Thus raindrops appear to cross the windows at $7.1°$ to the horizontal.

Example 19

A ship is sailing due north at a constant speed of 12 knots. A destroyer sailing at 36 knots is 30 nautical miles due east of the ship. At this moment, the destroyer is ordered to intercept the ship. Find

(a) the course which the destroyer should take,

(b) the velocity of the destroyer relative to the ship,

(c) the time taken for the destroyer to reach the ship.

[It is assumed that both the ship and the destroyer do not change their velocities.]

Solution . . .

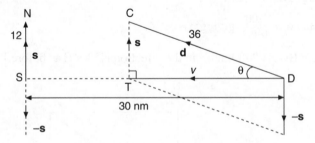

Fig. 13.53

Fig. 13.53 shows the positions of the ship S and the destroyer D. We reduce S to rest by introducing a velocity of 12 knots due south to both S and D.

Then the course of D is $\overrightarrow{DC}$ and, to intercept S, its track ($\overrightarrow{DT}$) must lie along DS.

(a) From $\triangle$DTC, $\sin\theta = \frac{12}{36}$ giving $\theta \approx 19.5°$.

Hence the course the destroyer should take is $270° + 19.5° = 289.5°$.

(b) The velocity of D relative to S is

$$\overrightarrow{DvS} = \overrightarrow{DT}$$

Therefore $|\overrightarrow{DrS}|^2 = 36^2 - 12^2$, giving $|\overrightarrow{DvS}| \approx 33.9$.

Hence $\overrightarrow{DvS}$ is 33.9 knots due W.

(c) Time taken $= \dfrac{30}{33.9}$ h ≈ 53 min

Hence the destroyer will intercept the ship in 53 minutes.

[By vectors, take **i** along DT and **j** along TC, then

$$\overrightarrow{DvS} = \mathbf{d} - \mathbf{s}$$

i.e., $v\mathbf{i} = (36\cos\theta)\mathbf{i} + (36\sin\theta)\mathbf{j} - 12\mathbf{j}$
$$= (36\cos\theta)\mathbf{i} + (36\sin\theta - 12)\mathbf{j}$$

Therefore $0 = 36\sin\theta - 12$ (equating the **j** components)

i.e. $\sin\theta = \dfrac{12}{36}$ giving $\theta \approx 19.5°$ as before.

Also $v = 36\cos\theta \approx 33.9$.

Hence $\overrightarrow{DvS}$ is 33.9 knots due W and the time taken can be calculated as before.]

▶ Example 20

To a man travelling in a car in the direction $060°$ at 40 km h^{-1}, the wind appears to be blowing from the east at 10 km h^{-1}. Find, by drawing or calculation, the true velocity of the wind.

▶ Solution . . .

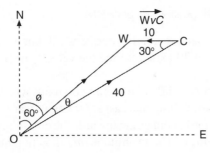

Fig. 13.54

(1) By calculation (using trigonometry)

Fig. 13.54 shows the vectors: $\overrightarrow{OC}$ = velocity of car, $\overrightarrow{OW}$ = true velocity of wind and $\overrightarrow{CW} = \overrightarrow{WvC}$ (the velocity of the wind relative to the car).

Since $\overrightarrow{WvC} = \overrightarrow{OW} - \overrightarrow{OC}$

$$\overrightarrow{OW} = \overrightarrow{WvC} + \overrightarrow{OC}$$

By the cosine rule,

$$|\overrightarrow{OW}|^2 = 40^2 + 10^2 - 2 \times 40 \times 10 \times \cos 30° \text{ giving } |\overrightarrow{OW}| \approx 31.7.$$

Also, $\dfrac{\sin\theta}{10} = \dfrac{\sin 30°}{31.7}$ giving $\theta \approx 9.1°$.

Hence the true velocity of the wind is 31.7 km h^{-1} towards the direction $(60° - 9.1°) = 50.9°$ or from the direction 230.9°.

(2) By calculation (using vectors)

By vectors, take **i** along $\overrightarrow{OE}$ and **j** along $\overrightarrow{ON}$.

$\overrightarrow{OC} = (40 \sin 60°)\mathbf{i} + (40 \cos 60°)\mathbf{j} = (20\sqrt{3})\mathbf{i} + 20\mathbf{j}$

$\overrightarrow{WvC} = -10\mathbf{i}$

$\overrightarrow{OW} = \overrightarrow{OC} + \overrightarrow{WvC} = (20\sqrt{3} - 10)\mathbf{i} + 20\mathbf{j}$

$|\overrightarrow{OW}|^2 = (20\sqrt{3} - 10)^2 + 20^2$ giving $|\overrightarrow{OW}| \approx 31.7$

Also, $\tan\emptyset = \dfrac{20\sqrt{3} - 10}{20}$ giving $\emptyset \approx 50.9°$.

Thus we obtain the same results as before.

(3) By drawing

First draw a sketch and label it with the information given (it should be a rough version of Fig. 13.54). The actual drawing must be done carefully. Choose a suitable scale to ensure reasonably accurate results, say 1 cm for 4 km h^{-1}.

Draw a north line ON as in Fig. 13.54.

From O, draw OC 10 cm long with $\angle$NOC = 60°.

From C, draw CW 2.5 cm long parallel to OE.

Join OW.

Measure OW (and convert to km h^{-1}) and $\angle$NOW.

Compare with the calculated values above.

Exercise 13F (*Answers on page 504*)

1. An aeroplane A is flying due N at 150 km h^{-1}. Aeroplane B is flying due east at 200 km h^{-1}. Find the velocity of B relative to A.

2. Two cars A and B are travelling on roads which cross at right angles. Car A is travelling due east at 60 km h^{-1}, car B is travelling at 40 km h^{-1} due north, both going towards the crossing. Find the velocity of B relative to A. [The magnitude *and* direction must be given].

3. A passenger is on the deck of a ship sailing due east at 25 km h^{-1}. The wind is blowing from the north-east at 10 km h^{-1}. What is the velocity of the wind relative to the passenger?

4. A road (running north-south) crosses a railway line at right angles. A passenger in a car travelling north at 60 km h^{-1} and 600 m south of the bridge, sees a train, travelling west at 90 km h^{-1}, which is 800 m east of the bridge. Find the velocity of the train relative to the car.

5. To a man in a car travelling at 20 km h^{-1} north-east, the wind appears to blow from the west with speed 16 km h^{-1}. Find the true velocity of the wind.

6. Aeroplane A is flying 400 km h^{-1} north-east and sees aeroplane B which is apparently flying north at 500 km h^{-1}. What is the true velocity of B?

7. An unidentified aircraft is reported as flying due north at 500 km h^{-1}. A fighter plane, which is 100 km on a bearing 225° from the unknown plane is ordered to contact it. If the fighter plane can fly 800 km h^{-1}, what course should it take? After how long will it be in contact?

8. A man on a ship steaming due south at 12 km h^{-1} sees a balloon apparently travelling due west at 15 km h^{-1}. Find the true velocity of the balloon.

9. Two ships A and B are 30 km apart with B due south of A. A is sailing at 10 km h^{-1} in the direction 120° while B is sailing at 15 km h^{-1} in the direction 45°.
   (a) Find the velocity of A relative to B.
   (b) Calculate the time taken for B to be due east of A.

10. A helicopter is flying on a course 060° with speed 100 km h^{-1}. An aeroplane, which is 50 km due east of the helicopter, can fly at 200 km h^{-1}. What course should the aeroplane take to intercept the helicopter?

11. To a ship sailing due N at 20 km h^{-1} another ship appears to be moving with a velocity of 12 km h^{-1} in the direction 120°. Find the true velocity of this ship.

12. A ship A is heading north at 20 km h^{-1} and at 1200 h is 50 km south-east of a ship B. If B steers at 25 km h^{-1} so as to *just* intercept A, find
   (a) the direction in which B must travel,
   (b) the time when interception takes place.

13. A man is walking along a horizontal road at 1.2 m s^{-1}. Rain is coming towards him and appears to be falling with a speed of 4 m s^{-1} in the direction which makes an angle of 60° with the horizontal. Find the actual speed of the rain and the angle this speed makes with the horizontal.
   Find the speed and the angle with the horizontal which the rain would appear to make if he walked at the same speed in the opposite direction.

Summary

1. Magnitude of vector $\mathbf{a} = |\mathbf{a}| = a$.

2. If $\mathbf{a} = k\mathbf{b}$, where k is a scalar (a number) $\neq 0$, then the vectors $\mathbf{a}$ and $\mathbf{b}$ are parallel, and in the same direction if $k > 0$, but in opposite directions if $k < 0$.

   $|\mathbf{a}| = |k| \times |\mathbf{b}|$

3. Conversely if $\mathbf{a}$ and $\mathbf{b}$ are parallel ($\mathbf{a} \neq 0$, $\mathbf{b} \neq 0$), then $\mathbf{a} = k\mathbf{b}$. P, Q and R are collinear if $\overrightarrow{PQ} = k\overrightarrow{QR}$ (or $\overrightarrow{PQ} = k\overrightarrow{PR}$) and conversely.

4. If $\overrightarrow{OA} = \mathbf{a}$, $\overrightarrow{OB} = \mathbf{b}$, $\mathbf{a} + \mathbf{b}$ is the diagonal OC of the parallelogram OACB.

5. $\mathbf{a} - \mathbf{b}$ is the vector from the end of $\mathbf{b}$ to the end of $\mathbf{a}$,
   $\mathbf{b} - \mathbf{a}$ is the vector from the end of $\mathbf{a}$ to the end of $\mathbf{b}$,
   where $\mathbf{a}$, $\mathbf{b}$ start from the same point.

6. If $m\mathbf{a} + n\mathbf{b} = p\mathbf{a} + q\mathbf{b}$ then $m = p$ and $n = q$.

7. The position vector of A is the vector $\overrightarrow{OA}$ where O is the origin.

8. $\mathbf{i}$ and $\mathbf{j}$ are unit vectors in the directions of the positive coordinate axes.

   Column vector form: $\begin{pmatrix} a \\ b \end{pmatrix} = a\mathbf{i} + b\mathbf{j}$

   If $\mathbf{r} = a\mathbf{i} + b\mathbf{j} = \begin{pmatrix} a \\ b \end{pmatrix}$, then $|\mathbf{r}| = \sqrt{a^2 + b^2}$, $\tan \theta = \dfrac{b}{a}$ (check for the correct quadrant).

9. The unit vector in the direction of $\mathbf{r}$ is $\hat{\mathbf{r}}$.
   If $\mathbf{r} = a\mathbf{i} + b\mathbf{j}$, then $\hat{\mathbf{r}} = \dfrac{a\mathbf{i} + b\mathbf{j}}{\sqrt{a^2 + b^2}}$.

10. **Composition of velocities**
    If a body has 2 velocities $\mathbf{a}$ and $\mathbf{b}$, the resultant velocity $\mathbf{c}$ is given by $\mathbf{c} = \mathbf{a} + \mathbf{b}$. If $\mathbf{a}$ and $\mathbf{b}$ are represented by the sides of a parallelogram, then $\mathbf{c}$ is represented by the diagonal as shown in Fig. 13.55.

11. **Resolution of velocities**
    It is useful to resolve a velocity $\mathbf{r}$ into 2 perpendicular components, usually along the x- and y-axes. Unit coordinate vectors $\mathbf{i}$ and $\mathbf{j}$ are often used as shown in Fig. 13.56.

    Also $|\mathbf{r}| = r = \sqrt{p^2 + q^2}$,

    $p = r \cos \theta$, $q = r \sin \theta$ and $\tan \theta = \dfrac{q}{p}$

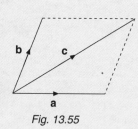

Fig. 13.55

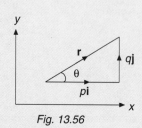

Fig. 13.56

12. Notation

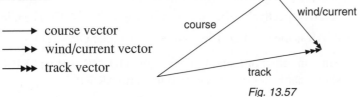

——→ course vector
——→→ wind/current vector
——→→→ track vector

Fig. 13.57

The track vector is the resultant of the other 2 vectors.

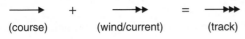

(course)   (wind/current)   (track)

13. Relative velocity

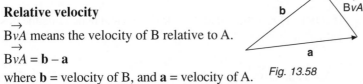

$\overrightarrow{BvA}$ means the velocity of B relative to A.

$\overrightarrow{BvA} = \mathbf{b} - \mathbf{a}$

where $\mathbf{b}$ = velocity of B, and $\mathbf{a}$ = velocity of A.

Fig. 13.58

Revision Exercise 13 (*Answers on page 505*)

1. A, B and C are points with position vectors $4\mathbf{p} - \mathbf{q}$, $\mu(\mathbf{p} + \mathbf{q})$ and $\mathbf{p} + 2\mathbf{q}$ respectively, relative to an origin O. Obtain expressions for $\overrightarrow{AB}$ and $\overrightarrow{AC}$. Given that B lies on AC, find the value of μ.   (C)

2. Points A and B have position vectors $\mathbf{a}$ and $\mathbf{b}$ respectively relative to an origin O (Fig. 13.59). The point D is such that $\overrightarrow{OD} = p\overrightarrow{OA}$ and the point E is such that $AE = qAB$.

   The line segments BD and OE intersect at X. If $OX = \frac{2}{5} OE$ and $XB = \frac{4}{5} DB$, express $\overrightarrow{OX}$ and $\overrightarrow{XB}$ in terms of $\mathbf{a}$, $\mathbf{b}$, p and q and hence evaluate p and q.   (C)

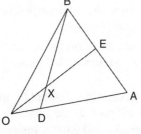

Fig. 13.59

3. The position vectors, relative to an origin O, of two points S and T are $2\mathbf{p}$ and $2\mathbf{q}$ respectively. The point A lies on OS and is such that OA = AS. The point B lies on OT produced and is such that OT = 2TB. The lines ST and AB intersect at R.

   Given that $\overrightarrow{AR} = \lambda\overrightarrow{AB}$ and that $\overrightarrow{SR} = \mu\overrightarrow{ST}$, express OR (**a**) in terms of $\mathbf{p}$, $\mathbf{q}$ and λ, (**b**) in terms of $\mathbf{p}$, $\mathbf{q}$, μ. Hence evaluate λ and μ and express $\overrightarrow{OR}$ in terms of $\mathbf{p}$ and $\mathbf{q}$.

4. The position vectors of points A and B relative to an origin O are **a** and **b** respectively. The point P is such that $\overrightarrow{OP} = 4\overrightarrow{OB}$. The midpoint of AB is the point Q. The point R is such that $\overrightarrow{OR} = \frac{8}{5}\overrightarrow{OQ}$.

Find, in terms of **a** and **b**, the vectors $\overrightarrow{OQ}$, $\overrightarrow{OR}$, $\overrightarrow{AR}$ and $\overrightarrow{RP}$. Hence show that R lies on AP and find the ratio AR:RP.

Given that the point S is such that $\overrightarrow{OS} = \mu\overrightarrow{OQ}$, find the value of μ such that PS is parallel to BA. (C)

5. P and Q have position vectors $2t\mathbf{i} + (t + 1)\mathbf{j}$ and $(t + 1)\mathbf{i} - (t + 2)\mathbf{j}$ respectively.

If $|\overrightarrow{OP}| = |\overrightarrow{OQ}|$ show that $3t^2 - 4t - 4 = 0$ and hence find the possible values of t.

6. $\overrightarrow{OA} = \mathbf{a}$ and $\overrightarrow{OB} = \mathbf{b}$. C is the midpoint of AB and D divides OB in the ratio 2:1. AD and OC intercept at P.

(a) Taking $\overrightarrow{OP} = p\overrightarrow{OC}$ and $\overrightarrow{AP} = q\overrightarrow{AD}$, find two vector expressions for $\overrightarrow{OP}$ and hence find the ratio OP:PC.

(b) E divides OB in the ratio 1:2 and AE meets OC at Q. By a similar method, find the ratio OQ:QC.

(c) Hence find the ratio OQ:QP:PC.

7. The position vectors of A, B and C are $-\mathbf{a} + 2\mathbf{b}$, $2\mathbf{a} + 3\mathbf{b}$ and $3\mathbf{a} + 5\mathbf{b}$ respectively. P divides BC in the ratio 3:4. Q lies on AB so that $AQ = \frac{2}{5}AB$. R lies on AC so that $\overrightarrow{CR} = 2\overrightarrow{AR}$. Find the position vectors of P, Q and R. Show that these points are collinear and state the ratio PQ:QR.

8. A river is 160 m wide and runs at 1.2 m s^{-1} between straight parallel banks. A man can row at 2 m s^{-1} in still water.

(a) If he rows in a direction perpendicular to the banks, how far downsteam will he land?

(b) At what acute angle (to the nearest degree) to the bank should he now row to return to his starting point?

9. A small aeroplane can fly at 200 km h^{-1} in still air. There is a wind of 50 km h^{-1} from the east. If the pilot wishes to fly due south, what course should he take and what is his ground speed?

The pilot keeps this course but the wind changes and the pilot finds that his ground speed is 200 km h^{-1} in the direction 190°. Calculate the new velocity of the wind.

10. An aeroplane can fly at 300 km h^{-1} relative to the air. If there is a wind of 60 km h^{-1} from the east, what is the shortest time whereby the aeroplane can reach a point 600 km south-west of its starting point?

11. An aeroplane has a speed of V km h^{-1} in still air and there is a wind of $\frac{V}{4}$ km h^{-1} blowing from the NE. Find the course that must be taken if the pilot wishes to reach a point due east.

12. A destroyer detects the presence of a vessel at a range of 30 nautical miles on a bearing of 060°. The vessel is steaming on a course of 150° at a speed of 15 knots. If the destroyer steams at 22 knots, determine either by drawing or by calculation the course the destroyer must steer so that its velocity relative to the vessel is in a direction 060°.

    Hence determine the time taken for the destroyer to intercept the vessel if neither changes course. (C)

13. A helicopter whose speed in still air is 40 km h^{-1} flies to an oil platform 60 km away on a bearing 060°. The wind velocity is 15 km h^{-1} from due north. Sketch a suitable triangle of velocities and find

    (a) the bearing on which the helicopter must fly,

    (b) the time taken to reach the platform. (C)

14. Two canoeists, A and B, can paddle in still water at 6 m s^{-1} and 5 m s^{-1} respectively. They both set off at the same time from the same point on one bank of a river which has straight parallel banks, 240 m apart, and which flows at 3 m s^{-1}. A paddles in the direction that will take him across the river by the shortest distance whilst B paddles in the direction that will take him across the shortest time. Determine

    (a) the direction in which A must paddle,

    (b) the direction in which B must paddle,

    (c) the time taken by each canoeist,

    (d) the distance between the points at which they land. (C)

15. A plane flies in a straight line from London to Rome, a distance of 1400 km on a bearing of 135°. Given that the plane's speed in still air is 380 km h^{-1}, that the wind direction is 225° and that the journey takes 4 hours, determine

    (a) the wind speed,

    (b) the direction the pilot should set for the flight.

    Find also the direction the pilot should set for the return flight, assuming that the speed and direction of the wind remain unchanged. (C)

16. A tanker is sailing on a fixed course due west at 30 km h^{-1}. At a time of 0900 a destroyer wishing to refuel is 160 km away on a bearing of 225° from the tanker. If the destroyer travels at 60 km h^{-1}, determine

    (a) the direction in which the destroyer should travel in order to reach the tanker,

    (b) the time at which the destroyer reaches the tanker. (C)

17. A cyclist is travelling due north at 20 km h^{-1} and finds that the wind relative to him appears to be blowing from a direction 040° with a speed of 30 km h^{-1}. Find the true speed and direction of the wind.

    Assuming that the speed and direction of the wind remain unchanged, find the speed of the wind relative to the cyclist when the cyclist is travelling due south at 20 km h^{-1}. (C)

18. An aircraft A is flying due east at 600 km h^{-1} and its bearing from aircraft B is 030°. If aircraft B has a speed of 1000 km h^{-1}, find the direction in which B must fly in order to intercept A. If the aircraft are initially 50 km apart, find the time taken, in minutes, for the interception to occur. (C)

19. An aircraft whose speed in still air is 300 km h^{-1} flies from A due north to B and back, where AB = 500 km. The wind velocity is 120 km h^{-1} from 240°. Find
    (a) the bearing on which the aircraft must fly for the outward journey,
    (b) the time of flight of the outward journey,
    (c) the bearing on which the aircraft must fly for the return journey. (C)

20. An aircraft is flying from point A to a point B 400 km north-east of A, and a wind is blowing from the west at 50 km h^{-1}. The speed of the aircraft in still air is 300 km h^{-1}. Find
    (a) the direction in which the aircraft must be headed,
    (b) the distance of the aircraft from B one hour after leaving A. (C)

21. (a) An aircraft flies in a straight line from a point A to a point B 200 km east of A.
        There is a wind blowing at 40 km h^{-1} from the direction 240° and the aircraft travels at 300 km h^{-1} in still air. Find
        (i) the direction in which the pilot must steer the aircraft,
        (ii) the time, to the nearest minute, for the journey from A to B.
    (b) To an observer in a ship sailing due north at 10 km h^{-1}, a second ship appears to be sailing due east at 24 km h^{-1}. Find the magnitude and direction of the actual velocity of the second ship. (C)

22. When a man walks at 4 km h^{-1} due west, the wind appears to blow from the south. When he walks 8 km h^{-1} due west, the wind now appears to blow from the south-west. Find, by drawing or calculation, the true velocity of the wind.

23. Two ships A and B leave a harbour at the same time, A sailing due N at 20 km h^{-1} and B sailing at 25 km h^{-1} in the direction 060°. Calculate

   (a) the velocity of B relative to A (stating the magnitude and direction),

   (b) the bearing of B from A in the subsequent motion,

   (c) the distance between the ships after 2 hours of sailing.

24. An aeroplane has a speed of V km h^{-1} in still air and flies in a straight line from A to B. There is a wind of speed $\frac{3}{4}V$ km h^{-1} blowing from a direction making an angle θ with AB where $\sin \theta = \frac{4}{5}$. Find

   (a) the angle which the intended course makes with AB,

   (b) the ground speed in terms of V.

25. A plane is scheduled to fly from London to Rome in $2\frac{1}{2}$ hours. Rome is 1 400 km from London and on a bearing of 135° from London. Given that there is a wind blowing from the north at 120 km h^{-1}, find by calculating or drawing

   (a) the speed of the plane in still air,

   (b) the course which the pilot should set.

   Assuming that the velocity of the wind and the speed of the plane in still air remain unchanged, find

   (c) the course which the pilot should set for the return journey,

   (d) the time taken, to the nearest minute. (C)

26. (a) An aircraft is flying due south at 350 km h^{-1}. The wind is blowing at 70 km h^{-1} from the direction θ°, where θ is acute. Given that the pilot is steering the aircraft in the direction 170°, find

   (i) the value of θ,

   (ii) the speed of the aircraft in still air.

   (b) A man who swims at 1.2 m s^{-1} in still water wishes to cross a river which is flowing between straight parallel banks at 2 m s^{-1}. He aims downstream in a direction making an angle of 60° with the bank. Find

   (i) the speed at which he travels,

   (ii) the angle which his resultant velocity makes with the bank. (C)

27. (a) Two particles, A and B, are 60 m apart with B due west of A. Particle A is travelling at 9 m s^{-1} in a direction 300° and B is travelling at 12 m s^{-1} in a direction 030°. Find

   (i) the magnitude and direction of the velocity of B relative to A,

   (ii) the time taken for B to be north of A.

   (b) A wind is blowing from the direction 320° at 30 km h^{-1}. Find, by drawing or by calculation, the magnitude and direction of the velocity of the wind relative to a man who is cycling due east at 18 km h^{-1}.

A man travels at 4 km h^{-1} due north for 3 hours, then at 3.5 km h^{-1} due west for $3\frac{1}{2}$ hours, and finally due south at 3 km h^{-1} for 4 hours. He is now where he first started. How is this possible?

Chapter 14

Matrices

A large number of computers in Singapore homes are made in Singapore, Japan, Taiwan or the United States. In a survey, existing users were asked their preference when it is time to replace their computers.

Of those who own a Singapore-made computer at present, 60% prefer a computer made in Singapore, 20% prefer a computer made in Japan, 10% prefer a computer made in the U.S., 7% prefer a computer made in Taiwan, while the rest prefer a computer made in other countries.

Of those who own a Japanese-made computer at present, 50% prefer a computer made in Japan, 25% prefer a computer made in Singapore, 13% prefer a computer made in the U.S., 10% prefer a computer made in Taiwan and the rest prefer a computer made in other countries.

Of those who own a U.S.-made computer at present, 40% prefer another computer made in the U.S., 30% prefer a computer made in Singapore, 18% prefer a computer made in Japan, 9% prefer a computer made in Taiwan and the rest prefer a computer made in other countries.

Of those who own a Taiwan-made computer at present, 36% prefer a computer made in Taiwan, 26% prefer a computer made in Singapore, 17% prefer a computer made in Japan, 8% prefer a computer made in the U.S. and the rest prefer a computer made in other countries.

Of those who own a computer made in other countries, 55% prefer a computer made in Singapore, 30% prefer a computer made in Japan, 10% prefer a computer made in the U.S., 3% prefer a computer made in Taiwan and the rest prefer a computer made in other countries.

You will agree that the above information is not readily assimilated. Can you organise the above information so that a person reading it can grasp it easily?

14.1 Matrix

Consider the following table which shows the purchase of T-shirts of sizes large (L), medium (M) and small (S), by a class of 22 boys and 18 girls.

Size	L	M	S
Boys	10	8	4
Girls	2	9	7

Such a table is called an array of data or a **matrix**. The plural form is **matrices**. If we were to record the purchase of T-shirts from a number of classes in the same format, it becomes unnecessary to label the matrix. The above matrix can then be written more concisely as

$$\begin{pmatrix} 10 & 8 & 4 \\ 2 & 9 & 7 \end{pmatrix} \text{ or } \begin{bmatrix} 10 & 8 & 4 \\ 2 & 9 & 7 \end{bmatrix}.$$

Both the round bracket ( ) and square bracket [ ] notations can be used. For our work, we will use the former.

Each number in the matrix is called an **element**. The element 10 in the first row and first column tells us that the boys purchased 10 size L T-shirts.

In the example above, the matrix has 2 rows and 3 columns. We say that it is a 2×3 (read as '2 by 3') matrix. This is also called the **order** of the matrix. In general, if a matrix has m rows and n columns, then the order of the matrix is $m \times n$, or simply a $m \times n$ matrix. A matrix is usually denoted by a capital letter.

For example,

$$A = \begin{pmatrix} 1 & 2 & 3 \\ 0 & 1 & 2 \end{pmatrix} \longleftarrow \begin{array}{l} \leftarrow \\ \leftarrow \end{array} \text{ 2 rows}$$

3 columns

is a 2×3 matrix,

and

$$B = \begin{pmatrix} 1 & 0 \\ 4 & 3 \\ 2 & 1 \end{pmatrix} \begin{array}{l} \leftarrow \\ \leftarrow \\ \leftarrow \end{array} \text{ 3 rows}$$

2 columns

is a 3×2 matrix.

Note that commas are not used to separate the elements of a matrix; thus $C = (2 \; 1)$ is a 1×2 matrix, whereas $(2,1)$ represents the coordinates of a point.

14.2 Equal Matrices

Equal matrices are matrices which are identical. They have the same order and the same corresponding elements.

14.3 Addition and Subtraction of Matrices

Matrices can only be **added** or **subtracted** if they are of the same order. To add 2 matrices, simply add the corresponding elements. The result will be a matrix of the **same order**.

For example, if $A = \begin{pmatrix} 1 & 0 \\ 2 & 1 \end{pmatrix}$ and $B = \begin{pmatrix} 2 & 1 \\ 1 & 0 \end{pmatrix}$,

then $A + B = \begin{pmatrix} 1 & 0 \\ 2 & 1 \end{pmatrix} + \begin{pmatrix} 2 & 1 \\ 1 & 0 \end{pmatrix} = \begin{pmatrix} 3 & 1 \\ 3 & 1 \end{pmatrix}$.

[order: (2×2) (2×2) (2×2)]

Subtraction is dealt in a similar manner where the corresponding elements are subtracted. Thus

$A - B = \begin{pmatrix} 1 & 0 \\ 2 & 1 \end{pmatrix} - \begin{pmatrix} 2 & 1 \\ 1 & 0 \end{pmatrix} = \begin{pmatrix} -1 & -1 \\ 1 & 1 \end{pmatrix}$.

[order: (2×2) (2×2) (2×2)]

14.4 Multiplication of a Matrix by a Number (a Scalar)

To multiply a matrix by a number, simply multiply each element by that number.

For example, if $A = \begin{pmatrix} 1 & 3 \\ 2 & 4 \end{pmatrix}$,

then $2A = \begin{pmatrix} 2 & 6 \\ 4 & 8 \end{pmatrix}$,

and $\frac{1}{2}A = \begin{pmatrix} \frac{1}{2} & \frac{3}{2} \\ 1 & 2 \end{pmatrix}$.

▶ **Example 1**

If $A = \begin{pmatrix} 1 & 2 \\ 4 & 5 \end{pmatrix}$, $B = \begin{pmatrix} 1 & 3 \\ 0 & 2 \end{pmatrix}$ and $X = \begin{pmatrix} p & 1 \\ -4 & q \end{pmatrix}$, find **(a)** $A + B$, **(b)** $A - B$,

(c) $3A$, **(d)** $\frac{1}{2}B$, **(e)** $2A + 3B$, **(f)** p and q if $A + X = B$.

▶ **Solution . . .**

(a) $A + B = \begin{pmatrix} 1 & 2 \\ 4 & 5 \end{pmatrix} + \begin{pmatrix} 1 & 3 \\ 0 & 2 \end{pmatrix}$

$= \begin{pmatrix} 2 & 5 \\ 4 & 7 \end{pmatrix}$

(b) $A - B = \begin{pmatrix} 1 & 2 \\ 4 & 5 \end{pmatrix} - \begin{pmatrix} 1 & 3 \\ 0 & 2 \end{pmatrix}$

$\qquad\quad = \begin{pmatrix} 0 & -1 \\ 4 & 3 \end{pmatrix}$

(c) $3A = 3 \begin{pmatrix} 1 & 2 \\ 4 & 5 \end{pmatrix}$

$\qquad\; = \begin{pmatrix} 3 & 6 \\ 12 & 15 \end{pmatrix}$

(d) $\frac{1}{2} B = \frac{1}{2} \begin{pmatrix} 1 & 3 \\ 0 & 2 \end{pmatrix}$

$\qquad\; = \begin{pmatrix} \frac{1}{2} & \frac{3}{2} \\ 0 & 1 \end{pmatrix}$

(e) $2A + 3B = 2 \begin{pmatrix} 1 & 2 \\ 4 & 5 \end{pmatrix} + 3 \begin{pmatrix} 1 & 3 \\ 0 & 2 \end{pmatrix}$

$\qquad\qquad = \begin{pmatrix} 2 & 4 \\ 8 & 10 \end{pmatrix} + \begin{pmatrix} 3 & 9 \\ 0 & 6 \end{pmatrix}$

$\qquad\qquad = \begin{pmatrix} 5 & 13 \\ 8 & 16 \end{pmatrix}$

(f) $A + X = B$

$\begin{pmatrix} 1 & 2 \\ 4 & 5 \end{pmatrix} + \begin{pmatrix} p & 1 \\ -4 & q \end{pmatrix} = \begin{pmatrix} 1 & 3 \\ 0 & 2 \end{pmatrix}$

$\begin{pmatrix} 1+p & 3 \\ 0 & 5+q \end{pmatrix} = \begin{pmatrix} 1 & 3 \\ 0 & 2 \end{pmatrix}$

$\therefore\ 1 + p\ = 1\ $ and $\ 5 + q = 2,$
giving $p = 0$ and $\qquad q = -3.$

14.5 Multiplication of 2 Matrices

2 matrices can only be multiplied if the number of *columns* in the first matrix is the same as the number of *rows* in the second matrix. We then say that the two matrices are **compatible** or **conformable**. We will illustrate the process of matrix multiplication using the 2×2 matrices. Other compatible matrices are multiplied in the same way.

If $A = \begin{pmatrix} a & b \\ c & d \end{pmatrix}$ and $B \begin{pmatrix} w & x \\ y & z \end{pmatrix}$,

then $AB = \begin{pmatrix} aw + by & ax + bz \\ cw + dy & cx + dz \end{pmatrix}.$

To obtain the element in the first row and first column of AB, multiply the elements in the first row of A by the corresponding elements in the first column of B and take the sum of the products.

First row of $A \longrightarrow \begin{pmatrix} \boxed{a \quad b} \\ c \quad d \end{pmatrix} \begin{pmatrix} \boxed{w} \quad x \\ \boxed{y} \quad z \end{pmatrix} \longrightarrow aw + by$

First column of B

To obtain the element in the first row and second column of AB, multiply the elements in the first row of A by the corresponding elements in the second column of B and the sum of the products.

First row of $A \longrightarrow \begin{pmatrix} \boxed{a \quad b} \\ c \quad d \end{pmatrix} \begin{pmatrix} w \quad \boxed{x} \\ y \quad \boxed{z} \end{pmatrix} \longrightarrow ax + bz$

Second column of B

Similarly, the elements in the second row of AB are obtained using the second row of A and the respective columns of B.

▶ **Example 2**

Given that $A = \begin{pmatrix} 0 & 1 \\ 2 & 3 \end{pmatrix}, B = \begin{pmatrix} 2 & 1 \\ 4 & 0 \end{pmatrix}$ and $C = \begin{pmatrix} 1 & 0 & 2 \\ 3 & 1 & 0 \end{pmatrix}$,

find the following products:

(a) AB

(b) BA

(c) BC

(d) CB

▶ **Solution . . .**

(a) $AB = \begin{pmatrix} 0 & 1 \\ 2 & 3 \end{pmatrix} \begin{pmatrix} 2 & 1 \\ 4 & 0 \end{pmatrix}$

$= \begin{pmatrix} 0 \times 2 + 1 \times 4 & 0 \times 1 + 1 \times 0 \\ 2 \times 2 + 3 \times 4 & 2 \times 1 + 3 \times 0 \end{pmatrix}$

$= \begin{pmatrix} 4 & 0 \\ 16 & 2 \end{pmatrix}$

(b) $BA = \begin{pmatrix} 2 & 1 \\ 4 & 0 \end{pmatrix} \begin{pmatrix} 0 & 1 \\ 2 & 3 \end{pmatrix}$

$= \begin{pmatrix} 2 \times 0 + 1 \times 2 & 2 \times 1 + 1 \times 3 \\ 4 \times 0 + 0 \times 2 & 4 \times 1 + 0 \times 3 \end{pmatrix}$

$= \begin{pmatrix} 2 & 5 \\ 0 & 4 \end{pmatrix}$

(c) $BC = \begin{pmatrix} 2 & 1 \\ 4 & 0 \end{pmatrix} \begin{pmatrix} 1 & 0 & 2 \\ 3 & 1 & 0 \end{pmatrix}$

$= \begin{pmatrix} 2 \times 1 + 1 \times 3 & 2 \times 0 + 1 \times 1 & 2 \times 2 + 1 \times 0 \\ 4 \times 1 + 0 \times 3 & 4 \times 0 + 0 \times 1 & 4 \times 2 + 0 \times 0 \end{pmatrix}$

$= \begin{pmatrix} 5 & 1 & 4 \\ 4 & 0 & 8 \end{pmatrix}$

(d) CB does not exist since the number of columns (3) in the first matrix (C) is not the same as the number of rows (2) in the second matrix (B).

Note:

(1) Parts (a) and (b) illustrate the fact that generally, $AB \neq BA$; that is matrix multiplication is **non-commutative**.

(2) Since $AB \neq BA$, we say that AB is the product of **pre-multiplying** B by A (A is before B) and BA is the product of **post-multiplying** B by A (A is after B).

(3) Part (c) illustrates the fact that if a matrix X has order ($p \times q$) and another matrix Y has order ($q \times r$), then XY has order ($p \times r$), observing that the number of columns (q) in X is the same as the number of rows (q) in Y.

▶ **Example 3**

The following tables show the purchase of T-shirts of sizes L, M and S by 2 classes X and Y.

Class X

Size	L	M	S
Boys	10	8	4
Girls	2	9	7

Class Y

Size	L	M	S
Boys	6	11	3
Girls	3	10	7

(a) Write down the purchase matrix for each class and find the combined purchase matrix for the 2 classes.

(b) The costs of the various sizes of T-shirts are shown below:

Size	L	M	S
Cost (in $)	10	8	6

Using matrix multiplication, find the total amount paid by the boys and the girls respectively.

▶ **Solution ...**

(a) Purchase matrix for class X: $\begin{pmatrix} 10 & 8 & 4 \\ 2 & 9 & 7 \end{pmatrix}$

Purchase matrix for class Y: $\begin{pmatrix} 6 & 11 & 3 \\ 3 & 10 & 7 \end{pmatrix}$

Combined purchase matrix:

$$\begin{pmatrix} 10 & 8 & 4 \\ 2 & 9 & 7 \end{pmatrix} + \begin{pmatrix} 6 & 11 & 3 \\ 3 & 10 & 7 \end{pmatrix}$$

$$= \begin{pmatrix} 16 & 19 & 7 \\ 5 & 19 & 14 \end{pmatrix}$$

(b) The boys purchased 16 L-sized T-shirts amounting to $16 \times \$10$, 19 M-sized T shirts amounting to $19 \times \$8$, and so on.

Hence we can represent the amount paid by the boys and girls respectively by the following matrix multiplication:

$$\begin{pmatrix} 16 & 19 & 7 \\ 5 & 19 & 14 \end{pmatrix} \begin{pmatrix} 10 \\ 8 \\ 6 \end{pmatrix}$$

$$= \begin{pmatrix} 16 \times 10 + 19 \times 8 + 7 \times 6 \\ 5 \times 10 + 19 \times 8 + 14 \times 6 \end{pmatrix}$$

$$= \begin{pmatrix} 354 \\ 286 \end{pmatrix}$$

Hence the boys paid \$354 and the girls paid \$286 for their T-shirts.

Exercise 14A *(Answers on page 505)*

1. State the order of each of the following matrices:

   (a) $(2 \quad 1)$

   (b) $\begin{pmatrix} 1 \\ 2 \end{pmatrix}$

   (c) $\begin{pmatrix} 2 & 5 \\ 1 & 3 \end{pmatrix}$

   (d) $\begin{pmatrix} 1 & 0 & 1 \\ 2 & 3 & 6 \end{pmatrix}$

   (e) $\begin{pmatrix} 2 & 1 \\ 0 & 3 \\ 4 & 1 \\ 1 & 1 \end{pmatrix}$

2. Express each of the following as a single matrix:

(a) $(1 \quad 2) + (2 \quad 3)$

(b) $\begin{pmatrix} 2 \\ -1 \end{pmatrix} + \begin{pmatrix} 0 \\ 6 \end{pmatrix}$

(c) $\begin{pmatrix} 1 & 0 \\ -3 & 1 \end{pmatrix} + \begin{pmatrix} 2 & -4 \\ -1 & 0 \end{pmatrix}$

(d) $\begin{pmatrix} 1 & 1 \\ 0 & 2 \\ -3 & 4 \end{pmatrix} + \begin{pmatrix} 0 & 3 \\ 1 & 2 \\ 0 & 4 \end{pmatrix}$

(e) $\begin{pmatrix} 3 & -4 & 1 & 2 \\ 1 & 5 & 0 & 3 \\ 2 & -2 & 3 & -1 \end{pmatrix} + \begin{pmatrix} 1 & 2 & -1 & 0 \\ 4 & 0 & 2 & 1 \\ 2 & -5 & 1 & 2 \end{pmatrix}$

3. Express each of the following as a single matrix:

(a) $(3 \quad 2) - (1 \quad 1)$

(b) $\begin{pmatrix} 3 \\ 4 \end{pmatrix} - \begin{pmatrix} 1 \\ -1 \end{pmatrix}$

(c) $\begin{pmatrix} 1 & 2 \\ 3 & 4 \end{pmatrix} - \begin{pmatrix} 0 & -1 \\ 2 & 1 \end{pmatrix}$

(d) $\begin{pmatrix} 0 & 2 & 5 \\ 2 & -1 & -1 \end{pmatrix} - \begin{pmatrix} 1 & 4 & 2 \\ 0 & 0 & -1 \end{pmatrix}$

(e) $\begin{pmatrix} 3 & -4 & 1 & 2 \\ 1 & 5 & 0 & 3 \\ 2 & -2 & 3 & -1 \end{pmatrix} - \begin{pmatrix} 1 & 2 & -1 & 0 \\ 4 & 0 & 2 & 1 \\ 2 & -5 & 1 & 2 \end{pmatrix}$

4. Express each of the following as a single matrix:

(a) $3\begin{pmatrix} 1 & 0 & 1 \\ 2 & 1 & 3 \\ 0 & 1 & 1 \end{pmatrix}$

(b) $-2\begin{pmatrix} 4 & -2 & 1 \\ -3 & 1 & 0 \end{pmatrix}$

(c) $4\begin{pmatrix} 1 & 3 \\ 2 & 1 \end{pmatrix} - \begin{pmatrix} 2 & 4 \\ 3 & 5 \end{pmatrix}$

(d) $\begin{pmatrix} 7 & 8 \\ 9 & 10 \end{pmatrix} - 2\begin{pmatrix} 1 & 0 \\ -1 & 2 \end{pmatrix}$

(e) $2\begin{pmatrix} 1 & 0 \\ 2 & 0 \\ 3 & 1 \end{pmatrix} - \frac{1}{2}\begin{pmatrix} 2 & 3 \\ 0 & 4 \\ 1 & 2 \end{pmatrix}$

5. If $A = \begin{pmatrix} 1 & 0 \\ 2 & 3 \end{pmatrix}$ and $B = \begin{pmatrix} 1 & -1 \\ 0 & 2 \end{pmatrix}$,

   (a) verify that $A + B = B + A$,
   (b) find $2A - 3B$.

6. If $A = \begin{pmatrix} 1 & 0 \\ 2 & 3 \end{pmatrix}$ and $B = \begin{pmatrix} 2 & 3 \\ 1 & 1 \end{pmatrix}$, find

   (a) AB,
   (b) BA.
   (c) Is $AB = BA$?

7. It is given that $A = (1 \ 2)$, $B = \begin{pmatrix} 3 \\ -1 \end{pmatrix}$ and $C = \begin{pmatrix} 2 & 1 \\ 4 & 3 \end{pmatrix}$.

   (a) State the orders of A, B and C.
   (b) Which of the following products exist?
   $$AB, \ BA, \ AC, \ CA, \ BC, \ CB$$
   For those which exist, evaluate them.

8. Given that $\begin{pmatrix} -3 \\ 5 \end{pmatrix} + 3\begin{pmatrix} 4 \\ -y \end{pmatrix} = \begin{pmatrix} x \\ y \end{pmatrix}$, find the values of x and y.

9. Given that $= \begin{pmatrix} 0 & 1 & 2 \\ 3 & 0 & 4 \end{pmatrix}\begin{pmatrix} 1 \\ m \\ 1 \end{pmatrix} = \begin{pmatrix} 4 \\ n \end{pmatrix}$, find the values of m and n.

10. If $A = \begin{pmatrix} a & 2 \\ 3 & 4 \end{pmatrix}$ and $B = \begin{pmatrix} 1 & 1 \\ 2 & b \end{pmatrix}$, find the values of a and b in each of the following:

   (a) $A + B = \begin{pmatrix} 5 & 3 \\ 5 & -7 \end{pmatrix}$

   (b) $A - B = \begin{pmatrix} 1 & 1 \\ 1 & 1 \end{pmatrix}$

   (c) $AB = \begin{pmatrix} 5 & -1 \\ 11 & -1 \end{pmatrix}$

11. A hot and cold drink vending machine dispenses drinks in 3 sizes: small (S), medium (M) and large (L). The numbers of drinks sold from 0800 h to 0900 h are shown in the following matrix:

	S	M	L
Hot	20	10	12
Cold	28	11	8

or $\begin{pmatrix} 20 & 10 & 12 \\ 28 & 11 & 8 \end{pmatrix}$

Similarly the numbers of drinks sold from 0900 h to 1000 h are shown by the matrix $\begin{pmatrix} 30 & 18 & 10 \\ 42 & 22 & 14 \end{pmatrix}$.

(a) Write down the matrix representing the sales of drinks from 0800 to 1000 h.

(b) The costs of drinks depend only on their sizes. The following table shows the costs in cents:

Size	S	M	L
Cost (in cents)	60	80	100

Using matrix multiplication, find the amounts collected for the hot and cold drinks respectively from 0800 h to 1000 h. Find also the total collection for the 2 hours.

12. A factory makes 3 models (X, Y and Z) of a toy using 4 different components (A, B, C and D).

The following table shows the numbers of each component used in each model:

Model	X	Y	Z
A	3	2	4
B	4	6	2
C	4	5	3
D	5	4	5

The cost (in $) of each component is shown below:

Component	A	B	C	D
Cost ($)	1	2	3	4

Using appropriate matrix multiplication, find

(a) how many of each component is needed to make
100 toys of model X,
150 toys of model Y,
and 200 toys of model Z respectively,

(b) how much it would cost to make one of each model of toys.

14.6 Algebra of 2 × 2 Matrices

We will now study 2×2 matrices in greater detail. In this and subsequent discussions, all matrices mentioned will be 2×2 matrices unless otherwise stated.

For matrices A, B and C, it can be shown that

$$(A + B) + C = A + (B + C)$$

and

$$(AB)C = A(BC)$$

These are called **associative laws** for addition and multiplication respectively.

It can also be shown that

$$A + B = B + A,$$
$$AB \neq BA \quad \text{in general.}$$

We say that A and B are **commutative** for addition but **not** commutative for multiplication.

▶ **Example 4**

Given that $A = \begin{pmatrix} 1 & 0 \\ 1 & 2 \end{pmatrix}$, $B = \begin{pmatrix} 2 & 1 \\ 4 & 3 \end{pmatrix}$, and $C = \begin{pmatrix} 0 & 1 \\ 2 & 3 \end{pmatrix}$, verify that

(a) $(A + B) + C = A + (B + C)$,

(b) $(AB)C = A(BC)$,

(c) $A + B = B + A$,

(d) $AB \neq BA$.

▶ **Solution . . .**

(a) $(A + B) + C = \left[\begin{pmatrix} 1 & 0 \\ 1 & 2 \end{pmatrix} + \begin{pmatrix} 2 & 1 \\ 4 & 3 \end{pmatrix} \right] + \begin{pmatrix} 0 & 1 \\ 2 & 3 \end{pmatrix}$

$= \begin{pmatrix} 3 & 1 \\ 5 & 5 \end{pmatrix} + \begin{pmatrix} 0 & 1 \\ 2 & 3 \end{pmatrix} = \begin{pmatrix} 3 & 2 \\ 7 & 8 \end{pmatrix}$

$A + (B + C) = \begin{pmatrix} 1 & 0 \\ 1 & 2 \end{pmatrix} + \left[\begin{pmatrix} 2 & 1 \\ 4 & 3 \end{pmatrix} + \begin{pmatrix} 0 & 1 \\ 2 & 3 \end{pmatrix} \right]$

$= \begin{pmatrix} 1 & 0 \\ 1 & 2 \end{pmatrix} + \begin{pmatrix} 2 & 2 \\ 6 & 6 \end{pmatrix} = \begin{pmatrix} 3 & 2 \\ 7 & 8 \end{pmatrix}$

$\therefore (A + B) + C = A + (B + C) = \begin{pmatrix} 3 & 2 \\ 7 & 8 \end{pmatrix}$

(b) $(AB)C = \left[\begin{pmatrix} 1 & 0 \\ 1 & 2 \end{pmatrix}\begin{pmatrix} 2 & 1 \\ 4 & 3 \end{pmatrix}\right]\begin{pmatrix} 0 & 1 \\ 2 & 3 \end{pmatrix}.$

$$= \begin{pmatrix} 2+0 & 1+0 \\ 2+8 & 1+6 \end{pmatrix}\begin{pmatrix} 0 & 1 \\ 2 & 3 \end{pmatrix}$$

$$= \begin{pmatrix} 2 & 1 \\ 10 & 7 \end{pmatrix}\begin{pmatrix} 0 & 1 \\ 2 & 3 \end{pmatrix}$$

$$= \begin{pmatrix} 0+2 & 2+3 \\ 0+14 & 10+21 \end{pmatrix}$$

$$= \begin{pmatrix} 2 & 5 \\ 14 & 31 \end{pmatrix}$$

$$A(BC) = \begin{pmatrix} 1 & 0 \\ 1 & 2 \end{pmatrix}\left[\begin{pmatrix} 2 & 1 \\ 4 & 3 \end{pmatrix}\begin{pmatrix} 0 & 1 \\ 2 & 3 \end{pmatrix}\right]$$

$$= \begin{pmatrix} 1 & 0 \\ 1 & 2 \end{pmatrix}\begin{pmatrix} 0+2 & 2+3 \\ 0+6 & 4+9 \end{pmatrix}$$

$$= \begin{pmatrix} 1 & 0 \\ 1 & 2 \end{pmatrix}\begin{pmatrix} 2 & 5 \\ 6 & 13 \end{pmatrix}$$

$$= \begin{pmatrix} 2+0 & 5+0 \\ 2+12 & 5+26 \end{pmatrix}$$

$$= \begin{pmatrix} 2 & 5 \\ 14 & 31 \end{pmatrix}$$

$$\therefore (AB)C = A(BC) = \begin{pmatrix} 2 & 5 \\ 14 & 31 \end{pmatrix}$$

(c) $A + B = \begin{pmatrix} 1 & 0 \\ 1 & 2 \end{pmatrix} + \begin{pmatrix} 2 & 1 \\ 4 & 3 \end{pmatrix}$

$$= \begin{pmatrix} 3 & 1 \\ 5 & 5 \end{pmatrix}$$

$$B + A = \begin{pmatrix} 2 & 1 \\ 4 & 3 \end{pmatrix} + \begin{pmatrix} 1 & 0 \\ 1 & 2 \end{pmatrix}$$

$$= \begin{pmatrix} 3 & 1 \\ 5 & 5 \end{pmatrix}$$

$$\therefore A + B = B + A = \begin{pmatrix} 3 & 1 \\ 5 & 5 \end{pmatrix}$$

(d) $AB = \begin{pmatrix} 1 & 0 \\ 1 & 2 \end{pmatrix}\begin{pmatrix} 2 & 1 \\ 4 & 3 \end{pmatrix}$

$$= \begin{pmatrix} 2 & 1 \\ 10 & 7 \end{pmatrix}$$

$$BA = \begin{pmatrix} 2 & 1 \\ 4 & 3 \end{pmatrix}\begin{pmatrix} 1 & 0 \\ 1 & 2 \end{pmatrix}$$

$$= \begin{pmatrix} 3 & 2 \\ 7 & 6 \end{pmatrix}$$

$$\therefore AB \neq BA$$

14.7 The Zero (or Null) Matrix

A **zero matrix** is one in which all its elements are 'zeros', and it is denoted by **0**. For 2×2 matrices, $0 = \begin{pmatrix} 0 & 0 \\ 0 & 0 \end{pmatrix}$.

It is easily shown that for a matrix A,

$$A + 0 = A = 0 + A$$
and
$$A0 = 0 = 0A \qquad .$$

In other words, the zero matrix behaves like the number 0 in the addition and multiplication of ordinary numbers. However, if we have 2 matrices A and B such that $AB = 0$, it does not necessarily mean that $A = 0$ and/or $B = 0$ as in ordinary algebra.

For example, if $A = \begin{pmatrix} 1 & 0 \\ 0 & 0 \end{pmatrix}$ and $B = \begin{pmatrix} 0 & 0 \\ 0 & 1 \end{pmatrix}$,

then $\qquad AB = \begin{pmatrix} 1 & 0 \\ 0 & 0 \end{pmatrix}\begin{pmatrix} 0 & 0 \\ 0 & 1 \end{pmatrix}$

$$= \begin{pmatrix} 0 & 0 \\ 0 & 0 \end{pmatrix}.$$

Thus $AB = 0$ but neither A nor B is a zero matrix.

14.8 The Unit (or Identity) Matrix

A **unit matrix** is one in which the elements in the leading diagonal (top left corner to bottom right corner) are 'ones' and the other elements are 'zeros'. It is denoted by the letter I.

Thus $I = \begin{pmatrix} 1 & 0 \\ 0 & 1 \end{pmatrix}$.

If $A = \begin{pmatrix} a & b \\ c & d \end{pmatrix}$,

then $AI = \begin{pmatrix} a & b \\ c & d \end{pmatrix}\begin{pmatrix} 1 & 0 \\ 0 & 1 \end{pmatrix} = \begin{pmatrix} a & b \\ c & d \end{pmatrix}$,

and $IA = \begin{pmatrix} 1 & 0 \\ 0 & 1 \end{pmatrix}\begin{pmatrix} a & b \\ c & d \end{pmatrix} = \begin{pmatrix} a & b \\ c & d \end{pmatrix}$.

Hence $\qquad AI = IA = A$.

Note that the unit matrix behaves like the number 1 in the ordinary multiplication of numbers.

14.9 Determinant of a Matrix

The **determinant** of a matrix $A = \begin{pmatrix} a & b \\ c & d \end{pmatrix}$ is defined to be $ad - bc$.
It is denoted by det A, $|A|$ or Δ.

▶ **Example 5**

Find the determinant of each of the following matrices:

(a) $A = \begin{pmatrix} 1 & 2 \\ 3 & 4 \end{pmatrix}$

(b) $B = \begin{pmatrix} 1 & 2 \\ 3 & 6 \end{pmatrix}$

▶ **Solution . . .**

(a) $\det A = 1 \times 4 - 2 \times 3$
$\qquad = 4 - 6$
$\qquad = -2$

(b) $\det B = 1 \times 6 - 2 \times 3$
$\qquad = 6 - 6$
$\qquad = 0$

In part (b) above, where det $B = 0$, B is said to be a **singular matrix**.

14.10 Inverse of a Matrix

The **inverse** of a matrix A is the matrix which, when multiplied with the matrix A, results in the unit matrix. It is denoted by A^{-1}.

Consider $A = \begin{pmatrix} 4 & -3 \\ 7 & -5 \end{pmatrix}$ and $B = \begin{pmatrix} -5 & 3 \\ -7 & 4 \end{pmatrix}$.

Then $\quad AB = \begin{pmatrix} 4 & -3 \\ 7 & -5 \end{pmatrix}\begin{pmatrix} -5 & 3 \\ -7 & 4 \end{pmatrix}$

$\qquad = \begin{pmatrix} 1 & 0 \\ 0 & 1 \end{pmatrix} = I,$

and $\quad BA = \begin{pmatrix} -5 & 3 \\ -7 & 4 \end{pmatrix}\begin{pmatrix} 4 & -3 \\ 7 & -5 \end{pmatrix}$

$\qquad = \begin{pmatrix} 1 & 0 \\ 0 & 1 \end{pmatrix} = I.$

Hence, we have $AB = BA = I$;
i.e. B is the inverse of A, or $B = A^{-1}$.

So, $\qquad \boxed{AA^{-1} = A^{-1}A = I}$, provided $\Delta \neq 0$

Note: A^{-1} exists only if $|A| \neq 0$ (refer to page 349).

▶ **Example 6**

For each of the following pairs of matices A and B, find AB and BA. What can you say about the matrices A and B?

(a) $A = \begin{pmatrix} 2 & 1 \\ 1 & 1 \end{pmatrix}, B = \begin{pmatrix} 1 & -1 \\ -1 & 2 \end{pmatrix}$

(b) $A = \begin{pmatrix} 2 & 7 \\ -1 & -3 \end{pmatrix}, B = \begin{pmatrix} -3 & -7 \\ 1 & 2 \end{pmatrix}$

(c) $A = \begin{pmatrix} 3 & 5 \\ 1 & 2 \end{pmatrix}, B = \begin{pmatrix} 2 & -5 \\ -1 & 3 \end{pmatrix}$

▶ **Solution . . .**

(a) $AB = \begin{pmatrix} 2 & 1 \\ 1 & 1 \end{pmatrix}\begin{pmatrix} 1 & -1 \\ -1 & 2 \end{pmatrix}$

$\qquad = \begin{pmatrix} 1 & 0 \\ 0 & 1 \end{pmatrix} = I$

$BA = \begin{pmatrix} 1 & -1 \\ -1 & 2 \end{pmatrix}\begin{pmatrix} 2 & 1 \\ 1 & 1 \end{pmatrix}$

$\qquad = \begin{pmatrix} 1 & 0 \\ 0 & 1 \end{pmatrix} = I$

Hence $AB = BA = I$.

(b) $AB = \begin{pmatrix} 2 & 7 \\ -1 & -3 \end{pmatrix}\begin{pmatrix} -3 & -7 \\ 1 & 2 \end{pmatrix}$

$\qquad = \begin{pmatrix} 1 & 0 \\ 0 & 1 \end{pmatrix} = I$

$$BA = \begin{pmatrix} -3 & -7 \\ 1 & 2 \end{pmatrix} \begin{pmatrix} 2 & 7 \\ -1 & -3 \end{pmatrix}$$

$$= \begin{pmatrix} 1 & 0 \\ 0 & 1 \end{pmatrix} = I$$

Hence $AB = BA = I$.

(c) $AB = \begin{pmatrix} 3 & 5 \\ 1 & 2 \end{pmatrix} \begin{pmatrix} 2 & -5 \\ -1 & 3 \end{pmatrix}$

$$= \begin{pmatrix} 1 & 0 \\ 0 & 1 \end{pmatrix} = I$$

$$BA = \begin{pmatrix} 2 & -5 \\ -1 & 3 \end{pmatrix} \begin{pmatrix} 3 & 5 \\ 1 & 2 \end{pmatrix}$$

$$= \begin{pmatrix} 1 & 0 \\ 0 & 1 \end{pmatrix} = I$$

Hence $AB = BA = I$.

In all the above cases, $AB = BA = I$. We say that B is the inverse of A, i.e. $B = A^{-1}$, or A is the inverse of B, i.e. $A = B^{-1}$.

Observation and Analysis

Now examine the relationship of each pair of matrices in Example 6 carefully.

(a) What do you notice about the *elements* in the leading diagonals (top left to bottom right) of matrices A and B?

(b) What do you notice about the *signs* of the elements in the other diagonals (top right to bottom left) of matrices A and B?

It would *appear* from the above observations that, in general, if $A = \begin{pmatrix} a & b \\ c & d \end{pmatrix}$, then its inverse $A^{-1} = B = \begin{pmatrix} d & -b \\ -c & a \end{pmatrix}$.

Let us test this out by examining the products AB and BA in general.

$$AB = \begin{pmatrix} a & b \\ c & d \end{pmatrix} \begin{pmatrix} d & -b \\ -c & a \end{pmatrix}$$

$$= \begin{pmatrix} ad - bc & 0 \\ 0 & ad - bc \end{pmatrix}$$

$$= (ad - bc) \begin{pmatrix} 1 & 0 \\ 0 & 1 \end{pmatrix}$$

$$= (ad - bc)I,$$

and $BA = \begin{pmatrix} d & -b \\ -c & a \end{pmatrix} \begin{pmatrix} a & b \\ c & d \end{pmatrix}$

$\qquad = \begin{pmatrix} ad - bc & 0 \\ 0 & ad - bc \end{pmatrix}$

$\qquad = (ad - bc) \begin{pmatrix} 1 & 0 \\ 0 & 1 \end{pmatrix}$

$\qquad = (ad - bc)I.$

Notice that in either case, the product is not only I, but I times the scalar $(ad - bc)$.

If we now take this scalar factor into consideration,
then $AB = (ad - bc)I$,

giving $A \times \dfrac{1}{ad - bc} B = I$,

or $\begin{pmatrix} a & b \\ c & d \end{pmatrix} \times \dfrac{1}{ad - bc} \begin{pmatrix} d & -b \\ -c & a \end{pmatrix} = I.$

You should verify this as an exercise.

So the inverse of $A = \begin{pmatrix} a & b \\ c & d \end{pmatrix}$ is $A^{-1} = \dfrac{1}{ad - bc} \begin{pmatrix} d & -b \\ -c & a \end{pmatrix}$

$\left(A^{-1} \neq \begin{pmatrix} d & -b \\ -c & a \end{pmatrix} \right).$

Do you know why A^{-1} appeared to be $\begin{pmatrix} d & -b \\ -c & a \end{pmatrix}$ in Example 6?

Recalling from section 14.9 that $ad - bc = \Delta$, we can rewrite A^{-1} as

$\dfrac{1}{\Delta} \begin{pmatrix} d & -b \\ -c & a \end{pmatrix}.$

If $\Delta = 0$, $\dfrac{1}{\Delta}$ is undefined; thus A^{-1} **exists only if $\Delta \neq 0$.**

▶ **Example 7**

State whether each of the following matrices has an inverse. Find the inverse if it exists.

(a) $A = \begin{pmatrix} 1 & 2 \\ 2 & 5 \end{pmatrix}$

(b) $B = \begin{pmatrix} 2 & 1 \\ 6 & 3 \end{pmatrix}$

(c) $C = \begin{pmatrix} 4 & 1 \\ 2 & 1 \end{pmatrix}$

► **Solution ...**

(a) $A = \begin{pmatrix} 1 & 2 \\ 2 & 5 \end{pmatrix}$

$\det A = 1 \times 5 - 2 \times 2$

$\qquad = 1$

Since $\det A \neq 0$, A^{-1} exists.

$A^{-1} = \dfrac{1}{\Delta} \begin{pmatrix} 5 & -2 \\ -2 & 1 \end{pmatrix}$ where $\Delta = 1$

$\qquad = \begin{pmatrix} 5 & -2 \\ -2 & 1 \end{pmatrix}$

(b) $B = \begin{pmatrix} 2 & 1 \\ 6 & 3 \end{pmatrix}$

$\det B = 2 \times 3 - 6 \times 1$

$\qquad = 0$

Since $\det B = 0$, B does not have an inverse.

(c) $C = \begin{pmatrix} 4 & 1 \\ 2 & 1 \end{pmatrix}$

$\det C = 4 \times 1 - 2 \times 1$

$\qquad = 2$

Since $\det C \neq 0$, C^{-1} exists.

$C^{-1} = \dfrac{1}{\Delta} \begin{pmatrix} 1 & -1 \\ -2 & 4 \end{pmatrix}$ where $\Delta = 2$

$\qquad = \dfrac{1}{2} \begin{pmatrix} 1 & -1 \\ -2 & 4 \end{pmatrix}$

$\qquad = \begin{pmatrix} \frac{1}{2} & \frac{1}{2} \\ -1 & 2 \end{pmatrix}$

Exercise 14B (Answers on page 505)

1. If $A = \begin{pmatrix} 1 & 2 \\ 3 & 4 \end{pmatrix}$ and $B = \begin{pmatrix} 0 & 1 \\ 2 & 3 \end{pmatrix}$,

    (a) verify that $A + B = B + A$,

    (b) find AB and BA. Is $AB = BA$?

2. Given that $A = \begin{pmatrix} 0 & 1 \\ 2 & 0 \end{pmatrix}$, $B = \begin{pmatrix} 1 & 1 \\ 0 & 3 \end{pmatrix}$ and $C = \begin{pmatrix} 2 & 1 \\ 0 & 4 \end{pmatrix}$, verify that

    (a) $(A + B) + C = A + (B + C)$,

    (b) $(AB)C = A(BC)$.

3. In each of the following, verify that A and B are inverses of each other by showing that $AB = BA = I$.

(a) $A = \begin{pmatrix} -7 & -4 \\ -5 & -3 \end{pmatrix}$ and $B = \begin{pmatrix} -3 & 4 \\ 5 & -7 \end{pmatrix}$

(b) $A = \begin{pmatrix} 1 & -1 \\ 1 & 1 \end{pmatrix}$ and $B = \begin{pmatrix} \frac{1}{2} & \frac{1}{2} \\ -\frac{1}{2} & \frac{1}{2} \end{pmatrix}$

(c) $A = \begin{pmatrix} \frac{1}{2} & -\frac{1}{2} \\ -\frac{1}{4} & \frac{3}{4} \end{pmatrix}$ and $B = \begin{pmatrix} 3 & 2 \\ 1 & 2 \end{pmatrix}$

4. Determine whether each of the following matrices has an inverse. Find the inverse if it exists.

(a) $A = \begin{pmatrix} 3 & 2 \\ 4 & 3 \end{pmatrix}$

(b) $B = \begin{pmatrix} 3 & 6 \\ 2 & 4 \end{pmatrix}$

(c) $C = \begin{pmatrix} 2 & -1 \\ -1 & 1 \end{pmatrix}$

(d) $D = \begin{pmatrix} 5 & 3 \\ 6 & 4 \end{pmatrix}$

(e) $E = \begin{pmatrix} 3 & 4 \\ 2 & 5 \end{pmatrix}$

(f) $F = \begin{pmatrix} \frac{3}{8} & \frac{1}{8} \\ \frac{1}{4} & -\frac{1}{4} \end{pmatrix}$

5. If $A = \begin{pmatrix} 2 & x \\ -1 & 2 \end{pmatrix}$ and det $A = 7$, find

(a) the value of x,
(b) A^{-1}.

6. It is given that $A = \begin{pmatrix} 2 & x \\ 0 & 4 \end{pmatrix}$ and $B = \begin{pmatrix} 6 & 2 \\ -x & \frac{1}{3} \end{pmatrix}$.

Find (a) x if det A = det B,
      (b) A^{-1},
      (c) B^{-1}.

7. If $A = \begin{pmatrix} 2 & 5 \\ 1 & 3 \end{pmatrix}$ and $B = \begin{pmatrix} 2 & 3 \\ 0 & 1 \end{pmatrix}$, calculate

(a) $(AB)^{-1}$,
(b) $A^{-1}B^{-1}$.
Is $(AB)^{-1} = A^{-1}B^{-1}$?

8. Given the matrices $A = \begin{pmatrix} 2 & 0 \\ 1 & 1 \end{pmatrix}$ and $B = \begin{pmatrix} 1 & 2 \\ 3 & 1 \end{pmatrix}$, verify that

$(AB)^{-1} = B^{-1}A^{-1}$.

9. If $A = \begin{pmatrix} 0 & 1 \\ 2 & 3 \end{pmatrix}$, $B = \begin{pmatrix} 2 & 1 \\ 0 & 2 \end{pmatrix}$, and $C = \begin{pmatrix} 0 & 3 \\ 1 & 2 \end{pmatrix}$, verify that

   (a) $A(B + C) = AB + AC$,

   (b) $(B + C)A = BA + CA$.

10. The square of a matrix A, written as A^2, is defined as $A^2 = AA$.

   If $A = \begin{pmatrix} 2 & 1 \\ 3 & 2 \end{pmatrix}$ and $B = \begin{pmatrix} 0 & 1 \\ 1 & 3 \end{pmatrix}$, find

   (a) A^2,   **(b)** B^2,

   (c) $(AB)^2$,   **(d)** A^2B^2.

   Is $(AB)^2 = A^2B^2$?

14.11 Simple Matrix Equations

A matrix equation involves an unknown matrix X just as an ordinary equation involves an unknown x. Examples of matrix equations are:

$$2X + \begin{pmatrix} 1 & 2 \\ 1 & 3 \end{pmatrix} = \begin{pmatrix} 2 & 0 \\ 1 & 4 \end{pmatrix}$$

$$\begin{pmatrix} 2 & 1 \\ 3 & 1 \end{pmatrix} X = \begin{pmatrix} 1 & 0 \\ 2 & 3 \end{pmatrix}$$

$$X \begin{pmatrix} 2 & 1 \\ 3 & 1 \end{pmatrix} = \begin{pmatrix} 1 & 0 \\ 2 & 3 \end{pmatrix}$$

To solve a matrix equation means to find the unknown matrix X. The process of solving a matrix equation is quite similar to that of solving an ordinary equation. However we have to bear in mind that in matrices, pre-multiplying and post-multiplying a matrix by another produce different results (i.e. $AB \neq BA$).

We summarise the rules for solving matrix equations below. These operations are applied to both sides of an equation:

1. Adding or subtracting the same matrix.
   For example, if $A + B = C$,
   then $A + B + D = C + D$ (adding a matrix D),
   and $A + B - D = C - D$ (subtracting a matrix D).

2. Multiplying or dividing by a non-zero scalar.
   For example, if $A + B = C$,
   then $k(A + B) = kC$ (multiplying by k, where k is a non-zero scalar),
   and $\frac{1}{k}(A + B) = \frac{1}{k}C$ (dividing by k, where k is a non-zero scalar).

3. Pre-multiplying or post-multiplying respectively by the same matrix.

For example, if $A + B = C$,

then $\qquad P(A + B) = PC$ (pre-multiplying by a matrix P),

and $\qquad (A + B)Q = CQ$ (post-multiplying by a matrix Q).

We will now solve the equations given as examples above.

▶ **Example 8**

Find the matrix X such that $2X + \begin{pmatrix} 1 & 2 \\ 1 & 3 \end{pmatrix} = \begin{pmatrix} 2 & 0 \\ 1 & 4 \end{pmatrix}$.

▶ **Solution ...**

$$2X + \begin{pmatrix} 1 & 2 \\ 1 & 3 \end{pmatrix} = \begin{pmatrix} 2 & 0 \\ 1 & 4 \end{pmatrix}$$

$$2X + \begin{pmatrix} 1 & 2 \\ 1 & 3 \end{pmatrix} - \begin{pmatrix} 1 & 2 \\ 1 & 3 \end{pmatrix} = \begin{pmatrix} 2 & 0 \\ 1 & 4 \end{pmatrix} - \begin{pmatrix} 1 & 2 \\ 1 & 3 \end{pmatrix}$$

(substracting $\begin{pmatrix} 1 & 2 \\ 1 & 3 \end{pmatrix}$ from both sides),

$$2X = \begin{pmatrix} 1 & -2 \\ 0 & 1 \end{pmatrix}$$

$$X = \frac{1}{2} \begin{pmatrix} 1 & -2 \\ 0 & 1 \end{pmatrix} \text{ (dividing both sides by 2)}$$

$$= \begin{pmatrix} \frac{1}{2} & -1 \\ 0 & \frac{1}{2} \end{pmatrix}$$

▶ **Example 9**

Find X in each of the following equations:

(a) $\begin{pmatrix} 2 & 1 \\ 3 & 1 \end{pmatrix} X = \begin{pmatrix} 1 & 0 \\ 2 & 3 \end{pmatrix}$ $\qquad$ **(b)** $X \begin{pmatrix} 2 & 1 \\ 3 & 1 \end{pmatrix} = \begin{pmatrix} 1 & 0 \\ 2 & 3 \end{pmatrix}$

▶ **Solution ...**

Let $A = \begin{pmatrix} 2 & 1 \\ 3 & 1 \end{pmatrix}$ and $B = \begin{pmatrix} 1 & 0 \\ 2 & 3 \end{pmatrix}$.

$\therefore A^{-1} = \dfrac{1}{2-3} \begin{pmatrix} 1 & -1 \\ -3 & 2 \end{pmatrix} = \begin{pmatrix} -1 & 1 \\ 3 & -2 \end{pmatrix}$

(a) The equation can be rewritten as

$\qquad AX = B$

$\therefore A^{-1}AX = A^{-1}B$ (pre-multiplying both sides by A^{-1})

$\qquad X = A^{-1}B$ (recall that $A^{-1}A = I$ and $IX = X$)

$$= \begin{pmatrix} -1 & 1 \\ 3 & -2 \end{pmatrix} \begin{pmatrix} 1 & 0 \\ 2 & 3 \end{pmatrix} = \begin{pmatrix} 1 & 3 \\ -1 & -6 \end{pmatrix}$$

(b) The equation can be rewritten as

$$XA = B$$
$$XAA^{-1} = BA^{-1} \text{ (post-multiplying both sides by } A^{-1}\text{)}$$
$$X = BA^{-1} \text{ (recalling } AA^{-1} = I \text{ and } XI = X\text{)}$$

$$= \begin{pmatrix} 1 & 0 \\ 2 & 3 \end{pmatrix} \begin{pmatrix} -1 & 1 \\ 3 & -2 \end{pmatrix}$$

$$= \begin{pmatrix} -1 & 1 \\ 7 & -4 \end{pmatrix}$$

▶ ## Example 10

Given that $A = \begin{pmatrix} 4 & 3 \\ 1 & 2 \end{pmatrix}$ and $B = \begin{pmatrix} 2 & 0 \\ 1 & 2 \end{pmatrix}$, find the matrix X such that

$XA - 5B = 2A$.

▶ ## Solution . . .

$$A^{-1} = \frac{1}{5} \begin{pmatrix} 2 & -3 \\ -1 & 4 \end{pmatrix}$$

$$XA - 5B = 2A$$
$$XA = 2A + 5B$$
$$XAA^{-1} = (2A + 5B)A^{-1}$$
$$XI = 2AA^{-1} + 5BA^{-1}$$
$$X = 2I + 5BA^{-1}$$

$$= 2 \begin{pmatrix} 1 & 0 \\ 0 & 1 \end{pmatrix} + 5 \begin{pmatrix} 2 & 0 \\ 1 & 2 \end{pmatrix} \frac{1}{5} \begin{pmatrix} 2 & -3 \\ -1 & 4 \end{pmatrix}$$

$$= \begin{pmatrix} 2 & 0 \\ 0 & 2 \end{pmatrix} + \frac{5}{5} \begin{pmatrix} 2 & 0 \\ 1 & 2 \end{pmatrix} \begin{pmatrix} 2 & -3 \\ -1 & 4 \end{pmatrix}$$

$$= \begin{pmatrix} 2 & 0 \\ 0 & 2 \end{pmatrix} + \begin{pmatrix} 4 & -6 \\ 0 & 5 \end{pmatrix}$$

$$= \begin{pmatrix} 6 & -6 \\ 0 & 7 \end{pmatrix}$$

14.12 Using Matrices to Solve Simultaneous Equations

You have already learned to solve simultaneous equations like

$$3x + 4y = 18 \ \ldots\ldots (1)$$

and $\quad 4x - y = 5 \ \ldots\ldots (2)$

in your lower secondary classes. You will now learn how to solve these equations using matrices.

We can rewrite the above equations in terms of matrices as follows:

$$\begin{pmatrix} 3x + 4y \\ 4x - y \end{pmatrix} = \begin{pmatrix} 18 \\ 5 \end{pmatrix}$$

This is the same as

$$\begin{pmatrix} 3 & 4 \\ 4 & -1 \end{pmatrix} \begin{pmatrix} x \\ y \end{pmatrix} = \begin{pmatrix} 18 \\ 5 \end{pmatrix}$$

or $\quad AX = B$,

where $A = \begin{pmatrix} 3 & 4 \\ 4 & -1 \end{pmatrix}, X = \begin{pmatrix} x \\ y \end{pmatrix}$ and $B = \begin{pmatrix} 18 \\ 5 \end{pmatrix}$.

To find X, we pre-multiply both sides by A^{-1}.

Thus $A^{-1}AX = A^{-1}B$

$$\therefore \quad X = A^{-1}B$$

But $A^{-1} = \dfrac{1}{-19} \begin{pmatrix} -1 & -4 \\ -4 & 3 \end{pmatrix}$

$$\therefore X = \frac{1}{-19} \begin{pmatrix} -1 & -4 \\ -4 & 3 \end{pmatrix} \begin{pmatrix} 18 \\ 5 \end{pmatrix}$$

$$= -\frac{1}{19} \begin{pmatrix} -38 \\ -57 \end{pmatrix}$$

$$= \begin{pmatrix} 2 \\ 3 \end{pmatrix}$$

i.e. $\begin{pmatrix} x \\ y \end{pmatrix} = \begin{pmatrix} 2 \\ 3 \end{pmatrix}$

or $x = 2$ and $y = 3$.

You may have noticed that this method of solving simultaneous equations appears to be more difficult than the method you have learned previously. However matrices can be used to solve more complicated systems of simultaneous equations involving more equations and unknowns. They are used with the aid of computers which can do large numbers of computations quickly.

▶ **Example 11**

Solve the following equations using the matrix method:
$$2x + 5y = 8$$
$$4x + 9y = 14$$

▶ **Solution . . .**

Rewrite the equations in matrix form:

$$\begin{pmatrix} 2 & 5 \\ 4 & 9 \end{pmatrix}\begin{pmatrix} x \\ y \end{pmatrix} = \begin{pmatrix} 8 \\ 14 \end{pmatrix}$$

or $AX = B$ . . . . . (1),

where $A = \begin{pmatrix} 2 & 5 \\ 4 & 9 \end{pmatrix}, X = \begin{pmatrix} x \\ y \end{pmatrix}$ and $B = \begin{pmatrix} 8 \\ 14 \end{pmatrix}$.

$$\therefore \quad A^{-1} = \frac{1}{-2}\begin{pmatrix} 9 & -5 \\ -4 & 2 \end{pmatrix}$$

Pre-multiply (1) by A^{-1}:

$$A^{-1}AX = A^{-1}B$$
$$IX = A^{-1}B$$

$$X = \frac{1}{-2}\begin{pmatrix} 9 & -5 \\ -4 & 2 \end{pmatrix}\begin{pmatrix} 8 \\ 14 \end{pmatrix}$$

$$X = -\frac{1}{2}\begin{pmatrix} 2 \\ -4 \end{pmatrix}$$

$$\begin{pmatrix} x \\ y \end{pmatrix} = \begin{pmatrix} -1 \\ 2 \end{pmatrix}$$

$$\therefore x = -1 \text{ and } y = 2.$$

Exercise 14C (Answers on page 505)

1. Given $A = \begin{pmatrix} 0 & 1 \\ 2 & 3 \end{pmatrix}$ and $B = \begin{pmatrix} 2 & 1 \\ 3 & 4 \end{pmatrix}$, find the matrix X such that
   $2X + 3A = 4B$.

2. If $A = \begin{pmatrix} 1 & 0 \\ 1 & 2 \end{pmatrix}$ and $B = \begin{pmatrix} 2 & 0 \\ 4 & 5 \end{pmatrix}$, solve the equation $4X - A = 2B - X$.

3. If $A = \begin{pmatrix} 2 & 1 \\ 4 & 0 \end{pmatrix}$ and $B = \begin{pmatrix} 2 & 0 \\ 8 & 1 \end{pmatrix}$, find the matrix X such that $XA = 2B$.

4. If $A = \begin{pmatrix} 1 & 0 \\ 1 & 2 \end{pmatrix}$ and $B = \begin{pmatrix} 1 & \frac{1}{2} \\ 5 & \frac{1}{2} \end{pmatrix}$, find the matrix X such that $\frac{1}{2}AX = B$.

5. If $A = \begin{pmatrix} 1 & 0 \\ 2 & 3 \end{pmatrix}$, $B = \begin{pmatrix} 1 & 1 \\ 2 & 3 \end{pmatrix}$ and $C = \begin{pmatrix} 0 & 1 \\ 3 & 3 \end{pmatrix}$, find the matrix X such that $AX - 2B = C$.

6. If $A = \begin{pmatrix} 5 & 2 \\ 1 & -2 \end{pmatrix}$, $B = \begin{pmatrix} 3 & -5 \\ 4 & 2 \end{pmatrix}$ and $C = \begin{pmatrix} -\frac{1}{3} & -3 \\ 14 & -4 \end{pmatrix}$, solve the equation $X(A + B) = 3C$.

Use the matrix method for questions 7 – 12.

7. Solve the simultaneous equations:
$$2x + 5y = 9$$
$$x + 3y = 5$$

8. Solve the simultaneous equations:
$$2x + y = 1$$
$$5x + 4y = 7$$

9. Solve the simultaneous equations:
$$4x + 4 = 3y$$
$$6x + 7 = 5y$$

10. Solve the simultaneous equations:
$$3x = 4y + 13$$
$$2x = 5y + 11$$

11. Find the coordinates of the point of intersection of the following lines:
$$5y = 2x - 20$$
$$2y = 3x - 19$$

12. Find the coordinates of the point of intersection of the following lines:
$$8x - 3y - 16 = 0$$
$$4x + 3y + 10 = 0$$

Summary

1. A **matrix** is a rectangular array of numbers. Each number is called an **element** of the matrix.

2. **Order of a matrix**

   If a matrix has m rows and n columns, then its **order** is $m \times n$, or we say that it is a $m \times n$ matrix.

3. **Equal matrices**

   Two matrices are equal if they are of the same order and have the same corresponding elements.

4. **Addition and subtraction of matrices**

   Matrices can only be added or subtracted if they are of the same order.

To add 2 matrices, simply add the corresponding elements. The results will be a matrix of the same order. Similarly, to subtract one matrix from another, simply subtract the corresponding elements.

Note that $A + B = B + A$, and $(A + B) + C = A + (B + C)$.

5. **Multiplication of a matrix by a number (scalar)**

To multiply a matrix by a number, simply multiply each element by that number.

6. **Multiplication of 2 matrices**

2 matrices A and B can only be multiplied to obtain the product AB if the number of *columns* in A is the same as the number of *rows* in B. We then say that A and B are **compatible** or **conformable**.

If the order of A is $m \times n$ and the order of B is $n \times p$, then their product AB is a matrix of order $m \times p$.

For 2×2 matrices, if $A = \begin{pmatrix} a & b \\ c & d \end{pmatrix}$ and $B = \begin{pmatrix} w & x \\ y & z \end{pmatrix}$,

then $AB = \begin{pmatrix} aw + by & ax + bz \\ cw + dy & cx + dz \end{pmatrix}$.

Note that $(AB)C = A(BC)$ and $AB \neq BA$ in general.

7. **The zero (or null) matrix**

A zero matrix is one in which all its elements are 0. It is denoted by **0**.

Note that $A + 0 = A = 0 + A$, and $A0 = 0 = 0A$.

8. **The unit (identity) matrix.**

A unit matrix I is a square matrix (number of rows = number of columns) where the elements in the leading diagonal are 'ones' and

the other elements are 'zeros'. For 2×2 matrices, $I = \begin{pmatrix} 1 & 0 \\ 0 & 1 \end{pmatrix}$.

Note that $AI = A = IA$.

9. **Determinant of a matrix**

The determinant of a square matrix A is denoted by $\det A$, $|A|$ or Δ.

For 2×2 matrices where $A = \begin{pmatrix} a & b \\ c & d \end{pmatrix}$, $\det A = ad - bc$.

10. **Inverse of a 2×2 matrix A**

The inverse of a matix A is denoted by A^{-1}.

If $A = \begin{pmatrix} a & b \\ c & d \end{pmatrix}$ and its determinant is Δ, then $A^{-1} = \dfrac{1}{\Delta} \begin{pmatrix} d & -b \\ -c & a \end{pmatrix}$ provided $\Delta \neq 0$.

If $\Delta = 0$, the inverse of A does not exist and A is then said to be a **singular matrix**.

11. Solving simultaneous equations

The simultaneous equations

$$a_1 x + b_1 y = c_1$$

and $a_2 x + b_2 y = c_2$

can be rewritten as $\begin{pmatrix} a_1 & b_1 \\ a_2 & b_2 \end{pmatrix} \begin{pmatrix} x \\ y \end{pmatrix} = \begin{pmatrix} c_1 \\ c_2 \end{pmatrix}$,

and can be solved by pre-multiplying both sides by $\begin{pmatrix} a_1 & b_1 \\ a_2 & b_2 \end{pmatrix}^{-1}$.

Revision Exercise 14 (*Answers on page 506*)

1. If $A = \begin{pmatrix} 2 & 5 \\ 1 & 2 \end{pmatrix}$ and $B = \begin{pmatrix} 1 & 0 \\ 6 & 3 \end{pmatrix}$, find

   (a) $A + 2B$,

   (b) $3A - B$.

2. Find the matrix M such that

   $$2M - \begin{pmatrix} 1 & 2 \\ 3 & 1 \end{pmatrix} = \begin{pmatrix} 5 & 6 \\ 1 & 3 \end{pmatrix}.$$

3. Evaluate (a) $\begin{pmatrix} 2 & 5 \\ -3 & -1 \end{pmatrix}\begin{pmatrix} 1 & 5 \\ 3 & 2 \end{pmatrix}$,

   (b) $\begin{pmatrix} 1 & 0 & 3 \\ 2 & 1 & 0 \end{pmatrix}\begin{pmatrix} 2 \\ 1 \\ 3 \end{pmatrix}$.

4. If $A = \begin{pmatrix} 2 & 1 \\ 4 & 3 \end{pmatrix}$, $B = \begin{pmatrix} 6 \\ -2 \end{pmatrix}$ and $C = (2 \ \ 4)$,

   (a) state the orders of A, B and C,

   (b) evaluate the products AB, BA, AC, CA, BC, CB if they exist.

5. If $A = \begin{pmatrix} -3 & 4 \\ 0 & 3 \end{pmatrix}$ and $B = \begin{pmatrix} 4 & -2 \\ 3 & 9 \end{pmatrix}$, verify that

   (a) $A + B = B + A$,

   (b) $AB \neq BA$.

6. If $A = \begin{pmatrix} 0 & 2 \\ 4 & 3 \end{pmatrix}$, $B = \begin{pmatrix} 1 & 0 \\ 3 & 2 \end{pmatrix}$ and $C = \begin{pmatrix} 2 & 1 \\ 0 & 3 \end{pmatrix}$, verify that

   (a) $(A + B) + C = A + (B + C)$,

   (b) $(AB)C = A(BC)$.

7. Given that $\begin{pmatrix} 1 & 2 & 3 \\ 0 & 1 & 2 \end{pmatrix}\begin{pmatrix} 2 \\ 3 \\ x \end{pmatrix} = \begin{pmatrix} 23 \\ y \end{pmatrix}$, find the values of x and y.

8. If $A = \begin{pmatrix} 2 & 4 \\ 1 & 3 \end{pmatrix}$, and $A\begin{pmatrix} 5x \\ 3 \end{pmatrix} = \begin{pmatrix} 22 \\ 7y \end{pmatrix}$, find the values of x and y.

9. Given that $\begin{pmatrix} 0 & 1 \\ 2b & 0 \end{pmatrix}\begin{pmatrix} -3 & -7 \\ 3a & 0 \end{pmatrix} = \begin{pmatrix} 0 & -2 \\ 6 & 4c \end{pmatrix} + \begin{pmatrix} 1 & 2 \\ 0 & -2 \end{pmatrix}$, find the values of a, b and c.

10. If $A = \begin{pmatrix} 2 & 1 \\ 8 & 5 \end{pmatrix}$, find **(a)** det A, **(b)** A^{-1}.

11. Given that $A = \begin{pmatrix} 2 & 1 \\ 5 & 4 \end{pmatrix}$, find

   (a) the matrix B such that $A + B = 0$,
   (b) the matrix C such that $AC = I$.

12. If $A = \begin{pmatrix} 4 & 5 \\ x & 3 \end{pmatrix}$ and $|A| = 2$, find

   (a) the value of x,
   (b) A^{-1},
   (c) A^2.

13. Given that $A = \begin{pmatrix} 2 & 4 \\ 3 & x \end{pmatrix}$, find

   (a) the value of x for which A has no inverse,
   (b) the value of x if $|A| = 8$,
   (c) A^{-1} if $x = 5$.

14. If $M = \begin{pmatrix} 3x & 0 \\ y & -y \end{pmatrix}$ and $M\begin{pmatrix} 3 \\ 4 \end{pmatrix} = \begin{pmatrix} 27 \\ -2 \end{pmatrix}$, find

   (a) the values of x and y,

   (b) $M\begin{pmatrix} 4 \\ 3 \end{pmatrix}$.

15. If $\begin{pmatrix} 1 & x \\ 2 & 1 \end{pmatrix}\begin{pmatrix} x^2 \\ 5 \end{pmatrix} = \begin{pmatrix} -6 \\ y \end{pmatrix}$, find the possible values of x and y.

16. If $A = \begin{pmatrix} x & x+1 \\ x+2 & x+3 \end{pmatrix}$, find

(a) $|A|$,

(b) A^{-1} in terms of x.

17. If $\begin{pmatrix} 1 & 3 \\ 4 & -2 \end{pmatrix} \begin{pmatrix} x \\ y \end{pmatrix} = \begin{pmatrix} -3 \\ 16 \end{pmatrix}$,

(a) write down a pair of simultaneous equations involving x and y,

(b) use the matrix method to find the values of x and y.

18. Use the matrix method to solve the simultaneous equations:
$$4x + 5y = 1$$
$$3x - 2y = 18$$

19. Using the matrix method, find the coordinates of the point of intersection of the following lines:
$$3y = 4x + 4$$
$$5y = 14 - 8x$$

20. A car-rental company rents out 3 makes of cars (x, y and z) on a daily basis. The numbers of different cars rented out the week before from Monday to Friday are given in the table below:

	x	y	z
Monday	20	12	16
Tuesday	24	10	18
Wednesday	18	20	15
Thursday	16	22	20
Friday	23	19	22

The rental (in $) of each make per day is as follows:

	x	y	z
Rental ($)	100	150	200

Using the appropriate matrix multiplication, find the amount received by the company on each of the five days and the total collection for the five days.

Maths Booster

If A and B are matrices, is it true that

(a) $(A + B)^2 = A^2 + 2AB + B^2$,

(b) $(A - B)^2 = A^2 - 2AB + B^2$,

(c) $(A + B)(A - B) = A^2 - B^2$?

Explain your conclusions.

Revision Paper 5 (Answers on page 512)

1. (a) Prove the identity $(\cos\theta + \sin\theta)^2 \equiv 2 - (\cos\theta - \sin\theta)^2$.
    (b) Solve the equation $\operatorname{cosec} 2\theta = -2.15$ for $0° \leq \theta \leq 360°$.

2. Show on a diagram a sketch of the curves $y = \cos 2x$ and $y = |2\sin x|$ for $0 \leq x \leq 2\pi$. State how many values of x will satisfy the equation $\cos 2x = |2\sin x|$ in the range.

3. In how many ways can a consonant and two vowels be chosen from the word 'EDUCATION'?

4. 5 boys and 5 girls are to be arranged in a straight line such that the shortest girl must be in front and the tallest boy must be at the back.
    (a) How many possible arrangements are there?
    (b) In addition, if the girls must be next to one another, find the number of possible arrangements.

5. (a) Find the coefficient of x^5 in the expansion of $(2x - 3)^7$.
    (b) If the first two terms in the expansion of $(ax + b)^5$ in descending powers of x are $32x^5 - 80x^4$, find the value of a and of b.

6. Find and simplify the first three terms in the expansions, in ascending powers of x, of $(1 + 3x)^4$ and $(2 - x)^4$ and hence find the coefficient of x^2 in the expansion of $(2 + 5x - 3x^2)^4$.

7. The position vectors of two points A and B referred to an origin O are $2\mathbf{i} - 3\mathbf{j}$ and $3\mathbf{i} + 4\mathbf{j}$ respectively. Find
    (a) $\overrightarrow{AB}$ in terms of $\mathbf{i}$ and $\mathbf{j}$,
    (b) angle AOB.

8. In $\triangle OAB$, $\overrightarrow{OA} = \mathbf{a}$, $\overrightarrow{OB} = \mathbf{b}$ and M is the midpoint of AB. T lies on OB where $\overrightarrow{OT} = \frac{1}{3}\overrightarrow{OB}$. OM and TA intersect at N. Taking $\overrightarrow{TN} = k\overrightarrow{TA}$ and $\overrightarrow{ON} = m\overrightarrow{OM}$, find two vector expressions for $\overrightarrow{ON}$ in terms of k, m, $\mathbf{a}$ and $\mathbf{b}$ and hence find
    (a) the values of k and m, and
    (b) the ratio ON:NM and TN:NA.

9. If $P = \begin{pmatrix} 1 & 0 \\ 2 & 3 \end{pmatrix}$ and $Q = \begin{pmatrix} 2 & 1 \\ 4 & 0 \end{pmatrix}$, find
    (a) $3P + 2Q$,
    (b) PQ,
    (c) QP.

10. (a) If $A = \begin{pmatrix} 1 & 2 \\ 3 & 4 \end{pmatrix}$ and $A\begin{pmatrix} 6 \\ 2x \end{pmatrix} = \begin{pmatrix} 26 \\ 29y \end{pmatrix}$, find the values of x and y.
    (b) Use the matrix method to solve the simultaneous equations:
    $$4x + 3y = 9$$
    $$3x - 2y = 11$$

Revision Paper 6 (Answers on page 512)

1. **(a)** Prove the identity
   $$(\cos\theta - \sin\theta)(\operatorname{cosec}\theta - \sec\theta) \equiv \sec\theta\operatorname{cosec}\theta - 2.$$
   (b) Solve the equation $3\sin^2\theta = 2\cos\theta + 2$ for values of θ in the range $0° \le \theta \le 360°$.

2. On one diagram, sketch the graphs of
   (a) $y = \sin 2x$, **(b)** $y = |\sin x|$ for $0 \le x \le 2\pi$.
   State the number of solutions of the equation $\sin 2x = |\sin x|$ in this range.

3. In how many ways can the letters of the word 'SINGAPORE' be arranged? If no two consonants are to be next to each other, how many ways are there?

4. A National Education Committee of 4 is to be chosen from 4 male teachers and 5 female teachers.
   (a) In how many ways can the Committee be formed?
   (b) In how many of these ways are both sexes represented on the Committee?

5. Find, in ascending powers of x, the first three terms in the expansions of **(a)** $(1 - 2x)^4$ and **(b)** $(2 - x)^5$.
   Hence find the coefficient of x^2 in the expansion of $(1 - 2x)^4(2 - x)^5$.

6. If the expansion of $(1 + ax)^n$ in ascending powers of x is $1 - 15x + 90x^2$, find the values of n and a.

7. OAB is a triangle with $\overrightarrow{OA} = \mathbf{a}$ and $\overrightarrow{OB} = \mathbf{b}$. OP lies on OA where OP:PA = 2:1 and Q lies on AB where AQ:QB = 2:1. OQ and PB intersect at R.
   (a) State $\overrightarrow{AB}$, $\overrightarrow{AQ}$, $\overrightarrow{OQ}$ and $\overrightarrow{PB}$ in terms of $\mathbf{a}$ and $\mathbf{b}$.
   (b) By taking $\overrightarrow{PR} = p\overrightarrow{PB}$, show that $\overrightarrow{PR} = \frac{2}{3}(1 - p)\mathbf{a} + p\mathbf{b}$.
   (c) If $\overrightarrow{OR} = q\overrightarrow{OQ}$ find the values of p and q.
   (d) Hence find the ratios OR:RQ and PR:RB.

8. At a certain time, two ships S and T are 20 km apart with T on a bearing of $060°$ from S. S is sailing due N at a speed of 15 km h^{-1} while T is sailing in the direction $330°$ with a speed 20 km h^{-1}.
   (a) Calculate the velocity of T relative to S.

   If S maintains the same direction but wishes to intercept T, find
   (b) by how much it must increase its speed,
   (c) the time taken for it to intercept T.

9. Given that $A = \begin{pmatrix} 3 & 1 \\ 0 & a \end{pmatrix}$, $B = \begin{pmatrix} 1 & b \\ 3 & 4 \end{pmatrix}$ and $C = \begin{pmatrix} 5 & 5 \\ 6 & c \end{pmatrix}$ and that $A + 2B = C$, find the values of a, b, and c.

10. If $X = \begin{pmatrix} x & x-1 \\ 6 & x+2 \end{pmatrix}$ and $|X| = 2$, find

    (a) the value of x,
    (b) X^{-1},
    (c) X^2.

Chapter 15

Differentiation

Suppose a tortoise travels a distance of 10 m in the first hour, and each subsequent hour it travels half the distance it covers in the previous hour. Thus in the second hour, it covers a distance of 5 m. The total distance it covers in the first 2 hours = 10 + 5 = 15 m.

Complete the table below to show the distance d m covered after n hours.

n (hours)	d (metres)
1	10
2	15
3	
4	
5	
6	
7	
8	
9	
10	

What do you observe about the values of d as n gets larger and larger? Do they get closer and closer to a certain value? If so, what is this value? Indeed this value is called the limit of d as n gets larger. You will learn more about limits in this chapter.

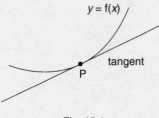

$y = f(x)$

tangent

P

Fig. 15.1

15.1 Gradient of a Curve

The gradient of a straight line is constant. It is equal to the ratio $\frac{y\text{-step}}{x\text{-step}}$ between any two points of the line. On a curve, however, the gradient is changing from one point to another. We define the gradient at any point on a curve therefore to be the gradient of the **tangent to the curve at that point** (Fig. 15.1).

We now find a **gradient function**, derived from the function represented by the curve, using a method called a **limiting process**. Consider the simple quadratic curve $y = x^2$ (Fig. 15.2) and take the point P(3,9) on that curve.

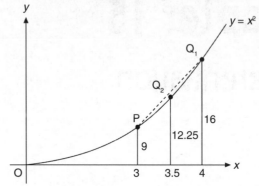

Fig. 15.2

Now take a point near P, say $Q_1(4,16)$. The gradient of the line PQ_1 is $\frac{16-9}{4-3} = 7$ which only approximately equals the gradient of the tangent at P.

To get a better approximation we try again, this time with $Q_2(3.5,12.25)$ which is closer to P.

The gradient of $PQ_2 = \frac{3.25}{0.5} = 6.5$.

Now see what happens if we repeat this process, taking positions of Q closer and closer to P, using a calculator (Fig. 15.3).

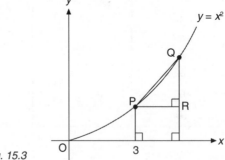

Fig. 15.3

Coordinates of Q	QR	PR	Gradient	
(3.3,10.89)	1.89	0.3	6.3	
(3.1,9.61)	0.61	0.1	6.1	
(3.01,9.060 1)	0.060 1	0.01	6.01	tending to 6
(3.001,9.006 001)	0.006 001	0.001	6.001	
(3.000 1,9.000 600 01)	0.000 600 01	0.0001	6.000 1	

The sequence of values suggests that as the position of Q gets closer and closer to P, the gradient approaches 6. We say that 6 is the **limiting value or limit** of the sequence. We use the symbol $\longrightarrow$ to mean 'tends to' or 'approaches'. Thus $P \longrightarrow Q$ is read as 'P tends to Q' or 'P approaches Q'. As $Q \longrightarrow P$, the gradient of $PQ \longrightarrow 6$ and **we take this limiting value as the gradient at P.**

Fig. 15.4 illustrates some lines through PQ for some positions of Q, showing how the gradients of these lines approach the gradient of the tangent PT.

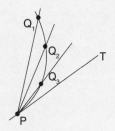

Fig. 15.4

15.2   General Method for the Gradient Function

To find the gradient at another point on the curve we must repeat the calculations. A better approach would be to find a formula for the gradient, using the same method.

To do this, we make use of two new and important notations, δx and δy.

Let δx (read as 'delta x' and used as a single symbol) be a small change in x, called the increment in x, and δy be the corresponding increment in y. So if x changes to $x + \delta x$, y will change to $y + \delta y$.

Using the same curve $y = x^2$, we consider a point $P(x,y)$ and a nearby point Q on the curve (Fig. 15.5).

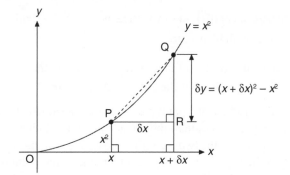

Fig. 15.5

$PR = \delta x$, $QR = \delta y$.

The coordinates of Q are $(x + \delta x, y + \delta y)$ and so $y + \delta y = (x + \delta x)^2$.

$$\begin{aligned} QR &= (x + \delta x)^2 - x^2 \\ &= x^2 + 2x\delta x + (\delta x)^2 - x^2 \\ &= 2x\delta x + (\delta x)^2 \end{aligned}$$

The gradient of $PQ = \dfrac{\delta y}{\delta x} = \dfrac{2x\delta x + (\delta x)^2}{\delta x} = 2x + \delta x$

Now we let $\delta x \longrightarrow 0$. The limiting value of $\dfrac{\delta y}{\delta x}$ will be $2x$, and we take this as the gradient at P.

When $x = 3$, the gradient $= 2(3) = 6$, as we have found out before. By using different values of x corresponding to different positions of P on the curve, we can obtain the gradient at any point on the curve. The function $x \longrightarrow 2x$ is called the **gradient function** for the curve $y = x^2$.

Each curve will have its own gradient function which we can find by the limiting method, known as 'working from first principles'.

We also use the symbol $\dfrac{dy}{dx}$ (read 'dee y by dee x') to represent the limiting value of $\dfrac{\delta y}{\delta x}$ as $\delta x \longrightarrow 0$. We write this as

$$\frac{dy}{dx} = \lim_{\delta x \to 0} \frac{\delta y}{\delta x}$$

where $\lim\limits_{\delta x \to 0}$ means 'take the limiting value when $\delta x \longrightarrow 0$'. (The curly δ is straightened to ordinary d to show that we have taken the limiting value.) So for the curve $y = x^2$, $\dfrac{dy}{dx} = 2x$.

If the equation of a curve is $y = f(x)$, we can also write its gradient as $f'(x)$. Thus if $y = f(x)$, $\dfrac{dy}{dx} = f'(x)$.

MATHS BULLETIN

Differentiation is a component of Calculus which is a very important branch of Mathematics. It was first developed by Sir Isaac Newton. Newton was born on Christmas Day in 1642 in the English village of Woolsthorpe. Newton studied Mathematics at Cambridge. He became one of the greatest scientists and mathematicians who ever lived.

Besides being the inventor of Calculus, he was also well known for his theory on gravitational force, said to be inspired by an apple dropping on his head when he was reading under an apple tree. He died in 1727 at the age of 85.

Surf the internet to find out more about Newton's life and achievements.

15.3 Meaning of $\dfrac{dy}{dx}$

The notation $\dfrac{dy}{dx}$ for the limiting value of $\dfrac{\delta y}{\delta x}$ as $\delta x \longrightarrow 0$ is appropriate as it is a reminder that $\dfrac{dy}{dx}$ is derived from $\dfrac{\delta y}{\delta x}$. We call this **differentiation** (as it uses the difference δx) and $\dfrac{dy}{dx}$ is called the **derivative** or the **differential coefficient** of y with respect to x. We shall use the abbreviation 'wrt' for 'with respect to'.

$\dfrac{dy}{dx}$ gives the gradient function for a curve and the value of $\dfrac{dy}{dx}$ at a given point is the gradient of the curve and therefore of the tangent there.

Now the gradient at a point measures the rate at which y is changing wrt x. The steeper the gradient the greater this rate of change. For example, on the curve $y = x^2$, the two quantities are each changing and the rate of change is $2x$. When $x = 3$, $y = 9$ but y is changing at that point 6 times as much as x is changing. $\dfrac{dy}{dx}$ measures this rate of change. This is what makes differentiation a powerful tool in Mathematics.

The idea and notation can be applied to any function. For example, if s is a function of t, $s = f(t)$, then $\dfrac{ds}{dt}$ is the rate of change of s wrt t.

If A is a function of r, $A = f(r)$, then $\dfrac{dA}{dr}$ is the rate of change of A wrt r.

15.4 The Derivative of ax^n

The finding of the gradient function from first principles can be tedious. We will now state a simple rule (which we shall not prove) to obtain the gradient function of ax^n, where a and n are constants.

The rule to differentiate ax^n:
Multiply the term by the index (n) and then reduce the index by 1.

For example, to find the derivative of $5x^3$:

the index 3 becomes a multiplier

$$3 \times 5x^2 \quad \leftarrow \text{the new index is } 3 - 1 = 2$$

The derivative of ax^n is nax^{n-1}.

What about the derivative of a constant, say $y = 5$? This is 0, as the gradient is always 0.

The derivative of a constant is 0.

> If $y = ax^n$, $\dfrac{dy}{dx} = nax^{n-1}$.
>
> If $y = k$ (a constant), $\dfrac{dy}{dx} = 0$.

More generally,

> If $y = ax^n + bx^m$,
>
> then $\dfrac{dy}{dx} = nax^{n-1} + mbx^{m-1}$,
>
> where a, b, m and n are constants.

This rule can be extended further to include sum (or difference) of more terms of the same form. Hence the differentiation of the sum of a number of terms is the sum of the differentiation of the individual terms.

Note that this rule is not applicable to functions such as $\sqrt{3x - 1}$ or $\dfrac{x+2}{x-1}$. We will deal with the differentiation of such functions later in the book.

▶ **Example 1**

Differentiate wrt x **(a)** $3x^5 + 7$, **(b)** $x^3 - \dfrac{1}{2}x^2 - \dfrac{1}{x}$, **(c)** $(2x - 3)^2$, **(d)** $\dfrac{4}{x^3}$, **(e)** $\sqrt{x}$, **(f)** $ax^3 + 2bx^2 - cx + 7$ where a, b and c are constants.

▶ **Solution . . .**

(a) If $y = 3x^5 + 7$, then $\dfrac{dy}{dx} = 5 \times 3x^{5-1} + 0 = 15x^4$.

Note:

Do not write $3x^5 + 7 = 15x^4$. This is incorrect. Use a letter such as y for the function and then write $\dfrac{dy}{dx}$.

(b) If $y = x^3 - \dfrac{1}{2}x^2 - \dfrac{1}{x} = x^3 - \dfrac{1}{2}x^2 - x^{-1}$

then $\dfrac{dy}{dx} = 3x^2 - 2 \times \dfrac{1}{2}x^1 - (-1)x^{-2} = 3x^2 - x + \dfrac{1}{x^2}$

Rewrite reciprocals such as $\dfrac{1}{x^2}$ in terms of negative indices before differentiating.

(c) Here we expand $(2x - 3)^2$ first. $(2x - 3)^2 = 4x^2 - 12x + 9$

If $y = 4x^2 - 12x + 9$, then $\dfrac{dy}{dx} = 8x - 12x^0 + 0 = 8x - 12$, as $x^0 = 1$.

(d) If $y = \dfrac{4}{x^3} = 4x^{-3}$, then $\dfrac{dy}{dx} = -3(4)x^{-3-1} = -12x^{-4}$,

which can be left in this form or written as $-\dfrac{12}{x^4}$.

(e) Here we rewrite $\sqrt{x}$ in index form:

If $y = \sqrt{x} = x^{\frac{1}{2}}$, then $\dfrac{dy}{dx} = \dfrac{1}{2} x^{-\frac{1}{2}}$ or $\dfrac{1}{2\sqrt{x}}$.

(f) If $y = ax^3 + 2bx^2 - cx + 7$, then $\dfrac{dy}{dx} = 3ax^2 + 4bx - cx^0 + 0$

$$= 3ax^2 + 4bx - c.$$

▶ **Example 2**

Find the coordinates of the points on the curve $y = x^3 - 3x^2 - 9x + 6$ where the gradient is 0.

▶ **Solution . . .**

The gradient $= \dfrac{dy}{dx}$.

$\dfrac{dy}{dx} = 3x^2 - 6x - 9 = 3(x^2 - 2x - 3) = 3(x - 3)(x + 1)$

If the gradient $= 0$, then $\dfrac{dy}{dx} = 0$ and so $3(x - 3)(x + 1) = 0$ which gives $x = 3$ or $x = -1$.

When $x = 3$, $y = 3^3 - 3(3^2) - 9(3) + 6 = -21$: coordinates $(3, -21)$.

When $x = -1$, $y = (-1)^3 - 3(-1)^2 - 9(-1) + 6 = 11$: coordinates $(-1, 11)$.

▶ **Example 3**

(a) Differentiate $A = 2\pi r^2 + 2\pi rh$ wrt r, where h is a constant.

(b) If $T = \dfrac{(3p+1)^2}{p}$, find $\dfrac{dT}{dp}$ and the values of p for $\dfrac{dT}{dp} = 0$.

▶ **Solution . . .**

(a) $\dfrac{dA}{dr} = 2 \times 2\pi r^1 + 2\pi rh^0$

$\qquad = 4\pi r + 2\pi h$

(b) Here we expand the numerator first.

$\dfrac{(3p+1)^2}{p} = \dfrac{9p^2 + 6p + 1}{p}$

$\qquad\qquad = 9p + 6 + \dfrac{1}{p}$ (dividing each term in the numerator by p)

$\qquad\qquad = 9p + 6 + p^{-1}$

Then $\dfrac{dT}{dp} = 9 + 0 + (-1)p^{-2} = 9 - \dfrac{1}{p^2}$

If $\dfrac{dT}{dp} = 0$, then $9 = \dfrac{1}{p^2}$ and $p = \pm\dfrac{1}{3}$.

Exercise 15A (Answers on page 506)

1. Differentiate the following wrt x:
   - (a) $5x$
   - (b) $4x^2$
   - (c) 7
   - (d) $3x^2 - 5$
   - (e) $3x^2 - x - 1$
   - (f) $x^3 - x^2 - x - 1$
   - (g) $1 - 3x^2$
   - (h) $(x - 1)^2$
   - (i) $\dfrac{4}{x}$
   - (j) $3x^2 + \dfrac{1}{x}$
   - (k) $(x - 2)^3$
   - (l) $\left(x - \dfrac{1}{x}\right)^2$
   - (m) $\dfrac{x^5}{5} + \dfrac{x^4}{4} + \dfrac{x^3}{3} + \dfrac{x^2}{2}$
   - (n) $\dfrac{x^3 - 2x^3 + x - 3}{x}$
   - (o) $\dfrac{(2x - 1)^2}{x^2}$
   - (p) $\dfrac{2x^2 - x - 1}{x^3}$
   - (q) $(\sqrt{x} + 1)^2$

2. Differentiate $s = 3t^2 - 4t - 2$ wrt t.

3. If $W = 3r^3 - 2r^2 + r - 3$, find $\dfrac{dW}{dr}$.

4. Given $u = (3t - 2)^2$, find $\dfrac{du}{dt}$.

5. $y = 4x^2 - \mu x + 6$. Given that the rate of change of y wrt x is 2 when $x = 1$, find the value of μ.

6. Find the gradient on the curve $y = 4x^3 - 10x + 1$ at the point where $x = -1$.

7. The gradient on the curve $y = ax^2 - 3x + 4$ where $x = -2$ is 13. Find the value of a.

8. Find the coordinates of the points on the curve $y = 3x^3 - 4x + 2$ where the gradient is 0.

9. Find the coordinates of the points on the curve $y = x^3 - 3x^2 + x - 5$ where the gradient is 1.

10. Find the values of z for which $\dfrac{dp}{dz} = 0$ where $P = 4z^3 - 2z^2 - 8z + 5$.

11. Show that there is only one point on the curve $y = x^4 - 32x + 10$ where the gradient is 0 and find its coordinates.

12. Given that $u = 4t^3 + 3t^2 - 6t - 1$, find the values of t for which $\dfrac{du}{dt} = 12$.

13. Find the values of t for which $\dfrac{ds}{dt} = 0$ given that $s = 4t^3 + t^2 - 2t - 5$.

14. Given $v = 4s^2 - 12s - 7$, find $\dfrac{dv}{ds}$. For what value of s is $\dfrac{dv}{ds} = 4$?

15. Given that the curve $y = ax^2 + \dfrac{b}{x}$ has a gradient of 5 at the point $(1,1)$, find the values of a and b. What is the gradient of the tangent to the curve at the point where $x = \dfrac{1}{2}$?

16. If the gradient on the curve $y = ax + \dfrac{b}{x}$ at the point $(-1,-1)$ is 5, find the values of a and b.

17. The curve given by $y = ax^3 + bx^2 + 3x + 2$ passes through the point $(1,2)$ and the gradient at that point is 7. Find the values of a and b.

18. Given $y = 2x^3 - 3x^2 - 12x + 5$, find the domain of x for which $\dfrac{dy}{dx} \geq 0$.

19. The function P is given by $P = \dfrac{a}{t} + bt^2$ and when $t = 1$, $P = -1$. The rate of change of P when $t = \dfrac{1}{2}$ is -5. Find the values of a and b.

20. Given that $R = mp^4 + np^2 + 3$, find $\dfrac{dR}{dp}$. When $p = 1$, $\dfrac{dR}{dp} = 12$ and when $p = \dfrac{1}{4}$, $\dfrac{dR}{dp} = -\dfrac{3}{4}$. Find the values of m and n.

15.5 Composite Functions

In part (c) of Example 1, to find the derivative of $(2x - 3)^2$, we first expand it into a polynomial. Similarly, if we want to find the derivative of $y = (3x - 2)^5$, we first expand it into a polynomial. This would be rather lengthy so we look for a neater method. To do this we take $(3x - 2)^5$ as a **composite** or **combined** function.

The function $y = (3x - 2)^5$ can be built up from two simpler functions, $u = 3x - 2$ and then $y = u^5$. We call u the **core** function.

Now u is a function of x so $\dfrac{du}{dx} = 3$. y is a function of the core u so $\dfrac{dy}{du} = 5u^4$. To obtain $\dfrac{dy}{dx}$ from these two derivatives, we use a rule for the derivative of composite functions (which we shall not prove):

$$\mathbf{\dfrac{dy}{dx} = \dfrac{dy}{du} \times \dfrac{du}{dx}}$$

where y is a function of u and u is a function of x.

Note:

du cannot be cancelled on the right-hand side as these are not fractions but derivatives. However the notation suggests the result and is easy to remember.

Hence, $\dfrac{dy}{dx} = 5u^4 \times 3 = 15u^4 = 15(3x - 2)^4$.

▶ Example 4

Find $\dfrac{dy}{dx}$ given that $y = (x^2 - 3x + 1)^4$.

▶ Solution

Take $u = x^2 - 3x + 1$ as the core. Then $y = u^4$.

$\dfrac{dy}{du} = 4u^3$, differentiating y wrt the core u.

$\dfrac{du}{dx} = 2x - 3$, differentiating the core wrt x.

Multiplying these two derivatives to obtain $\dfrac{dy}{dx}$:

$$\dfrac{dy}{dx} = 4u^3 \times (2x - 3) = 4(2x - 3)(x^2 - 3x + 1)^3.$$

▶ Example 5

Find $\dfrac{dy}{dx}$ if $y = (ax^2 + bx + c)^n$.

▶ Solution . . .

Take $u = ax^2 + bx + c$ and then $y = u^n$.

$\dfrac{dy}{du} = nu^{n-1}$ and $\dfrac{du}{dx} = 2ax + b$.

Then $\dfrac{dy}{dx} = nu^{n-1} \times (2ax + b) = n(2ax + b)(ax^2 + bx + c)^{n-1}$.

With practice, $\dfrac{dy}{dx}$ can be written down in two steps on one line.

Suppose $y = (\mathbf{core})^n$ [**core** being a function of x]

$$\begin{array}{cc} \textit{Step 1} & \textit{Step 2} \\[4pt] \dfrac{dy}{dx} = n(\mathbf{core})^{n-1} & \times \quad \dfrac{d(\mathrm{core})}{dx} \\[4pt] \uparrow & \uparrow \\ \text{derivative of } (\mathbf{core})^n & \text{derivative of core} \\ \text{wrt core} & \text{wrt } x \end{array}$$

Generalising, if $y = [f(x)]^n$, then $\dfrac{dy}{dx} = n[f(x)]^{n-1} \cdot f'(x)$ where $f'(x)$ is the differentiation of $f(x)$ wrt x.

▶ Example 6

Differentiate $\dfrac{2}{x^2 - 3x + 1}$ wrt x.

▶ Solution . . .

Take $y = 2\underset{\mathbf{core}}{(x^2 - 3x + 1)^{-1}}$

Then $\dfrac{dy}{dx} = 2(-1)(x^2 - 3x + 1)^{-2} \times \underset{\text{derivative of core wrt } x}{(2x - 3)}$

$$= \dfrac{-2(2x - 3)}{(x^2 - 3x + 1)^2}$$

▶ **Example 7**

Given that $s = 3t - \dfrac{1}{1-2t}$, find **(a)** $\dfrac{ds}{dt}$ and **(b)** the values of s when $\dfrac{ds}{dt} = \dfrac{25}{9}$.

▶ **Solution . . .**

(a) $s = 3t - \underset{\text{core}}{(1-2t)^{-1}}$

$$\frac{ds}{dt} = 3 - (-1)(1-2t)^{-2}(-2)$$

$$= 3 - \frac{2}{(1-2t)^2} \qquad \text{derivative of core wrt } t$$

(b) If $3 - \dfrac{2}{(1-2t)^2} = \dfrac{25}{9}$, then $\dfrac{2}{(1-2t)^2} = \dfrac{2}{9}$, i.e. $9 = (1-2t)^2$.

Hence $9 = 1 - 4t + 4t^2$ or $4t^2 - 4t - 8 = 0$,

which gives $t^2 - t - 2 = 0$ or $(t-2)(t+1) = 0$ and $t = 2$ or -1.

When $t = 2$, $s = 6 - \dfrac{1}{1-4} = 6\dfrac{1}{3}$,

and when $t = -1$, $s = -3 - \dfrac{1}{3} = -3\dfrac{1}{3}$.

Exercise 15B (Answers on page 506)

1. Differentiate the following wrt x:

    (a) $(x-3)^5$ **(b)** $(3x-1)^7$ **(c)** $(5-2x)^3$

    (d) $(4x-5)^{10}$ **(e)** $(4x-3)^4$ **(f)** $(x^2-x+1)^3$

    (g) $(3-x-2x^2)^5$ **(h)** $\dfrac{1}{x-2}$ **(i)** $\dfrac{4}{1-3x}$

    (j) $\dfrac{4}{3+2x}$ **(k)** $(x-\dfrac{1}{2})^4$ **(l)** $\dfrac{1}{x^2+3}$

    (m) $\dfrac{4}{x^2-x-1}$ **(n)** $(ax+b)^n$ **(o)** $\dfrac{2}{(2x-3)^4}$

    (p) $\dfrac{1}{(1-3x-2x^2)^3}$ **(q)** $(2x-\dfrac{1}{2x})^3$

2. If $s = (2t-1)^3$, find **(a)** $\dfrac{ds}{dt}$ and **(b)** the value of t for which $\dfrac{ds}{dt} = 24$.

3. If $v = (3t^2 - 2t + 1)^2$, find the value of $\dfrac{dv}{dt}$ when $t = -1$.

4. Given that $A = \dfrac{t^2}{2} - \dfrac{(1-t)^3}{5}$, find $\dfrac{dA}{dt}$ and simplify the result. Hence find the value of t for which $\dfrac{dA}{dt} = 1$.

5. If $s = \dfrac{3}{4-2r}$, find $\dfrac{ds}{dr}$ and the values of s when $\dfrac{ds}{dr} = \dfrac{1}{6}$.

6. The equation of a curve is $y = 2x - \dfrac{4}{x+1}$. Find **(a)** $\dfrac{dy}{dx}$ and **(b)** the gradient of the curve when $x = -3$.

7. Find the gradient of the curve $y = \dfrac{3}{x^2 - 2x + 1}$ where $x = 2$.

8. If $y = \dfrac{1}{x+1}$, find the coordinates of the points where the gradient is $-\dfrac{1}{4}$.

9. If $y = \dfrac{1}{(x-3)^2}$, find the coordinates of the point where the gradient $= 2$.

10. Given that $v = \dfrac{3}{1-4t}$, find (a) $\dfrac{dv}{dt}$, (b) the values of t when $\dfrac{dv}{dt} = 3$.

11. If $y = 3t + 1 + \dfrac{1}{1+2t}$, find (a) $\dfrac{dy}{dt}$ and (b) the values of t when $\dfrac{dy}{dt} = 2\dfrac{1}{2}$.

12. When $x = 1$, the gradient of the curve $y = \dfrac{1}{3+ax}$ is 2. Find the values of a.

13. Given that $L = \dfrac{1}{a+bx}$ and that $L = 1$ and $\dfrac{dL}{dx} = 3$ when $x = 1$, find the values of a and b.

14. The curve $y = \dfrac{1}{a+bx}$ passes through the point $(1, -1)$ and its gradient at that point is 2. Find the values of a and b.

15.6 The Second Differential Coefficient $\dfrac{d^2y}{dx^2}$

If y is a function of x, then $\dfrac{dy}{dx}$ is also a function of x (or a constant).

Hence we can differentiate $\dfrac{dy}{dx}$ wrt x. This gives the **second differential coefficient** $\dfrac{d\left(\frac{dy}{dx}\right)}{dx}$ which is written as $\dfrac{d^2y}{dx^2}$ (read 'dee two y by dee x two') for brevity. The 2's are not squares but symbolise differentiating twice.

The square of $\dfrac{dy}{dx}$ is written as $\left(\dfrac{dy}{dx}\right)^2$.

$\dfrac{d^2y}{dx^2}$ is sometimes also written as $f''(x)$ where $y = f(x)$.

▶ **Example 8**

Find $\dfrac{d^2y}{dx^2}$ and $\left(\dfrac{dy}{dx}\right)^2$ if

(a) $y = 2x^3 - 3x^2 + 1$, (b) $y = (4x - 1)^3$, (c) $y = \dfrac{1}{2-3x}$.

▶ **Solution . . .**

(a) $\dfrac{dy}{dx} = 6x^2 - 6x$

$\dfrac{d^2y}{dx^2} = 12x - 6$

$\left(\dfrac{dy}{dx}\right)^2 = (6x^2 - 6x)^2$ $\left(\text{which is quite different from } \dfrac{d^2y}{dx^2}\right)$

(b) $\dfrac{dy}{dx} = 3(4x - 1)^2 \times 4 = 12(4x - 1)^2$

$\dfrac{d^2y}{dx^2} = 24(4x - 1) \times 4 = 96(4x - 1)$

$\left(\dfrac{dy}{dx}\right)^2 = 144(4x - 1)^4.$

(c) $y = (2 - 3x)^{-1}$

$\dfrac{dy}{dx} = (-1)(2 - 3x)^{-2} \times (-3) = 3(2 - 3x)^{-2}$

$\dfrac{d^2y}{dx^2} = 3(-2)(2 - 3x)^{-3} \times (-3) = 18(2 - 3x)^{-3}$

$\left(\dfrac{dy}{dx}\right)^2 = \dfrac{9}{(2 - 3x)^4}$

As we shall see, $\dfrac{d^2y}{dx^2}$ has important applications. It is also possible to find further derivatives, such as $\dfrac{d^3y}{dx^3}$, etc. but we shall not use these.

Exercise 15C (Answers on page 506)

1. Find $\dfrac{dy}{dx}$ and $\dfrac{d^2y}{dx^2}$ for the following:

   (a) $4x^3 - 5x^2 + 8$ **(b)** $(2x - 7)^3$ **(c)** $(1 - 4x)^4$

   (d) $\dfrac{1}{x}$ **(e)** $x^2 - \dfrac{1}{x}$ **(f)** $\dfrac{3}{2 - x}$

   (g) $x^4 - x^2 - \dfrac{1}{x^2}$

2. If $s = 3t^2 - \dfrac{2}{t^2}$, find $\dfrac{ds}{dt}$ and $\dfrac{d^2s}{dt^2}$.

3. If $y = (ax + 2)^2$ and $\dfrac{d^2y}{dx^2} = 18$, find the values of a.

4. $y = ax^3 + bx$. Given that $\dfrac{dy}{dx} = -1\dfrac{1}{4}$ and that $\dfrac{d^2y}{dx^2} = 3$ when $x = \dfrac{1}{2}$, find the values of a and b.

5. For the function $y = (ax + b)^2$, $\dfrac{dy}{dx} = -6$ when $x = \dfrac{1}{3}$ and $\dfrac{d^2y}{dx^2} = 18$. Find the values of a and b.

6. If the gradient of the curve $y = 2x^3 + \mu x^2 - 5$ is -2 when $x = 1$, find the value of μ and the value of $\dfrac{d^2y}{dx^2}$ at that point.

7. If $y = \dfrac{1}{2-x}$, find $(\dfrac{dy}{dx})^2$ and $\dfrac{d^2y}{dx^2}$. Show that $y\dfrac{d^2y}{dx^2} = 2(\dfrac{dy}{dt})^2$.

8. If $s = 3t^3 - 30t^2 + 36t + 2$, find the values of t for which $\dfrac{ds}{dt} = 0$ and the value of t for which $\dfrac{d^2s}{dt^2} = 0$.

9. If $y = 2x^3 - 4x^2 + 9x - 5$, what is the range of values of x for which $\dfrac{d^2y}{dx^2} \geq 0$?

15.7 Differentiation of the Product of Two Functions

$y = (3x - 1)^3(x^2 + 5)^2$ is a product of two functions of x: $(3x - 1)^3$ and $(x^2 + 5)^2$. Each of these can be differentiated but how can we find $\dfrac{dy}{dx}$? As we shall see, the result is NOT the product of their derivatives.

Let $y = uv$ where u and v are each functions of x.

Suppose x has an increment δx. This will produce increments δu in u and δv in v, and finally produce an increment δy in y.

So $y + \delta y = (u + \delta u)(v + \delta v) = uv + u\delta v + v\delta u + (\delta u)(\delta v)$.

Then $\delta y = u\delta v + v\delta u + (\delta u)(\delta v)$

and $\dfrac{\delta y}{\delta x} = u\dfrac{\delta v}{\delta x} + v\dfrac{\delta u}{\delta x} + \dfrac{\delta u}{\delta x}\delta v$.

Now let $\delta x \longrightarrow 0$. Consequently $\delta u \longrightarrow 0$, $\delta v \longrightarrow 0$, $\dfrac{\delta u}{\delta x} \longrightarrow \dfrac{du}{dx}$,

$\dfrac{\delta v}{\delta x} \longrightarrow \dfrac{dv}{dx}$ and $\dfrac{\delta y}{\delta x} \longrightarrow \dfrac{dy}{dx}$.

So, as $\delta x \longrightarrow 0$, $\dfrac{dy}{dx} \longrightarrow u\dfrac{dv}{dx} + v\dfrac{du}{dx}$.

Hence we have the **product rule** for $y = uv$:

$$\dfrac{dy}{dx} = u\dfrac{dv}{dx} + v\dfrac{du}{dx}$$

where u and v are functions of x.

As the result is symmetrical in u and v, it does not matter which function is chosen as u or v.

▶ **Example 9**

Differentiate $(3x - 2)(x^3 + 4)$ wrt x.

▶ **Solution . . .**

Take $u = 3x - 2$, $v = x^3 + 4$.

$\dfrac{du}{dx} = 3$, $\dfrac{dv}{dx} = 3x^2$

Then $\dfrac{dy}{dx} = u\dfrac{dv}{dx} + v\dfrac{du}{dx}$

$\qquad = (3x - 2) \times 3x^2 + (x^3 + 4) \times 3$

$\qquad = 9x^3 - 6x^2 + 3x^3 + 12$

$\qquad = 12x^3 - 6x^2 + 12$

▶ Example 10

Differentiate $x^3(2x - 1)^4$ wrt x.

▶ Solution . . .

Take $u = x^3$, $v = (2x - 1)^4$.

$\dfrac{dy}{dx} = x^3 \times 4(2x - 1)^3 \times 2 + (2x - 1)^4 \times 3x^2$

$\qquad\quad\; u \qquad\quad \dfrac{dv}{dx} \qquad\quad v \qquad\quad \dfrac{du}{dx}$

In this example, we simplify as far as possible and leave the result in factor form.

$\dfrac{dy}{dx} = x^2(2x - 1)^3[x \times 8 + (2x - 1)3]$

$\qquad = x^2(2x - 1)^3(14x - 3)$

▶ Example 11

Differentiate $(3x - 1)^3(x^2 + 5)^2$ wrt x.

▶ Solution . . .

$\dfrac{dy}{dx} = (3x - 1)^3 \times 2(x^2 + 5) \times 2x + (x^2 + 5)^2 \times 3(3x - 1)^2 \times 3$

$\qquad = (3x - 1)^2(x^2 + 5)[(3x - 1) \times 4x + (x^2 + 5) \times 9]$

$\qquad = (3x - 1)^2(x^2 + 5)(12x^2 - 4x + 9x^2 + 45)$

$\qquad = (3x - 1)^2(x^2 + 5)(21x^2 - 4x + 45)$

Exercise 15D (Answers on page 506)

1. Differentiate each of the following products wrt x. Leave the answers in simplified factor form.

(a) $x(x - 2)^2$
(b) $x^2(x^2 - 1)$
(c) $(x^2 + 1)(x^3 - 1)$
(d) $(x + 1)^2(x - 2)^3$
(e) $x^5(1 - 2x)^2$
(f) $(1 - x)^2(3 - x)^3$
(g) $x^2(x^2 - x - 1)^3$
(h) $x^2(x^2 - 3)^3$
(i) $(3x - 2)^2(2x^2 - 1)$
(j) $(x^2 + 1)^2(2x - 1)^3$
(k) $\sqrt{x}\,(x^3 - 1)^2$
(l) $x(\sqrt{x} - 1)^2$
(m) $2x(1 - 2x)^3$
(n) $\sqrt{x - 1}\,(x + 1)^4$
(o) $(x^2 - x - 2)(x + 1)^3$
(p) $(3x - 1)^2(2x + 3)^3$

2. Find the gradient of the tangent to the curve $y = (x + 1)(x - 2)^3$ at the point where $x = 1$.

3. Given that $y = ax^2(x - 1)^3$ and that $\dfrac{dy}{dx} = 32$ when $x = 2$, find the value of a.

4. Find $\dfrac{dy}{dx}$ and $\dfrac{d^2y}{dx^2}$ if $y = x(x + 1)^3$.

5. Find $\dfrac{dy}{dx}$ and $\dfrac{d^2y}{dx^2}$ if $y = x(2x - 1)^4$.

6. For what values of x does the curve $y = x^2(x - 1)^3$ have zero gradient?

7. f, g and h are three functions of x. By taking f as u and gh as v, show that $\dfrac{d(fgh)}{dx} = gh\dfrac{df}{dx} + f\dfrac{d(gh)}{dx}$ and deduce that $\dfrac{d(fgh)}{dx} = gh\dfrac{df}{dx} + fh\dfrac{dg}{dx} + fg\dfrac{dh}{dx}$.

Hence differentiate $x(x + 1)^2(x + 2)^3$ wrt x.

15.8 Differentiation of the Quotient of Two Functions

We can also find a formula for differentiating a quotient of two functions, such as $\dfrac{x+1}{x-1}$.

Suppose $y = \dfrac{u}{v}$ where u and v are functions of x.

Let x have an increment δx. Then u and v will have increments δu and δv respectively, and y will have an increment δy.

Now $y + \delta y = \dfrac{u + \delta u}{v + \delta v}$ and therefore

$$\delta y = \frac{u + \delta u}{v + \delta v} - \frac{u}{v} = \frac{uv + v\delta u - uv - u\delta v}{v(v + \delta v)} = \frac{v\delta u - u\delta v}{v(v + \delta v)}$$

Then $\dfrac{\delta y}{\delta x} = \dfrac{v\frac{\delta u}{\delta x} - u\frac{\delta v}{\delta x}}{v(v + \delta v)}$

Now let $\delta x \longrightarrow 0$. Then $\delta u \longrightarrow 0$, $\delta v \longrightarrow 0$, $\dfrac{\delta u}{\delta x} \longrightarrow \dfrac{du}{dx}$, $\dfrac{\delta v}{\delta x} \longrightarrow \dfrac{dv}{dx}$ and $\dfrac{\delta y}{\delta x} \longrightarrow \dfrac{dy}{dx}$.

So we obtain the **quotient formula** for the differentiation of $y = \dfrac{u}{v}$:

$$\frac{dy}{dx} = \frac{v\frac{du}{dx} - u\frac{dv}{dx}}{v^2}$$

This formula is not symmetrical in u and v so it is important to get the terms in the right order. An informal way of remembering this formula is *'bottom dee top minus top dee bottom all over bottom squared'* where 'top' = u, 'bottom' = v.

Note:

The quotient formula can also be derived using the product formula as follows:

Suppose $y = \dfrac{u}{v}$, which can be written as $y = uv^{-1}$.

Using the product formula,

$$\frac{dy}{dx} = u\frac{dv^{-1}}{dx} + v^{-1}\frac{du}{dx}$$

$$= u(-v^{-2}\frac{dv}{dx}) + v^{-1}\frac{du}{dx}$$

$$= \frac{-u}{v^2}\frac{dv}{dx} + \frac{1}{v}\frac{du}{dx}$$

$$= \frac{-u}{v^2}\frac{dv}{dx} + \frac{v}{v^2}\frac{du}{dx}$$

$$= \frac{v\frac{du}{dx} - u\frac{dv}{dx}}{v^2}$$

Note:

It is unnecessary to use this formula for functions with a constant numerator such as $\dfrac{k}{\sqrt{x-2}}$ (take as $k(x-2)^{-\frac{1}{2}}$) or functions with a single term denominator such as $\dfrac{x-2x^3}{x^2}$ (divide first).

▶ **Example 12**

Differentiate **(a)** $\dfrac{x-1}{x+1}$, **(b)** $\dfrac{x^2+1}{x^2-x-1}$, **(c)** $\dfrac{x}{\sqrt{x+1}}$ wrt x.

▶ **Solution . . .**

(a) Here $u = x-1$, $v = x+1$, $\dfrac{du}{dx} = 1$, $\dfrac{dv}{dx} = 1$

$$\frac{dy}{dx} = \frac{(x+1)(1)-(x-1)(1)}{(x+1)^2} = \frac{2}{(x+1)^2}$$

(b) $u = x^2 + 1$, $v = x^2 - x - 1$, $\dfrac{du}{dx} = 2x$, $\dfrac{dv}{dx} = 2x - 1$

$$\frac{dy}{dx} = \frac{(x^2-x-1)(2x)-(x^2+1)(2x-1)}{(x^2-x-1)^2}$$

$$= \frac{2x^3-2x^2-2x-2x^3-2x+x^2+1}{(x^2-x-1)^2} = \frac{-x^2-4x+1}{(x^2-x-1)^2}$$

(c) $u = x$, $v = (x+1)^{\frac{1}{2}}$, $\dfrac{du}{dx} = 1$, $\dfrac{dv}{dx} = \dfrac{1}{2}(x+1)^{-\frac{1}{2}}$

$$\frac{dy}{dx} = \frac{(x+1)^{\frac{1}{2}}(1) - x\frac{1}{2}(x+1)^{-\frac{1}{2}}}{[(x+1)^{\frac{1}{2}}]^2} = \frac{(x+1)^{\frac{1}{2}} - \frac{x}{2}(x+1)^{-\frac{1}{2}}}{x+1}$$

To simplify this, multiply the numerator and denominator by $2(x+1)^{\frac{1}{2}}$.

$$\frac{dy}{dx} = \frac{2(x+1)-x}{2(x+1)(x+1)^{\frac{1}{2}}} = \frac{x+2}{2(x+1)^{\frac{3}{2}}}$$

▶ **Example 13**

If $y = \dfrac{x}{3x+2}$, show that $\dfrac{dy}{dx} = \dfrac{2}{(3x+2)^2}$ and find $\dfrac{d^2y}{dx^2}$.

▶ **Solution . . .**

$$\frac{dy}{dx} = \frac{(3x+2)(1)-x(3)}{(3x+2)^2} = \frac{2}{(3x+2)^2}$$

To find $\dfrac{d^2y}{dx^2}$ we rewrite $\dfrac{dy}{dx}$ as $2(3x+2)^{-2}$ which is a composite function.

$$\therefore \frac{d^2y}{dx^2} = 2(-2)(3x+2)^{-3} \times 3$$

Exercise 15E *(Answers on page 507)*

1. Differentiate the following wrt x, simplifying where possible:

   (a) $\dfrac{x}{x+2}$ (b) $\dfrac{x+1}{x+2}$ (c) $\dfrac{x-1}{2x+1}$

   (d) $\dfrac{3x-2}{x^2+1}$ (e) $\dfrac{x^2+2}{x-1}$ (f) $\dfrac{x^2+x-1}{1-x}$

   (g) $\dfrac{x}{\sqrt{x-2}}$ (h) $\dfrac{2x}{\sqrt{2x+1}}$ (i) $\dfrac{x^3}{x^2+1}$

   (j) $\dfrac{x}{\sqrt{x^2-2}}$ (k) $\dfrac{x^2}{3x+1}$ (l) $\dfrac{x-1}{2-x}$

   (m) $\dfrac{3x-4}{x^2+1}$ (n) $\dfrac{x+1}{x^2+1}$

2. If $y = \dfrac{x}{x+1}$, find $\dfrac{dy}{dx}$ and $\dfrac{d^2y}{dx^2}$. Hence show that

   $(1+x)\dfrac{d^2y}{dx^2} + 2\dfrac{dy}{dx} = 0$.

3. If $y = \dfrac{x}{2x-1}$, show that $\dfrac{dy}{dx} = \dfrac{-1}{(2x-1)^2}$ and find $\dfrac{d^2y}{dx^2}$.

4. Given that $y = \dfrac{x}{2x+3}$, find $\dfrac{dy}{dx}$ and $\dfrac{d^2y}{dx^2}$.

5. If $y = \dfrac{x}{\sqrt{x^2+3}}$, find $\dfrac{dy}{dx}$ and $\dfrac{d^2y}{dx^2}$.

6. If $y = \sqrt{\dfrac{x}{x+1}}$, find $\dfrac{dy}{dx}$ and $\dfrac{d^2y}{dx^2}$.

7. Find $\dfrac{dy}{dx}$ if $y = \sqrt{\dfrac{x+1}{x-1}}$.

8. The equation of a curve is $y = \dfrac{x^2}{x-2}$. Find the values of x for which $\dfrac{dy}{dx} = 0$.

9. Given that $y = \dfrac{x+a}{x+2}$ and that $\dfrac{dy}{dx} = -\dfrac{1}{25}$ when $x = 3$, find the value of a.

10. If $y = \dfrac{x}{\sqrt{x^2+x+1}}$, find $\dfrac{dy}{dx}$.
    Hence find the x-coordinate of the point on the curve where $\dfrac{dy}{dx} = 0$.

Summary

1. If $y = f(x)$ then $\dfrac{dy}{dx} = f'(x)$ is the gradient function. The value of $f'(x)$ is the gradient at a given point.

2. $\dfrac{dy}{dx}$ is the derivative or differential coefficient of y wrt x. It measures the rate of change of y wrt x.

3. If $y = ax^n$, $\dfrac{dy}{dx} = nax^{n-1}$; if $y = k$ (a constant), $\dfrac{dy}{dx} = 0$.

4. The derivative of a sum of terms is the sum of the derivatives of the separate terms.

5. If $y = f(u)$ where u is a function of x, $\dfrac{dy}{dx} = \dfrac{dy}{du} \times \dfrac{du}{dx}$.

6. $\dfrac{d(\frac{dy}{dx})}{dx}$ is the second differential coefficient of y wrt x, written as $\dfrac{d^2y}{dx^2}$ or as $f''(x)$ if $y = f(x)$.

7. **Product rule:** If $y = uv$, $\dfrac{dy}{dx} = v\dfrac{du}{dx} + u\dfrac{dv}{dx}$.

8. **Quotient rule:** If $y = \dfrac{u}{v}$, $\dfrac{dy}{dx} = \dfrac{v\frac{du}{dx} - u\frac{dv}{dx}}{v^2}$

Revision Exercise 15 (Answers on page 507)

1. Differentiate the following wrt x:
   (a) $(x-5)^3$
   (b) $(1-2x)^5$
   (c) $\dfrac{2}{1-4x}$
   (d) $(2x^2-1)^3$
   (e) $(1-3x-2x^2)^3$
   (f) $\dfrac{1}{x(1-x)}$
   (g) $(2x - \dfrac{1}{x})^3$
   (h) $\dfrac{x^3 - 2x^2 + 1}{2x^2}$
   (i) $\dfrac{(x-1)(x+4)}{x}$
   (j) $\dfrac{1-3x}{2} - \dfrac{2}{1-3x}$

2. If $y = x^3 - 3x^2 + 7$, for what range of values of x is $\dfrac{dy}{dx} \le 0$?

3. Find the gradient of the curve $y = 5 + 2x - 3x^2$ at each of the points where it meets the x-axis.

4. Differentiate wrt x
   (a) $(x-1)^3(3-2x)^2$,   (b) $\dfrac{\sqrt{x}}{1+x}$.

5. Given that $s = 3t^2 - 4t + 1$, find the rate of change of s wrt t when $s = 5$.

6. If $y = 4x - \dfrac{1}{1-2x}$, find $\dfrac{dy}{dx}$ and $\dfrac{d^2y}{dx^2}$.

7. For the function $y = 2x^3 - 4x$, find $\dfrac{dy}{dx}$ and $\dfrac{d^2y}{dx^2}$.
   Hence find the value of $\dfrac{\frac{dy}{dx}}{\sqrt{1 + \frac{d^2y}{dx^2}}}$ when $x = 2$.

8. If $A = \dfrac{1}{1+\mu r}$ where μ is a constant > 0 and the rate of change of A wrt r is $-\dfrac{5}{9}$ when $r = 0.4$, find the value of μ.

9. The tangent at the point (a,b) on the curve $y = 1 - x - 2x^2$ has a gradient of 7. Find the values of a and b.

10. The curve $y = \dfrac{a}{x} + bx$ (a, b are constants) passes through the points A$(1,-1)$ and B$(4,-11\frac{1}{2})$.
   (a) Find the value of a and of b.
   (b) Show that the tangent to the curve at the point where $x = -2$ is parallel to AB.

11. If $y = (x + 2)\sqrt{1-x}$, find $\dfrac{dy}{dx}$ and $\dfrac{d^2y}{dx^2}$.
   Find also the coordinates of the point on the curve where the tangent is parallel to the x-axis.

12. The line $y = x + 1$ meets the curve $y = x^2 - x - 2$ at the points A and B. Find the gradients of the tangents to the curve at these points.

13. If $p = 2s^3 - s^2 - 28s$, find the values of s which make $\dfrac{dp}{ds} = 0$ and for these values of s, find the value of $\dfrac{d^2p}{ds^2}$.

14. The gradient of the curve $y = ax^2 + bx + 2$ at the point $(2,12)$ is 11. Find the values of a and b.

15. If $y = x^3 + 3x^2 - 9x + 2$, for what range of values of x is $\dfrac{dy}{dx}$ negative?

16. Given that $y = (x + 2)^2 - (x - 2)^3$, find the range of values of x for which $\dfrac{dy}{dx} \geq 0$.

17. If $y = \dfrac{A}{x} + Bx$, where A and B are constants, show that
   $$x^2\frac{d^2y}{dx^2} + x\frac{dy}{dx} = y.$$

18. If $y = \dfrac{x}{2x+1}$, find the value of $\dfrac{\frac{d^2y}{dx^2}}{[1+(\frac{dy}{dx})^2]^{\frac{3}{2}}}$ when $x = 0$.

Maths Booster

Can you find a function whose gradient function is same as the function itself? [You can do some research in your school library and learn more about it.]

Chapter 16

Applications of Differentiation

Suppose you have 400 m of fencing material and wish to use it to form 3 sides of a rectangular plot of land along the side of a canal which makes up the fourth side of the rectangular enclosure.

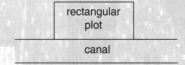

Discuss how you would ensure that the area of the plot is as large as possible.

Later in this chapter, you will learn a convenient method which can be employed to solve the above problem.

16.1 Tangents and Normals

As we have seen, if $y = f(x)$ is the equation of a curve, then $\dfrac{dy}{dx}$ gives the gradient of the tangent at any point (Fig. 16.1). The gradient of the tangent at $P(x_1, y_1)$ is the value of $\dfrac{dy}{dx}$ when $x = x_1$. If we denote this value by m_1, then the equation of the tangent is $y - y_1 = m_1(x - x_1)$.

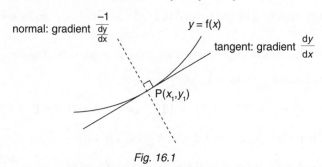

normal: gradient $\dfrac{-1}{\frac{dy}{dx}}$

$y = f(x)$

tangent: gradient $\dfrac{dy}{dx}$

$P(x_1, y_1)$

Fig. 16.1

Associated with the tangent is the **normal**, which is perpendicular to the tangent. The gradient of the tangent is $\dfrac{dy}{dx}$, so the gradient of the normal is $-\dfrac{1}{\frac{dy}{dx}}$. If we denote the value of $-\dfrac{1}{\frac{dy}{dx}}$ at $P(x_1, y_1)$ by m_2, then the equation of the normal is $y - y_1 = m_2(x - x_1)$.

▶ **Example 1**

Find the equations of the tangent and the normal to the curve $y = x^2 - 2x - 3$ at the point where it meets the positive x-axis.

▶ **Solution . . .**

When $y = 0$, $x^2 - 2x - 3 = (x - 3)(x + 1) = 0$. Hence the curve meets the positive x-axis where $x = 3$.

$\dfrac{dy}{dx} = 2x - 2$ and when $x = 3$, $\dfrac{dy}{dx} = 4$.

We write this briefly as $\left(\dfrac{dy}{dx}\right)_{x=3} = 4$, meaning the *value* of $\dfrac{dy}{dx}$ when $x = 3$.

The equation of the tangent is then $y = 4(x - 3)$, i.e. $y = 4x - 12$.

The gradient of the normal $= -\dfrac{1}{4}$ so the equation of the normal is $y = -\dfrac{1}{4}(x - 3)$, i.e. $4y + x = 3$.

▶ **Example 2**

(a) Find the equation of the normal to the curve $y = x + \dfrac{4}{x}$ at the point P where $x = 4$.

(b) If the normal meets the curve again at N, find the coordinates of N (Fig. 16.2).

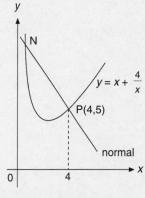

$y = x + \dfrac{4}{x}$

P(4,5)

normal

Fig. 16.2

► **Solution . . .**

(a) The coordinates of P are $\left(4, 4 + \dfrac{4}{4}\right)$, i.e. (4,5).

$\dfrac{dy}{dx} = 1 - \dfrac{4}{x^2}$ so $\left(\dfrac{dy}{dx}\right)_{x=4} = 1 - \dfrac{1}{4} = \dfrac{3}{4}$.

Hence the gradient of the normal $= -\dfrac{4}{3}$.

The equation of the normal is $y - 5 = -\dfrac{4}{3}(x - 4)$, i.e. $3y + 4x = 31$.

(b) To find where the normal meets the curve, we solve the simultaneous

equations $3y + 4x = 31$ and $y = x + \dfrac{4}{x}$.

$x + \dfrac{4}{x} = \dfrac{31 - 4x}{3}$, i.e. $3x^2 + 12 = 31x - 4x^2$ or $7x^2 - 31x + 12 = 0$.

Then $(7x - 3)(x - 4) = 0$ which gives $x = 4$ or $\dfrac{3}{7}$.

$x = 4$ is the point P so the coordinates of N are $\left(\dfrac{3}{7}, \dfrac{3}{7} + \dfrac{4}{\frac{3}{7}}\right)$,

i.e. $\left(\dfrac{3}{7}, \dfrac{205}{21}\right)$.

► **Example 3**

(a) Find the x-coordinate of the point(s) on the curve $y = 2x^3 + x^2 - 2x + 1$ where the tangent(s) to the curve is (are) parallel to the line $y = 2x$.

(b) Is there any part of the curve where the tangent is parallel to the line $y + 3x = 1$?

► **Solution . . .**

(a) $\dfrac{dy}{dx} = 6x^2 + 2x - 2$ and this must equal 2 (the gradient of $y = 2x$).

Then $6x^2 + 2x - 2 = 2$ which gives $3x^2 + x - 2 = 0$ or $(3x - 2)(x + 1) = 0$.

Hence $x = \dfrac{2}{3}$ or $- 1$.

At these points the tangents to the curve are parallel to $y = 2x$.

(b) If $\dfrac{dy}{dx} = 6x^2 + 2x - 2 = -3$ (the gradient of $y + 3x = 1$), then

$6x^2 + 2x + 1 = 0$. But this equation has no real solutions. Hence the gradient of the curve is never equal to -3 and there is no part of the curve where the tangent is parallel to $y + 3x = 1$.

Exercise 16A *(Answers on page 507)*

1. Find the equations of the tangent and the normal to the following curves at the given point:

    (a) $y = x^2 - 2$; $x = -3$ **(b)** $y = 2x^3$; $x = 1$

    (c) $y = 1 - x - 3x^2$; $x = -1$ **(d)** $y = 2x^3 - x - 1$; $x = -1$

    (e) $y = \dfrac{4}{x}$; $x = -2$ **(f)** $y = \dfrac{3}{x+1}$; $y = 1$

    (g) $y = \dfrac{1}{1 - 2x}$; $y = -1$ **(h)** $y = 2x + \dfrac{4}{x}$; $x = -2$

(i) $y = 2x^2 - 3;\ x = 2$ **(j)** $y = 1 - x - 3x^2 - x^3;\ x = -1$

(k) $y = 3 - \dfrac{2}{x};\ y = 7$ **(l)** $y = \dfrac{2}{1 - 2x};\ y = 1$

2. The tangent to the curve $y = x^2 - 2x + 3$ at a certain point is parallel to the line $y = x$. Find the equation of the tangent and the coordinates of the point where it meets the x-axis.

3. Find **(a)** the coordinates of the point on the curve $y = 3x^2 + 2x + 1$ where the tangent is parallel to the line $4x + y = 5$, and **(b)** the equation of the normal at that point.

4. **(a)** Find the equation of the tangent to the curve $y = x^3 - 2x^2 + x$ at the origin.

     (b) At what point does it meet the curve again?

5. The normal to the curve $y = 2x - \dfrac{1}{1 - x}$ where $x = 2$, meets the curve again at the point P. Find

     (a) the equation of the normal,

     (b) the coordinates of P,

     (c) the equation of the tangent at P.

6. The normal to the curve $y = 2x - \dfrac{1}{x + 1}$ at the point where $x = 1$ meets the curve again at a second point. Find the x-coordinate of this point.

7. A and B are points on the curve $y = 2x - \dfrac{6}{x}$ whose x-coordinates are 1 and 3 respectively. Find the equations of the tangents at A and B and the coordinates of the point where they intersect.

8. **(a)** The normal at the point A(−1,2) on the curve $y = 3 - x^2$ meets the curve again at B. Find **(i)** the equation of the normal at A and **(ii)** the coordinates of B.

     (b) Find the coordinates of the point C on the curve where the curve is parallel to the normal at A.

16.2   Stationary Points: Maxima and Minima

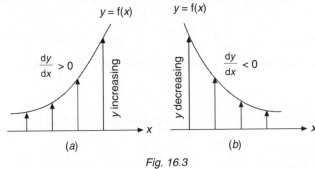

Fig. 16.3

In Fig. 16.3(a), on any stretch of the curve $y = f(x)$ where $\dfrac{dy}{dx} > 0$, the curve slopes upwards. Hence y increases as x increases.

Similarly if $\dfrac{dy}{dx} < 0$ (Fig. 16.3(b)), y decreases as x increases.

At any point where $\dfrac{dy}{dx} = 0$, f(x) has a **stationary** value and is neither increasing nor decreasing. Such a point is a **stationary** point.

There are three types of stationary points: **maximum**, **minimum** and **point of inflexion** (Fig. 16.4).

Maximum and minimum points are also called **turning points** as the tangent 'turns round' at these points.

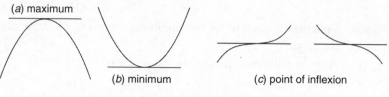

(*a*) maximum   (*b*) minimum   (*c*) point of inflexion

Fig. 16.4

The essential condition for a stationary point is $\dfrac{dy}{dx} = 0$.

If this equation has solutions, they are the x-coordinates of the stationary points. We then test for the type of points. A curve may have one or more, or none of these points.

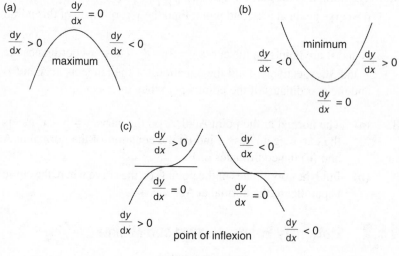

Fig. 16.5

Maximum point

$\dfrac{dy}{dx}$ passes from positive values through 0 to negative values (Fig. 16.5(a)).

Minimum point

$\dfrac{dy}{dx}$ passes from negative values through 0 to positive values (Fig. 16.5(b)).

Point of inflexion

$\dfrac{dy}{dx}$ has the same sign on each side of the zero value (Fig. 16.5(c)).

Note that maximum and minimum apply only in the neighbourhood of the stationary point. The values of the function at this point are not necessarily the greatest and least values of the function overall.

16.2.1   *Stationary Point for a Quadratic Function*

We have already seen that the quadratic function $y = ax^2 + bx + c$ *always* has either a maximum (when $a < 0$) or a minimum point ($a > 0$).

As $\dfrac{dy}{dx} = 2ax + b$, this equation always has a solution.

▶ **Example 4**

Which type of stationary point does $y = 1 - 2x - 2x^2$ have and what is the value of y at that point? Illustrate with a sketch.

▶ **Solution . . .**

As $a = -2 < 0$, the curve has a maximum point.

$\dfrac{dy}{dx} = -2 - 4x$ and $\dfrac{dy}{dx} = 0$ gives $x = -\dfrac{1}{2}$.

So the curve has a maximum point at $\left(-\dfrac{1}{2}, 1\dfrac{1}{2}\right)$ (Fig. 16.6)

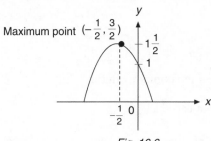

Fig. 16.6

16.2.2   *The Sign Test for Stationary Points*

To determine the nature of a stationary point on a curve means to decide if a stationary point is a maximum point, a minimum point or a point of inflexion. Unlike the case of a quadratic function, we do not know the nature of the stationary point by examining the equation of the curve. A simple test to decide on the nature of a stationary point is to examine the **sign** of $\dfrac{dy}{dx}$ on each side of that point. This is called the 'sign test'. The following examples illustrate the use of this test.

▶ **Example 5**

Find the nature of the stationary points on the curve $y = 4x^3 - 3x^2 - 6x + 2$.

▶ **Solution . . .**

$\dfrac{dy}{dx} = 12x^2 - 6x - 6 = 6(2x^2 - x - 1) = 6(2x + 1)(x - 1)$

$\dfrac{dy}{dx} = 0$ when $x = -\dfrac{1}{2}$ or 1.

First consider $x = -\frac{1}{2}$.

We examine the sign of $\frac{dy}{dx}$ when x is slightly less than $-\frac{1}{2}$ (denoted by $-\frac{1}{2}^-$) and the sign of $\frac{dy}{dx}$ when x is slightly more than $-\frac{1}{2}$ (denoted by $-\frac{1}{2}^+$).

Since $\frac{dy}{dx} = 6(2x + 1)(x - 1)$, we can obtain the sign of $\frac{dy}{dx}$ by noting the signs of the factors $(2x + 1)$ and $(x - 1)$.

x	$-\frac{1}{2}^-$	$-\frac{1}{2}$	$-\frac{1}{2}^+$
sign of $\frac{dy}{dx}$ = sign of $(2x + 1)(x - 1)$	$(-)(-) = +$	0	$(+)(-) = -$
sketch of tangent	/	—	\

The sketch of the curve around $x = -\frac{1}{2}$ is $\frown$, i.e. there is a maximum point at $x = -\frac{1}{2}$.

When $x = -\frac{1}{2}$, $y = 4\left(-\frac{1}{8}\right) - 3\left(\frac{1}{2}\right) - 6\left(-\frac{1}{2}\right) + 2$

$= 3\frac{3}{4}$ (a maximum value),

and the maximum point is $\left(-\frac{1}{2}, 3\frac{3}{4}\right)$.

Now consider the other value, $x = 1$, and examine the sign of $\frac{dy}{dx}$ when x is slightly less than 1 and when x is slightly more than 1.

x	1^-	1	1^+
sign of $\frac{dy}{dx}$ = sign of $(2x + 1)(x - 1)$	$(+)(-) = -$	0	$(-)(-) = +$
sketch of tangent	\	—	/

The sketch of the curve around $x = 1$ is $\smile$, i.e. there is a minimum point at $x = 1$.

When $x = 1$, $y = -3$ (a minimum value) and the minimum point is $(1, -3)$.

▶ **Example 6**

What type of stationary point(s) does the curve $y = x^3 - 3x^2 + 3x - 1$ have?

▶ **Solution . . .**

$$\frac{dy}{dx} = 3x^2 - 6x + 3 = 3(x^2 - 2x + 1) = 3(x-1)^2$$

$\frac{dy}{dx} = 0$ gives $x = 1$. There is only one stationary point on the curve.

x	1^-	1	1^+
sign of $\frac{dy}{dx}$ = sign of $(x-1)^2$	+	0	+
sketch of tangent	/	—	/

The sketch of the curve is $\smile$, so the stationary point is a point of inflexion.

When $x = 1$, $y = 0$. Hence the point of inflexion is $(1, 0)$.

▶ **Example 7**

Examine the nature of the stationary point(s) on the curve $y = x^3 - x^2 + 5x - 1$.

▶ **Solution . . .**

$\frac{dy}{dx} = 3x^2 - 2x + 5$. For stationary points, $3x^2 - 2x + 5 = 0$. This equation has no solutions, so the curve has no stationary points.

16.2.3   The $\frac{d^2y}{dx^2}$ Test for Maxima and Minima

The sign test is adequate for simple functions but $\frac{d^2y}{dx^2}$ can also be used to test for maxima and minima.

Around a maximum point, $\frac{dy}{dx}$ passes from positive to negative so it is a *decreasing* function (Fig. 16.7). Hence the gradient of $\frac{dy}{dx}$, i.e. $\frac{d^2y}{dx^2}$, is negative at that point.

Around a minimum point, $\frac{dy}{dx}$ passes from negative to positive so it is an *increasing* function (Fig. 16.8). Hence the gradient of $\frac{dy}{dx}$, i.e. $\frac{d^2y}{dx^2}$, is positive at that point.

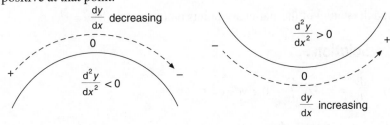

Fig. 16.7   Fig. 16.8

Maximum point:	Minimum point:
$\dfrac{dy}{dx} = 0$ and $\dfrac{d^2y}{dx^2} < 0$	$\dfrac{dy}{dx} = 0$ and $\dfrac{d^2y}{dx^2} > 0$

If $\dfrac{d^2y}{dx^2} = 0$, this test is indecisive. For such cases the sign test should be used (see Example 9).

▶ **Example 8**

Find the types of stationary points on the curve $y = 4x + \dfrac{1}{x}$ and the coordinates of these points.

▶ **Solution . . .**

$\dfrac{dy}{dx} = 4 - \dfrac{1}{x^2}$

If $\dfrac{dy}{dx} = 0$, then $x^2 = \dfrac{1}{4}$ and $x = \pm\dfrac{1}{2}$.

$\dfrac{d^2y}{dx^2} = \dfrac{2}{x^3}$

When $x = +\dfrac{1}{2}$, $\dfrac{d^2y}{dx^2} > 0$ so this is a minimum point at $\left(\dfrac{1}{2}, 4\right)$.

When $x = -\dfrac{1}{2}$, $\dfrac{d^2y}{dx^2} < 0$ so this is a maximum point at $\left(-\dfrac{1}{2}, -4\right)$.

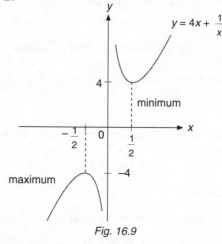

Fig. 16.9

▶ **Example 9**

Find the nature of the stationary points on **(a)** $y = x^3$, **(b)** $y = x^4$.

▶ **Solution . . .**

(a) $\dfrac{dy}{dx} = 3x^2$ so $\dfrac{dy}{dx} = 0$ gives $x = 0$.

$\dfrac{d^2y}{dx^2} = 6x = 0$ when $x = 0$.

x	0^-	0	0^+
sign of $\dfrac{dy}{dx}$ = sign of $3x^2$	+	0	+
sketch of tangent	/	—	/

The sign test shows that this is a point of inflexion at $(0,0)$ (Fig. 16.10(a)).

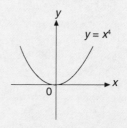

Fig. 16.10(a)

(b) $\dfrac{dy}{dx} = 4x^3$ and again $\dfrac{dy}{dx} = 0$ gives $x = 0$.

$\dfrac{d^2y}{dx^2} = 12x^2 = 0$ when $x = 0$.

x	0^-	0	0^+
sign of $\dfrac{dy}{dx}$ = sign of $4x^3$	–	0	+
sketch of tangent	\	—	/

The sign test shows that this is a minimum point at $(0,0)$ (Fig. 16.10(b)).

Fig. 16.10(b)

Exercise 16B *(Answers on page 507)*

1. For each of the following functions, find **(i)** the x-coordinates and the nature of the stationary points (if any) and **(ii)** the value of the function at these points.

   (a) $7 - 6x - x^2$ **(b)** $x^2 - 3x$

   (c) $x^3 - 3x - 2$ **(d)** $x^5 - 2$

   (e) $2x^3 + 3x^2 - 36x + 4$ **(f)** $2x^3 - x^2 + 1$

   (g) $3x^4 - 4x^3 + 1$ **(h)** $x + \dfrac{25}{x}$

   (i) $3x - \dfrac{1}{x}$ **(j)** $x^3 - 6x^2 + 12x + 2$

   (k) $x^3 + 3x - 2$ **(l)** $x^3 + 3x^2 + 4x + 4$

   (m) $x^2 + \dfrac{16}{x^2}$ **(n)** $3x^2 - 5x - 2$

   (o) x^6 **(p)** $x^3 + x^2 + 1$

   (q) $x^3 - x^2 - 5x - 1$ **(r)** $x^3 + 3x^2 + 3x - 4$

   (s) $x - \dfrac{1}{9x}$ **(t)** $x + \dfrac{1}{x-1}$

   (u) $x^2 + \dfrac{16}{x}$ **(v)** $2x - \dfrac{6}{5-3x}$

2. The function $y = ax^3 - 12x + 2$ has a turning point where $x = 2$. Find **(a)** the value of a, **(b)** the nature of this turning point.

3. The function $y = 2x^3 + ax^2 - 12x - 4$ has a minimum point where $x = 1$. Find **(a)** the value of a, **(b)** the position of the maximum point.

4. The function $y = x^3 + ax^2 - 7x - 1$ has a stationary value where $x = 1$. Find **(a)** the value of a and **(b)** the type and coordinates of the stationary points.

5. Find **(a)** the positions and nature of the stationary points on the curve $y = x^3 - 2x^2 + 1$ and **(b)** the coordinates of the point where the gradient on the curve is a minimum.

6. For what value of t is $s = t^3 - 9t^2 + 15t - 10$
   (a) a maximum,   **(b)** a minimum?
   For what value of t is $\dfrac{ds}{dt}$ a minimum?

7. Given that $v = 1 - t + 2t^2 - t^3$, find the value of t for which $\dfrac{dv}{dt}$ is a maximum and explain why it is a maximum.

8. The function $y = ax^3 + bx^2 - 12x + 13$ passes through the point $(1,0)$ and has a stationary point where $x = -1$. Find
   (a) the value of a and of b,
   (b) the type and the x-coordinates of the stationary points.

9. Find the value of x for which $y = 4x^3 - x^2 - 2x + 1$ has
   (a) a maximum,   **(b)** a minimum value.
   Hence find the values of θ $(0° \le \theta \le 360°)$ for the function $T = 4\cos^3\theta - \cos^2\theta - 2\cos\theta + 1$ at its maximum and minimum values.

10. For the function $A = \pi r^3 - 6r^2 + 3$, find, in terms of π, the values of r at the stationary points, and find out which type each point is.

11. If $y = 4x^3 + 3ax^2 + 48x - 3$, in what interval must a *not* lie if y has stationary points? If $a = 10$, find the x-coordinates and the nature of the stationary points.

12. Find the type and position of the stationary point(s) on the curve $y = \dfrac{1}{x-1} + \dfrac{1}{2-x}$.

16.3   Maximum and Minimum Problems

The methods we have learnt can be used to find the maximum and minimum values of a quantity which varies under certain conditions.

▶ **Example 10**

Two numbers x and y are connected by the relation $x + y = 6$. Find the values of x and y which give a stationary point of the function $T = 2x^2 + 3y^2$ and determine whether they make T a maximum or minimum.

▶ Solution . . .

We must express T in terms of *one* of the variables x or y.

Choosing x, $y = 6 - x$ and $T = 2x^2 + 3(6 - x)^2$.

For a stationary point, we let $\dfrac{dT}{dx} = 0$.

Then $\dfrac{dT}{dx} = 4x - 6(6 - x) = 10x - 36 = 0$ and so $x = 3.6$ and $y = 2.4$.

To decide whether this gives a maximum or minimum, we find $\dfrac{d^2T}{dx^2}$.

$\dfrac{d^2T}{dx^2} = 10$ which is positive.

Hence T will have a minimum value when $x = 3.6$, $y = 2.4$.

▶ Example 11

A cylindrical can (with lid) of radius r cm is made from 300 cm² of thin sheet metal.

(a) Show that its height, h cm, is given by $h = \dfrac{150 - \pi r^2}{\pi r}$.

(b) Find r and h so that the can contains the maximum possible volume. Hence find this volume.

▶ Solution . . .

(a) The surface area A of a cylinder radius r, height h is given by
$A = 2\pi r^2 + 2\pi rh = 300$.

Hence $2\pi rh = 300 - 2\pi r^2$ and $h = \dfrac{150 - \pi r^2}{\pi r}$.

(b) The volume $V = \pi r^2 h$ and V is to be maximized. We must express V in terms of one variable and so we substitute for h from (a).

Then $V = \pi r^2\, \dfrac{150 - \pi r^2}{\pi r} = r(150 - \pi r^2) = 150r - \pi r^3$.

To find the maximum value of V, let $\dfrac{dV}{dr} = 0$.

$\dfrac{dV}{dr} = 150 - 3\pi r^2 = 0$ and so $3\pi r^2 = 150$ giving $r = \sqrt{\dfrac{50}{\pi}} \approx 4$ cm.

Checking that this is a maximum, $\dfrac{d^2V}{dr^2} = -6\pi r$ which is < 0.

From (a), when $r = 4$ cm, $h = \dfrac{150 - 50}{\pi \times 4} \approx 8$ cm.

Hence to obtain the maximum volume, the radius = 4 cm and the height = 8 cm. The maximum volume is then $\pi r^2 h = \pi 4^2 \times 8 = 402$ cm³.

[Note that the height = the diameter. A can of this shape will give maximum volume for a given surface area.]

▶ Example 12

The length of a closed rectangular box is 3 times its width (Fig. 16.11). If its volume is 972 cm³, find the dimensions of the box if the surface area is to be a minimum.

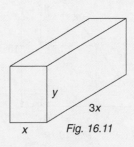

Fig. 16.11

▶ **Solution . . .**

Take the width as x cm, length $3x$ cm and let the height be y cm for the moment.

The volume $V = 3x^2y = 972$, i.e. $x^2y = 324$ ....(1)

The surface area $A = 6x^2 + 6xy + 2xy = 6x^2 + 8xy$ ....(2)

We must now express A in terms of one variable.

From (1), $y = \dfrac{324}{x^2}$

and so $A = 6x^2 + 8x\dfrac{324}{x^2} = 6x^2 + \dfrac{2592}{x}$, and $\dfrac{dA}{dx} = 12x - \dfrac{2592}{x^2}$.

To minimize A, we let $\dfrac{dA}{dx} = 0$.

Then $12x - \dfrac{2592}{x^2} = 0$, giving $12x^3 = 2592$ or $x^3 = 216$. Hence $x = 6$.

To verify that this is a minimum, $\dfrac{d^2A}{dx^2} = 12 + \dfrac{2 \times 2592}{x^3}$ which will be positive.

From (1), when $x = 6$, $y = 324 \div 36 = 9$.

Hence the dimensions are 18 cm by 6 cm by 9 cm for the minimum surface area.

▶ **Example 13**

Triangle ABC is isosceles with AB = AC = 20 cm and BC = 24 cm (Fig. 16.12). A rectangle PQRS is drawn inside the triangle with PQ on BC, and S and R on AB and AC respectively.

(a) If PQ = $2x$ cm, show that the area A cm^2 of the rectangle is given by $A = \dfrac{8x(12 - x)}{3}$.

(b) Hence find the value of x for which A is a maximum.

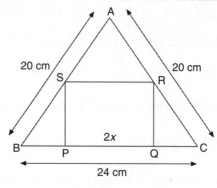

Fig. 16.12

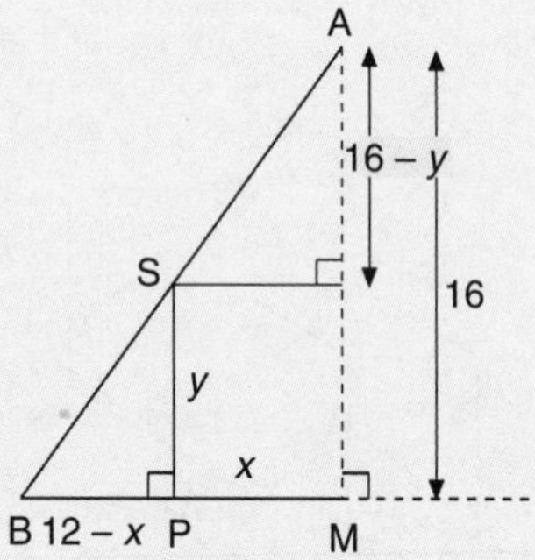

▶ **Solution . . .**

(a) We need to know the height of the rectangle.

Let SP = y cm (Fig. 16.13).

If M is the midpoint of BC, then BM = 12, BP = $12 - x$ and, by Pythagoras' Theorem, AM = 16.

From $\triangle$SBP, $\tan \angle SBP = \dfrac{y}{12 - x}$

and from $\triangle$ABM, $\tan \angle SBP = \dfrac{16}{12} = \dfrac{4}{3}$.

Fig. 16.13

Then $\dfrac{y}{12-x} = \dfrac{4}{3}$ so $y = \dfrac{4(12-x)}{3}$.

Hence $A = 2xy = \dfrac{8x(12-x)}{3}$.

(b) $A = \dfrac{96x - 8x^2}{3} = 32x - \dfrac{8x^2}{3}$ and $\dfrac{\mathrm{d}A}{\mathrm{d}x} = 32 - \dfrac{16x}{3}$.

When $\dfrac{\mathrm{d}A}{\mathrm{d}x} = 0$, $x = 6$.

$\dfrac{\mathrm{d}^2A}{\mathrm{d}x^2} = -\dfrac{16}{3}$ which is negative, thus confirming that this gives a maximum.

Exercise 16C *(Answers on page 507)*

1. Given that $x + y = 8$, find the minimum value of $x + y^2$.

2. Find the minimum value of $x^2 - xy + y^2$ given that $x + y = 10$.

3. x and y are numbers such that $x + y = 4$. Find the minimum value of $x^2 + xy + 2y^2$.

4. Given that $u = 3 + 4t^2 - 2t^3$, find the maximum value of u for the domain $0 \le t \le 2$, showing that it is a maximum.

5. If $s = 7 + 8t + 5t^2 - t^3$, find the value of t which gives a minimum value of s, showing that it is a minimum.

6. What is the minimum value of $x + \dfrac{1}{x}$ if $x > 0$?

7. If $R = \dfrac{V^2}{4} + \dfrac{500}{V}$, find the value of V for which R is a minimum.

8. A rectangular box, with a lid, is made of thin metal. Its length is $2x$ cm and its width is x cm. If the box must have a volume of 72 cm^3,
    (a) show that the area $A \text{ cm}^2$ of metal used is given by
    $$A = 4x^2 + \dfrac{216}{x},$$
    (b) find the value of x so that A is a minimum.

9. The cost $\$C$ of running a boat on a trip is given by $C = 4v^2 + \dfrac{1\,000}{v}$ where v is the average speed in km h^{-1}. Find the value of v for which the cost is a minimum.

10. It is estimated that the load L which can safely be placed on a beam of width x, length y and height h is given by $L = \dfrac{4xy^2}{h}$. If $h = 30$ and $x + y = 15$, find the greatest load that the beam can bear.

11. A piece of wire of length 20 cm is formed into the shape of a sector of a circle of radius r cm and angle θ radians.

    (a) Show that $\theta = \dfrac{20-2r}{r}$ and that the area of the sector is $r(10-r)$ cm^2.

    (b) Hence find the values of r and θ to give the maximum area.

12. A cylinder is placed inside a circular cone of radius 18 cm and height 12 cm so that its base is level with the base of the cone, as shown in Fig. 16.14.

    (a) If the radius of the cylinder is r cm, show that its height h cm is given by $h = \dfrac{2}{3}(18-r)$.

    (b) Hence find the value of r to give the maximum possible volume of the cylinder and find this volume in terms of π.

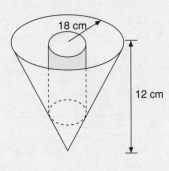

Fig. 16.14

13. A straight line passes through the point (2,3) and its gradient is m. It meets the positive x- and y- axes at A and B respectively.

    (a) State the equation of the line in terms of m.

    (b) Show that $OA = 2 - \dfrac{3}{m}$ and find a similar expression for OB.

    (c) Show that the area of $\triangle OAB = 6 - \dfrac{9}{2m} - 2m$.

    (d) Hence find the value of m for which this area is a minimum, showing that it is a minimum.

14. From a rectangular piece of thin cardboard 16 cm by 10 cm, the shaded squares each of side x cm are removed (Fig. 16.15). The remainder is folded up to a form a tray.

    (a) Show that the volume V cm^3 of this tray is given by $V = 4(x^3 - 13x^2 + 40x)$.

    (b) Hence find a possible value of x which will give the maximum value of V.

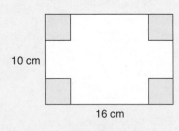

Fig. 16.15

15. The cost of making x articles per day is $\$\left(\dfrac{1}{2}x^2 + 50x + 50\right)$ and the selling price of each one is $\$\left(80 - \dfrac{1}{4}x\right)$. Find

    (a) the daily profit in terms of x,

    (b) the value of x to give the maximum profit.

16. Ship A is at O at noon and is sailing due east at 10 km h^{-1} (Fig. 16.16). At the same time, ship B is 100 km due south of O and is sailing at 20 km h^{-1} due north.

    (a) State the distances in km of A and B from O after t hours.

    (b) Show that the distance S km between A and B is then given by $S^2 = 500t^2 - 4000t + 10\,000$.

    (c) Find the value of t for which S^2 is a minimum and hence find the minimum distance between the ships.

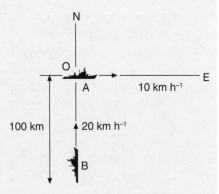

Fig. 16.16

17. The dimensions of a cylinder of radius r are such that the sum of its length and its circumference is 8π cm.
    (a) Show that its length is $\pi(8 - 2r)$ cm.
    (b) Hence state its volume in terms of r and find the value of r which gives the maximum value.

18. In Fig. 16.17, ABCD is a rectangle which fits inside the semicircle of radius 10 cm and centre O.

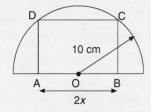

    (a) If AB = $2x$ cm, show that the area A cm^2 of the rectangle is given by $A^2 = 4x^2(100 - x^2)$.
    (b) Find the value of x which makes A^2 a maximum.
    (c) Hence find the maximum area of the rectangle.

Fig. 16.17

19. In Fig. 16.18, ABCD is a rectangle where AB = 9 m and AD = 6 m. CE = 4 m and FE is parallel to AD. X is a point on FE where XF = x m and M is the midpoint of BC. FInd

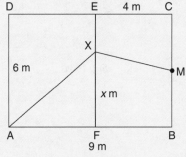

    (a) AX^2 and XM^2 in terms of x,
    (b) the value of x for which AX^2 + XM^2 is a minimum.

Fig. 16.18

20. In $\triangle$ABC, $\angle$BAC = 60°, AB = 4 cm and AC = 2 cm. P lies on AB extended where BP = x cm, while Q lies on AC extended where CQ = y cm. Given that $x + y = 10$, show that PQ$^2 = 3x^2 - 24x + 112$ and find the value of x which will make PQ^2 a minimum. State the ratio of BC:PQ in that case.

21. The position vectors $\mathbf{r}_A$ and $\mathbf{r}_B$ of two points A and B are given by $\mathbf{r}_A = 2t\mathbf{i} + (1 + t)\mathbf{j}$ and $\mathbf{r}_B = (t + 1)\mathbf{i} - (t + 2)\mathbf{j}$.
    (a) Find the values of t for which OA is perpendicular to OB where O is the origin.
    (b) Find the vector $\overrightarrow{AB}$ in terms of t.
    (c) Find the value of t for which $|\overrightarrow{AB}|^2$ is a minimum.
    (d) Hence find the shortest distance between A and B.

22. A can is in the shape of a closed cylinder with a hemisphere at one end (Fig. 16.19). Its volume is 45π cm^3. Taking r cm as the radius of the cylinder and h cm as its height, show that

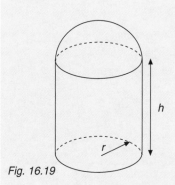

    (a) $r^2h + \dfrac{2r^3}{3} = 45$,
    (b) the external surface area A of the can is given by
        $A = \dfrac{5\pi r^2}{3} + \dfrac{90\pi}{r}$.
    (c) Hence find the value of r for which A is a minimum and find the minimum value of A.
        (Volume of a sphere = $\dfrac{4\pi r^3}{3}$, surface area of a sphere = $4\pi r^2$.)

Fig. 16.19

23. ABC is an isosceles triangle with AB = AC = 10 cm and ∠BAC = 60°. A particle P starts from B and moves along BA at a speed of 2 cm s^{-2}. Another particle Q starts from A at the same time and moves along AC at a speed of 4 cm s^{-1}.

(a) Write down the distances of P and Q from A at time t seconds after the start.

Find

(b) an expression for PQ^2 in terms of t, and

(c) the value of t for which PQ^2 is a minimum.

(d) Hence find the minimum length of PQ.

24. Fig. 16.20 shows a framework in the shape of a rectangular box made from straight pieces of wire. The total length of these pieces is 60 cm.

(a) Show that $y = (15 - 5x)$ cm.

(b) Find an expression for the volume enclosed by the framework in terms of x and hence find

(c) the value of x which makes this volume a maximum and

(d) the maximum volume.

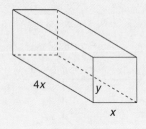

Fig. 16.20

25. A piece of wire 48 cm long is divided into two parts. One part is formed into the shape of a circle of radius r cm while the other part is formed into a square of side x cm.

(a) Show that $r = \dfrac{24 - 2x}{\pi}$.

(b) Find an expression in terms of x for the total area A of the two shapes and hence calculate (correct to 3 significant figures) the value of x for which A is a minimum.

26. In ΔABC, ∠A = 60°, AB = x cm and AC = y cm where $x + 2y = k$ (a constant). Find an expression for BC^2 in terms of x and k and hence find the ratio $x:y$ for which BC^2 is a minimum.

27. ABCD is a square of side 10 cm. P lies on BC where BP = x cm and Q lies on CD where CQ = $\dfrac{3x}{2}$ cm.

(a) Find an expression in terms of x for the area of ΔAPQ and hence

(b) find the value of x which makes this area a minimum.

28. A rectangular box has a square cross-section and the sum of its length and the perimeter of this cross-section is 2 m. If the length of the box is x m, show that its volume V m^3 is given by $V = \dfrac{x(2 - x)^2}{16}$. Hence find the maximum volume of the box.

29. Fig. 16.21 shows part of the parabola $y = 8x - x^2$ with a rectangle ABCD which fits between the curve and the x-axis. Taking AB = $2x$, show that

(a) OB = $x + 4$,

(b) the area of ABCD = $32x - 2x^3$ units^2. Hence find the value of x which makes this area a maximum and state the maximum area.

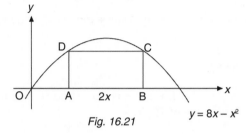

Fig. 16.21

16.4 Small Increments: Approximate Changes

Given a function $y = f(x)$, suppose x is changed by an increment δx to become $x + \delta x$. Then y changes by an increment δy. We can find an approximate value for δy in a simple way using $\dfrac{dy}{dx}$, provided δx **is small**.

In Fig. 16.22, A is the point on $y = f(x)$ where $x = k$. AB = δx and BC = δy. AT is the tangent at A and the gradient of this tangent $= \left(\dfrac{dy}{dx}\right)_{x=k}$.

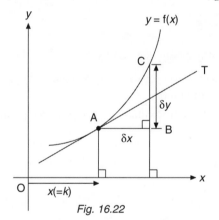

Fig. 16.22

Now if δx is small, we can take $\dfrac{BC}{AB} = \dfrac{\delta y}{\delta x}$ to be approximately equal to the gradient of the tangent at A.

Then $\dfrac{\delta y}{\delta x} \approx \left(\dfrac{dy}{dx}\right)_{x=k}$ and so

$$\delta y \approx \left(\frac{dy}{dx}\right)_{x=k} \times \delta x \ .$$

▶ **Example 14**

If $y = \dfrac{27}{x^2}$, find the approximate change in y if x is increased from 3 to 3.01.

▶ **Solution . . .**

Here $k = 3$.

$\dfrac{dy}{dx} = -\dfrac{54}{x^3}$ and so $\left(\dfrac{dy}{dx}\right)_{x=3} = -2$.

Then $\delta y \approx \left(\dfrac{dy}{dx}\right)_{x=3} \times \delta x = -2 \times 0.01 = -0.02$.

Note that the negative value indicates a *decrease* in the value of y.

▶ **Example 15**

Given that $T = x^3 - 2x^2 + 1$ and x is decreased from 2 to 1.985, find the approximate new value of T.

▶ **Solution . . .**

$\dfrac{dT}{dx} = 3x^2 - 4x$ so $\left(\dfrac{dT}{dx}\right)_{x=2} = 4$.

Then $\delta T \approx \left(\dfrac{dT}{dx}\right)_{x=2} \times \delta x$

$\qquad\qquad = 4 \times (-0.015)$ (as x was decreased)
$\qquad\qquad = -0.06$

Hence the approximate new value of $T = 2^3 - 2(2^2) + 1 - 0.06 = 0.94$.

▶ **Example 16**

The volume V of a sphere is given by $V = \dfrac{4\pi r^3}{3}$ where r is the radius.

(a) State an expression for the approximate change in V if r is changed by a small amount δr.

(b) Hence find the approximate percentage change in V if r is increased by 1%.

▶ **Solution . . .**

(a) $\dfrac{dV}{dr} = 4\pi r^2$

$\delta V \approx \left(\dfrac{dV}{dr}\right) \times \delta r = 4\pi r^2 \times \delta r$.

(b) If r is increased by 1% then $\delta r = 0.01r$.

The percentage increase in $V \approx \dfrac{\delta V}{V} \times 100\% = \dfrac{4\pi r^2 \delta r}{\frac{4}{3}\pi r^3} \times 100\%$

$\qquad\qquad\qquad = \dfrac{3}{r} \times 0.01r \times 100\% = 3\%$

▶ **Example 17**

If $y = 3 - x + 2x^2$ and x is increased from 4 by an amount $\dfrac{r}{100}$ where r is small, find in terms of r

(a) the approximate change in y,

(b) the percentage change in y.

► **Solution . . .**

(a) $\dfrac{dy}{dx} = -1 + 4x$ and $\left(\dfrac{dy}{dx}\right)_{x=4} = 15$.

Then $\delta y \approx 15 \times \dfrac{r}{100} = \dfrac{3r}{20}$.

(b) The original value of y was $3 - 4 + 32 = 31$ and the percentage change

in $y = \dfrac{\delta y}{y} \times 100\% \approx \dfrac{\frac{3r}{20}}{31} \times 100\% = \dfrac{15r}{31}\%$.

► **Example 18**

If $y = 2x^2 - 3x + 1$, find the positive value of x for which $y = 3$. Hence find the approximate increase in x which will change y from 3 to 3.015.

► **Solution . . .**

When $y = 3$, $2x^2 - 3x + 1 = 3$, so $2x^2 - 3x - 2 = 0$ or $(2x + 1)(x - 2) = 0$, giving $x = 2$ (positive value).

$\dfrac{dy}{dx} = 4x - 3$ and $\left(\dfrac{dy}{dx}\right)_{x=2} = 5$; $\delta y = 0.015$.

Then substituting $\delta y \approx \left(\dfrac{dy}{dx}\right)_{x=2} \times \delta x$,

$$0.015 = 5\delta x \text{ giving } \delta x \approx 0.003.$$

Exercise 16D (Answers on page 508)

1. If $y = x^2 - x + 1$, find the approximate change in y when x is increased from 4 to 4.025.

2. Given the function $y = x^3 + x^2 - 4$, x is increased from 4 to 4.05. What is the approximate change in y?

3. If $z = 2x^2 - 7$, find the approximate change in z when x is decreased from 4 to 3.99.

4. Given that $y = (x + 2)^5$, find the approximate change in y when x is increased from 2 to 2.005.

5. Given that $y = (x^2 - x - 1)^4$, find the change in y following an increase in x from 2 to 2.01.

6. For the function $T = \dfrac{5}{s+1}$, find the approximate new value of T due to an increase in s from 9 to 9.1.

7. $P = \left(1 - \dfrac{1}{x}\right)^3$. When $x = 2$, it is decreased by 3%. Find the approximate percentage change in P.

8. Find the approximate change in T for the function $T = 4 + 3u - 2u^2$ when u is increased by 5% from the value of 2.

9. The radius of a circle is increased by 5%. Calculate the approximate percentage increase in
   (a) the circumference,
   (b) the area of the circle.

10. A piece of wire of length 20 cm is shaped into the form of a sector of a circle of radius r cm and angle θ radians.
    (a) Show that the area A cm^2 of the sector is given by $A = r(10 - r)$.
    (b) If r is increased by 2% when $r = 2.5$ cm, find the approximate percentage change in A.

11. The height of a cone is 20 cm but the radius of its circular base is increased from 10 cm to 10.01 cm. Find the approximate change in the volume of the cone in terms of π.

12. If $y = x^3 - 3x^2$, find, in terms of k, (a) the approximate increase in y if x is increased from 4 to $4 + k$, where k is small and (b) the approximate percentage change in y.

13. Each side of a cube is increased by $p\%$ where p is small. What is the approximate percentage increase in the volume of the cube in terms of p?

14. $y = x^2 - \dfrac{1}{1 - x}$. If x is increased from 3 to 3.001, find the approximate change in y.

15. If x is decreased from 5 to 4.98 in the function $y = \dfrac{2}{x - 1}$, what is the approximate percentage change in y?

16. Find the positive value of x when $y = 4$ for the function $y = x^2 - 5x - 2$. Hence find the approximate change in x when y changes from 4 to 4.02.

17. The y-coordinate of a point in the first quadrant on the curve $y = 3x^2 - 8x - 1$ is 2. Find its x-coordinate. What is the approximate change in x if the point is moved to a position on the curve where $y = 2.04$?

18. For the function $y = 3x^2 + ax + b$, where a and b are constants, when x changes from 2 to 2.02, y changes from 2 to 2.12 approximately. Find the values of a and b.

19. In an experiment to find the values of T from the formula $T = \dfrac{2}{x^2 + 4}$, values of x are read from a measuring device. A value of x is read as 2.04 but should be 2. What is the approximate error in the value of T?

20. U is calculated from the formula $U = \dfrac{2}{x-1}$. Measurements of x are taken but they are liable to an error of $\pm 1.5\%$. When x is measured as 3, what are the greatest and least values of U?

21. Given that $v = \dfrac{1}{u} + \dfrac{1}{1-u}$, find the approximate change in v when u is increased from 2 to 2.04.

22. For the function $A = \dfrac{1}{(r-1)^2}$, a small change in r when $r = 2(r-1)^2$ produces a 2% reduction in the value of A. Find the approximate change in r.

16.5 Connected Rates of Change

When a circle increases in size, the rate at which its area increases is connected to the rate at which its radius increases since its area is related to its radius.

In general, if $y = f(x)$ and the rates of increase of x and y wrt time t are $\dfrac{dx}{dt}$ and $\dfrac{dy}{dt}$ respectively, then using the rule of combined functions, we have $\dfrac{dy}{dt} = \dfrac{dy}{dx} \times \dfrac{dx}{dt}$.

▶ **Example 19**

Some oil is spilt onto a level surface and spreads out in the shape of a circle. The radius r cm of the circle is increasing at the rate of 0.5 cm s^{-1}. At what rate is the area of the circle increasing when the radius is 5 cm?

▶ **Solution . . .**

The rate of change of the radius wrt time $(t) = \dfrac{dr}{dt} = 0.5$.

We wish to find the rate of change of the area A, i.e. $\dfrac{dA}{dt}$.

We now use the rule $\dfrac{dA}{dt} = \dfrac{dA}{dr} \times \dfrac{dr}{dt}$.

We know that $A = \pi r^2$ so $\dfrac{dA}{dr} = 2\pi r = 2\pi \times 5$.

Then $\dfrac{dA}{dt} = 2\pi \times 5 \times 0.5 = 15.7$ cm^2 s^{-1}.

▶ **Example 20**

Water is emptied from a cylindrical tank of radius 20 cm at the rate of 2.5 litres s^{-1} and fresh water is added at the rate of 2 litres s^{-1} (Fig. 16.23). At what rate is the water level in the tank changing?

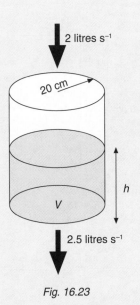

2 litres s^{-1}

20 cm

h

V

2.5 litres s^{-1}

Fig. 16.23

▶ **Solution . . .**

Let the depth of water be h cm at time t s.

The rate of change of the volume V cm^3 of the water
$= \dfrac{\mathrm{d}V}{\mathrm{d}t} = +2000 - 2500 = -500$ cm^3 s^{-1}.
(1 litre = 1000 cm^3; so 2000^3 cm of water is flowing in and 2500 cm^3 of water is flowing out, per second).

The rate of change of the water level $= \dfrac{\mathrm{d}h}{\mathrm{d}t}$ which we have to find.

Then $\dfrac{\mathrm{d}V}{\mathrm{d}t} = \dfrac{\mathrm{d}V}{\mathrm{d}h} \times \dfrac{\mathrm{d}h}{\mathrm{d}t}$.

Since $V = \pi r^2 h$ and $\dfrac{\mathrm{d}V}{\mathrm{d}h} = 400\pi$,

therefore $-500 = 400\pi \times \dfrac{\mathrm{d}h}{\mathrm{d}t}$ giving $\dfrac{\mathrm{d}h}{\mathrm{d}t} = \dfrac{-500}{400\pi} = -0.40$ cm s^{-1}.

The water level is *falling* at the rate of 0.4 cm s^{-1}.

▶ **Example 21**

A hollow circular cone is held upside down with its axis vertical (Fig. 16.24). Liquid is added at the constant rate of 20 cm^3 s^{-1} but leaks away through a small hole in the vertex at the constant rate of 15 cm^3 s^{-1}. At what rate is the depth of the liquid in the cone changing when it is 12 cm?

▶ **Solution . . .**

If V cm^3 is the volume of the liquid in the cone at time t s, then
$\dfrac{\mathrm{d}V}{\mathrm{d}t} = +20 - 15 = 5$ cm^3 s^{-1}.

Let h cm be the height of the liquid at time t s. We have to find $\dfrac{\mathrm{d}h}{\mathrm{d}t}$.

$\dfrac{\mathrm{d}V}{\mathrm{d}t} = \dfrac{\mathrm{d}V}{\mathrm{d}h} \times \dfrac{\mathrm{d}h}{\mathrm{d}t}$ so we find a relation between V and h.

Taking r as the radius of the water surface, from Fig. 16.25 we have:

$\tan\theta = \dfrac{4}{20} = \dfrac{r}{h}$ so $r = \dfrac{h}{5}$ and $V = \dfrac{1}{3}\pi r^2 h = \dfrac{\pi h^3}{75}$.

Then $\dfrac{\mathrm{d}V}{\mathrm{d}h} = \dfrac{\pi h^2}{25}$.

So $\dfrac{\mathrm{d}V}{\mathrm{d}t} = 5 = \dfrac{\pi \times 12^2}{25} \times \dfrac{\mathrm{d}h}{\mathrm{d}t}$

and $\dfrac{\mathrm{d}h}{\mathrm{d}t} = \dfrac{25 \times 5}{\pi \times 144} \approx 0.28$ cm s^{-1}.

The depth of liquid is rising at the rate of 0.28 cm s^{-1}.

Note that in this example the rate of change of the depth depends on how much liquid is already in the cone as the cross-section is not constant.

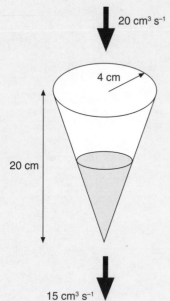

20 cm^3 s^{-1}

4 cm

20 cm

15 cm^3 s^{-1}

Fig. 16.24

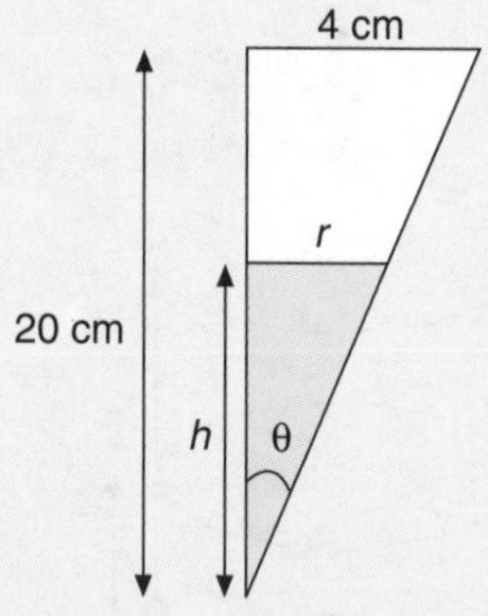

4 cm

20 cm

r

h θ

Fig. 16.25

▶ Example 22

The pressure P units and the volume V m^3 of a quantity of gas stored at a constant temperature in a cylinder are related by Boyle's Law $PV = k$ (a constant). At a certain time, the volume of gas in the cylinder is 30 m^3 and its pressure is 20 units. If the gas is being compressed at the rate of 6 m^3 s^{-1}, at what rate is the pressure changing?

▶ Solution . . .

$PV = k$ so $k = 20 \times 30 = 600$ units m^3.

The relation between P and V is $PV = 600$ or $P = \dfrac{600}{V}$.

Now $\dfrac{dP}{dt} = \dfrac{dP}{dV} \times \dfrac{dV}{dt}$ and $\dfrac{dP}{dV} = -\dfrac{600}{V^2}$.

We are given that $\dfrac{dV}{dt} = -6$ (decreasing).

So $\dfrac{dP}{dt} = -\dfrac{600}{30^2} \times (-6) = 4$ units per second (increasing).

▶ Example 23

A street lamp is 8 m high. A man of height 1.6 m walks along the street away from the lamp at a steady rate of 1 m s^{-1}. At what rate is the length of his shadow changing?

▶ Solution . . .

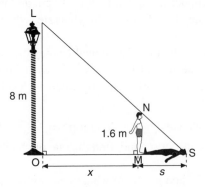

Fig. 16.26

In Fig. 16.26, L is the lamp and OL = 8 m.
MN = 1.6 m is the man and MS = s m his shadow.
Let OM = x m.

Now $\dfrac{dx}{dt} =$ rate at which the man is walking = 1 m s^{-1}. We require $\dfrac{ds}{dt}$.

$\dfrac{ds}{dt} = \dfrac{ds}{dx} \times \dfrac{dx}{dt}$ so we find the relation between s and x.

$\tan \angle NSM = \dfrac{1.6}{s} = \dfrac{8}{x + s}$ which gives $s = \dfrac{x}{4}$.

Then $\dfrac{ds}{dx} = \dfrac{1}{4}$.

Hence $\dfrac{ds}{dt} = \dfrac{1}{4} \times 1 = 0.25$ m s^{-1} which is the rate at which the length of his shadow is increasing.

Exercise 16E *(Answers on page 508)*

1. At what rate is the area of a circle decreasing when its radius is 8 cm and decreasing at 0.4 cm s^{-1}?

2. The area of a circle is decreasing at the rate of 2 cm^2 s^{-1}. How fast is the radius decreasing when the area is 9π cm^2?

3. The radius r cm of a sphere is 10 cm and it is increasing at the rate of 0.25 cm s^{-1}. At what rate is (a) the volume, (b) the surface area, increasing?
   (For a sphere, volume = $\dfrac{4\pi r^3}{3}$ and surface area = $4\pi r^2$.)

4. A spherical balloon is being inflated by blowing on 2×10^3 cm^3 of air per second. At what rate is its radius increasing when its diameter is 20 cm?

5. ABC is a triangle with $\angle$B = 90° and AB has a fixed length of 8 cm. The length of BC is increasing at 0.5 cm s^{-1}. At what rate is the area of the triangle increasing?

6. A closed cylinder is of fixed length 10 cm but its radius is increasing at the rate of 1.5 cm s^{-1}. Find the rate of increase of its total surface area when the radius is 4 cm. (Leave the answer in terms of π.)

7. A circular cylinder has a diameter of 40 cm and is being filled with water at the rate of 1.5 litres s^{-1}. At what rate is the water level rising?

8. The length of each side of a cubical framework of straight wires is expanding at the rate of 0.02 m s^{-1}. At what rate in cm^3 s^{-1} is the volume of the framework changing when each side is 0.2 m long?

9. x and y are connected by the equation $y = \dfrac{x^2 - 3}{x}$. If x is changing at a rate of 0.3 units per second, find the rate of change of y when $x = 3$.

10. $y = (2r^2 - r + 1)^3$ and $x = 4r$. At what rate is y changing with respect to x when $r = 0.5$?

11. The height of a cone remains constant at 20 cm. The radius of the base is 5 cm and is increasing at 0.2 cm s^{-1}. At what rate is the volume of the cone changing?

12. The volume V cm^3 of liquid in a container is given by $V = 2x^3 - 4x^2 + 5$ where x cm is the depth of the liquid. At what rate is the volume increasing when $x = 4$ and is increasing at the rate of 1.5 cm s^{-1}?

13. Liquid escapes from a circular cylinder of radius 5 cm at a rate of 50 cm^3 $^{-1}$s. How fast is the level of the liquid in the cylinder falling?

14. A hollow cone of radius 15 cm and height 25 cm, is held vertex down with its axis vertical. Liquid is poured into the cone at the rate of 500 cm³ s⁻¹. How fast is the level of the liquid rising when the radius of its surface is 10 cm?

15. In an electrical circuit, the resistance $R = \dfrac{10}{I}$ where I is the current flowing in the circuit. If I is increasing at 0.05 units per second, what is the rate of change of R when $R = 5$ units?

16. Two quantities p and q are related by the equation $(p - 1)(q + 2) = k$ where k is a constant. When $p = 5$ units, q is 7 units and q is changing at the rate of 0.04 units per second. Find the rate at which p is changing.

17. Water is being poured into a cylinder of radius 10 cm at a rate of 360 cm³ s⁻¹ but leaks out at a rate of 40 cm³ s⁻¹. At what speed is the water level changing?

18. In Fig. 16.27, the sides of the rectangle ABCD are 18 cm and 10 cm. The rectangle KLMN lies inside ABCD and the shaded area has a width of x cm at each side.

    (a) Express the shaded area in terms of x.

    (b) If the shaded area is $\dfrac{8}{15}$ of the area of ABCD, find the value of x.

    (c) The area of KLMN varies as x decreases at a constant rate of 0.25 cm s⁻¹. Find the rate at which the shaded area is decreasing when it is $\dfrac{8}{15}$ of the area of ABCD.

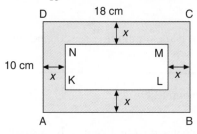

Fig. 16.27

19. A hemispherical bowl contains liquid as shown in Fig. 16.28. The volume V cm³ of liquid is given by $V = \dfrac{1}{3}\pi h^2(24 - h)$ where h is the greatest depth of the liquid in cm. If liquid is poured into the bowl at the rate of 100 cm³ s⁻¹, at what rate is the greatest depth of the liquid increasing when it is 2 cm? (Leave the answer in terms of π.)

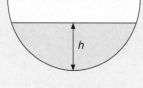

Fig. 16.28

20. Sand falls on to level ground at a rate of 1000 cm³ s⁻¹ and piles up in the form of a circular cone whose vertical angle is 60°.

    (a) Given that $\tan 30° = \dfrac{1}{\sqrt{3}}$, show that the radius r of the base is given by $r = \dfrac{h}{\sqrt{3}}$ where h is the height.

    (b) Show that the volume V of the pile is $\dfrac{\pi h^3}{9}$.

    (c) Hence find the rate at which the height of the pile is increasing when $h = 20$ cm.

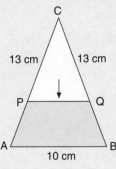

Fig. 16.29

21. In Fig. 16.29, ABC is an isosceles triangle where AC = BC = 13 cm and AB = 10 cm. PQ moves towards AB at a steady rate of 0.5 cm s⁻¹ keeping parallel to AB. If PQ is x cm from C, show that

   (a) $PQ = \dfrac{5x}{6}$ cm,

   (b) the shaded area = $\dfrac{5}{12}(144 - x^2)$ cm².

   (c) Hence find the rate at which the shaded area is decreasing when PQ is moving half way towards AB from C.

22. (a) If $\dfrac{dL}{dt} = k$ where k is a number, show that $\dfrac{dL^2}{dt} = 2kL$.

   (b) ABC is a triangle in which $\angle CAB = 60°$ and AB is of fixed length 5 cm. If AC = 8 cm, show that BC = 7 cm.

   (c) Taking AC = x cm and L = length of BC, find an expression for L^2 in terms of x.

   (d) Find $\dfrac{dL^2}{dt}$ when $x = 8$ and is increasing at 1 cm s⁻¹.

   (e) Hence, using (a), find the rate at which the length of BC is changing.

Summary

1. Gradient of tangent to $y = f(x)$ is $\dfrac{dy}{dx}$.

   Gradient of normal is $-\dfrac{1}{\frac{dy}{dx}}$.

2. For a stationary point (maximum, minimum or point of inflexion), $\dfrac{dy}{dx} = 0$.

   The stationary point is maximum if $\dfrac{d^2y}{dx^2} < 0$, and minimum if $\dfrac{d^2y}{dx^2} > 0$.

   If $\dfrac{d^2y}{dx^2} = 0$, use the sign test.

3. If $y = f(x)$ and x is changed from a value k by a small increment δx, $\delta y \approx \left(\dfrac{dy}{dx}\right)_{x=k} \times \delta x$.

4. If $y = f(x)$, $\dfrac{dy}{dt} = \dfrac{dy}{dx} \times \dfrac{dx}{dt}$.

Revision Exercise 16 (Answers on page 508)

1. For the function $y = x^3 - 6x^2 - 15x + 3$, find the range of values of x for which $\dfrac{dy}{dx} > 0$.

2. For what value of x does the function $y = 4x^3 - 6x^2 - 9x + 5$ have a minimum stationary point?

3. The area of a circle increases from 25π to 25.5π. Calculate the approximate increase in the radius.

4. The variables x and y are related by the equation $y = \dfrac{2x-6}{x}$.

   (a) Obtain an expression for $\dfrac{dy}{dx}$ and hence find an expression for the approximate increase in y as x increases from 4 to $4 + p$, where p is small.

   (b) Given that x and y are functions of t and that $\dfrac{dy}{dt} = 0.4$, find the corresponding rate of change of x when $y = 1$. (C)

5. The area, A cm^2, of the image of a rocket on a radar screen is given by the formula $A = \dfrac{12}{r^2}$, where r km is the distance of the rocket from the screen. The rocket is approaching at 0.5 km s^{-1}. When the rocket is 10 km away, at what rate is the area of the image changing? When A is changing at 0.096 cm^2 s^{-1}, how far away is the rocket? (C)

6. A piece of wire, 60 cm long, is bent to form the shape shown in Fig. 16.30. This shape consists of a semicircular arc, radius r cm, and three sides of a rectangle of height x cm.
   Express x in terms of r and hence show that the area enclosed, A cm^2, is given by $A = 60r - 2r^2 - \dfrac{\pi r^2}{2}$.
   Hence determine, to 3 significant figures, the value of r for which A is either a maximum or a minimum. Determine whether this value of r makes A a maximum or a minimum.

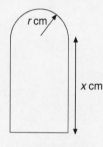

Fig. 16.30

7. If $y = 10 - x + 5x^2$, find the approximate percentage change in y when x is increased by $p\%$ (p small) when $x = 4$.

8. Under a heating process, the length, x cm, of each side of a metal cube increases from an initial value of 9.9 cm at a constant rate of 0.005 cm s^{-1}. Express the volume, V cm^3, and the surface area, A cm^2, of the cube in terms of x.
   Write down expressions for $\dfrac{dV}{dx}$ and $\dfrac{dA}{dx}$. Hence find

   (a) the rate at which V is increasing when the cube has been heated for 20 s,

   (b) the approximate increase in A as x increases from 10 to 10.001 cm. (C)

9. $R = \dfrac{V^3}{25} + \dfrac{10\,800}{V}$. Find the value of V for which R is least.

10. A piece of wire, 100 cm in length, is divided into two parts. One part is bent to form an equilateral triangle of side x cm and the other is bent to form a square of side y cm. Express y in terms of x and hence show that A cm^2, the total area enclosed by the two shapes, is such that $A = \dfrac{\sqrt{3}}{4}x^2 + \dfrac{(100 - 3x)^2}{16}$.
   Calculate the value of x for which A has a stationary value.
   Determine whether this value of x makes A a maximum or a minimum. (C)

11. Show that the equation of the normal to the curve $y = 2x + \dfrac{6}{x}$ at the point $(2,7)$ is $y + 2x = 11$. Given that this normal meets the curve again at P, find the x-coordinate of P. (C)

12. Fig. 16.31 shows a solid body which consists of a right circular cylinder fixed, with no overlap, to a rectangular block. The block has a square base of side $2x$ cm and a height of x cm. The cylinder has a radius of x cm and a height of y cm. Given that the total volume of the solid is 27 cm^3, express y in terms of x.

Hence show that the total surface area, A cm^2, of the solid is given by

$$A = \frac{54}{x} + 8x^2.$$

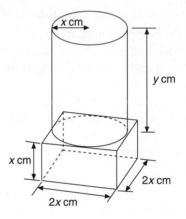

Fig. 16.31

Find

(a) the value of x for which A has a stationary value,

(b) the value of A and of y corresponding to this value of x. Determine whether the stationary value of A is a maximum or a minimum. (C)

13. Fig. 16.32 shows part of the curve $y = 4 + 3x - x^2$ and the line $2y - 2 = x$. $OB = b$ and BCD is parallel to the y-axis.

(a) Express the length of CD in terms of b.

(b) Hence find the value of b for which the length of CD is a maximum.

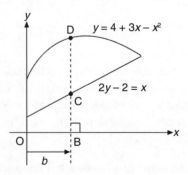

Fig. 16.32

14. A circular cylinder of height $2h$ cm is fitted inside a sphere of radius 10 cm. Find an expression for the radius of the cylinder in terms of h and hence find the maximum volume of the cylinder.

15. A piece of wire, of fixed length L cm, is bent to form the boundary OPQO of a sector of a circle (Fig. 16.33). The circle has centre O and radius r cm. The angle of the sector is θ radians.

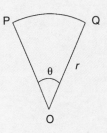

Show that the area, A cm^2, of the sector is given by $A = \frac{1}{2}rL - r^2$.

(a) Find a relationship between r and L for which A has a stationary value and find the corresponding value of θ. Determine the nature of this stationary value.

(b) Show that, for this value of θ, the area of the triangle OPQ is approximately 45.5% of the area of the sector OPQ. (C)

Fig. 16.33

16. A line of gradient m ($m < 0$) passes through the point (3,2) and meets the axes at P and Q. Find the coordinates of P and Q in terms of m and show that the area of $\triangle$POQ is $6 - \frac{2}{m} - \frac{9m}{2}$. Hence find the minimum area of $\triangle$POQ.

17. A rectangular box without a lid is made from thin cardboard. The sides of the base are $2x$ cm and $3x$ cm and the height of the box is h cm. If the total surface area is 200 cm^2, show that $h = \frac{20}{x} - \frac{3x}{5}$ and hence find the dimensions of the box to give the maximum volume.

18. Show that the height of a circular cone of volume V and radius r is given by $\frac{3V}{\pi r^2}$. If V remains constant but r is increased by 2%, find the approximate percentage change in h.

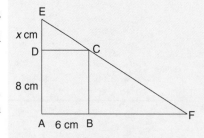

19. In Fig. 16.34, ABCD is a rectangle with AB = 6 cm and AD = 8 cm. DE = x cm. EC meets AB produced at F. Find the value of x which gives the minimum area of $\triangle$AFE and show that it is a minimum.

Fig. 16.34

20. Given the function $y = ax^3 + bx^2 + cx + d$, find the values of a, b, c and d if the curve
(a) passes through the point (0,–3),
(b) has a stationary point at (–1,1),
(c) has the value of $\frac{d^2y}{dx^2} = 2$ when $x = 1$.

21. Find the nature of the stationary points on the curve $y = 3x^4 + 4x^3 + 2$.

22. A cylinder of radius r cm is placed upright inside a cone so that the top of the cylinder is 4 cm above the top of the cone as in Fig. 16.35. The cone has a radius of 6 cm and a height of 18 cm. The part of the cylinder inside the cone is h cm deep.
(a) Show that $h + 3r = 18$.
(b) Find an expression in terms of r for the volume of the cylinder.
(c) Hence find the value of h for which the volume of the cylinder is a maximum.

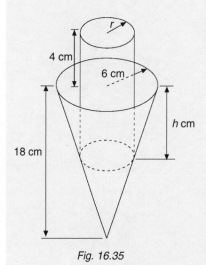

Fig. 16.35

23. (a) If $\frac{1}{u} + \frac{1}{v} = 2$, show that $u = \frac{v}{2v-1}$ and that this equals $\frac{1}{2}\left(1 + \frac{1}{2v-1}\right)$.

(b) If v is increased by 2% when it is 2, find the percentage change in u.

24. A water trough 100 cm long has a cross section in the shape of a vertical trapezium ABCD as shown in Fig. 16.36. AB = 30 cm and AD and BC are each inclined at 60° to the horizontal. The trough is placed on level ground and is being filled at the rate of 10 litres s^{-1}.

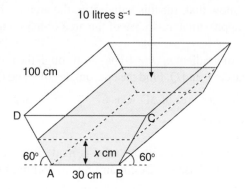

Fig. 16.36

(a) Given that $\tan 60° = \sqrt{3}$, show that the volume V cm^3 of water in the trough when it is x cm deep is given by
$$V = 100x\left(30 + \frac{x}{\sqrt{3}}\right).$$

(b) Hence calculate the rate at which the water level is rising when $x = 15$ cm.

25. Point A moves along the positive x-axis away from the origin O at a speed of 4 cm s^{-1} where OA > 5 cm. B is a fixed point on the positive y-axis where OB = 20 cm. P is a fixed point on the positive x-axis where OP = 5 cm and Q lies on the line joining B and A with PQ parallel to the y-axis.

(a) Show that when OA = x cm, PQ = $20\left(1 - \frac{5}{x}\right)$ cm.

(b) Hence find the speed of Q along PQ as A moves when (i) $x = 12$ cm, (ii) $x = 20$ cm.

(c) Obtain an expression in terms of x for the acceleration of Q along PQ.

26. In $\triangle$OAB, $\angle$AOB = 60°, OA = 10 cm and OB = 4 cm. P lies on OA where OP = x cm and Q lies on OB. Given that the area of $\triangle$OPQ is twice that of $\triangle$OAB, find in terms of x,

(a) OQ,

(b) PQ^2.

Hence find the value of x which will make PQ^2 a minimum, and the corresponding length of OQ.

27. Find the point of intersection P of the curves $y^2 = 4x$ and $4y = x^2$ and sketch the parts of these curves which lie between the origin O and P. A lies on $y^2 = 4x$ with x-coordinte 2. B is a variable point (x, y) on the curve $4y = x^2$, lying between O and P. Find an expression for the area of $\triangle OAB$ and hence find the maximum area of this triangle.

Maths Booster

The figure below shows a rectangular box 80 cm long, 50 cm wide and 10 cm high.

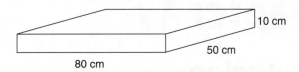

10 cm

50 cm

80 cm

Identical balls of radius 5 cm are to be packed into the box. What is the maximum number of balls you can pack into it?

Chapter 17

Integration

On graph paper, draw the graph of $y = x^2 - 4x + 5$ for the domain $0 \le x \le 5$ using the scale of 1 cm for 1 unit on both axes. Discuss ways you can estimate the area of the region between the curve, the x-axis and the lines $x = 0$ and $x = 5$. Estimate this area.

Compare your answer to the actual area which is $16\frac{2}{3}$ unit^2.

You will learn how to find the exact value of such areas later in this chapter.

17.1 Anti-differentiation

If we differentiate $y = 3x^2 - 4x + 3$, we obtain $\dfrac{dy}{dx} = 6x - 4$.

Supposing we are given $\dfrac{dy}{dx} = 6x - 4$, can we do a reverse operation,

i.e. **anti-differentiate**, to find y?

Let us review the process of differentiation for $y = ax^n$.

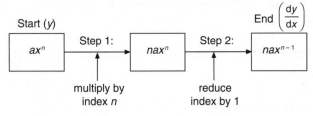

Now *reverse* the process.

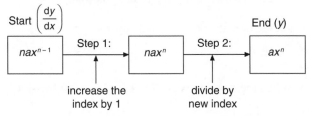

So by reversing the process, we can obtain y from $\dfrac{dy}{dx}$.

If we start with $\dfrac{dy}{dx} = nax^{n-1}$, we obtain $y = ax^n$.

If we start with $\dfrac{dy}{dx} = ax^n$ and apply the reverse process, we get:

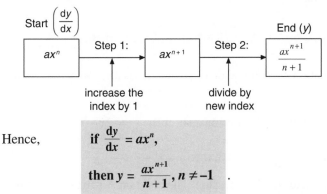

Hence,   **if $\dfrac{dy}{dx} = ax^n$,**

   then $y = \dfrac{ax^{n+1}}{n+1}, n \neq -1$.

This process of anti-differentiation is actually called **integration**. We **integrate** ax^n wrt x. ax^n is the **integrand** and the result is called the **integral**. A notation for this will be given later. Note that we have excluded the case when the index n is -1 as integration of x^{-1}, using the above rule, will result in $\dfrac{x^0}{0}$ which is undefined. In fact, the integral of x^{-1} is a special function. However we will not go into this as it is beyond the scope of the present syllabus.

▶ **Example 1**

Integrate the following wrt x: **(a)** x^3 **(b)** $2x^2$ **(c)** $4x$ **(d)** 7 **(e)** $\dfrac{3}{x^2}$

▶ **Solution . . .**

We show here the steps taken to obtain the integral. With practice these would not be written down, only the result.

(a) Increase the index by 1 to 4, then divide by 4.

Result $\dfrac{x^4}{4}$.

(b) When the new index is 3, then divide by 3. The factor 2 is left as it is.

Result $\dfrac{2x^3}{3}$.

(c) $4x = 4x^1$. When the new index is 2, divide by 2.

Result $\dfrac{4x^2}{2} = 2x^2$. (Always simplify where possible.)

(d) $7 = 7x^0$. When the new index is 1, divide by 1.

Result $\dfrac{7x^1}{1} = 7x$.

(e) $\dfrac{3}{x^2} = 3x^{-2}$. When the new index is $-2 + 1 = -1$, divide by -1.

Result $\dfrac{3x^{-1}}{-1} = -\dfrac{3}{x}$.

Now check each result by differentiation and verify that the original expression is obtained.

Before we go further there is one important point to note. This is discussed in the next section.

17.2 The Arbitrary Constant: Indefinite Integral

As in differentiation, the integral of a sum of terms is the sum of the separate integrals.

If $y = x^2 - 3x + c$ where c is any constant, then $\dfrac{dy}{dx} = 2x - 3$.

Now if we start with $\dfrac{dy}{dx} = 2x - 3$, then $y = x^2 - 3x$.

But this is not the original expression. The constant c is missing and so it must be added to the result. The correct result is $x^2 - 3x + c$. c is called the **arbitrary constant** as its value is not known, unless we are given further information. **It must always be added to an integral.** Such an integral is called an **indefinite integral**.

It is easy to get confused between differentiation and integration. It may help to remember:

Differentiation: multiply by the index and then **D**ecrease the index.

Integration: **I**ncrease the index and then divide by the new index.

▶ **Example 2**

Integrate wrt x **(a)** $2x^3 - 3x + 1$, **(b)** $(2x - 3)^2$, **(c)** $\dfrac{x^4 - 3x + 1}{2x^3}$.

▶ **Solution ...**

(a) Integrate each term: $\dfrac{2x^4}{4} - \dfrac{3x^2}{2} + \dfrac{x^1}{1} + c = \dfrac{x^4}{2} - \dfrac{3x^2}{2} + x + c$

(b) Expand first: $4x^2 - 12x + 9$

Now integrate: $\dfrac{4x^3}{3} - \dfrac{12x^2}{2} + 9x + c = \dfrac{4x^3}{3} - 6x^2 + 9x + c$

(c) Divide by $2x^3$ first: $\dfrac{x}{2} - \dfrac{3x^{-2}}{2} + \dfrac{x^{-3}}{2}$

Now integrate: $\dfrac{x^2}{2(2)} - \dfrac{3x^{-1}}{2(-1)} + \dfrac{x^{-2}}{2(-2)} + c = \dfrac{x^2}{4} + \dfrac{3}{2x} - \dfrac{1}{4x^2} + c$

17.2.1 Notation

The symbol for integration is $\int$. For example we write $\int 3x\, dx$. This means that the integrand $3x$ is to be integrated wrt x.

So $\qquad \int 3x\, dx = \dfrac{3x^2}{2} + c$ and $\int u^2\, du = \dfrac{u^3}{3} + c.$

> **If $\dfrac{dy}{dx} = f(x)$, then $y = \int f(x)\, dx + c$** .

▶ **Example 3**

Find
(a) $\int x^5\, dx$, **(b)** $\int dx$, **(c)** $\int 2t^3\, dt$, **(d)** $\int (s^2 - 2s + 3)\, ds$,

(e) $\int (p - 1)(2 - p)\, dp$.

▶ **Solution ...**

(a) $\int x^5\, dx = \dfrac{x^6}{6} + c$

(b) $\int dx$ means $\int 1\, dx = \int x^0\, dx = x + c$

(c) Here the variable is t: $\int 2t^3\, dt = \dfrac{2t^4}{4} + c = \dfrac{t^4}{2} + c.$

(d) If the integrand is a polynomial, it must be placed *in brackets* between the $\int$ sign and ds.

$\int (s^2 - 2s + 3)\, ds = \dfrac{s^3}{3} - \dfrac{2s^2}{2} + 3s + c = \dfrac{s^3}{3} - s^2 + 3s + c$

(e) Expand first.

$\int (-2 + 3p - p^2)\, dp = -2p + \dfrac{3p^2}{2} - \dfrac{p^3}{3} + c$

Note that an integral such as $\int 4x\, dy$ is not possible unless x can first be expressed in terms of y.

Exercise 17A (Answers on page 508)

1. Find the indefinite integrals of the following wrt x:

   (a) $4x$ (b) $4x^3$ (c) -7

   (d) $3x^2$ (e) $3-x$ (f) $4x^4$

   (g) $2x^5$ (h) x^2-3 (i) $1-x-x^2$

   (j) $x^2 - \dfrac{x}{4}$ (k) $1-3x-4x^2$ (l) $x^5 - 3x^2$

   (m) $\dfrac{2}{x^3}$ (n) $(x+2)^2$ (o) $(x-1)^3$

   (p) $1 - \dfrac{1}{3x^4}$ (q) $(2-x)^2$ (r) $x^2 - \dfrac{1}{x^2}$

   (s) $(x+2)(x-3)$ (t) $x + \dfrac{1}{x^2}$ (u) $\dfrac{x+1}{3x^3}$

   (v) $(x^2+2)(x-1)$ (w) $4x^{-3}+1$ (x) $4x^{-\frac{1}{3}} + x^2$

   (y) $1 + \sqrt{x}$ (z) $x - \dfrac{1}{\sqrt{x}}$

2. Find the following:

   (a) $\displaystyle\int (x-4)\,dx$ (b) $\displaystyle\int \dfrac{3}{y^2}\,dy$

   (c) $\displaystyle\int \dfrac{dx}{3}\ \left(\text{i.e. } \int \dfrac{1}{3}\,dx\right)$ (d) $\displaystyle\int \left(2 - \dfrac{1}{x^2}\right) dx$

   (e) $\displaystyle\int (3x-2)\,dx$ (f) $\displaystyle\int \dfrac{2t}{3}\,dt$

   (g) $\displaystyle\int \dfrac{4}{y^2}\,dy$ (h) $\displaystyle\int \left(\dfrac{1}{u^2} + \dfrac{2}{u^3}\right) du$

3. Find the following:

   (a) $\displaystyle\int \dfrac{u+1}{u^3}\,du$ (b) $\displaystyle\int (3r-2)^2\,dr$

   (c) $\displaystyle\int (3p-2)(p-3)\,dp$ (d) $\displaystyle\int (1-x)^3\,dx$

   (e) $\displaystyle\int \left(\dfrac{4t^3 - 3t^3 - 1}{3t^2}\right) dt$ (f) $\displaystyle\int \left(s - \dfrac{1}{2s}\right)^2 ds$

   (g) $\displaystyle\int (1-4s)(2+3s)\,ds$ (h) $\displaystyle\int \left(\dfrac{x+1}{2}\right)^2 dx$

   (i) $\displaystyle\int \left(x^3 - \dfrac{x}{2}\right) dx$ (j) $\displaystyle\int (1-2y)^2\,dy$

   (k) $\displaystyle\int \left(2t^3 - 4t + \dfrac{1}{3}\right) dt$ (l) $\displaystyle\int \left(2x + \dfrac{3}{2x}\right)^2 dx$

   (m) $\displaystyle\int \left(\dfrac{2t^4 + t^2 - 2}{t^4}\right) dt$ (n) $\displaystyle\int p(2p+3)(3p-2)\,dp$

17.2.2   Determining the Arbitrary Constant

If $\dfrac{dy}{dx} = 2x - 3$, then by integration, $y = x^2 - 3x + c$ ......(1),

where c is an arbitrary constant.

The value of c can be determined if we are given further information, like a value of x and the corresponding value of y. If we substitute this pair of values of x and y into equation (1), we can then obtain the value of c. If we then put this value of c back into equation (1), the resulting equation is the equation of the curve whose gradient function is $2x - 3$.

▶ **Example 4**

Find y given that $\dfrac{dy}{dx} = 2x - 3$ and that $y = -4$ when $x = 1$.

▶ **Solution . . .**

If $\dfrac{dy}{dx} = 2x - 3$, then $y = \displaystyle\int (2x - 3)\, dx = x^2 - 3x + c$.

This is the indefinite integral and is illustrated in Fig. 17.1. For all values of c, the family of curves $y = x^2 - 3x + c$ are parallel, one vertically above the other. The equations could be $y = x^2 - 3x$ or $y = x^2 - 3x + 5$ etc.

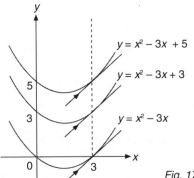

Fig. 17.1

For any value of x (say 3), the gradient on each curve at $x = 3$ is 3 as $\dfrac{dy}{dx} = 2x - 3$ and the tangents at these points are parallel.

Further information is therefore needed to identify a particular member of the family. In this example, we have the necessary information to find c.

When $x = 1$, $y = 1 - 3 + c = -4$ so $c = -2$. Hence $y = x^2 - 3x - 2$.

▶ **Example 5**

The gradient of the tangent at a point on a curve is given by $x^2 + x - 2$. Find the equation of the curve if it passes through $(2,1)$.

▶ **Solution . . .**

Gradient $= \dfrac{dy}{dx} = x^2 + x - 2$.

Then $y = \displaystyle\int (x^2 + x - 2)\, dx = \dfrac{x^3}{3} + \dfrac{x^2}{2} - 2x + c$.

When $x = 2$, $y = \dfrac{8}{3} + \dfrac{4}{2} - 4 + c = 1$. Hence $c = \dfrac{1}{3}$.

The equation of the curve is $y = \dfrac{x^3}{3} + \dfrac{x^2}{2} - 2x + \dfrac{1}{3}$

or $6y = 2x^3 + 3x^2 - 12x + 2$.

▶ **Example 6**

A curve has a turning point at the point $(-1,1)$. If the gradient is given by $6x^2 + ax - 12$, find the value of a and the equation of the curve.

▶ **Solution . . .**

$\dfrac{dy}{dx} = 6x^2 + ax - 12$

When $x = -1$, $\dfrac{dy}{dx} = 0$.

Then $6 - a - 12 = 0$ giving $a = -6$.

So $\dfrac{dy}{dx} = 6x^2 - 6x - 12$.

Hence $y = \displaystyle\int (6x^2 - 6x - 12)\, dx = 2x^3 - 3x^2 - 12x + c$.

When $x = -1$, $y = -2 - 3 + 12 + c = 1$, so $c = -6$.

The equation is $y = 2x^3 - 3x^2 - 12x - 6$.

▶ **Example 7**

For a curve $y = f(x)$, $\dfrac{d^2y}{dx^2} = 6x - 2$. Given that $y = 11$ and $\dfrac{dy}{dx} = 10$ when $x = 2$, find the equation of the curve.

▶ **Solution . . .**

$\dfrac{d^2y}{dx^2}$ is obtained by differentiating $\dfrac{dy}{dx}$ wrt x. Then $\dfrac{dy}{dx}$ is found by integrating $\dfrac{d^2y}{dx^2}$ wrt x.

$\dfrac{dy}{dx} = \displaystyle\int \dfrac{d^2y}{dx^2}\, dx = \int (6x - 2)\, dx = 3x^2 - 2x + c$

But $\dfrac{dy}{dx} = 10$ when $x = 2$.

Then $12 - 4 + c = 10$, giving $c = 2$

$\dfrac{dy}{dx} = 3x^2 - 2x + 2$

Now we integrate again to find y.

$y = \displaystyle\int (3x^2 - 2x + 2)\, dx = x^3 - x^2 + 2x + c_1$.

When $x = 2$, $y = 8 - 4 + 4 + c_1 = 11$ so $c_1 = 3$.

Hence the equation is $y = x^3 - x^2 + 2x + 3$.

Exercise 17B (Answers on page 509)

1. A curve is given by $\dfrac{dy}{dx} = 2x - 1$. If it passes through the point $(2,6)$, find its equation.

2. If a curve is given by $\dfrac{dy}{dx} = x(x - 1)$, find **(a)** its equation if it passes through the point $(1,0)$ and **(b)** the nature and coordinates of its turning points.

3. Given that $\dfrac{dy}{dx} = 1 - 5x$ and that $y = -5$ when $x = 2$, find the value of y when $x = 1$.

4. The rate of change of a quantity P is given by $\dfrac{dp}{dt} = t + 2$. If $P = 5$ when $t = 2$, find the value of P when $t = 3$.

5. Given that $\dfrac{d^2y}{dx^2} = 2x + 1$ and that $\dfrac{dy}{dx} = y = 3$ when $x = -1$, find y in terms of x.

6. Given that $\dfrac{d^2y}{dx^2} = 3$, find y in terms of x if $\dfrac{dy}{dx} = 4$ and $y = 6$ when $x = 2$.

7. A curve has gradient $x^2 - 4x + 3$ at the point (x, y) on the curve and it passes through the point $(3, -1)$. Find **(a)** its equation and **(b)** the types and coordinates of its turning points.

8. For the function $y = f(x)$, $\dfrac{dy}{dx} = x^2 + kx$ where k is a constant. If y has a turning point at the point $(3, -2)$, find the value of k and the value of y when $x = 4$.

9. If $\dfrac{dy}{dt} = 1 - \dfrac{1}{t^2}$, find the value of y when $t = 4$ if $y = 4$ when $t = 1$.

10. If $\dfrac{dy}{dx} = 6x^2 + 4x - 5$ and $y = 10$ when $x = 2$, find the value of y when $x = 3$.

11. The rate of change of a quantity L with respect to t is given by $\dfrac{dL}{dt} = 3t - 2$. If $L = 3$ when $t = 2$, find the value of L when $t = 4$.

12. A curve passes through the point $(1, 0)$ and its gradient at any point (x, y) on the curve is $3x^2 - 2x - 1$. Find **(a)** the equation of the curve, and **(b)** the coordinates of the points where y has a maximum and minimum value, identifying each one.

13. Given that $\dfrac{d^2y}{dx^2} = 3 - kt$ where k is a constant and that $\dfrac{dy}{dx} = -6$ when $t = -1$ and 9 when $t = 2$, find the value of k. If $y = -\dfrac{5}{6}$ when $t = 1$, find y in terms of t.

14. A quantity u varies with respect to t so that $\dfrac{du}{dt} = a + bt$ where a and b are constants. Given that it has a maximum value of $5\dfrac{1}{2}$ when $t = 1$ and that its rate of change when $t = 2$ is -3, find u in terms of t.

17.3 Area Under a Curve

An important application of integration is in finding the area under a given curve $y = f(x)$. Up to now, such areas could only be found approximately, for example, by counting squares or by the trapezium rule. Using calculus, we can now find the exact value of areas bounded by curves.

Fig. 17.2 shows part of a curve $y = f(x)$. The shaded area A lies between the curve and the x-axis, bounded by the ordinates at a and b. This area is called the area under the curve between a and b.

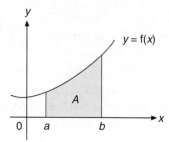

Fig. 17.2

We now show a method of finding A. For the moment we can only deal with areas which lie above the x-axis.

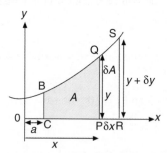

Fig. 17.3

Let P be a point on the x-axis where $OP = x$ (Fig. 17.3). $PQ = y$, $OC = a$ and CB is perpendicular to the x-axis. The shaded area under the curve from a to x is A.

Now take an increment δx in x to reach R and draw the ordinates RS. $RS = y + \delta y$ and the increment in $A = \delta A =$ the area PRSQ.

QT and US are drawn parallel to the x-axis (Fig. 17.4).
Area of rectangle PRTQ $< \delta A <$ area of rectangle PRSU.

i.e. $y\delta x < \delta A < (y + \delta y)\delta x$ so $y < \dfrac{\delta A}{\delta x} < y + \delta y$.

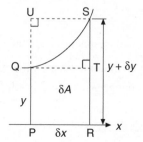

Fig. 17.4

Now if $\delta x \to 0$, $\delta y \to 0$ and $y + \delta y \to y$.

The left-hand term of the inequality (y) remains fixed at y but the right-hand term ($y + \delta y) \to y$. Hence $\dfrac{\delta A}{\delta x} \to y$ and in the limit $\dfrac{dA}{dx} = y$.

We then have
$$A = \int y \, dx + c = \int f(x) \, dx + c \ .$$

We can find c from the fact that $A = 0$ when $x = a$.

▶ Example 8

Find the area under the curve $y = x^2 + 2$ between $x = 1$ and $x = 3$ (Fig. 17.5).

▶ Solution . . .

$A = \int y \, dx = \int (x^2 + 2) \, dx = \dfrac{x^3}{3} + 2x + c$

Now when $x = 1$, $A = 0$.

Hence $0 = \dfrac{1}{3} + 2 + c$, giving $c = -2\dfrac{1}{3}$.

Then $A_1^x = \dfrac{x^3}{3} + 2x - 2\dfrac{1}{3}$ where A_1^x means the area between the ordinates

1 and x ($x > 1$).

To calculate the area from 1 to 3, substitute $x = 3$.

$A_1^3 = 9 + 6 - 2\dfrac{1}{3} = 12\dfrac{1}{3}$ units^2.

(If we require the area from 1 to 2, i.e. A_1^2, then we put $x = 2$.)

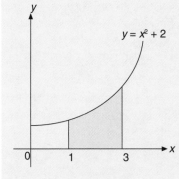

$y = x^2 + 2$

Fig. 17.5

▶ Example 9

Find the area under the curve $y = 2 + x - x^2$.

▶ Solution . . .

The curve meets the x-axis where $y = 0$,
i.e. where $2 + x - x^2 = (2 - x)(1 + x) = 0$,
giving $x = -1$ or $x = 2$ (Fig. 17.6).

So $A = \int (2 + x - x^2) \, dx = 2x + \dfrac{x^2}{2} - \dfrac{x^3}{3} + c$.

But $A = 0$ when $x = -1$.

Hence $0 = -2 + \dfrac{1}{2} + \dfrac{1}{3} + c$, giving $c = 1\dfrac{1}{6}$.

Then $A_{-1}^x = 2x + \dfrac{x^2}{2} - \dfrac{x^3}{3} + 1 \ $.

Now put $x = 2$ to obtain the required area.

$A_{-1}^2 = 4 + 2 - \dfrac{8}{3} + 1\dfrac{1}{6} = 4\dfrac{1}{2}$ units^2.

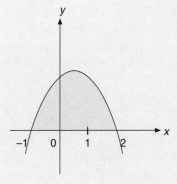

Fig. 17.6

17.4 Definite Integrals

We can shorten the above process by using the concept of a **definite integral**.

Suppose A_a^x is the area under $y = f(x)$ from a to x (Fig. 17.7).

Then $A = \int f(x)\,dx = g(x) + c$ where $g(x)$ is the indefinite integral of $f(x)$.

Now when $x = a$, $A = 0$ so $0 = g(a) + c$, giving $c = -g(a)$.

Hence $A_a^x = g(x) - g(a)$.

Now we put $x = b$

and $A_a^b = g(b) - g(a)$.

$\qquad$ = (value of the integral at b) – (value of the integral at a)

We write this as $\int_a^b f(x)\,dx$ and it is called the **definite integral** of $f(x)$ wrt x between the **limits** a (the lower limit) and b (the upper limit). The arbitrary constant c disappears in the subtraction.

Hence if $y = f(x)$, the area under the curve between the x coordinates a and b is:

$$\int_a^b f(x)\,dx = g(b) - g(a)$$

where $g(x)$ is the indefinite integral of $f(x)$.

This is only true if $f(x) \geq 0$. We will investigate what happens if $f(x) < 0$ later.

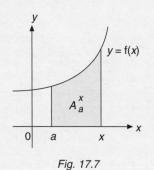

Fig. 17.7

▶ ## Example 10

Find the area under the curve $y = x^3 + 2$ from $x = -1$ to $x = 2$ (Fig. 17.8).

▶ ## Solution . . .

$$A = \int_{-1}^{2} y\,dx$$

$$= \int_{-1}^{2} (x^3 + 2)\,dx$$

$$= \left[\frac{x^4}{4} + 2x\right]_{-1}^{2} \quad \text{upper limit}$$
$$\qquad\qquad\qquad\qquad \text{lower limit}$$

$g(x) = \dfrac{x^4}{4} + 2x + c$

$g(x)$ is placed in square brackets with the limits at the right. The arbitrary constant is not included.

$$= \left(\frac{2^4}{4} + 2 \times 2\right) \quad - \quad \left(\frac{(-1)^4}{4} + 2 \times (-1)\right)$$

Substitute the **upper** limit to obtain $g(b)$, the value when $b = 2$.

Substitute the **lower** limit to obtain $g(a)$, the value when $a = -1$.

$$= 8 \qquad\qquad - \qquad \left(\frac{1}{4} - 2\right)$$

$$= 8 \qquad\qquad - \qquad \left(-1\frac{3}{4}\right)$$

$$= 9\frac{3}{4} \ \text{units}^2$$

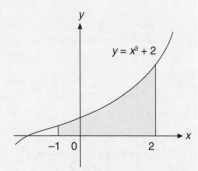

Fig. 17.8

▶ **Example 11**

(a) Find the coordinates of **(i)** the point A where the curves $y = (x + 1)^2$ and $y = (x - 3)^2$ intersect and **(ii)** the points where the curves meet the x-axis.

(b) Hence find the area of the region enclosed by the curves and the x-axis.

▶ **Solution ...**

(a) **(i)** The curves meet where $(x + 1)^2 = (x - 3)^2$ i.e. where $x = 1$.
Hence the coordinates of A are (1,4).

(ii) $y = (x + 1)^2$ meets $y = 0$ where $x = -1$, i.e., the point $(-1,0)$.
$y = (x - 3)^2$ meets $y = 0$ where $x = 3$, i.e., the point $(3,0)$.

(b) The curves are shown in Fig. 17.9. The area required is divided into two parts because the boundary changes at A ($x = 1$).

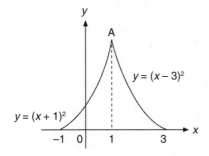

Fig. 17.9

Total area $= \displaystyle\int_{-1}^{1} (x + 1)^2 \, dx + \int_{1}^{3} (x - 3)^2 \, dx$

$= \displaystyle\int_{-1}^{1} (x^2 + 2x + 1) \, dx + \int_{1}^{3} (x^2 - 6x + 9) \, dx$

$= \left[\dfrac{x^3}{3} + x^2 + x \right]_{-1}^{1} + \left[\dfrac{x^3}{3} - 3x^2 + 9x \right]_{1}^{3}$

$= \left(\dfrac{1}{3} + 1 + 1 \right) - \left(-\dfrac{1}{3} + 1 - 1 \right) + (9 - 27 + 27) - \left(\dfrac{1}{3} - 3 + 9 \right)$

substitute   substitute   substitute   substitute
upper limit 1   lower limit −1   upper limit 3   lower limit 1

$= \dfrac{7}{3} + \dfrac{1}{3} + 9 - \dfrac{19}{3}$

$= \dfrac{16}{3}$ units^2

In the next two examples, only the *value* of the definite integral is to be found.

▶ **Example 12**

Find $\displaystyle\int_{-4}^{-2} \left(x - \frac{1}{x^2}\right) dx$.

▶ **Solution . . .**

$$\int_{-4}^{-2} \left(x - \frac{1}{x^2}\right) dx = \left[\frac{x^2}{2} + \frac{1}{x}\right]_{-4}^{-2}$$

$$= \underbrace{\left(\frac{(-2)^2}{2} + \frac{1}{-2}\right)}_{\substack{\text{substitute the upper} \\ \text{limit } (-2)}} - \underbrace{\left(\frac{(-4)^2}{2} + \frac{1}{-4}\right)}_{\substack{\text{substitute the lower} \\ \text{limit } (-4)}}$$

$$= \left(2 - \frac{1}{2}\right) - \left(8 - \frac{1}{4}\right)$$

$$= -6\frac{1}{4}$$

▶ **Example 13**

Evaluate $\displaystyle\int_{-2}^{0} (1 - t - t^2) \, dt$.

▶ **Solution . . .**

$$\int_{-2}^{0} (1 - t - t^2) \, dt = \left[t - \frac{t^2}{2} - \frac{t^3}{3}\right]_{-2}^{0}$$

$$= [0] - \left[-2 - \frac{(-2)^2}{2} - \frac{(-2)^3}{3}\right]$$

$$= 0 - \left(-1\frac{1}{3}\right) = 1\frac{1}{3}$$

▶ **Example 14**

The volume V of the liquid in a container leaks out at the rate of $30t$ cm^3 s^{-1} where t is the time in seconds. Find the amount of liquid lost in the third second.

▶ **Solution . . .**

$\dfrac{dV}{dt} = -30t$ (decreasing)

The third second is between $t = 2$ and $t = 3$.

So we find (value of V when $t = 3$) − (value of V when $t = 2$) using a definite integral.

Change of volume $= \displaystyle\int_{2}^{3} \frac{dV}{dt} \, dt = \int_{2}^{3} (-30t) \, dt = \left[-15t^2\right]_{2}^{3} = -135 - (-60)$

$$= -75$$

Hence 75 cm^3 of liquid was lost in the third second.

► **Example 15**

(a) Show from a diagram that
$$\int_a^c f(x)\,dx = \int_a^b f(x)\,dx + \int_b^c f(x)\,dx \text{ where } a < b < c.$$

(b) Given that $\int_2^5 f(x)\,dx = 10$, find (if possible) the values of

(i) $\int_2^5 2f(x)\,dx,$

(ii) $\int_2^5 [f(x) + 1]\,dx$

(iii) $\int_2^3 [f(x) - 2]\,dx + \int_3^5 f(x)\,dx,$

(iv) $\int_2^5 \left[1 - \frac{1}{2}f(x)\right] dx,$

(v) $\int_2^5 [f(x)]^2\,dx.$

► **Solution . . .**

(a) From Fig. 17.10, $\int_a^c f(x)\,dx = \text{area } A + \text{area } B$
$$= \int_a^b f(x)\,dx + \int_b^c f(x)\,dx$$

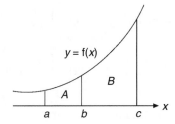

Fig. 17.10

(b) **(i)** $\int_2^5 2f(x)\,dx = 2\int_2^5 f(x)\,dx = 2 \times 10 = 20$

(ii) $\int_2^5 [f(x) + 1]\,dx = \int_2^5 f(x)\,dx + \int_2^5 1\,dx$
$$= 10 + \big[x\big]_2^5$$
$$= 10 + (5 - 2) = 13$$

(iii) $\int_2^3 [f(x) - 2]\,dx + \int_3^5 f(x)\,dx = \int_2^3 f(x)\,dx - \int_2^3 2\,dx + \int_3^5 f(x)\,dx$
$$= \int_2^5 f(x)\,dx - \big[2x\big]_2^3$$
$$= 10 - (6 - 4) = 8$$

(iv) $\int_2^5 \left[1 - \frac{1}{2}f(x)\right] dx = \int_2^5 1\,dx - \frac{1}{2}\int_2^5 f(x)\,dx$
$$= (5 - 2) - 5 = -2$$

(v) Not possible, as f(x) is not known.

Exercise 17C (Answers on page 509)

1. (a) $\displaystyle\int_{-2}^{1} dx$ (b) $\displaystyle\int_{-1}^{0} x\, dx$

(c) $\displaystyle\int_{-2}^{1} x^2\, dx$ (d) $\displaystyle\int_{0}^{3} (2x-1)\, dx$

(e) $\displaystyle\int_{-2}^{-1} (1-x)\, dx$ (f) $\displaystyle\int_{-2}^{2} x^3\, dx$

(g) $\displaystyle\int_{1}^{3} \frac{1}{x^2}\, dx$ (h) $\displaystyle\int_{-3}^{-1} (x-x^2)\, dx$

(i) $\displaystyle\int_{-1}^{2} (p-2)(p-3)\, dp$ (j) $\displaystyle\int_{a}^{b} dx$

(k) $\displaystyle\int_{t}^{2t} (u^2-3)\, du$ (l) $\displaystyle\int_{1}^{3} \frac{x-3}{x^3}\, dx$

(m) $\displaystyle\int_{-2}^{0} t(t^2-1)\, dt$ (n) $\displaystyle\int_{-3}^{-2} \left(\frac{1}{x^2} - \frac{1}{x^3}\right) dx$

(o) $\displaystyle\int_{-2}^{-1} 3x^2\, dx$ (p) $\displaystyle\int_{1}^{3} x^3\, dx$

(q) $\displaystyle\int_{0}^{3} x(3-x)\, dx$ (r) $\displaystyle\int_{-4}^{0} (3-2x)\, dx$

(s) $\displaystyle\int_{1}^{2} (x+1)(x+2)\, dx$ (t) $\displaystyle\int_{1}^{2} \left(x - \frac{1}{x^2}\right) dx$

(u) $\displaystyle\int_{-2}^{2} (x^3 - x^2 + x)\, dx$ (v) $\displaystyle\int_{1}^{2} (3x^2 + x^{-2})\, dx$

(w) $\displaystyle\int_{0}^{8} (5x^{\frac{2}{3}} - 2x)\, dx$ (x) $\displaystyle\int_{0}^{1} \left(\sqrt{x} + \frac{1}{\sqrt{x}}\right) dx$

2. If $\displaystyle\int_{0}^{a} (x-4)\, dx = 10$, find the values of a.

3. Given that $\displaystyle\int_{0}^{r} (2x-1)\, dx = 12$, find the values of r.

4. Given that $\displaystyle\int_{1}^{2} (x+p)\, dx = 3$, find the value of p.

5. If $\displaystyle\int_{0}^{3} (t^2 + \mu)\, dt = 3$, find the value of μ.

6. Find the value of u if $\displaystyle\int_{u}^{2u} \frac{1}{x^2}\, dx = \frac{1}{4}$.

7. Find the areas under the following curves between the coordinates given:
(a) $y = 4 - x^2; x = -2, x = 0$ (b) $y = x(3-x); x = 0, x = 3$

(c) $y = \frac{1}{2}x^2; x = 1, x = 2$ (d) $y = 3 - 2x - x^2; x = -3, x = 1$

(e) $y = 2 - x^2$; $x = -1$, $x = 1$ (f) $2y = 1 + x^2$; $x = -2$, $x = 1$

(g) $y = x^3 + 2$; $x = 0$, $x = 2$ (h) $y = x^2 - x - 2$; $x = -3$, $x = -1$

8. Find the area bounded by the curve $y = 2x - 2x^2$ and the positive x- and y-axes.

9. Find the area under the curve $y = x^2 + 3$ between the coordinates (a) $x = 0$ and $x = 2$, (b) $x = -2$ and $x = 2$. Using a sketch of the curve, explain the relation between the two areas.

10. The area under the curve $y = x^2 + ax - 5$ between the lines $x = 1$ and $x = 3$ is $14\frac{2}{3}$ units^2. Find the value of a.

11. If the area under the curve $y = \frac{x^2}{3}$ between $x = 2$ and $x = k$, where k is a constant, is 8 times the area under the curve between $x = 1$ and $x = 2$, find the value of k.

12. Given that $\frac{dA}{dt} = 2t^2 - t + 5$, find the change in the value of A between $t = 1$ and $t = 3$.

13. If $\frac{dT}{dt} = t^2 - t + 1$, find the change in T as t changes from 1 to 2.

14. The rate of change of a quantity P is given by $\frac{dP}{dt} = \frac{10}{t^2} + t$ for $t > 2$. Find the change in the value of P when t increases from 3 to 5.

15. If $\frac{d^2y}{dx^2} = 2x - 1$, find the increase in y as x increases from 2 to 4 given that $\frac{dy}{dx} = 6$ when $x = 2$.

16. The curve $y = ax^2 + bx + c$ passes through the points $(0,-2)$ and $(1,-3)$ and its gradient where $x = 2$ is 5. Find (a) the value of a, of b and of c, and (b) the area under the curve between the lines $x = 2$ and $x = 3$.

17. (a) If $\int_0^a (x - 1)\, dx = \frac{1}{2} \int_0^a (x + 1)\, dx$, find the value of a.

(b) Given that $\int_1^6 f(x)\, dx = 7$, evaluate (i) $\int_1^6 3f(x)\, dx$,

(ii) $\int_1^6 [2 - f(x)]\, dx$, (iii) $\int_1^3 [f(x) - 2]\, dx + \int_3^6 f(x)\, dx$.

18. Fig. 17.11 shows part of the line $y + 2x = 5$ and the curve $y = x(4 - x)$, which meet at A.

(a) Find the coordinates of A.

(b) Hence find the area of the shaded region.

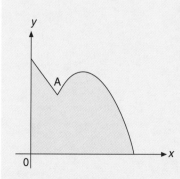

Fig. 17.11

19. The curve $y = 4 - x^2$ meets the positive x-axis at B and the curve $y = x(4 - x)$ meets the positive x-axis at C. The curves intersect at A. Find

(a) the coordinates of A, B and C,

(b) the area of the region ABC bounded by the curves and the x-axis.

20. (a) If $y = x^2 - 4x + 4$, find (i) where the curve meets the y-axis and (ii) the x-coordinate m of the minimum point on the curve.

(b) Sketch on the same diagram the graph of $y = 4 - x^2$ for $-2 \le x \le 0$ and the graph of $y = x^2 - 4x + 4$ for $0 \le x \le m$.

(c) Hence find the total area under the two curves.

17.5 Further Notes on Areas

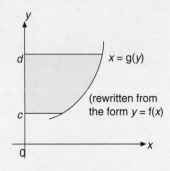

Fig. 17.12

(I) Area between a curve and the y-axis

The area between $y = f(x)$ and the x-axis for $a \le x \le b$ is $\int_a^b y \, dx$.

Similarly, the area between $y = f(x)$ and the y-axis is $\int_c^d x\,dy$ where c and d are the limits on the y-axis and the equation of the curve is expressed in the form $x = g(y)$ (Fig. 17.12).

▶ ## Example 16

Fig. 17.13 shows part of the curve $(y - 1)^2 = x - 1$. Find the area of the shaded region.

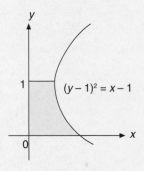

Fig. 17.13

▶ ## Solution . . .

The area $= \int_0^1 x\,dy$ as 0 and 1 are the limits for y.

The equation of the curve is rewritten as $x = (y - 1)^2 + 1 = y^2 - 2y + 2$.

So the area is $\int_0^1 (y^2 - 2y + 2)\,dy = \left[\dfrac{y^3}{3} - y^2 + 2y \right]_0^1$

$$= \left(\frac{1}{3} - 1 + 2 \right) - (0) = 1\frac{1}{3} \text{ units}^2.$$

II Area under the x-axis

The curve $y = x^2 - 3x + 2 = (x - 2)(x - 1)$ meets the x-axis where $x = 1$ and $x = 2$ (Fig. 17.14).

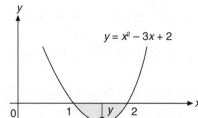

Fig. 17.14

For all points in the domain $1 < x < 2$, y will be negative, so $\int y\,dx$ will also be negative for this domain.

$$\int_1^2 y\,dx = \int_1^2 (x^2 - 3x + 2)\,dx = \left[\frac{x^3}{3} - \frac{3x^2}{2} + 2x\right]$$

$$= \left(\frac{8}{3} - 6 + 4\right) - \left(\frac{1}{3} - \frac{3}{2} + 2\right)$$

$$= \frac{3}{2} - \frac{5}{6}$$

$$= -\frac{1}{6} \text{ which is negative as expected.}$$

The numerical value of $\int y\,dx$ is $\frac{1}{6}$ and this is the area below the x-axis.

If part of a curve lies below the x-axis, the area between that part and the x-axis is $-\int y\,dx$ (Fig. 17.15).

If a curve lies partly above and partly below the x-axis (Fig. 17.16), the total area will be $\int_a^b y\,dx - \int_b^c y\,dx$.

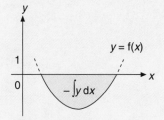

Fig. 17.15

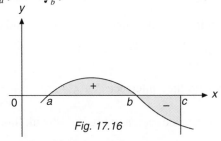

Fig. 17.16

The two parts are evaluated separately. Hence a sketch of the curve must be made to check if any part is below the x-axis.

Similarly the area of a region between a curve and the y-axis on the left of the y-axis will be negative. Its numerical value is $-\int x\,dy$.

▶ **Example 17**

Find the area between the curve $y = x(x - 2)$ and the x-axis from $x = -1$ to $x = 2$.

▶ **Solution . . .**

The curve meets the x-axis at $x = 0$ and $x = 2$ (Fig. 17.17).

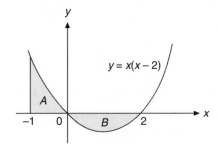

Fig. 17.17

Area $A = \int_{-1}^{0} (x^2 - 2x)\, dx = \left[\dfrac{x^3}{3} - x^2\right]_{-1}^{0} = (0) - \left(-\dfrac{1}{3} - 1\right) = 1\dfrac{1}{3}$

Area $B = -\int_{0}^{2} (x^2 - 2x)\, dx = -\left[\dfrac{x^3}{3} - x^2\right]_{0}^{2} = -\left[\left(\dfrac{8}{3} - 4\right) - (0)\right] = 1\dfrac{1}{3}$

Hence the total area is $1\dfrac{1}{3} + 1\dfrac{1}{3} = 2\dfrac{2}{3}$ units^2.

Note that $\int_{-1}^{2} (x^2 - 2x)\, dx = \left[\dfrac{x^3}{3} - x^2\right]_{-1}^{2}$

$$= \left(\dfrac{8}{3} - 4\right) - \left(-\dfrac{1}{3} - 1\right) = 0$$

which is the correct value for this *integral* but not for the *area*.

(III) Area between a curve and a line, or between two curves

▶ **Example 18**

Find the area enclosed by the curve $y = 5 + x - x^2$ and the line $y = x + 4$.

▶ **Solution . . .**

First we find where they intersect: $5 + x - x^2 = x + 4$, i.e. $x^2 = 1$ giving $x = 1$ or -1.

So we require the shaded region in Fig. 17.18 with limits $x = -1$ and $x = 1$.

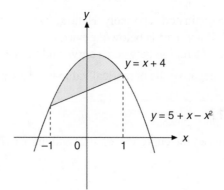

Fig. 17.18

Now the area under the curve

$$= \int_{-1}^{1} (5 + x - x^2)\, dx$$

and the area under the line

$$= \int_{-1}^{1} (x + 4)\, dx.$$

Hence the shaded area $= \int_{-1}^{1} (5 + x - x^2)\, dx - \int_{-1}^{1} (x + 4)\, dx.$

Since these two definite integrals have the same limits, they can be combined into one definite integral:

$$\int_{-1}^{1} [(5 + x - x^2) - (x + 4)]\, dx = \int_{-1}^{1} (5 + x - x^2 - x - 4)\, dx$$

$$= \int_{-1}^{1} (1 - x^2)\, dx$$

$$= \left[x - \frac{x^3}{3} \right]_{-1}^{1}$$

$$= \left(1 - \frac{1}{3} \right) - \left(-1 + \frac{1}{3} \right) = \frac{4}{3}$$

Hence the area enclosed is $\frac{4}{3}$ units^2.

In Fig. 17.19, $y = f(x)$ and $y = g(x)$ are two curves such that $f(x) > g(x)$ for $a \le x \le b$.

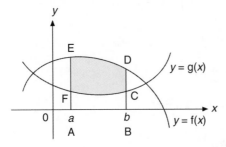

Fig. 17.19

Then $\int_{a}^{b} f(x) \, dx =$ area ABDE and $\int_{a}^{b} g(x) \, dx =$ area ABCF.

Hence the area between the curves, i.e. the shaded area

$\quad =$ ABDE $-$ ABCF

$$= \int_{a}^{b} [f(x) - g(x)] \, dx.$$

> **Area between $y = f(x)$ and $y = g(x)$ for $a \le x \le b$**
>
> $$= \int_{a}^{b} [f(x) - g(x)] \, dx,$$
>
> **where $f(x) > g(x)$.**

This rule is still true if parts of either curve are below the x-axis (provided $f(x) > g(x)$) as the next example shows.

▶ **Example 19**

Find the area enclosed by the curves $y_1 = x^2$ and $y_2 = x^2 - 2x$ and the lines $x = 1$ and $x = 3$ (Fig. 17.20).

▶ **Solution . . .**

We require the shaded area.
$y_2 = x^2 - 2x = x(x - 2)$, so it meets the x-axis at $x = 0$ and $x = 2$.
Consider the regions A, B and C.

$$A = \int_{1}^{2} y_1 \, dx$$

$$B = -\int_{1}^{2} y_2 \, dx \text{ (as } y_2 \text{ is below the } x\text{-axis in this interval).}$$

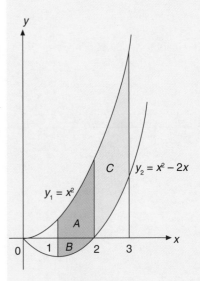

Fig. 17.20

So $\int_1^2 y_1\, dx - \int_1^2 y_2\, dx = A + B.$

Hence the rule is true for areas crossing the x-axis.

$C = \int_2^3 y_1\, dx - \int_2^3 y_2\, dx$ (as both y_1 and y_2 are above the x-axis)

Hence the total shaded area $A + B + C$

$$= \int_1^2 (y_1 - y_2)\, dx + \int_2^3 (y_1 - y_2)\, dx$$

$$= \int_1^3 (y_1 - y_2)\, dx$$

$$= \int_1^3 (x^2 - x^2 + 2x)\, dx$$

$$= \left[x^2\right]_1^3 = 9 - 1 = 8 \text{ units}^2.$$

▶ **Example 20**

The tangents at $x = 0$ and $x = 3$ on the curve $y = 2x - x^2 - 1$ meet at T.

(a) Find the equations of these tangents and the coordinates of T.

(b) Calculate the area of the region bounded by the curve and the tangents.

▶ **Solution . . .**

The curve and the tangents are shown in Fig. 17.21.

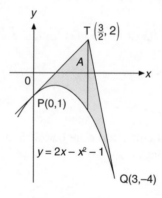

Fig. 17.21

If $y = 2x - x^2 - 1$, then $\dfrac{dy}{dx} = 2 - 2x$.

(a) The tangent at P(0,– 1) has gradient 2.
Hence its equation is $y + 1 = 2x$.
The tangent at Q(3,–4) has gradient $2 - 6 = -4$.
Hence its equation is $y + 4 = -4(x - 3)$, i.e. $y = -4x + 8$.

These lines intersect where $2x - 1 = -4x + 8$, i.e. $x = 1\frac{1}{2}$.

When $x = 1\frac{1}{2}$, $y = 2x - 1 = 2$.

Therefore the coordinates of T are $\left(1\frac{1}{2}, 2\right)$.

(b) The shaded area is divided into two parts, A and B as the boundary line changes at $T\left(x = \frac{3}{2}\right)$.

$$\text{Area of A} = \int_0^{\frac{3}{2}} [(2x - 1) - (2x - x^2 - 1)]\, dx$$

$$= \int_0^{\frac{3}{2}} x^2\, dx = \left[\frac{x^3}{3}\right]_0^{\frac{3}{2}} = \frac{9}{8}$$

$$\text{Area of B} = \int_{\frac{3}{2}}^3 [(-4x + 8) - (2x - x^2 - 1)]\, dx$$

$$= \int_{\frac{3}{2}}^3 (x^2 - 6x + 9)\, dx$$

$$= \left[\frac{x^3}{3} - 3x^2 + 9x\right]_{\frac{3}{2}}^3$$

$$= (9 - 27 + 27) - \left(\frac{27}{24} - \frac{27}{4} + \frac{27}{2}\right) = \frac{27}{24} = \frac{9}{8}$$

Hence the total shaded area is $\frac{9}{4}$ units^2.

Exercise 17D *(Answers on page 509)*

1. Find the area of the region bounded by the curve $y = x^2 - 9$ and the x-axis.

2. Calculate the area enclosed by the curve $y = 3x - x^2$, the x-axis and the lines $x = -1$, $x = 2$.

3. Find where the curve $y = x^2 - x - 1$ meets the line $y = 5$. Hence find the area of the region bounded by the curve and the line $y = 5$.

4. Part of the curve $y = x(x - 1)(x - 2)$ is shown in Fig. 17.22. Find the values of a and b. Hence find the area of the region enclosed by the curve and the x-axis from $x = 0$ to $x = b$.

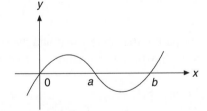

Fig. 17.22

5. Find the area of the region enclosed by the following curves or lines:
   (a) $y = 2x,\ y = x^2$ **(b)** $y = x^2,\ y = 4$
   (c) $y = x^2 - 2,\ y = \frac{1}{2}x^2$ **(d)** $y = x^2,\ y = x^3$
   (e) $y = 2x^2,\ y = x + 1$ **(f)** $y = x(2 - x),\ y = x$
   (g) $y = 2 - x^2,\ y = -2$ **(h)** $y = x^2 + 3,\ y = 5 - x$
   (i) $y = x^2 - 1,\ y = x + 1$

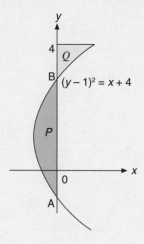

Fig. 17.23

6. In Fig. 17.23, the curve $(y-1)^2 = x + 4$ meets the y-axis at A and B.
    (a) Find the coordinates of A and B.
    (b) Calculate the areas of
        (i)   the shaded region P,   (ii)   the shaded region Q.

7. For a curve, $\dfrac{dy}{dx} = 2x + k$ where k is a constant, and the curve has a turning point where $x = 2$.
    (a) If it passes through the point $(-1, 8)$, find its equation.
    (b) The line $y = x + 3$ meets the curve at points A and B. Find the coordinates of A and B.
    (c) Hence find the area of the region enclosed by the curve and the line.

8. (a) Sketch the curve $y = x(3 - x)$.
    (b) Find the equation of the normal to the curve at the origin and the x-coordinate of the point where this normal meets the curve again.
    (c) Find the area of the region bounded by the curve and the normal.

9. The normal at the point A $(x = 0)$ on the curve $y = 2 - x - x^2$ meets the curve again at B. Find (a) the coordinates of B, (b) the area of the region bounded by the curve and the normal.

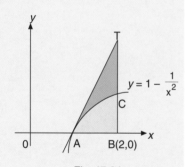

Fig. 17.24

10. Fig. 17.24 shows part of the curve $y = 1 - \dfrac{1}{x^2}$. Find
    (a) the coordinates of the point A where the curve meets the x-axis,
    (b) the equation of the tangent to the curve at A.
    (c) The line through B(2,0) parallel to the y-axis meets the curve at C and the tangent at T. Find the ratio of the areas of the shaded regions ABC and ACT.

11. Fig. 17.25 shows part of the curve $y = x^2$ and the line $y = 4$. The line AB is drawn through A(0,2) with gradient -1 to meet the curve at B. Find
    (a) the coordinates of B,
    (b) the ratio of the shaded areas P and Q.

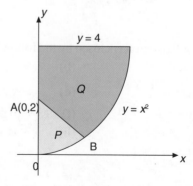

Fig. 17.25

12. **(a)** Sketch the curve $y = x(4 - x)$.

   (b) Find the equations of the tangents to the curve at the origin O and at the point where $x = 3$.

   (c) If these tangents meet at T, find the x-coordinate of T and the area of the region enclosed by the tangents and the curve.

13. Fig. 17.26 shows part of the curve $y = x^2 - x + 2$ and line UV.

   (a) Find the coordinates of U and V and the equation UV.

   (b) Hence find the area of the shaded region.

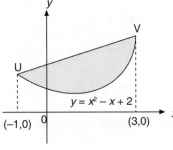

Fig. 17.26

14. Fig. 17.27 shows part of the curve $y = 5 - x - x^2$ and the line $y = 2x + 1$ which meet at A and B. Find

   (a) the x-coordinate of A and of B, and

   (b) the area of the shaded region.

15. Fig. 17.28 shows part of the curves $y = \dfrac{2}{x^2}$ and $y = x^2 - 4x$.

   A is the point $(1,2)$ and BC is part of the line $x = 3$. Find the area of the shaded region.

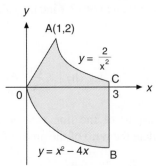

Fig. 17.28

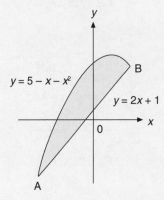

Fig. 17.27

Summary

1. If $\dfrac{dy}{dx} = f(x)$, then $y = \displaystyle\int f(x)\, dx + c$ (indefinite integral).

2. If $\dfrac{dy}{dx} = ax^n$, $y = \dfrac{ax^{n+1}}{n+1} + c$, $(n \neq -1)$.

3. Definite integral $\displaystyle\int_a^b f(x)\, dx = \Big[g(x)\Big]_a^b = g(b) - g(a)$ where $g(x)$ is the indefinite integral of $f(x)$.

4. Area beween $y = f(x)$, the x-axis and $x = a$, $x = b$ (Fig. 17.29 (a))

$$= \int_a^b y \, dx = \int_a^b f(x) \, dx.$$

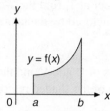

Fig. 17.29(a)

5. If $f(x) < 0$ for $a \le x \le b$, the area $= -\int_a^b f(x) \, dx.$

6. Area between $y = f(x)$ and the y-axis for $c \le y \le d$ (Fig. 17.29 (b))

$$= \int_c^d x \, dy \text{ where } x \text{ is found in terms of } y.$$

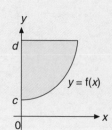

Fig. 17.29(b)

7. Area between $y = f(x)$ and $y = g(x)$ for $a \le x \le b$ and $f(x) > g(x)$ (Fig. 17.29 (c))

$$= \int_a^b [f(x) - g(x)] \, dx.$$

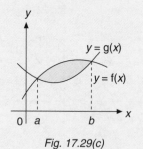

Fig. 17.29(c)

Revision Exercise 17 *(Answers on page 509)*

1. On a curve for which $\dfrac{dy}{dx} = p + x$, where p is a constant, the tangent at the point $(2,5)$ has a gradient of -2. Find the value of p and the equation of the curve.

2. Evaluate **(a)** $\displaystyle\int_{-2}^{-1} (x - \frac{1}{x^2}) \, dx$, **(b)** $\displaystyle\int_1^2 \frac{x+1}{x^3} \, dx$.

3. Fig. 17.30 shows part of the line $y = 2x$ and part of the curve $y = 4x - x^2$. Calculate the ratio of the areas of the regions P and Q.

(C)

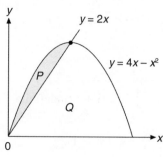

Fig. 17.30

4. Fig. 17.31 shows part of the curve $y = x^2 - 2x + 2$ and a chord PQ. Find

    (a) the coordinates of P and Q,

    (b) the ratio of the area of the shaded region A to the area of the shaded region B.   (C)

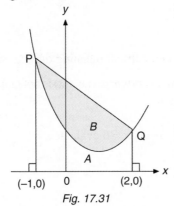

Fig. 17.31

5. Fig. 17.32 shows part of the curve $y = 5 + 4x - x^2$. A is the maximum point of the curve. Find

    (a) the coordinates of A,

    (b) the equation of OA,

    (c) the area of the shaded region.

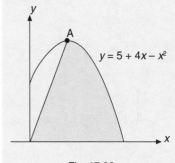

Fig. 17.32

6. Fig. 17.33 shows part of the curve $y = 6x - x^2$ and the line $y = 3x$. Show that the area enclosed by the curve and the x-axis is 36 units^2. Calculate the ratio of the areas of the regions marked A and B.   (C)

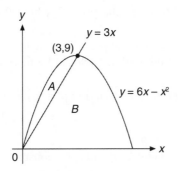

Fig. 17.33

7. The tangent at the point (2,4) on the curve $y = x^2$ meets the x-axis at A.

    (a) Find the coordinates of A.

    (b) Find the area of the region bounded by the curve, the x-axis and the tangent.

8. The part of the curve $y = 4 - x^2$ lying in the first quadrant meets the y-axis at A and the x-axis at B. C lies on the curve and the equation of OC is $y = 3x$, where O is the origin.
  (a) Find the coordinates of A, B and C.
  (b) Find the ratio of the area of the region OAC to the area of the region OBC.

9. **(a)** Explain the geometrical meaning of the result $\int_0^6 f(x)\, dx = 0$ if $f(x)$ is not zero everywhere (i.e. $f(x)$ is not graphically represented by the x-axis.)

  (b) Given that $\int_0^4 p(x)\, dx = 6$ evaluate

  (i) $\int_0^4 3p(x)\, dx$,

  (ii) $\int_0^4 [2 - p(x)]\, dx$,

  (iii) $\int_0^2 [p(x) - 2]\, dx + \int_2^4 [p(x) + 1]\, dx$.

10. Fig. 17.34 shows part of the curve $(y - 2)^2 = x + 4$ and part of the line $y = \dfrac{1}{2}x$. Find **(a)** the coordinates of B, **(b)** the area of the shaded region.

11. Fig. 17.35 shows part of the curve $y = x - \dfrac{1}{x^2}$. Given that C is the point (2,0), find
  (a) the equation of the tangent to the curve at the point A,
  (b) the coordinates of the point T where this tangent meets the x-axis,
  (c) the coordinates of the point B where the curve meets the x-axis,
  (d) the area of the region enclosed by the curve and the lines AT and BT,
  (e) the ratio of the area found in part (d) to the area of the triangle ATC. (C)

12. $y = ax^2 + bx + c$ where a, b and c are constants. Given $\int_{-1}^1 xy\, dx = 0$, find the value of b. If $y = 2$ when $x = 1$ and $\int_{-1}^1 y\, dx = 0$, find the value of a and of c.

13. Sketch the graph of $y = |x^2 - 2x|$. Hence find $\int_0^3 |x^2 - 2x|\, dx$.

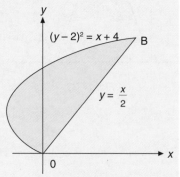

Fig. 17.34

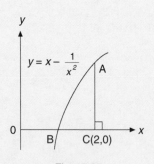

Fig. 17.35

You may have learnt that the volume of a sphere with radius r is $\frac{4}{3}\pi r^3$ without actually knowing why it is true. Integration provides a neat way of proving this fact.

Consider an area enclosed by a curve $y = f(x)$ and the line $x = a$ and $x = b$. It has been established in Calculus that when this area is rotated about the x-axis, the volume (V) generated is given by the formula $V = \pi\int_{a}^{b} y^2 \, dx$. This is illustrated in Fig. (17.36) for the curve $y = x^2$ between $x = 1$ and $x = 2$.

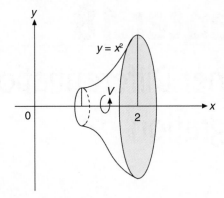

Fig. 17.36

The equation of a circle with radius r and centre at the origin O is $x^2 + y^2 = r^2$ (see Fig. 17.37). If we rotate the shaded area about the x-axis, we will get a sphere of radius r.

Hence the volume of the sphere, using the above formula is

$$V = \pi\int_{-r}^{r} y^2 \, dx.$$

Proceed from here to obtain the well-established formula for volume of a sphere, i.e. $V = \frac{4}{3}\pi r^3$.

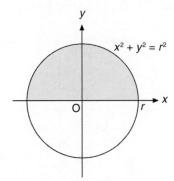

Fig. 17.37

Chapter 18

Further Differentiation and Integration

In Fig. 18.1, OAPB is a sector of a circle centre O, radius r and angle x radians. CA is perpendicular to OA.

Can you find the areas of the following?

(a) ΔOAB

(b) ΔOAC

(c) Sector OAB

By comparing these areas, deduce that:

$$\sin x < x < \tan x$$

Keep this result in mind. We shall be using it later.

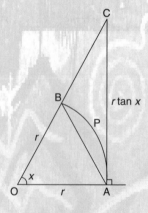

Fig. 18.1

18.1 Differentiation of Trigonometric Functions

Before we can differentiate trigonometric functions we need to find an important limit, i.e. $\lim\limits_{x \to 0} \dfrac{\sin x}{x}$ where x is in radians.

Using a calculator, the following values of $\sin x$ and x were obtained:

x (radians)	$\sin x$
0.2	0.198 669
0.1	0.099 83
0.05	0.049 979
0.01	0.009 999 8
0.001	0.000 999 9

This shows that when x is small, $\sin x \approx x$. It would suggest that $\lim\limits_{x \to 0} \dfrac{\sin x}{x} = 1$. Here is a simple proof of this.

We use the result in the discussion earlier, i.e. $\sin x < x < \tan x$.

Dividing by $\sin x$, $1 < \dfrac{x}{\sin x} < \dfrac{1}{\cos x}$.

Now as $x \to 0$, $\cos x \to 1$ and $\dfrac{1}{\cos x} \to 1$.

The left-hand term (1) is fixed at 1 and the right-hand term $\left(\dfrac{1}{\cos x}\right) \to 1$.

Hence the middle term $\left(\dfrac{x}{\sin x}\right)$ must $\to 1$. Therefore $\lim\limits_{x \to 0} \dfrac{x}{\sin x} = 1$.

In a more convenient form,

$$\lim_{x \to 0} \frac{\sin x}{x} = 1$$

Note: For the result $\lim\limits_{x \to 0} \dfrac{\sin x}{x} = 1$ to be valid, x must be in radians.

18.1.1 *Differentiation of sin x*

We can now find the derivative of $\sin x$ (x in radians).

Let $y = \sin x$. If x takes an increment δx, the corresponding increment in y will be δy.

Then $y + \delta y = \sin(x + \delta x)$ so $\delta y = \sin(x + \delta x) - \sin x$.

To simplify this, we need to use the trigonometric identity:

$\sin(A + B) - \sin(A - B) \equiv 2 \cos A \sin B$ ....(1)

We shall not prove identity (1) as it is beyond the scope of the present syllabus.

Now if we take $A + B = x + \delta x$ and $A - B = x$, then $A = x + \dfrac{\delta x}{2}$, $B = \dfrac{\delta x}{2}$.

Hence, using the result (1), $\delta y = 2 \cos\left(x + \dfrac{\delta x}{2}\right) \sin\left(\dfrac{\delta x}{2}\right)$.

Then $\dfrac{\delta y}{\delta x} = \dfrac{2 \cos(x + \frac{\delta x}{2}) \sin(\frac{\delta x}{2})}{\delta x} = \cos\left(x + \dfrac{\delta x}{2}\right) \dfrac{\sin(\frac{\delta x}{2})}{\frac{\delta x}{2}}$.

If $\delta x \to 0$, then $\dfrac{\delta y}{\delta x} \to \dfrac{dy}{dx}$, $\cos\left(x + \dfrac{\delta x}{2}\right) \to \cos x$ and the limit of $\dfrac{\sin(\frac{\delta x}{2})}{\frac{\delta x}{2}}$ is 1 (as $\dfrac{\delta x}{2}$ also $\to 0$). Hence $\dfrac{dy}{dx} = \cos x$.

$$\frac{d}{dx} \sin x = \cos x \qquad x \text{ in radians}$$

Note that $\dfrac{d}{dx}\sin x$ is another way of writing $\dfrac{d\sin x}{dx}$, which is also the same as writing $\dfrac{dy}{dx}$ when $y = \sin x$.

The gradient at any point on the sine curve is the value of $\cos x$ at that point (Fig. 18.2).

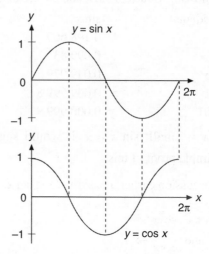

Fig. 18.2

▶ **Example 1**

Differentiate **(a)** $\sin 3x$, **(b)** $\sin(ax + b)$, **(c)** $\sin^2 x$, **(d)** $\sin^3(3x - 2)$.

▶ **Solution . . .**

(a) $y = \sin 3x$

We treat this as a composite function, i.e. $y = \sin u$ where $u = 3x$.

$\dfrac{dy}{du} = \cos u$ and $\dfrac{du}{dx} = 3$.

Then $\dfrac{dy}{dx} = \dfrac{dy}{du} \times \dfrac{du}{dx} = \cos u \times 3 = 3\cos 3x$.

Compare $\dfrac{dy}{dx}$ with y. Note the function **sin** is differentiated first to give cos, then the angle **3x** differentiated to give 3.

(b) $y = \sin(ax + b)$

Taking $y = \sin u$ where $u = ax + b$,

$\dfrac{dy}{dx} = \dfrac{dy}{du} \times \dfrac{du}{dx} = \cos u \times a = a\cos(ax + b)$

Note this result for future use:

$$\dfrac{d}{dx}\sin(ax + b) = a\cos(ax + b)$$

First differentiate the function, then differentiate the angle.

(c) $y = \sin^2 x$

Treat this as a power of the function $\sin x$, as $\sin^2 x$ means $(\sin x)^2$.

Take $y = u^2$ where $u = \sin x$.

First differentiate as a **power**, i.e. $\dfrac{dy}{du}$, then differentiate the function **sin**, i.e. $\dfrac{du}{dx}$.

$$\dfrac{dy}{dx} = \quad 2\sin x \qquad \times \qquad \cos x \qquad = 2\sin x \cos x$$

$$\underset{\substack{\text{differentiate} \\ \sin^2 x \text{ to get} \\ 2\sin x}}{} \qquad \underset{\substack{\text{differentiate} \\ \sin x \text{ to get} \\ \cos x}}{}$$

(d) $y = \sin^3(3x - 2)$

First differentiate as a power, then differentiate sin and then the angle.

$$\dfrac{dy}{dx} = 3\sin^2(3x - 2) \quad \times \quad \cos(3x - 2) \quad \times \qquad 3$$

$$\underset{\substack{\text{differentiate } \sin^3 \\ \text{to get } 3\sin^2}}{} \qquad \underset{\substack{\text{differentiate sin} \\ \text{to get cos}}}{} \qquad \underset{\substack{\text{differentiate} \\ 3x - 2 \text{ to get } 3}}{}$$

The sequence is
$$\sin^3(3x - 2)$$
power first — function second — variable last

Hence $\dfrac{dy}{dx} = 9\sin^2(3x - 2)\cos(3x - 2)$.

Using this method, we can obtain the following results:

> **If $y = \sin^n(ax + b)$,**
>
> **then $\dfrac{dy}{dx} = na\sin^{n-1}(ax + b)\cos(ax + b)$.**

▶ **Example 2**

Differentiate $\sin x^\circ$ wrt x.

▶ **Solution . . .**

We must first convert the angle to radians.

$x^\circ = \dfrac{\pi x}{180}$ radians

If $y = \sin \dfrac{\pi x}{180}$, then

$\dfrac{dy}{dx} = \cos \dfrac{\pi x}{180} \times \dfrac{\pi}{180}$ or $\dfrac{\pi}{180}\cos x^\circ$.

Note that the result is NOT $\cos x^\circ$. All formulae in calculus for trigonometric functions are only true for radian measure. Angles in degrees must be converted to radians.

▶ **Example 3**

Differentiate wrt x **(a)** $x\sin x$, **(b)** $\sqrt{1 - \sin x}$ wrt x.

► **Solution . . .**

(a) This is a product of x and $\sin x$.

If $y = x \sin x$, then $\dfrac{dy}{dx} = x \cos x + \sin x$.

(b) If $y = (1 - \sin x)^{\frac{1}{2}}$, $\dfrac{dy}{dx} = \dfrac{1}{2}(1 - \sin x)^{-\frac{1}{2}} \times (-\cos x)$

$$= \frac{-\cos x}{2\sqrt{1 - \sin x}}.$$

► **Example 4**

Find the values of x for $0 < x < \pi$ which satisfy the equation

$\dfrac{d}{dx}(x - \sin x) = \cos^2 x.$

► **Solution . . .**

$\dfrac{d}{dx}(x - \sin x) = 1 - \cos x$

Hence $1 - \cos x = \cos^2 x$

i.e. $\cos^2 x + \cos x - 1 = 0$

$\cos x = \dfrac{-1 \pm \sqrt{1 + 4}}{2}$

$\qquad = 0.618 \text{ or } - 1.618 \text{ (not admissible)}$

$\qquad x = 0.905 \text{ or } 5.38 \text{ radians}$

18.1.2 Differentiation of cos x

To differentiate, we recall that,

$\sin\!\left(\dfrac{\pi}{2} - x\right) = \cos x,$

and $\cos\!\left(\dfrac{\pi}{2} - x\right) = \sin x.$

So $\dfrac{d(\cos x)}{dx} = \dfrac{d \sin(\frac{\pi}{2} - x)}{dx}$

$\qquad\qquad = \cos\!\left(\dfrac{\pi}{2} - x\right) \times (-1) = -\cos\!\left(\dfrac{\pi}{2} - x\right)$

$\qquad\qquad = -\sin x.$

$$\frac{d}{dx}\cos x = -\sin x \qquad x \text{ in radians}$$

It follows that $\qquad \dfrac{d}{dx}\cos(ax + b) = -a \sin(ax + b)$

and $\qquad \dfrac{d}{dx}\cos^n(ax + b) = -na \cos^{n-1}(ax + b) \sin(ax + b).$

▶ Example 5

Differentiate **(a)** $\cos 5x$, **(b)** $\cos^2\left(\frac{x}{2}+3\right)$, **(c)** $\dfrac{\sin 2x}{\cos 3x}$.

▶ Solution . . .

(a) $y = \cos 5x$

Using the same procedure as before, $\dfrac{dy}{dx} = -\sin 5x \times 5$
$$= -5 \sin 5x.$$

(b) $y = \cos^2\left(\frac{x}{2}+3\right)$

$\dfrac{dy}{dx} = 2\cos\left(\frac{x}{2}+3\right) \times \left(-\sin\left(\frac{x}{2}+3\right)\right) \times \frac{1}{2}$

$\qquad = -\sin\left(\frac{x}{2}+3\right)\cos\left(\frac{x}{2}+3\right)$

(c) $y = \dfrac{\sin 2x}{\cos 3x}$

Using the quotient rule,

$\dfrac{dy}{dx} = \dfrac{(\cos 3x)(2\,\cos 2x) - (\sin 2x)(-3\,\sin 3x)}{\cos^2 3x}$

$\qquad = \dfrac{2\,\cos 3x \cos 2x + 3\,\sin 3x \sin 2x}{\cos^2 3x}.$

▶ Example 6

Find the values of $\theta(0 < \theta < 2\pi)$ for which $y = \dfrac{\sin\theta}{3-\cos\theta}$ is stationary.

▶ Solution . . .

Using the quotient rule,

$\dfrac{dy}{d\theta} = \dfrac{(3-\cos\theta)(\cos\theta) - \sin\theta(\sin\theta)}{(3-\cos\theta)^2} = \dfrac{3\,\cos\theta - (\cos^2\theta + \sin^2\theta)}{(3-\cos\theta)^2}$

$\qquad = \dfrac{3\,\cos\theta - 1}{(3-\cos\theta)^2}$

Then $\dfrac{dy}{d\theta} = 0$ when $3\cos\theta - 1 = 0$ i.e. when $\cos\theta = \dfrac{1}{3}$
and therefore $\theta = 1.23$ or $2\pi - 1.23 = 5.05$ radians.

▶ Example 7

Differentiate $\sec x$.

▶ Solution . . .

Let $y = \sec x = \dfrac{1}{\cos x} = (\cos x)^{-1}$.

$\dfrac{dy}{dx} = -1(\cos x)^{-2} \times (-\sin x) = \dfrac{\sin x}{\cos^2 x}$

$\qquad\qquad\qquad = \dfrac{1}{\cos x} \cdot \dfrac{\sin x}{\cos x} = \sec x \tan x.$

▶ **Example 8**

Find the equation of the tangent to the curve $y = \sin 2x \cos x$ at the point where $x = \dfrac{\pi}{6}$.

▶ **Solution . . .**

If $y = \sin 2x \cos x$, using the product rule,

$\dfrac{dy}{dx} = (\sin 2x)(-\sin x) + (\cos x)(2 \cos 2x).$

When $x = \dfrac{\pi}{6}$, $y = \sin \dfrac{\pi}{3} \cos \dfrac{\pi}{6}$

$\qquad = \dfrac{\sqrt{3}}{2} \cdot \dfrac{\sqrt{3}}{2} = \dfrac{3}{4}$

and $\dfrac{dy}{dx} = -\sin \dfrac{\pi}{3} \sin \dfrac{\pi}{6} + 2 \cos \dfrac{\pi}{6} \cos \dfrac{\pi}{3}$

$\qquad = -\dfrac{\sqrt{3}}{2} \cdot \dfrac{1}{2} + 2 \cdot \dfrac{\sqrt{3}}{2} \cdot \dfrac{1}{2}$

$\qquad = \dfrac{\sqrt{3}}{4}$

Equation of tangent at $x = \dfrac{\pi}{6}$ is $y - \dfrac{3}{4} = \dfrac{\sqrt{3}}{4}\left(x - \dfrac{\pi}{6}\right)$ or $4y = \sqrt{3}\left(x - \dfrac{\pi}{6}\right) + 3$

18.1.3   Differentiation of tan x

If $y = \tan x = \dfrac{\sin x}{\cos x}$, then using the quotient rule,

$\dfrac{dy}{dx} = \dfrac{(\cos x)(\cos x) - (\sin x)(-\sin x)}{\cos^2 x} = \dfrac{\cos^2 x + \sin^2 x}{\cos^2 x} = \dfrac{1}{\cos^2 x} = \sec^2 x$

$$\dfrac{d}{dx} \tan x = \sec^2 x \qquad x \text{ in radians}$$

Then $\qquad \dfrac{d}{dx} \tan (ax + b) = a \sec^2 (ax + b)$

and $\qquad \dfrac{d}{dx} \tan^n (ax + b) = na \tan^{n-1}(ax + b) \sec^2 (ax + b).$

▶ **Example 9**

Differentiate wrt x **(a)** $x \tan 2x$, **(b)** $\sin x \tan x$.

▶ **Solution . . .**

(a)   If $y = x \tan 2x$, $\dfrac{dy}{dx} = x \sec^2 2x \times 2 + \tan 2x$

$\qquad\qquad\qquad\qquad = 2x \sec^2 2x + \tan 2x.$

(b)   If $y = \sin x \tan x$, $\dfrac{dy}{dx} = \sin x \sec^2 x + \tan x \cos x$

$\qquad\qquad\qquad\qquad\quad = \sin x \sec^2 x + \sin x$

$\qquad\qquad\qquad\qquad\quad = (\sin x)(\sec^2 x + 1).$

Exercise 18A (Answers on page 509)

1. Differentiate wrt x:

   (a) $\sin 3x$ (b) $\sin \dfrac{x}{2}$ (c) $\cos \dfrac{x}{4}$

   (d) $\tan 3x$ (e) $\operatorname{cosec} x$ (f) $x \sin x$

   (g) $x^2 \sin 2x$ (h) $\cos(2x^2 - 1)$ (i) $\sin\left(\dfrac{\pi}{3} - x\right)$

   (j) $\tan \dfrac{x}{2}$ (k) $x \sin x + \cos x$ (l) $\dfrac{\cos x}{2 - \sin x}$

   (m) $\cos^3 2x$ (n) $x \cos x - \sin 2x$ (o) $\sin 3x \cos 2x$

   (p) $\sqrt{4 + \sin^2 2x}$ (q) $\cos^3(1 - 3x^2)$ (r) $\sqrt{\tan 2x}$

2. Differentiate wrt x:

   (a) $\cos 3x$ (b) $\sin \dfrac{x}{3}$ (c) $\cos(2x^2 - 1)$

   (d) $\sin^3 2x$ (e) $\tan\left(\dfrac{x}{3} - 2\right)$ (f) $\sin \dfrac{x}{2} \cos 2x$

   (g) $\dfrac{1 - \sin x}{1 + \sin x}$ (h) $x^2 \tan \dfrac{x}{2}$ (i) $\cos x^2$

   (j) $x(\cos 2x - \sin x)$

3. If $y = \sin 2x$, find $\dfrac{dy}{dx}$ and $\dfrac{d^2y}{dx^2}$, and show that $\dfrac{d^2y}{dx^2} + 4y = 0$.

4. If $y = x \sin 2x$, find the value of $\dfrac{dy}{dx}$ when $x = \dfrac{\pi}{2}$.

5. Given $y = A \cos 2x + B \sin 2x$, where A and B are constants, show that $\dfrac{d^2y}{dx^2} + 4y = 0$. If $y = 3$ when $x = \dfrac{\pi}{2}$ and $\dfrac{dy}{dx} = 4$ when $x = 0$, find the value of A and of B.

6. If $y = \cos \theta + 2 \sin \theta$, find the values of θ $(0 < \theta < 2\pi)$ for which $\dfrac{dy}{d\theta} = 0$.

7. Find $\dfrac{dy}{dx}$ if $y = (\sin x + \cos 2x)^2$.

8. Solve the equation $\dfrac{d}{dx}(x + \sin 2x) = 2$ for $0 < x < \pi$.

9. If $y = \dfrac{\sin x}{1 + \cos x}$, find $\dfrac{dy}{dx}$ and $\dfrac{d^2y}{dx^2}$.

10. (a) Show that if $y = 2 \sin x - \cos x$, then $\dfrac{dy}{dx} = 0$ when $\tan x = -2$. Hence find the values of x $(0 < x < 2\pi)$ where y has stationary values.

    (b) Find the value of x $(0 < x < 2\pi)$ for which $y = \dfrac{3\cos x}{2 - \sin x}$ is stationary. Hence find the maximum and minimum values of y.

11. Find the equations of the tangents to the curve $y = \sin x$ where $x = 0$ and $x = \pi$.

12. Find the equation of the tangent to the curve $y = \cos x$ where $x = \frac{\pi}{2}$.

18.2 Integration of Trigonometric Functions

When we differentiate $y = \sin x$, we get $\dfrac{dy}{dx} = \cos x$.

So $\int \cos x \, dx = \sin x + c$.

More generally, if $y = \sin(ax + b)$, then $\dfrac{dy}{dx} = a \cos(ax + b)$.

Therefore $\boxed{\int \cos(ax + b) \, dx = \dfrac{1}{a} \sin(ax + b) + c}$.

When we differentiate $y = \cos x$, we get $\dfrac{dy}{dx} = -\sin x$.

So $\int \sin x \, dx = -\cos x + c$.

More generally, if $y = \cos(ax + b)$, then $\dfrac{dy}{dx} = -a \sin(ax + b)$.

Therefore $\boxed{\int \sin(ax + b) \, dx = -\dfrac{1}{a} \cos(ax + b) + c}$.

When we differentiate $y = \tan x$, we get $\dfrac{dy}{dx} = \sec^2 x$.

So $\int \sec^2 x \, dx = \tan x + c$.

More generally, if $y = \tan(ax + b)$, then $\dfrac{dy}{dx} = a \sec^2(ax + b)$.

Therefore $\boxed{\int \sec^2(ax + b) \, dx = \dfrac{1}{a} \tan(ax + b) + c}$.

For all these results, x must be in radians.

▶ **Example 10**

Integrate **(a)** $\int \sin 3x \, dx$, **(b)** $\int \cos \dfrac{x}{2} \, dx$.

▶ **Solution . . .**

(a) $\int \sin 3x \, dx = \dfrac{-\cos 3x}{3} + c = -\dfrac{1}{3} \cos 3x + c$

(b) $\int \cos \dfrac{x}{2} \, dx = \dfrac{\sin \frac{x}{2}}{\frac{1}{2}} + c = 2 \sin \dfrac{x}{2} + c$

▶ **Example 11**

Find the area of the shaded region in Fig. 18.3 between the part OA of the curve $y = \sin x$ and the line OA, where O is the origin and A is the point $\left(\frac{\pi}{2}, 1\right)$.

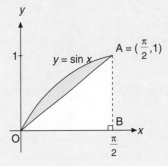

Fig. 18.3

▶ **Solution . . .**

The shaded area is the area under the curve minus the area of $\triangle OBA$ where AB is perpendicular to the x-axis.

$$\text{Area} = \int_0^{\frac{\pi}{2}} \sin x \, dx - \frac{1}{2} \times \frac{\pi}{2} \times 1$$

$$= \left[-\cos x\right]_0^{\frac{\pi}{2}} - \frac{\pi}{4}$$

$$= \left(-\cos \frac{\pi}{2}\right) - (-\cos 0) - \frac{\pi}{4} = 0 - (-1) - \frac{\pi}{4} = 1 - \frac{\pi}{4} \text{ units}^2$$

▶ **Example 12**

Differentiate $\sin^2 2x$ wrt x. Hence find $\int_0^{\frac{\pi}{4}} \sin 2x \cos 2x \, dx$.

▶ **Solution . . .**

$$\frac{d}{dx}(\sin^2 2x) = 2 \sin 2x \cdot \cos 2x \cdot 2$$

$$= 4 \sin 2x \cos 2x$$

Hence, $\int_0^{\frac{\pi}{4}} 4 \sin 2x \cos 2x \, dx = \left[\sin^2 2x\right]_0^{\frac{\pi}{4}}$

$$4 \int_0^{\frac{\pi}{4}} \sin 2x \cos 2x \, dx = \sin^2 \frac{\pi}{2} - 0$$

$$= 1$$

$$\therefore \quad \int_0^{\frac{\pi}{4}} \sin 2x \cos 2x \, dx = \frac{1}{4}$$

Exercise 18B (Answers on page 510)

1. Integrate the following wrt x:

   (a) $\sin 2x$ (b) $\cos 4x$ (c) $\sin \frac{x}{2}$

   (d) $3 \sin 3x$ (e) $\sec^2 3x$ (f) $\cos 2x - \sin x$

   (g) $\sin x + \cos x$ (h) $\cos\left(\frac{x}{2} + \frac{\pi}{4}\right)$ (i) $\cos 5x$

   (j) $\sin\left(\frac{\pi}{4} - x\right)$ (k) $\sec^2 \frac{x}{2}$ (l) $\cos 2x - \sin x$

   (m) $\cos 2x + \sec^2 x$ (n) $2 \sin x + \frac{1}{2} \sin 2x$

2. Evaluate the following:

(a) $\displaystyle\int_0^{\frac{\pi}{2}} \cos x \, dx$ (b) $\displaystyle\int_0^{\frac{\pi}{2}} \sin x \, dx$

(c) $\displaystyle\int_0^{\frac{\pi}{2}} \sin 2x \, dx$ (d) $\displaystyle\int_0^{\frac{\pi}{4}} \sec^2 x \, dx$

(e) $\displaystyle\int_0^{\frac{\pi}{2}} (\sin 2x - \cos x) \, dx$ (f) $\displaystyle\int_0^{\frac{\pi}{2}} (\cos 2x + 2 \sin x) \, dx$

(g) $\displaystyle\int_{\frac{\pi}{6}}^{\frac{\pi}{3}} \sin \frac{3x}{2} \, dx$ (h) $\displaystyle\int_0^{\frac{\pi}{3}} \sin 3x \, dx$

(i) $\displaystyle\int_0^{\pi} \cos \, dx$ (j) $\displaystyle\int_0^{\pi} \cos 2x \, dx$

(k) $\displaystyle\int_0^{\frac{5\pi}{12}} \cos \left(2x + \frac{\pi}{6}\right) x \, dx$

3. If $\dfrac{dy}{d\theta} = \dfrac{1}{\theta^2} + \dfrac{1}{2} \cos 2\theta$, and $y = 1$ when $\theta = \dfrac{\pi}{2}$, find y in terms of θ.

4. Find the area of the region enclosed by the curve $y = \sin x$ and the x-axis from $x = 0$ to $x = \pi$.

5. Differentiate $\dfrac{1}{1 + \cos x}$ wrt x. Hence find the area of the region under the curve $y = \dfrac{\sin x}{(1 + \cos x)^2}$ between $x = 0$ and $x = \dfrac{\pi}{2}$.

6. Sketch the curves $y = \cos x$ and $y = \sin x$ for $0 \leq x \leq \dfrac{\pi}{2}$. Find **(a)** the value of x where the curves intersect, **(b)** the area of the region bounded by the two curves and the x-axis.

7. Find the area of the region enclosed by the x-axis, the y-axis, the curve $y = \cos x$ and the line $x = \dfrac{\pi}{6}$.

18.3 Integration of Powers of the Linear Function ax + b

If $y = (ax + b)^{n+1}$, then $\dfrac{dy}{dx} = (n + 1)a(ax + b)^n$.

Hence $\displaystyle\int (n + 1)a(ax + b)^n dx = (ax + b)^{n+1}$

and so
$$\int (ax + b)^n dx = \frac{(ax + b)^{n+1}}{(n+1)a} + c \; ; n \neq -1.$$

This result only applies to a **linear function** $ax + b$. The integration of powers of non-linear functions such as $ax^2 + b$ cannot be done in this way and is beyond the scope of this book.

► Example 13

Find **(a)** $\int (2x-1)^3 dx$, **(b)** $\int \dfrac{dx}{(3x+2)^2}$, **(c)** $\int_1^5 \sqrt{2x-1}\ dx$.

(a) Here $a = 2$, $b = -1$ and $n = 3$.

So $\int (2x-1)^3\ dx = \dfrac{(2x-1)^4}{4\times 2} + c = \dfrac{1}{8}(2x-1)^4 + c$

(b) $\int \dfrac{dx}{(3x+2)^2}$ is short for $\int \dfrac{1}{(3x+2)^2}\ dx = \dfrac{(3x+2)^{-1}}{(-1)(3)} + c$

$$= -\frac{1}{3}(3x+2)^{-1} + c$$

$$= -\frac{1}{3(3x+2)} + c$$

(c) $\int_1^5 \sqrt{2x-1}\ dx = \int_1^5 (2x-1)^{\frac{1}{2}}\ dx$

$$= \left[\frac{(2x-1)^{\frac{3}{2}}}{2\times\frac{3}{2}} \right]_1^5$$

$$= \left(\frac{1}{3}\times 9^{\frac{3}{2}} \right) - \left(\frac{1}{3}\times 1^{\frac{3}{2}} \right) = 9 - \frac{1}{3} = 8\frac{2}{3}$$

► Example 14

Find the area bounded by the curve $y = \dfrac{1}{\sqrt{2x-3}}$, the x-axis and the lines $x = 2$, $x = 6$.

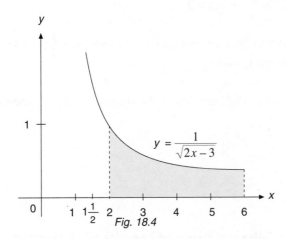

Fig. 18.4

As $\sqrt{2x-3}$ is positive for $x > 1\frac{1}{2}$, y is real and positive in the area required.

Area $= \displaystyle\int_2^6 (2x-3)^{-\frac{1}{2}}\ dx = \left[\dfrac{(2x-3)^{\frac{1}{2}}}{2\times\frac{1}{2}} \right]_2^6$

$$= \left[(2x-3)^{\frac{1}{2}} \right]_2^6$$

$$= (9^{\frac{1}{2}}) - (1^{\frac{1}{2}})$$

$$= 2\ \text{units}^2$$

Exercise 18C (Answers on page 510)

1. Integrate the following wrt x:

(a) $(2x - 3)^2$

(b) $(2x + 5)^4$

(c) $(x - 2)^{-3}$

(d) $\sqrt{x - 3}$

(e) $\dfrac{1}{(3x - 2)^2}$

(f) $(2x + 3)^{-\frac{1}{2}}$

(g) $\dfrac{1}{\sqrt{2x + 3}}$

(h) $(3 - 4x)^3$

(i) $\dfrac{1}{\sqrt{3 - 2x}}$

(j) $(3x + 2)^4$

(k) $(4x - 1)^{\frac{1}{3}}$

(l) $(2x - 5)^{-\frac{1}{2}}$

(m) $\sqrt[3]{4x - 1}$

(n) $(1 - 2x)^{-2}$

2. Find the value of the following:

(a) $\displaystyle\int_0^1 (2x + 1)^2 \, dx$

(b) $\displaystyle\int_1^5 \sqrt{3x + 1} \, dx$

(c) $\displaystyle\int_0^1 (3x - 1)^2 \, dx$

(d) $\displaystyle\int_{-5}^0 \sqrt{1 - 3x} \, dx$

(e) $\displaystyle\int_{\frac{2}{3}}^{\frac{4}{3}} (3x - 4)^3 \, dx$

(f) $\displaystyle\int_{-2}^2 \sqrt{2x + 5} \, dx$

(g) $\displaystyle\int_1^6 \dfrac{dx}{\sqrt{x + 3}}$

(h) $\displaystyle\int_1^2 (3x - 2)^3 \, dx$

3. Calculate the area bounded by the curve $y = (3x + 1)^{-2}$, the x-axis and the lines $x = 1$, $x = 3$.

4. Calculate the area bounded by the curve $y = \dfrac{1}{2}(x^3 + 4)$, the y-axis and the line $y = 6$.

5. Find the area bounded by the curve $y = \sqrt{2x - 1}$ and the line $y = \dfrac{1}{2}x + \dfrac{1}{2}$.

18.4 Differentiation of Logarithmic Functions

First we have to recall the value of another important limit, which we dealt with in Chapter 7 (p 161), namely

$$\lim_{t \to \infty}\left(1 + \frac{1}{t}\right)^t = e$$

Its importance is that it is taken as the base of **natural logarithms**, i.e. $\log_e x$ (written as $\ln x$.)

> **If $y = \log_e x = \ln x$, then $e^y = x$.**
>
> **If $y = e^x$, then $\ln y = x$.**

Similar to other logarithms, $\ln 1 = 0$, $\ln e = 1$ and if $0 < x < 1$, $\ln x$ is negative. If $x \le 0$, $\ln x$ is undefined.

So for example, if $y = e^{2x+3}$, then $\ln y = 2x + 3$;

if $y = 2e^{3x}$, then $\ln y = \ln 2 + \ln e^{3x} = \ln 2 + 3x$.

We shall now see why such a strange number is chosen as a base for logarithms.

18.4.1 Differentiation of ln x

Take $y = \ln x$ and let x have an increment δx. Consequently, y has an increment δy.

Then $y + \delta y = \ln(x + \delta x)$ and $\delta y = \ln(x + \delta x) - \ln x = \ln\left(\dfrac{x + \delta x}{x}\right)$.

Hence $\dfrac{\delta y}{\delta x} = \dfrac{1}{\delta x} \ln\left(\dfrac{x + \delta x}{x}\right) = \ln\left(1 + \dfrac{\delta x}{x}\right)^{\frac{1}{\delta x}}$.

To make use of the above limit, write $\dfrac{\delta x}{x} = \dfrac{1}{t}$ so $\dfrac{1}{\delta x} = \dfrac{t}{x}$.

Then $\dfrac{\delta y}{\delta x} = \ln(1 + \dfrac{1}{t})^{\frac{t}{x}} = \dfrac{1}{x} \ln(1 + \dfrac{1}{t})^t$.

Now let $\delta x \to 0$. Consequently, $\delta y \to 0$, $\dfrac{\delta y}{\delta x} \to \dfrac{dy}{dx}$, $t \to \infty$ and $(1 + \dfrac{1}{t})^t \to e$.

Using these, we have $\dfrac{dy}{dx} = \dfrac{1}{x} \ln e = \dfrac{1}{x}$ as $\ln e = \log_e e = 1$.

$$\frac{d}{dx} \ln x = \frac{1}{x}$$

This is a very important and simple result, and it shows why e is taken as the base of natural logarithms.

18.4.2 Differentiation of ln f(x)

Using the result in the preceding section and the rule for a composite function, we can now differentiate $\ln f(x)$.

Suppose $y = \ln f(x)$.

Take $u = f(x)$ and so $y = \ln u$.

$\dfrac{dy}{du} = \dfrac{1}{u}$ and $\dfrac{du}{dx} = \dfrac{d}{dx} f(x) = f'(x)$

$\dfrac{dy}{dx} = \dfrac{dy}{du} \times \dfrac{du}{dx} = \dfrac{1}{u} \times f'(x) = \dfrac{f'(x)}{f(x)}$

$$\frac{d}{dx} \ln f(x) = \frac{f'(x)}{f(x)}$$

▶ **Example 15**

Differentiate wrt x **(a)** $\ln (ax + b)$, **(b)** $\ln (x^2 - 3x + 1)$, **(c)** $\ln \sin 3x$,
(d) $x^2 \ln x$, **(e)** $\dfrac{\ln x}{x+1}$.

▶ **Solution …**

(a) Here $f(x) = ax + b$.

$$\frac{d}{dx} \ln(ax + b) = \frac{a}{ax + b} \text{ as } f'(x) = \frac{d}{dx}(ax + b) = a.$$

(b) $\dfrac{d}{dx} \ln(x^2 - 3x + 1) = \dfrac{2x - 3}{x^2 - 3x + 1}$ (as $f'(x) = 2x - 3$)

(c) $\dfrac{d}{dx} \ln \sin 3x = \dfrac{3 \cos 3x}{\sin 3x} = 3 \cot 3x$

(d) $y = x^2 \ln x$ is the product of x^2 and $\ln x$.

So $\dfrac{dy}{dx} = 2x \ln x + x^2 \dfrac{d}{dx} \ln x = 2x \ln x + x^2 \times \dfrac{1}{x} = 2x \ln x + x.$

(e) $y = \dfrac{\ln x}{x+1}$ as a quotient of two functions.

Hence $\dfrac{dy}{dx} = \dfrac{(x+1)\frac{1}{x} - \ln x}{(x+1)^2} = \dfrac{x + 1 - x \ln x}{x(x+1)^2}.$

▶ **Example 16**

Find $\dfrac{dy}{dx}$ if **(a)** $y = \ln(x + 1)(3x - 2)^2$, **(b)** $y = \ln\left(\dfrac{\sqrt{x+1}}{2x-1}\right)$.

▶ **Solution …**

(a) We could differentiate directly but it is easier to simplify the logarithm first.

$\ln(x + 1)(3x - 2)^2 = \ln(x + 1) + \ln(3x - 2)^2 = \ln(x + 1) + 2 \ln(3x - 2).$

Now differentiate:
$$\frac{dy}{dx} = \frac{1}{x+1} + 2\left(\frac{3}{3x-2}\right) = \frac{3x - 2 + 6(x+1)}{(x+1)(3x-2)} = \frac{9x + 4}{(x+1)(3x-2)}$$

(b) Similarly, we simplify the logarithm before differentiation. Thus,

$$\ln\left(\frac{\sqrt{x+1}}{2x-1}\right) = \ln\sqrt{x+1} - \ln(2x - 1)$$

$$= \ln(x + 1)^{\frac{1}{2}} - \ln(2x - 1)$$

$$= \frac{1}{2}\ln(x + 1) - \ln(2x - 1)$$

Differentiating, $\dfrac{dy}{dx} = \dfrac{1}{2}\left(\dfrac{1}{x+1}\right) - \dfrac{2}{2x-1} = \dfrac{(2x-1) - 4(x+1)}{2(x+1)(2x-1)}$

$$= \frac{-2x - 5}{2(x+1)(2x-1)}$$

Exercise 18D (Answers on page 510)

1. Differentiate the following wrt x and simplify where possible:

(a) $\ln 5x$ (b) $\ln x^2$ (c) $\ln (3x - 1)$

(d) $\ln (\sin x)$ (e) $\ln (x + \tan x)$ (f) $\ln (\cos 2x)$

(g) $\ln (\cos^2 x)$ (h) $\ln \left(\sin \frac{x}{2}\right)$ (i) $\ln (2x^2 - 4x - 1)$

(j) $\ln \sqrt{2x - 5}$ (k) $\ln \left(\frac{1}{\sqrt{x}}\right)$ (l) $x \ln x$

(m) $\dfrac{\ln x}{x^2}$ (n) $\ln(x \cos x)$ (o) $\cos(\ln x)$

(p) $\ln x \ln 3x$ (q) $(x^2 + 1)\ln(x - 1)$ (r) $(\ln x)^2$

(s) $\ln(\cos 3x)$ (t) $(x - 1) \ln 2x$ (u) $\ln (x + \sin x)$

(v) $\ln(x + 3)(2x - 1)$ (w) $\ln \left(\frac{x - 4}{x + 3}\right)$

2. If $y = \ln(x + 1)(x - 2)$, show that $\dfrac{dy}{dx} = \dfrac{2x - 1}{x^2 - x - 2}$.

3. If $y = \ln(3x + 1)(2x - 1)$, find and simplify $\dfrac{dy}{dx}$.

4. Given that $y = \ln \left(\dfrac{x - 2}{x + 1}\right)$, find $\dfrac{dy}{dx}$ in its simplest form.

5. Differentiate $\ln(x - \sin x)$. Hence find the gradient on the curve $y = \ln(x - \sin x)$ where $x = \pi$.

6. Differentiate $\dfrac{\sin x}{1 - \cos x}$. Hence show that $\dfrac{d}{dx} \ln \dfrac{\sin x}{1 - \cos x} = -\operatorname{cosec} x$.

7. Differentiate $\dfrac{\cos x}{1 + \sin x}$. Hence show that $\dfrac{dy}{dx} \ln \dfrac{\cos x}{1 + \sin x} = -\sec x$.

18.5   Differentiation of Exponential Functions

Let us look at another limit, namely

$$\lim_{t \to 0} \left(\frac{e^t - 1}{t}\right).$$

Again we shall not be able to prove what this limit is but the following set of values obtained from a calculator will suggest an answer.

t	$\dfrac{e^t - 1}{t}$
0.1	1.051 709
0.01	1.005 016
0.001	1.000 500
0.0001	1.000 050
0.000 01	1.000 000

As t approaches 0, it appears that $\left(\dfrac{e^t - 1}{t}\right)$ tends to 1, which is in fact true.

We shall assume this limit to find the differentiation of the function e^x from first principles.

18.5.1   Differentiation of e^x

Consider $y = e^x$ .... (1)

then $y + \delta y = e^{x + \delta x}$ .... (2)

(2) − (1) $\delta y = e^{x + \delta x} - e^x$

$\qquad\qquad = e^x.e^{\delta x} - e^x$

$\qquad\qquad = e^x(e^{\delta x} - 1)$

$\qquad \dfrac{\delta y}{\delta x} = e^x \dfrac{(e^{\delta x} - 1)}{\delta x}$

To make use of the limit in the preceding section, write $\delta x = t$.

Then $\dfrac{\delta y}{\delta x} = e^x \dfrac{(e^t - 1)}{t}$.

Now let $\delta x \to 0$, so $t \to 0$ and $\dfrac{e^t - 1}{t} \to 1$.

Using these, we have

$\dfrac{dy}{dx} = e^x$.

Hence $\qquad \boxed{\dfrac{d}{dx} e^x = e^x}$.

This result makes e^x a unique function. It is the only function whose derivative is itself. The gradient at a point on the curve $y = e^x$ equals the value of y at that point.

18.5.2   Differentiation of $e^{f(x)}$

We can also differentiate composite functions of the type $e^{f(x)}$.

If $y = e^{f(x)}$ and $u = f(x)$, then $y = e^u$.

$\dfrac{dy}{du} = e^u$ and $\dfrac{du}{dx} = f'(x)$.

Hence $\dfrac{dy}{dx} = \dfrac{dy}{du} \times \dfrac{du}{dx} = e^u f'(x) = f'(x)e^{f(x)}$.

$$\boxed{\dfrac{d}{dx} e^{f(x)} = f'(x)e^{f(x)}}$$

▶ **Example 17**

Differentiate wrt x **(a)** e^{3x-2}, **(b)** $e^{\sin 2x}$, **(c)** xe^{-2x}.

▶ **Solution . . .**

(a) $\dfrac{de^{3x-2}}{dx} = 3e^{3x-2}$ as $\dfrac{d(3x-2)}{dx} = 3$.

(b) $\dfrac{d}{dx} e^{\sin 2x} = (2 \cos 2x) e^{\sin 2x}$

(c) $y = xe^{-2x}$ is a product.

$\qquad \dfrac{dy}{dx} = e^{-2x} + x(-2e^{-2x}) = e^{-2x}(1 - 2x)$

▶ **Example 18**

Find the coordinates of the point of intersection of the curves $y = e^{2x-1}$ and $y = e^{2-x}$ and the gradient of each curve at that point.

▶ **Solution . . .**

At the point of intersection, $e^{2x-1} = e^{2-x}$ so $2x - 1 = 2 - x$ and $x = 1$. The coordinates of the point are (1,e).

For $y = e^{2x-1}$, $\dfrac{dy}{dx} = 2e^{2x-1} = 2e$ when $x = 1$.

For $y = e^{2-x}$, $\dfrac{dy}{dx} = -e^{2-x} = -e$ when $x = 1$.

Exercise 18E (Answers on page 510)

1. Differentiate the following wrt x:

   (a) e^{4x}

   (b) e^{5x-1}

   (c) e^{5-3x}

   (d) e^{x^2}

   (e) $e^{\cos x}$

   (f) xe^x

   (g) $(2x-4)e^{-\frac{x}{2}}$

   (h) e^{ax+b}

   (i) e^{x^2+2x-1}

   (j) $e^x \sin x$

   (k) $\dfrac{e^x + 1}{e^x}$

   (l) $\dfrac{e^x}{x+1}$

   (m) $x^2 e^{-x}$

   (n) $e^x - e^{-x}$

   (o) $e^{-x}(\cos x - \sin x)$

   (p) $(3x+2)e^{-2x}$

   (q) $e^{2x} \ln x$

   (r) $\dfrac{e^x}{e^x - 1}$

   (s) $\dfrac{xe^x}{x-1}$

   (t) $e^{2x} \cos 2x$

   (u) $\dfrac{e^x}{x}$

   (v) $x^3 e^{2x}$

   (w) $(e^x - e^{-x})^2$

2. Find the coordinates of the point where the curves $y = e^{5x-2}$ and $y = e^{4-x}$ meet and the gradient of each curve at that point.

3. If $y = (x-3)e^{-2x}$, find the range of values of x for which $\dfrac{dy}{dx} > 0$.

4. If $y = xe^{3x}$ find $\dfrac{dy}{dx}$ and $\dfrac{d^2y}{dx^2}$. Hence find the value of x for which y has a stationary point and state the nature of that point.

5. Given that $y = x^2 e^{2x}$, find the values of x for which y is stationary.

6. If $y = (x^2 - 3)e^{-x}$, find the values of x where y is stationary and the nature of these points.

7. If $y = e^x \cos x$, find $\dfrac{dy}{dx}$ and $\dfrac{d^2y}{dx^2}$. Use these to find the values of x $(0 < x < 2\pi)$ where y has stationary points and state the nature of these points.

8. Find $\dfrac{dy}{dx}$ and $\dfrac{d^2y}{dx^2}$ for $y = e^x(\cos x + \sin x)$.
   Hence find the values of x $(0 < x < 2\pi)$ where y is stationary and the nature of the stationary points.

9. Given that $y = e^x \sin x$, prove that $\dfrac{d^2 y}{dx^2} - 2\dfrac{dy}{dx} + 2y = 0$.

10. Find the gradient on the curve $y = e^{2x} \cos x$ where $x = 0$.

11. If $y = a^x$, show that $\ln y = x \ln a$ and hence find $\dfrac{dy}{dx}$.

12. If $\dfrac{d}{dx}\left(\dfrac{\sin x}{e^x}\right) = \dfrac{f(x)}{e^x}$, find $f(x)$.

18.6 Integration of Exponential Functions

As $\dfrac{de^x}{dx} = e^x$,

then
$$\int e^x \, dx = e^x + c \ .$$

Also since $\dfrac{de^{ax+b}}{dx} = ae^{ax+b}$,

then
$$\int e^{ax+b} \, dx = \frac{1}{a} e^{ax+b} + c \ .$$

Note that this result holds only for the linear function $ax + b$.

▶ ## Example 19

Find **(a)** $\displaystyle\int 3e^{4x+5} \, dx$, **(b)** $\displaystyle\int_2^3 e^{3-2x} \, dx$.

▶ ## Solution . . .

(a) $\displaystyle\int 3e^{4x+5} \, dx = \frac{3e^{4x+5}}{4} + c$

(b) $\displaystyle\int_2^3 e^{3-2x} \, dx = \left[\frac{e^{3-2x}}{-2}\right]_2^3$

$$= \frac{1}{-2}\left[e^{-3} - e^{-1}\right]$$

$$= \frac{1}{-2}\left[\frac{1}{e^3} - \frac{1}{e}\right] \quad \text{or} \quad \frac{1}{2}\left[\frac{1}{e} - \frac{1}{e^3}\right]$$

Such results are usually left in terms of e. If required, a calculator can be used to evaluate the numerical value.

▶ ## Example 20

Sketch the graphs of $y = e^{2x}$ and $y = e^{4x}$ for $x \geq 0$. Shade and find the area of the region enclosed by the curves $y = e^{2x}$ and $y = e^{4x}$ and the lines $x = 1$ and $x = 2$.

▶ **Solution . . .**

$$\text{Area} = \int_1^2 (e^{4x} - e^{2x})\, dx$$

$$= \left[\frac{e^{4x}}{4} - \frac{e^{2x}}{2} \right]_1^2$$

$$= \left(\frac{e^8}{4} - \frac{e^4}{2} \right) - \left(\frac{e^4}{4} - \frac{e^2}{2} \right)$$

$$= \frac{1}{4}e^8 - \frac{3}{4}e^4 + \frac{1}{2}e^2$$

$$= \frac{e^2}{4}(e^6 - 3e^2 + 2)\ \text{units}^2$$

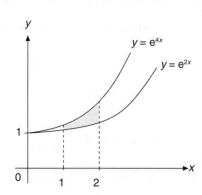

Exercise 18F *(Answers on page 510)*

1. Find the following: .

   (a) $\displaystyle\int e^{3x}\, dx$ (b) $\displaystyle\int e^{-x}\, dx$ (c) $\displaystyle\int e^{2-x}\, dx$

   (d) $\displaystyle\int \left(e^x + \frac{1}{e^x}\right)^2 dx$ (e) $\displaystyle\int e^{-3x}\, dx$ (f) $\displaystyle\int e^{1-2x}\, dx$

2. Evaluate the following, giving the result in terms of e:

   (a) $\displaystyle\int_0^1 e^{4x}\, dx$ (b) $\displaystyle\int_{-1}^0 e^{-x}\, dx$ (c) $\displaystyle\int_{-1}^{-3} e^{1-x}\, dx$

   (d) $\displaystyle\int_1^3 e^{2x-1}\, dx$ (e) $\displaystyle\int_{-2}^0 \frac{2}{e^{2x}}\, dx$ (f) $\displaystyle\int_1^2 e^{-2x}\, dx$

   (g) $\displaystyle\int_{-2}^0 e^{-\frac{x}{2}}\, dx$ (h) $\displaystyle\int_{-1}^1 e^{2-x}\, dx$

3. P is a function of t such that $\dfrac{dp}{dt} = e^{-3t}$ and $P = 3$ when $t = 0$. Find P in terms of t.

4. Calculate the area of the region enclosed by the curves $y = e^x$ and $y = e^{2x}$ and the line $x = 1$.

5. Find $\displaystyle\int \frac{e^x + 1}{e^x}\, dx$.

6. (a) The gradient of a curve is given by $\dfrac{dy}{dx} = e^{2x}$ and it passes through the point $\left(0, \frac{1}{2}\right)$. Find the equation of the curve.

   (b) Find the area of the region enclosed by the curve, the x-axis and the lines $x = 0$ and $x = 1$.

Summary

1. For x in radians, a and b as constants:

$$\frac{d}{dx} \sin(ax+b) = a\cos(ax+b), \int \cos(ax+b)\,dx = \frac{1}{a}\sin(ax+b) + c$$

$$\frac{d}{dx} \cos(ax+b) = -a\sin(ax+b), \int \sin(ax+b)\,dx = -\frac{1}{a}\cos(ax+b) + c$$

$$\frac{d}{dx} \tan(ax+b) = a\sec^2(ax+b), \int \sec^2(ax+b)\,dx = \frac{1}{a}\tan(ax+b) + c$$

2. $\int (ax+b)^n\,dx = \dfrac{(ax+b)^{n+1}}{a(n+1)} + c$ for all values of n, *except* $n = -1$.

3. $\ln x = \log_e x$; $e \approx 2.718\,3$

4. If $y = \ln x$, $x = e^y$; if $y = e^{ax+b}$, $\ln y = ax + b$.

5. $\dfrac{d}{dx} \ln x = \dfrac{1}{x}$

6. $\dfrac{d}{dx} \ln f(x) = \dfrac{f'(x)}{f(x)}$

7. $\dfrac{d}{dx} e^x = e^x$

8. $\dfrac{d}{dx} e^{f(x)} = f'(x)e^{f(x)}$

9. $\int e^x\,dx = e^x + c$

10. $\int e^{ax+b}\,dx = \dfrac{1}{a} e^{ax+b} + c$

Revision Exercise 18 (Answers on page 510)

1. If $y = x\sin x$, find $\dfrac{d^2y}{dx^2}$.

2. Evaluate $\displaystyle\int_0^\alpha \cos x\,dx$ when $\tan\alpha = \dfrac{3}{4}\ \left(0 < \alpha < \dfrac{\pi}{2}\right)$.

3. Calculate the area of the region enclosed by the curve $y = \sin x$, the tangent at the point $(0,0)$ to this curve and the line $x = \dfrac{\pi}{2}$.

4. Differentiate wrt x (a) $\dfrac{x}{\cos x}$, (b) $\dfrac{1+\sin x}{1-\sin x}$, (c) $\dfrac{\sin x}{\sin x + \cos x}$.

5. Evaluate $\displaystyle\int_{\frac{\pi}{8}}^{\frac{3\pi}{8}} 4\sec^2 2x\,dx$.

6. Sketch the curve $y = |\sin x|$ for $0 \le x \le 2\pi$.
   Evaluate $\displaystyle\int_0^{2\pi} |\sin x|\,dx$.

7. Find the values of $x\ (0 \le x \le 2\pi)$ for which $y = \dfrac{1+\sin x}{\sin x + \cos x}$ is stationary. State the maximum and minimum values of y.

8. If $y = \sin 2\theta$, find the approximate change in y when θ is increased from $\dfrac{\pi}{6}$ to $\dfrac{\pi}{6} + 0.01$.

9. If $y = a \sin 2x$, where a is a constant, satisfies the equation $\dfrac{d^2 y}{dx^2} + 8y = 4 \sin 2x$, find the value of a.

10. Evaluate the following:

(a) $\displaystyle\int_0^1 e^{1-2x}\, dx$ (b) $\displaystyle\int_{-2}^0 e^{1-\frac{x}{2}}\, dx$

(c) $\displaystyle\int_a^b e^{kt}\, dt$ (k is a constant)   (d) $\displaystyle\int_{-3}^{-1} e^{2-x}\, dx$

(e) $\displaystyle\int_0^1 \dfrac{e}{e^{2x}}\, dx$

11. Find the gradient of the curve $y = \ln(x + \sin 2x)$ where $x = \dfrac{\pi}{2}$.

12. Sketch the curve $y = e^{-2x}$ for $x > 0$ and find the area of the region enclosed by the curve, the y-axis, the x-axis and the line $x = 1$.

13. Fig. 18.5 shows part of the curves $y = e^{x-2}$ and $y = e^{-x}$ which intersect at P. Find **(a)** the coordinates of P and **(b)** the area of the shaded region in terms of e.

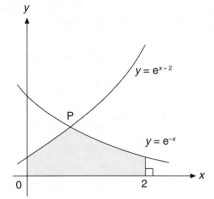

Fig. 18.5

14. Find the values of x at the turning points on the curve $y = (x^2 + x - 1)e^{-x}$ and determine the nature of these points.

15. If $\dfrac{d}{dx}\left(\dfrac{x^2 + 1}{e^x}\right) = \dfrac{f(x)}{e^x}$, find f($x$).

16. Differentiate $\ln(x\sqrt{x+1}$ wrt x, simplifying your result.

17. Find the value of x at the turning point on the curve $y = \dfrac{\ln x}{x}$ and find out whether it is a maximum or a minimum point.

18. Find the approximate change in $\ln x$ if x is increased from 2 to 2.01.

19. If $y = e^{3x} - 2e^{-3x}$, show that $\dfrac{d^2y}{dx^2} = 9y$.

20. Find the value of k if $y = e^{kx} \sin 2x$ satisfies the equation
    $$\dfrac{d^2y}{dx^2} + 2\dfrac{dy}{dx} + 5y = 0.$$

21. If $y = \dfrac{e^{-x}}{\cos x}$, find the value of $\dfrac{dy}{dx}$ when $x = 0$.

22. Given that $y = e^{ax} \sin bx$, where a and b are constants, show that
    $$\dfrac{d^2y}{dx^2} = e^{ax}[(a^2 - b^2) \sin bx + 2ab \cos bx].$$

23. Differentiate $e^{2x}(2x - 1)$ wrt x. Hence find the value of $\displaystyle\int_0^1 xe^{2x}\, dx$.

24. Show that $y = x^2 \ln\left(\dfrac{1}{x}\right)$ has only one turning point and determine if it is a maximum or minimum point. Also find the value of y at the point.

25. Given that $y = \cos(e^x)$, show that $\dfrac{d^2y}{dx^2} - \dfrac{dy}{dx} + ye^{2x} = 0$.

26. Sketch the curves $y = e^x$ and $y = 2 + 3e^{-x}$ and show that the coordinates of their point of intersection are $(\ln 3, 3)$. Hence find the area of the region enclosed by the two curves and the y-axis.

27. **(a)** Sketch on the same diagram the curves $y = e^x$ and $y = e^{-x}$.

    (b) Add a sketch of the curve $y = \dfrac{1}{2}(e^x + e^{-x})$.

    (c) If $y = \dfrac{1}{2}(e^x + e^{-x})$, find $\dfrac{dy}{dx}$ and $\left(\dfrac{dy}{dx}\right)^2$.

    (d) Show that $1 + \left(\dfrac{dy}{dx}\right)^2 = y^2$.

    (e) The length s of the arc of a curve $y = f(x)$ from $x = a$ to $x = b$ is given by $s = \displaystyle\int_a^b \sqrt{1 + \left(\dfrac{dy}{dx}\right)^2}\, dx$. Find the length of the arc of $y = \dfrac{1}{2}(e^x + e^{-x})$ from $x = -1$ to $x = 1$.

Maths Booster

The world's population is increasing exponentially and is described as a population explosion. Various mathematical models have been developed to predict the future population of the world. One of the simpler models involves the following formula:

The population P of the earth t years after Jan 1, 2000 can be projected by the formula $P = ke^{\frac{t}{50}}$, where k is a constant.

On Jan 1, 2000, the world population was approximately 6 billion. Assuming the population is increasing at a constant rate of $c\%$ per year, find c.

At this rate, in which year will the population reach 10 000 000 000?

Chapter 19

Application of Differentiation and Integration to Kinematics

In this chapter we are going to study the motion of a body in a straight line. An interesting experiment concerning this relates to the famous Leaning Tower of Pisa. For centuries before the time of Galileo, all scholars, including scientists and mathematicians, believed in Aristotle's theory that the rate at which bodies fell was proportional to the weights of the bodies. Legend has it that Galileo tested Aristotle's theory by climbing to the top of the Leaning Tower of Pisa and simultaneously dropping two cannon balls, one many times the weight of the other. It was observed that both balls hit the ground at the same time, thus disproving Aristotle's theory. Galileo had conjectured that all objects, irrespective of their weights, would fall at the same rate in a vacuum and he was subsequently proven right.

19.1 Motion in a Straight Line

Kinematics is the study of the motion of a body without taking into consideration how the motion is caused. We will now study the motion of a particle moving in a straight line.

Consider a particle P moving along a straight line X'OX (Fig. 19.1).

A 'particle' is a body small enough for its dimensions to be ignored.

Fig. 19.1

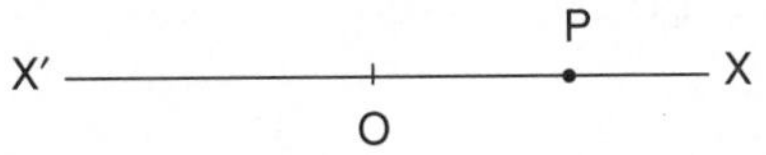

The position of the particle P is given by its **displacement** from the point O. The term 'displacement', if you recall in Chapter 13, is a vector defining the distance in a given direction. In Fig. 19.1, displacements of the particle to the right of O are taken to be positive and those to the left of O are taken to be negative.

The rate of change of distance travelled with respect to time is the **speed**.

Average speed is $\dfrac{\text{distance travelled}}{\text{time taken}}$.

Speed is usually measured in m s^{-1} and sometimes in cm s^{-1} or km h^{-1}.

If the direction is to be taken into account, then we speak of the **velocity** of the body. The magnitude of the vector velocity is the speed.

Suppose a body moves a small distance δs during a small time interval δt. Then the average speed is $\dfrac{\delta s}{\delta t}$. Now as $\delta t \to 0$, we shall have the limiting value of the average speed, i.e. the speed at a particular instant or the **instantaneous** speed. Using the usual notation, $\lim\limits_{\delta t \to 0} \dfrac{\delta s}{\delta t} = \dfrac{ds}{dt}$. So if s is the distance travelled in time t and s is a function of t, then $\dfrac{ds}{dt}$ will give the speed v at a given instant.

$$v = \frac{ds}{dt} \text{ where } s \text{ is a function of } t \qquad \ldots \ldots (1)$$

If v itself is changing, then we have the rate of change of speed v with respect to t, called the **acceleration** (a).

Now
$$a = \frac{dv}{dt} = \frac{d(\frac{ds}{dt})}{dt} = \frac{d^2s}{dt^2} \text{ where } v \text{ is a function of } t \qquad \ldots \ldots (2)$$

Acceleration is the rate of *change* of the velocity with respect to time and hence its standard unit is metres per second *per second*, written m s^{-2}.

A positive acceleration means that the speed is increasing, while a negative acceleration (or a **deceleration** or **retardation**) means that the speed is decreasing.

If we are given the speed v as a function of t, we can find the position of the particle by integration. Thus, from (1), we have $\dfrac{ds}{dt} = v$.

$$\therefore \quad s = \int v \, dt \quad \ldots \ldots (3)$$

Similarly, if we are given the acceleration a, we can find the speed v. Thus from (2), we have $\dfrac{dv}{dt} = a$.

$$\therefore \quad v = \int a \, dt \quad \ldots \ldots (4)$$

▶ **Example 1**

A particle starts from a point O and moves in a straight line so that its distance s cm from O after time t seconds is given by $s = 2t^2 - \dfrac{t^3}{6}$. Find

(a) its initial velocity and acceleration,
(b) the time after the start when it comes to a momentary halt,
(c) its distance from O at this time.
(d) What maximum velocity does it reach before that time?
(e) After what time does the particle pass through O again?

▶ **Solution . . .**

If $s = 2t^2 - \dfrac{t^3}{6}$, then the velocity $v = \dfrac{ds}{dt} = 4t - \dfrac{t^2}{2}$ ... (1)

and the acceleration $a = \dfrac{dv}{dt} = 4 - t$. .... (2)

(a) When $t = 0$ (the start), $v = 0$ and $a = 4$. The particle starts from rest (motionless) with an acceleration of 4 cm s^{-2}.

From (2), note that the acceleration decreases to 0 in the first 4 seconds and then becomes negative.

(b) From (1), $v = 0$ when $4t - \dfrac{t^2}{2} = 0$, i.e. $t\left(4 - \dfrac{t}{2}\right) = 0$ which gives $t = 0$ (the start) or $t = 8$.

At $t = 8$, $a = 4 - 8 = -4$ so the particle stops and instantly reverses direction, moving back towards O. Such a position, where $v = 0$ but $a \neq 0$, is called 'instantaneous rest'.

(c) When $t = 8$, $s = 2(8)^2 - \dfrac{8^3}{6} = \dfrac{128}{3}$ cm.

(d) The maximum velocity occurs when $\dfrac{dv}{dt} = 0$.

From (2), this occurs when $t = 4$ and v is then $4(4) - \dfrac{16}{2} = 8$ cm s^{-1}.

(e) $s = 0$ when $2t^2 - \dfrac{t^3}{6} = 0$, i.e. $t^2\left(2 - \dfrac{t}{6}\right) = 0$ which gives $t = 0$ or $t = 12$.

Hence the particle passes through O again after 12 seconds, now moving in the reverse direction.

The following diagram shows the features of the motion.

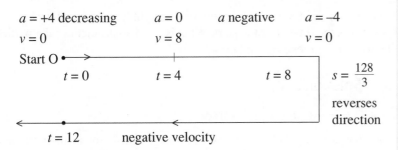

At time $t = 8$, the displacement = distance travelled = $\dfrac{128}{3}$.

At time $t = 12$, the displacement = 0 but the distance travelled was $\dfrac{256}{3}$. The particle reversed during that time.

▶ **Example 2**

The distance s m of a particle moving in a straight line measured from a fixed point O on the line is given by $s = t^2 - 3t + 2$ where t is the time in seconds from the start. Find

(a) its initial distance from O,
(b) its initial velocity and in which direction,
(c) its initial acceleration,
(d) the times when it passes through O and with what velocity,
(e) when and where it is at instantaneous rest.

▶ **Solution . . .**

(a) At the start, $t = 0$. Then $s = 2$ m. The particle starts 2 m from O.

(b) $v = \dfrac{ds}{dt} = 2t - 3$
When $t = 0$, $v = -3$, i.e. in the direction towards O.

(c) $a = \dfrac{dv}{dt} = 2$
The acceleration is constant, i.e. 2 m s^{-2}.

(d) $s = 0$ when $t^2 - 3t + 2 = (t - 2)(t - 1) = 0$, i.e. when $t = 2$ or 1.
When $t = 1$, $v = -1$ and when $t = 2$, $v = 1$.

(e) The particle is at instantaneous rest when $v = 0$, i.e. when $t = 1\frac{1}{2}$

seconds. Then $s = \left(1\frac{1}{2}\right)^2 - 3\left(1\frac{1}{2}\right) + 2 = -0.25$ m.

Putting these facts together, the following diagrammatic representation of the motion can be made:

$t = 1\dfrac{1}{2}$ $t = 1$ Start $t = 0$, $s = 2$

$v = 0$ $v = -1$ $v = -3$, $a = 2$

reverses   ← 0.25 m   2m

$t = 2$ velocity increasing $a = 2$

$v = 1$

▶ Example 3

The velocity v of a particle moving in a straight line is given by $v = t^2 - 3t$ where t is the time after the start. What is the displacement of the particle between the times $t = 2$ and $t = 4$?

▶ Solution . . .

$v = \dfrac{ds}{dt} = t^2 - 3t$ so $s = \displaystyle\int (t^2 - 3t)\, dt$

The displacement is the distance between the positions of the particle at times $t = 2$ and $t = 4$, so it is the value of the definite integral

$$\int_2^4 (t^2 - 3t)\, dt = \left[\frac{t^3}{3} - \frac{3t^2}{2} \right]_2^4$$

$$= \left(\frac{64}{3} - \frac{48}{2} \right) - \left(\frac{8}{3} - \frac{12}{2} \right) = \frac{2}{3}$$

Note:

As we have seen in Example 1, this is not necessarily equal to the actual distance travelled by the particle. It may have gone, for example, 8 units to the left followed by $8\frac{2}{3}$ units to the right.

▶ Example 4

The acceleration a m s^{-2} of a particle moving in a straight line is given by $a = 2t - 5$ where t is the time in seconds from the start. If the initial velocity was 4 m s^{-1}, find

(a) the velocity at time t,
(b) the times when the particle is at instantaneous rest,
(c) the distance from the starting point O after 5 seconds,
(d) the distance travelled in the sixth second.

▶ Solution . . .

(a) $a = \dfrac{dv}{dt} = 2t - 5$

$v = \displaystyle\int 2t - 5 \, dt$

$\quad = \dfrac{2t^2}{2} - 5t + c$

$\quad = t^2 - 5t + c$

Initially, $t = 0$, $v = 4$,
so $4 = c$.
Hence $v = t^2 - 5t + 4$.

(b) When the particle is at instantaneous rest,
$v = 0$,
so $t^2 - 5t + 4 = 0$.
$(t - 1)(t - 4) = 0$
$t = 1$ or 4
∴ the particle is at instantaneous rest when $t = 1$ and 4.

(c) $v = \dfrac{ds}{dt} = t^2 - 5t + 4$

$s = \displaystyle\int t^2 - 5t + 4 \; dt$

The distance from O after 6 s is the displacement when $t = 6$, and this is $s_1 = \displaystyle\int_0^6 t^2 - 5t + 4 \; dt$

$$= \left[\frac{t^3}{3} - \frac{5t^2}{2} + 4t \right]_0^6$$
$$= (72 - 90 + 24) = 6 \text{ m}$$

(d) To answer this part, we note from parts (a) and (b) that the particle moves in the positive direction, comes to rest at $t = 1$, then moves with negative velocity (hence negative direction), comes to rest again after 4 s and reverses direction (positive direction) and thereafter continues in the positive direction.

The sixth second is the time interval starting from $t = 5$ to $t = 6$ (just as the first second is the time interval starting from $t = 0$ to $t = 1$).

Hence the distance travelled in the 6th second is

$$s_2 = \int_5^6 t^2 - 5t + 4 \; dt$$

$$= \left[\frac{t^3}{3} - \frac{5t^2}{2} + 4t \right]_5^6$$

$$= [72 - 90 + 24] - \left[\frac{125}{3} - \frac{125}{2} + 20 \right] = 6\frac{5}{6} \text{ m}$$

Exercise 19A (Answers on page 511)

1. A particle, moving in a straight line, starts from rest and its displacement s m from a fixed point of the line is given by $s = t^2 - kt$ where k is a constant and t is the time (in seconds) afer the start. If it comes to instantaneous rest after 2 seconds, find
    (a) the value of k,
    (b) the initial velocity of the particle.

2. The distance s m of a particle moving in a straight line measured from a fixed point O on the line is given by $s = t^2 - 2t$ where t is the time in seconds after the start.
    (a) What is the initial velocity of the particle?
    (b) When is the particle at instantaneous rest?
    (c) When does it pass through O for the second time?
    (d) What is the acceleration of the particle?

3. For a particle moving in a straight line, its displacement s m from a point O on the line is given by $s = t^2 - 5t + 6$, where t is the time in seconds from the start. Find
    (a) the initial distance of the particle from O,
    (b) its initial velocity,
    (c) when it is at instantaneous rest,
    (d) at what time(s) after the start it passes through O,
    (e) the distance travelled in the first 3 seconds.

4. A small body moves along the x-axis so that its distance x from the origin at time t s is given by $x = 2t^3 - 15t^2 + 24t + 20$. Find
   (a) the velocity with which it starts,
   (b) when it is at instantaneous rest,
   (c) the minimum distance of the body from the origin.
   (d) Between what times is the particle moving towards the origin?
   (e) What is its acceleration at the times in (d)?

5. A particle moves in a straight line. Its displacement s m from a fixed point on the line is given by $s = t^2 - 4t - 5$, at a time t after the start, where $t \geq 0$. Find
   (a) where the particle starts and its initial velocity,
   (b) when and where it comes to instantaneous rest,
   (c) when it passes through the fixed point,
   (d) its acceleration.

6. A particle moves along the x-axis, and its x-coordinate at time t s after the start is given by $x = 2t^3 - 9t^2 + 12t - 1$ for $t \geq 0$.
   (a) Find its x-coordinate and the velocity at the start.
   (b) At what times does the particle come to instantaneous rest?
   (c) When is its acceleration zero?

7. The velocity v cm s^{-1} of a particle moving in a straight line is given by $v = 6t - kt^2$, where k is a constant and t s is the time from the start. If its acceleration is 0 when $t = 1$, find
   (a) the value of k,
   (b) the time when the particle comes to instantaneous rest,
   (c) the maximum velocity of the particle.

8. An object moving in a straight line has acceleration a m s^{-2} after t s where $a = 6t$. Initially, its velocity is 4 m s^{-1} and its distance from a fixed point on the line is 10 m. Find the velocity of the object when $t = 3$ s and its distance from the fixed point at this instant.

9. The velocity v m s^{-1} of a particle after t s is given by $v = 6t + 3t^2$.
   (a) When is the particle moving at a velocity of 24 m s^{-1}?
   (b) Find its acceleration at this instant.
   (c) Find the distance travelled in the third second.

10. A particle, starting from rest, attains an acceleration a m s^{-2} after t s where $a = 4t + 2$.
    (a) Find its velocity after 2 s.
    (b) Calculate the distance travelled between $t = 2$ and $t = 4$.

11. The velocity v m s^{-1} of a particle after t s is given by $v = 6t^2 + 2t + 1$. After 1 s, its distance from its initial position is 6 m.
    (a) How far has it travelled in the first 3 s?
    (b) Find its acceleration when $t = 5$.

12. A body moves so that its velocity v m s^{-1} is given by $v = 48t - 8t^2$.
   (a) Find the times when the body is instantaneously at rest.
   (b) Find the accelerations at these instants.
   (c) Find the distance travelled between those instants.

19.2 s–t Graphs

Fig. 19.2 is a graph showing the relation between the distance or displacement s (in metres) and time t (in seconds). It is called an *s–t* **graph**. We have already learnt that the gradient of the graph $\dfrac{ds}{dt}$ represents the velocity in m s^{-1}. From the graph, we note the following facts:

1. The starting or initial position A of the body is 3 m from a reference position O. The initial velocity is given by the gradient at A and is positive. The body is moving away from O in the positive direction.

2. From A to B, the body moves further away from O but its velocity is decreasing, as the gradient is decreasing.

3. At B, 7 m from O and 5 s from the start, the gradient is zero, i.e. the velocity is zero. The body is momentarily at rest.

4. From B to C, the gradient is negative. Hence the velocity is negative, i.e. the body is moving back towards O and arrives there after 8 s from the start. Note that the *distance* travelled up to this time is $4 + 7 = 11$ m but the *displacement* from O at this time is zero. As this graph always shows the displacement of the body at any time, it is better described as a **displacement-time graph**.

5. The body reaches position D (4 m from O in the opposite direction to B) after 10 s, and is again momentarily at rest.

6. From D to E, the body is now moving in the positive direction and reaches O again after 12 s from the start.

If s is given as a a function of t, the velocity can be found by obtaining the value of $\dfrac{ds}{dt}$. Otherwise, an approximate value can be obtained by fitting a tangent to the curve and measuring its gradient.

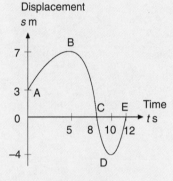

Fig. 19.2

19.3 v–t Graphs

Another useful graph is the *v–t* **graph**, which relates velocity to time. Fig. 19.3 shows an example of such a graph.

The gradient of the graph, $\dfrac{dv}{dt}$, represents the acceleration. There is no indication of the displacement of the body. From the graph, we note the following facts:

1. The body starts at $t = 0$ from rest (i.e. with zero initial velocity). From O to A, the velocity increases until it reaches 10 m s^{-1} at time 5 s. Since OA is a straight line, the acceleration is constant or **uniform** and is equal to $\dfrac{10}{2} = 2$ m s^{-2}. At A, the acceleration ceases.

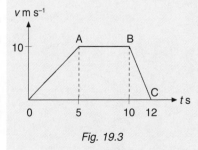

Fig. 19.3

2. From A to B, the body moves with uniform velocity (10 m s⁻¹).

3. From B to C, the velocity decreases steadily. The acceleration is negative. A negative acceleration is called a **deceleration** or a **retardation**. In this case, the retardation is uniform and is equal to $\frac{10}{2}$ =5 m s⁻². The body comes to rest again at t = 12 s.

19.3.1 Area under the v–t Graph

The area under a v–t graph provides us with additional information. In the centre part of the graph in Fig. 19.3, the body is moving with a uniform velocity of 10 m s⁻¹ for 5 s. Hence the distance covered is 50 m. The area under this part of the curve is 10 m s⁻¹ × 5 s = 50 m. So the area under a v–t graph is numerically equal to the distance covered by the body (strictly speaking, the displacement of the body).

If v is measured in m s⁻¹ and t in s, the area will give the distance in m; if v is in km h⁻¹ and t in h, the area represents the distance measured in km.

(In general, if v is a function of t, the area under the graph would be

$$\int v\, dt = \int \frac{ds}{dt}\, dt = \int ds = s \text{ with the appropriate limits taken.})$$

▶ **Example 5**

A train starts from rest from station P and accelerates uniformly for 2 min, reaching a speed of 60 km h⁻¹. It maintains this speed for 10 min and then retards uniformly for 3 min to come to rest at station Q. Find
(a) the distance PQ in km,
(b) the average speed of the train,
(c) the acceleration in m s⁻².

▶ **Solution . . .**

The v–t graph is shown in Fig. 19.4. OA is a straight line as the acceleration is uniform. AB is a straight section parallel to the t-axis as the velocity is constant at 60 km h⁻¹. BC is also straight, with a negative gradient, as the retardation is uniform. v is marked in km h⁻¹ and, to be consistent, t is also marked in h.

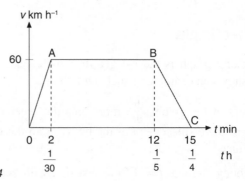

Fig. 19.4

(a) The area under the graph represents the distance travelled.

Area of trapezium OABC = $\frac{1}{2}$ (AB + OC) × 60

$$= \frac{1}{2}\left(\frac{10}{60} + \frac{15}{60}\right) \times 60 = 12.5$$

Hence the distance PQ is 12.5 km.

(b) The average speed = $\dfrac{\text{total distance travelled}}{\text{time taken}}$

$$= \frac{12.5}{\frac{1}{4}} = 50 \text{ km h}^{-1}$$

(c) To find the acceleration in m s^{-2}, we work in m and s.

Now 60 km h^{-1} = $\dfrac{60 \times 1\,000}{60 \times 60} = \dfrac{50}{3}$ m s^{-1}

Hence the acceleration = $\dfrac{\frac{50}{3}}{120} \approx 0.14$ m s^{-2}.

▶ Example 6

An MRT train starts from station X and accelerates uniformly to a speed of 20 m s^{-1}. It maintains this speed and then retards uniformly until it comes to rest at station Y. The distance between the stations is 2 km. The total time taken is 2 min. If the retardation is twice the acceleration in magnitude, find

(a) the length of time for which the train is travelling at constant speed,

(b) the acceleration.

▶ Solution . . .

We first draw the *v-t* graph (Fig. 19.5). OA is a straight line as the acceleration is uniform. AB is a straight line parallel to the *t*-axis as the speed is constant. BC is also straight with a negative gradient, as the retardation is uniform. *v* is marked in m s^{-1}, while *t* is marked in s to be consistent with *v*.

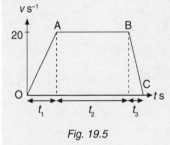

Fig. 19.5

Suppose the train takes t_1, t_2 and t_3 seconds for the 3 parts of the journey as indicated in Fig. 19.5.

(a) The train travels at constant speed for t_2 seconds.

The total time taken is 120 s, i.e. $t_1 + t_2 + t_3 = 120$ s.

The area under the graph represents the distance travelled, i.e. area of trapezium OABC represents the distance between station X and station Y or 2000 m.

Therefore $\frac{1}{2}(t_2 + 120) \times 20 = 2000$

$$t_2 + 120 = 200$$
$$t_2 = 80$$

Hence the train travels at a constant speed for 80s.

(b) Let the acceleration be *a* m s^{-2}.

Then the retardation is $2a$ m s^{-2}.

The gradient of OA gives the acceleration

$$\frac{20}{t_1} = a$$

or $t_1 = \dfrac{20}{a}$

Similarly the retardation is given by

$$\frac{20}{t_3} = 2a$$

or $t_3 = \frac{10}{a}$.

We know that the journey takes 120 s,

i.e. $t_1 + t_2 + t_3 = 120$

so $\quad \frac{20}{a} + 80 + \frac{10}{a} = 120$

which simplifies to $\frac{2}{a} + \frac{1}{a} = 4$ or $\frac{3}{a} = 4$,

giving $a = \frac{3}{4}$.

Hence the acceleration is $\frac{3}{4}$ m s^{-2}.

▶ **Example 7**

A car is travelling at a constant speed of 72 km h^{-1} and passes a stationary police car. The police car immediately gives chase, accelerating uniformly to reach a speed of 90 km h^{-1} in 10 s and continues at this speed until it overtakes the other car. Find

(a) the time taken by the police car to catch up with the car,

(b) the distance travelled by the police car when this happens.

▶ **Solution . . .**

The v–t graphs of the car and the police car are shown in Fig. 19.6. The constant speed of the car is represented by the straight line PQ. OAB is the graph of the speed of the police car.

We work in m and s, so 72 km h^{-1} = 20 m s^{-1} and 90 km h^{-1} = 25 m s^{-1}.

(a) Let the time taken by the police car to overtake the other car be t s. When this happens, both cars would have covered the same distance, therefore area of OABC = area of OPQC,

i.e. $\frac{1}{2}[t + (t - 10)] \times 25 = 20 \times t$.

Verify that this gives $t = 25$ s.

Hence the police car takes 25 s to catch up with the car.

(b) The distance travelled by the police car is the same as the distance covered by the other car, and this is $20 \times 25 = 500$ m.

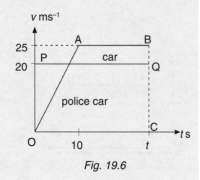

Fig. 19.6

19.4 Constant Acceleration

Let us consider the special case of motion in a straight line when the acceleration (or retardation) is constant. We can then derive a set of equations which will be useful in solving problems connected with constant acceleration. Suppose a body, moving with constant acceleration a, has an initial velocity u. At time t, let its displacement be s and its velocity be v (all in consistent units).

1. We know $\dfrac{dv}{dt} = a$ (a = constant)

$$\therefore v = \int a \, dt$$
$$= at + c \quad (c = \text{constant})$$

If the initial velocity is u (when $t = 0$),

then $u = 0 + c$

$$c = u$$
$$\therefore v = at + u$$

or $\boxed{v = u + at}$ ....(1)

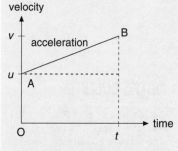

Fig. 19.7

We can also derive this equation using the $v - t$ graph shown in Fig. 19.7.

Acceleration = gradient of AB

i.e. $a = \dfrac{v - u}{t}$

or $at = v - u$

Rearranging,

$$v = u + at \quad \text{which is equation (1)}$$

2. Velocity is $\dfrac{ds}{dt} = v$

$$\therefore s = \int v \, dt$$
$$= \int (u + at) \, dt$$
$$= ut + \dfrac{at^2}{2} + k \quad (k = \text{constant})$$

If the initial displacement is 0, then $k = 0$.

$$\therefore \quad \boxed{s = ut + \dfrac{1}{2} at^2} \quad ....(2)$$

3. From (1) we get $a = \dfrac{v - u}{t}$.

Substituting it into (2), we get $s = ut + \dfrac{v - u}{2} t$.

i.e. $\boxed{s = \dfrac{1}{2}(u + v)t}$ ....(3)

Alternatively, we can obtain equations (2) and (3) using the $v - t$ graph (Fig. 19.7) as follows:

The area under the graph represents the displacement. Hence

$$s = \dfrac{1}{2}(u + v) \times t \quad \text{which is equation (3)}$$

Substituting for v in equation (2),

$$s = \dfrac{1}{2}(u + u + at) \times t$$

Simplifying,

$$s = ut + \dfrac{1}{2} at^2 \quad \text{which is equation (2)}$$

4. From the equation (1), $t = \left(\dfrac{v - u}{a} \right)$.

Substituting for t in equation (3),

$$s = \dfrac{1}{2}(u + v)\left(\dfrac{v - u}{a} \right)$$

i.e. $2as = v^2 - u^2$

or

$$\boxed{v^2 = u^2 + 2as} \quad ....(4)$$

These four equations are applicable *only* to a body travelling in a straight line with constant acceleration (or retardation in which case the value of *a* would be negative). They can be used to solve problems instead of using a *v–t* graph or in conjunction with it. Solutions will often involve solving simultaneous equations.

MATHS BULLETIN

Galileo was born in Pisa in 1564. His father was Vincenzo Galilei who was well known for his musical studies. Galileo studied at the University of Pisa. He later became a mathematics professor at the University of Pisa and subsequently a mathematics professor at the University of Padua. He was both a great mathematician and a scientist and contributed a lot to both fields. He was deeply involved in the study of mechanics and in experiments related to the subject. Among his other achievements were the invention of the microscope and the discovery of the satellites of Jupiter. He died in the year 1642.

Surf the internet to find out more about Galileo's life and achievements.

▶ **Example 8**

A particle travelling in a straight line with constant acceleration 4 m s^{-2} passes a point O when its velocity is 12 m s^{-1}. It passes another point P after a further 3 s. Find the velocity of the particle at P and the distance OP.

▶ **Solution . . .**

Let us consider the motion of the particle from the moment it passes O. Suppose the velocity of the particle at P is *v* m s^{-1} and the distance OP is *s* m.

Using the equation $v = u + at$,

we have

$$v = 12 + 4(3)$$
$$= 24$$

Hence the velocity of the particle at P is 24 m s^{-1}.

Using the equation $s = \frac{1}{2}(u + v) \times t$,

we have

$$s = \frac{1}{2}(12 + 24) \times 3 = 54.$$

Hence the distance OP is 54 m.

▶ **Example 9**

A particle, moving in a straight line with constant acceleration, travels 10 m in the first second and 15 m in the second second. Find
(a) its initial velocity,
(b) its acceleration,
(c) the distance travelled in the third second.

▶ **Solution . . .**

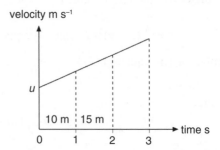

Fig. 19.8

The *v–t* graph is shown in Fig. 19.8.

Let the initial velocity be u m s^{-1} and the acceleration be a m s^{-2}.

Consider motion in the first second.

Using the equation $s = ut + \frac{1}{2}at^2$,

we have $\qquad 10 = u + \frac{1}{2}a$

or $\qquad 2u + a = 20.$ $\qquad$ ....(1)

Similarly, consider motion in the first two seconds.

We have $\qquad 25 = u \times 2 + \frac{1}{2} \times a \times 2^2$

or $\qquad 2u + 2a = 25.$ $\qquad$ ....(2)

Solving equations (1) and (2), we obtain
$u = 7.5$ and $a = 5$.

Hence,
(a) the initial velocity is 7.5 m s^{-1}, and
(b) the acceleration is 5 m s^{-2}.
(c) The distance travelled in the first three seconds is s m given by

$s = 7.5 \times 3 + \frac{1}{2} \times 5 \times 3^2 = 45$.

Hence the distance travelled in the third second
= distance travelled in 1st 3 seconds – distance travelled in 1st
2 seconds
= (45 – 25) m
= 20 m.

▶ **Example 10**

A bus leaves a bus stop and accelerates uniformly for 10 s over a distance
of 100 m. It then moves uniformly with the speed it has attained for 30 s
and finally retards uniformly to rest at the next stop. If the two bus stops
are 1 km apart, find
(a) the maximum velocity,
(b) the acceleration,
(c) the total time taken between the two stops.

▶ **Solution . . .**

The v–t graph is shown in Fig. 19.9. Consider motion in the first 10 s.

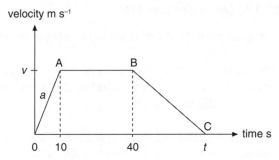

Fig. 19.9

(a) Using the equation $s = \frac{1}{2}(u + v) \times t$, the maximum speed v m s^{-1} is given by $100 = \frac{1}{2}(0 + v) \times 10$, giving $v = 20$.
Hence the maximum speed is 20 m s^{-1}.

(b) Using the equation $v = u + at$, the acceleration a m s^{-2} is given by $20 = 0 + a \times 10$, giving $a = 2$.
Hence the acceleration is 2 m s^{-2}.

(c) Let the total time taken be t s.
Area of OABC represents the distance travelled which is 1000 m,
i.e. $\frac{1}{2}(30 + t) \times 20 = 1000$, giving $t = 70$.
Hence the total time taken is 70 s.

▶ **Example 11**

Two particles P and Q are moving on the same horizontal line towards each other. P passes point A on the line with speed 8 m s^{-1} and constant acceleration $\frac{3}{4}$ m s^{-2}. Simultaneously, Q passes point B on the line with speed 4 m s^{-1} and constant acceleration $\frac{5}{4}$ m s^{-2}. Given that the distance AB is 64 m, calculate
(a) the time taken for the particles to collide,
(b) the distance from A of the point of collision.

▶ **Solution . . .**

(a) Let the time taken be t seconds.
Using the formula $s = ut + \frac{1}{2}at^2$, P will travel a distance of
$8t + \frac{1}{2} \times \frac{3}{4}t^2$ m and Q a distance of $4t + \frac{1}{2} \times \frac{5}{4}t^2$ m.
These distances total 64 m.
Then $8t + \frac{3}{8}t^2 + 4t + \frac{5}{8}t^2 = 64$, i.e. $t^2 + 12t - 64 = 0$.
Hence $(t + 16)(t - 4) = 0$, giving $t = -16$ (not admissible) or $t = 4$.
Thus they collide after 4 seconds.

(b) The distance from A of the point of collision is then
$8 \times 4 + \frac{3}{8} \times 16 = 38$ m.

Exercise 19B (Answers on page 511)

(All acceleration are to be taken as uniform and in a straight line.)

1. A car starts from rest, accelerates at 0.8 m s^{-2} for 10 s and then continues at a steady speed for a further 20s. Draw the v-t graph and find the total distance travelled.

2. A car starts from rest, accelerating at 1 m s^{-2} for 10 s. It then continues at a steady speed for a further 20 s and decelerates to rest in 5 s. Find **(a)** the distance travelled in m, **(b)** the average speed in m s^{-1} and **(c)** the time taken to cover half the distance.

3. Two cars start from the same place. One accelerates at 1 m s^{-2} for 10 s, the other accelerates at 0.8 m s^{-2} for 20 s. Both cars continue with the speed then reached. How long after the start will the second car overtake the first and at what distance?

4. A car accelerates from rest to reach a certain speed in 10 min. It then continues at this speed for another 10 min and decelerates to rest in a further 5 min. The total distance covered is 17.5 km. Find the steady speed reached.

5. Two trains, A and B, starting together from rest, arrive together at rest 10 min later. Train A accelerates uniformly at 0.125 m s^{-2} for 2 min, continues at the steady speed reached for another 4 min and then retards uniformly to rest. Train B accelerates uniformly for 5 min and then retards uniformly to rest.
    Draw both journeys on the same v-t graph and find
    (a) the distance (in m) travelled,
    (b) the acceleration of train B,
    (c) the distance between the two trains after 3 min.

6. A car travelling at a constant velocity of 20 m s^{-1} passes a stationary sports car. Ten seconds afterwards, the sports car accelerates uniformly at 3 m s^{-2} to reach a speed of 30 m s^{-1} with which it continues. Draw the v-t graphs of both cars together and find when and where the sports car overtakes the first car.

7. In rising from rest to rest in 8 s, a lift accelerates uniformly to its maximum speed and then retards uniformly. The retardation is one-third the acceleration and the distance travelled is 20 m. Find the acceleration, the retardation and the maximum speed reached.

8. An electric train takes 3 min to travel between two stations 2 970 m apart. The train accelerates uniformly to a speed of 18 m s^{-1} and then travels for a time at this speed before retarding uniformly to rest at the second station.
    If the acceleration and retardation are in the ratio 2:3, calculate the times for which the train was accelerating and travelling at a steady speed.

9. A particle starts with the velocity 3 m s^{-1} and accelerates at 0.5 m s^{-2}. What is its velocity after (a) 3 s, (b) 10 s, (c) t s? How far has it travelled in these times?

10. A body, decelerating at 0.8 m s^{-2}, passes a certain point with a speed of 30 m s^{-1}. Find its velocity after 10 s, the distance covered in that time and how much further the body will go until it stops.

11. A particle travelling with an acceleration of 0.75 m s^{-2} passes a point O at a speed of 5 m s^{-1}. How long will it take to cover a distance of 250 m from O? What will its speed be at that time?

12. If a particle passes a certain point at a speed of 5 m s^{-1} and is accelerating at 3 m s^{-2}, how far will it travel in the next 2 s? How long will it take (from the start) to travel 44 m?

13. A car, retarding uniformly, passes over three cables, P, Q and R set at right angles to the path of the car and 11 m apart. It takes 1 s between P and Q and 1.2 s between Q and R. Find
    (a) its retardation,
    (b) its velocity when it crosses P,
    (c) its distance beyond R when it comes to rest.   (C)

14. A car, slowing down with uniform retardation, passes a stationary man. 20 s after passing the man the car is 40 m from him and 30 s after passing him it is 50 m away. Find the speed of the car as it passes the man. Find the distance from the man where the car comes to rest. Draw a sketch of the v–t graph.

15. A body passes a certain point A of the straight line on which it is moving with uniform acceleration. One second afterwards it is 11 m beyond A and in the next second it travels a further 13 m. Find the velocity it had when it passed A, and how far it travels in the third second after passing A.

16. Two particles A and B are moving in the same direction on parallel horizontal lines. They pass a certain point O at the same time, A moving with a speed of 3 m s^{-1} and constant acceleration rate of 0.5 m s^{-2} and B moving with a speed of 4 m s^{-1} and constant acceleration 0.2 m s^{-2}.
    If the speeds of A and B are equal after t seconds, calculate
    (a) the value of t,
    (b) the distance between the particles at that time.

17. Two particles P and Q are moving on the same horizontal straight line towards each other. P passes a point A on the line at the speed of 4 m s^{-1} and a uniform acceleration 1 m s^{-2}. At the same instant, Q passes a point B on the line at the speed of 6 m s^{-1} and a uniform deceleration 0.5 m s^{-2}. If the distance AB is 44 m, calculate
    (a) the time taken for the particles to collide,
    (b) the distance from A of the point of collision.

Summary

1. If distance s is a function of t, then
$$\text{velocity } v = \frac{ds}{dt},$$
$$\text{acceleration } a = \frac{dv}{dt} = \frac{d^2 s}{dt^2}.$$

2. If acceleration a is a function of t, then
$$v = \int a \, dt,$$
$$s = \int v \, dt.$$

3. When a body is instantaneously at rest, $v = 0$.

4. A negative acceleration is a retardation (or deceleration).

5. For an s–t graph, the gradient of the graph represents velocity.

6. For a v–t graph, the gradient of the graph represents acceleration; the area under the graph represents displacement.

7. Equations of motion with constant acceleration:
$$v = u + at$$
$$s = \frac{1}{2}(u + v)t$$
$$s = ut + \frac{1}{2}at^2$$
$$v^2 = u^2 + 2as$$
where s = displacement, u = initial velocity, v = velocity at time t, a = acceleration.

Revision Exercise 19 (Answers on page 511)

1. A point moves on the x-axis and its position at time t is given by $x = t(t^2 - 6t + 12)$. Show that its velocity at the origin is 12 and find its position when it comes to instantaneous rest. If v is its velocity and a its acceleration at time t, show that $a^2 = 12v$.

2. A particle is travelling in a straight line and its distance s cm from a fixed point on the line after t seconds is given by $s = 12t - 15t^2 + 4t^3$. Find
   (a) the velocity and acceleration after 3 seconds,
   (b) the distance between the two points where it is at instantaneous rest.

3. A particle P travels in a straight line so that its distance, s metres, from a fixed point O is given by $s = 11 + 6t^2 - t^3$ where t is the time in seconds measured from the start of the motion. Calculate
   (a) the velocity of P after 3 seconds,
   (b) the velocity of P when its acceleration is instantaneously zero,
   (c) the average velocity of P over the first two seconds.

4. A particle starts from a fixed point O and moves in a straight line. Its distance s from O at time t seconds from the start is given by $s = \frac{1}{3}t^3 - 2t^2 + 3t$. Find an expression for the velocity v of the particle in terms of t. At what times from the start is the particle at instantaneous rest? What is its displacement between those times?

5. A point A moves along the positve x-axis away from the origin O at a speed of 4 cm s^{-1} where OA > 5 cm. B is a fixed point on the positive y-axis where OB = 20 cm. P is a fixed point on the positive x-axis where OP = 5 cm and Q lies on the line joining B and A with PQ parallel to the y-axis.

(a) Show that when OA = x cm, PQ = $20(1 - \frac{5}{x})$ cm.

(b) Hence find the speed of Q along PQ as A moves when
(i) $x = 12$ cm, (ii) $x = 20$ cm.

(c) Obtain an expression in terms of x for the acceleration of Q along PQ.

6. A particle passes a fixed point O with a velocity of 3 and moves in a straight line with acceleration a given by $a = 3 - 2t$ where t is the time in seconds after passing O. Find the velocity and the distance of the particle O when $t = 2$.

7. A particle, moving in a straight line, passes through a fixed point O with a velocity of 8 m s^{-1}. Its acceleration, a m s^{-2}, t seconds after passing O, is given by $a = 12 - 6t$. Find
(i) the velocity of the particle when $t = 2$,
(ii) the displacement of the particle from O when $t = 2$. (C)

8. A particle travelling in a straight line passes a fixed point O with a velocity of $1\frac{1}{2}$ m s^{-1}. It moves in such a manner that, t seconds after passing O, its acceleration a m s^{-2}, is given by $a = p + qt$, where p and q are constants.

Given that its velocity is $3\frac{1}{2}$ m s^{-1} when $t = 2$ and that it comes instantaneously to rest when $t = 3$, calculate the value of p and of q. Find the distance travelled by the particle between $t = 1$ and $t = 2$. (C)

9. A particle moves in a straight line and its distance s from a fixed point O of the line at time t is given by $s = 4 \sin 2t$.
(a) Show that its velocity v and its acceleration a at time t are given by $v = 2\sqrt{16 - s^2}$ and $a = -4s$.
(b) Find the greatest distance from O reached by the particle.

10. Two particles A and B are moving in the same direction on parallel horizontal tracks. At a certain point, the particle A, travelling at a speed of 7 m s^{-1} and accelerating uniformly at 1.5 m s^{-2}, overtakes B, travelling at 3 m s^{-1} and accelerating uniformly at 2.5 m s^{-2}. Calculate the period of time which elapses before B overtakes A.
If, after this time, B then ceases to accelerate and continues at a constant speed, calculate the time taken for A to overtake B again.

11. Two particles, X and Y, are moving in the same direction on parallel horizontal tracks. At a certain point O, the particle X, travelling with a speed of 16 m s^{-1} and retarding uniformly at 6 m s^{-2}, overtakes Y, which is travelling at 8 m s^{-1} and accelerating uniformly at 2 m s^{-2}. Calculate
(a) the distance of Y from O when the velocities of X and Y are equal,
(b) the velocity of X when Y overtakes X. (C)

12. A man running a 100 m race accelerates uniformly from rest for the first T seconds and reaches a velocity of 10 m s^{-1}. He maintains this velocity for the rest of the race. His time for the race is 12 s. Sketch a velocity-time graph.

Calculate

(a) the value of T,

(b) the acceleration,

(c) the distance the man runs before he reaches his maximum speed.

(C)

13. A car moves along a straight level road, accelerating from rest at a constant rate for 9.6 s over a distance of S_1 m until it reaches a speed of V m s^{-1}. Express S_1 in terms of V.

It then accelerates at a constant rate of 2.5 m s^{-2} over a distance of S_2 m until it reaches a speed of 25 m s^{-1}. Express S_2 in terms of V.

Given that the car has now travelled a total distance of 152 m, calculate the possible values of V. Using the smaller of these values, calculate the time taken to attain a speed of 25 m s^{-1} from rest. (C)

14. A motorcyclist travelling along a straight road passes a fixed point O with a speed of 20 m s^{-1} and continues at this speed for t_1 seconds. Over the next t_2 seconds, he accelerates at a constant rate to a speed of 30 m s^{-1}. He then brings the motorcycle to rest in a further t_3 seconds by retarding at a constant rate. His acceleration and retardation are of equal magnitude.

(a) Sketch a velocity-time graph to illustrate the motion of the motorcyclist after passing O.

(b) Obtain an equation connecting t_2 and t_3.

(c) Given that the total distance and the total time represented by the graph are 748 m and 40 s respectively, calculate t_1, t_2 and t_3.

(C)

15. During a certain stage of its journey, a train decelerates uniformly from a speed of 25 m s^{-1} to a speed of 15 m s^{-1} which it maintains for a time before accelerating uniformly to its former speed of 25 m s^{-1}. Sketch a velocity-time graph to illustrate this stage.

Given that, for this stage of the journey, the total distance travelled is 12 000 m, the total time taken is 720 seconds and the magnitude of the acceleration is twice that of the deceleration, calculate

(a) the time during which the train is accelerating,

(b) the speed of the train 180 seconds after the start of this stage,

(c) the speed of the train 660 seconds after the start of this stage.

(C)

16. A car starts from rest and accelerates at 1 m s⁻² to reach a speed of 90 km h⁻¹. It maintains this speed for 5 minutes and then slows down uniformly to a speed of 36 km h⁻¹ while covering a distance of 350 m. It then continues at this speed for 10 minutes and is brought to rest with uniform deceleration in a further 15 seconds. Sketch a v–t graph of the motion and hence or otherwise calculate
   (a) the total time in minutes taken over the journey,
   (b) the total distance travelled in km correct to 3 significant figures.

17. A straight horizontal track joins two stations A and B which are a distance D km apart.

A train starts from rest at A, accelerates at a constant rate over a distance $\dfrac{D}{4}$ km before reaching a velocity V km h⁻¹ which it maintains for a further distance $\dfrac{D}{2}$ km before retarding at a constant rate and coming to rest at B.

A second train completes the journey from A to B in T hours by starting from rest at A, accelerating at a constant rate for $\dfrac{T}{4}$ hours, reaching the velocity V km h⁻¹ which it maintains for $\dfrac{T}{2}$ hours, before retarding at a constant rate and coming to rest at B. For each train, calculate the average velocity for the journey and state which train completes the journey in a shorter time. (C)

18. A car travels a distance of 46.8 km in 32 minutes. First it accelerates uniformly from rest to reach a speed of v m s⁻¹, then continues at this speed for 20 minutes and finally retards uniformly to rest. Calculate the value of v in m s⁻¹.
Given also that the magnitude of the retardation is half that of the acceleration, find the acceleration in m s⁻².

19. Two particles P and Q are 45 m apart on a smooth horizontal plane. P starts moving towards Q at a speed of 3 m s⁻¹ and constant acceleration 0.5 m s⁻². At the same instant, Q starts moving towards P in the same straight line at the speed of 6 m s⁻¹ and a constant retardation rate of a m s⁻². If they meet when Q has just come to momentary rest, calculate the time taken for the particles to meet.

20. Particles A and B are moving in the same direction along parallel horizontal lines. At time $t = 0$, A, travelling at a speed of 6 m s⁻¹ and a constant acceleration rate of 1.6 m s⁻², overtakes B travelling at a speed of 4 m s⁻¹ and a constant acceleration rate of 2 m s⁻². Calculate
   (a) the value of t when B overtakes A,
   (b) the speeds of A and B at that instant.
   (c) If at that time, the acceleration of B is reduced to 1 m s⁻², after what time interval will A overtake B?

Maths Booster

Two MRT trains A and B start from rest and approach each other from two stations 0.9 km apart (so that the fronts of the trains are 0.9 km apart). Train A, which is 90 m long, moves with a constant acceleration of 6 m s^{-2} and Train B, which is 110 m long, moves with a constant acceleration of 5 m s^{-2}, until they pass each other completely.

Find the time taken for this to happen.

Revision Paper 7 (Answers on page 512)

1. Differentiate the following wrt x, simplifying your answers.

    (a) $\left(x - \dfrac{1}{2x}\right)^2$

    (b) $\dfrac{1-2x}{x+2}$

    (c) $(x-2)^2(2x-3)^3$

2. (a) Find the equation of the normal to the curve $y = \dfrac{1}{x} - 2x$ at the point where $x = 1$.

    (b) Find the values of $\dfrac{d^2y}{dx^2}$ on the curve $y = 2x(x-3)^2$ where $\dfrac{dy}{dx} = 0$.

3. (a) Find (i) the range of values of x for which the function $x^3 - 3x^2 - 9x + 1$ has a positive gradient, (ii) the nature of the stationary points on the curve and the values of x where they occur.

    (b) Find the maximum value of $(x + b)(a - x)$ where a and b are constants.

4. (a) The radius r of a sphere increases from 2 to 2.01. Find the approximate change in the surface area A. $[A = 4\pi r^2]$.

    (b) The radius r of a sphere is increasing at a constant rate of 0.02 cm s^{-1}. Find the rate at which the volume is increasing when $r = 3$ cm. $[V = \dfrac{4}{3}\pi r^3]$.

    (c) The volume V of a sphere decreases by approximately 6% when the radius decreases by $p\%$. Find the value of p.

5. Find (a) $\displaystyle\int \dfrac{2x^2 + 3}{x^2}\, dx$,

    (b) $\displaystyle\int_{-1}^{2} (x-2)^2\, dx$,

    (c) $\displaystyle\int_{-5}^{0} \dfrac{dx}{\sqrt{5-x}}$.

6. Calculate the area of the region lying between the curve $y = x^2 - 3x + 2$, the x-axis and the lines $x = -1$, $x = 2$.

7. (a) Sketch the curve $y = 1 + e^x$.
    Find (b) the equation of the tangent to this curve at the point $(1, 1 + e)$ and (c) the coordinates of the point where this tangent cuts the y-axis. (d) Hence find the area enclosed by the curve, this tangent and the y-axis. [Leave your answer in terms of e.]

8. (a) Find $\dfrac{dy}{dx}$ if $y = \ln\left(\dfrac{x-2}{x+2}\right)$, simplifying your answer.

    (b) Hence evaluate $\displaystyle\int_{0}^{1} \dfrac{1}{x^2 - 4}\, dx$.

9. A particle moves along a straight line so that its velocity v m s^{-1} at time t seconds from the start is given by $v = t^2 - 4t$.
    (a) Find the time after the start when the particle is at instantaneous rest.
    (b) What is the velocity of the particle when its acceleration is zero?
    (c) Find the displacement of the particle during the first 3 seconds of motion.

10. A car accelerates uniformly from rest to reach a speed of 24 m s^{-1}, continues at this speed for 20 seconds and then decelerates uniformly to stop at the traffic lights. The total time from start to stop was 35 seconds. Given that the magnitude of the deceleration was twice that of the acceleration, calculate
    (a) the total distance travelled,
    (b) the rate of acceleration,
    (c) the time taken to travel the first half of the journey.

Revision Paper 8 (*Answers on page 512*)

1. Differentiate the following wrt x, simplifying your answers.
    (a) $\ln(x\sqrt{x^2+1})$

    (b) $\dfrac{\ln x}{x^2}$

    (c) $\dfrac{e^{-x}}{x+1}$

2. The gradient of the curve $y = \dfrac{a}{x} + bx^2$ at the point $(1, -1)$ is -8. Find the values of a and b. Hence find the equation of the tangent to the curve where $x = 2$.

3. (a) Given that $A = 3r + \dfrac{1}{r}$, find the rate of change of r with respect to t when $r = 2$, if the rate of change of A with respect to t is $\dfrac{11}{8}$.
    (b) A cone of radius 6 cm and height 24 cm is held vertex down with its axis vertical. Water is poured into the cone at the rate of 90 cm^3 s^{-1}. At what rate is the water level rising when its greatest depth is 12 cm?

4. A piece of wire 120 cm long is bent into the shape shown in Fig. R8.1. Show that the area A cm^2 is given by $A = 480x - 60x^2$. Hence find the value of x which gives the maximum area.

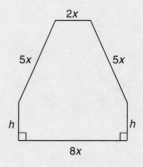

Fig. R8.1

5. Evaluate (a) $\displaystyle\int_{-5}^{0} \dfrac{dx}{(5-x)^2}$,

    (b) $\displaystyle\int_{0}^{\frac{\pi}{2}} 2\cos 3x \, dx$,

    (c) $\displaystyle\int_{0}^{1} \dfrac{e^x - 1}{e^{2x}} \, dx$.

6.   Fig R8.2 shows part of the curve $y = 2 - x - x^2$ and the lines $y = 2$ and $y = -5$. Find the area of the shaded region.

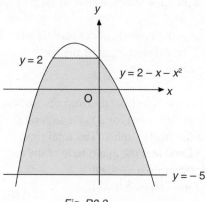

Fig. R8.2

7.   A curve passes through the point $(0,2)$ and its gradient at any point (x,y) on the curve is $1 - x - 2x^2$. Find
     (a)   the equation of the curve,
     (b)   the coordinates of the turning points on the curve, stating the nature of each one,
     (c)   the equation of the tangent to the curve at the point where $x = 1$.

8.   **(a)**   Differentiate $\tan^3 x$ wrt x.
     (b)   Show that $\tan^4 x = \sec^2 x \tan^2 x - \sec^2 x + 1$.
     (c)   Hence, using these results, find $\int \tan^4 x \, dx$.

9.   A particle moves on a straight line so that its velocity v m s^{-1} t seconds after passing through a fixed point O on the line is given by $v = 12e^{-\frac{t}{3}}$.
     (a) State its velocity at O. Find **(b)** its acceleration 3 seconds after passing O and **(c)** its displacement from O at that time.

10. **(a)**   When the driver of a car has to stop, he takes a certain time t seconds before he puts on the brakes. The car then immediately decelerates at the uniform rate of a m s^{-2}. When travelling at a uniform speed of 10 m s^{-1}, the car covers a distance of 15 m before coming to a stop and when travelling at 20 m s^{-1}, the car covers a distance of 50 m. Find the value of t and of a.
     With these values, what is the shortest distance in which the driver can stop the car if it is travelling with a speed of 24 m s^{-1} and an acceleration of 2 m s^{-2}?

     (b)   Two bodies A and B are travelling along parallel straight lines. At a certain instant, A has a speed of 15 m s^{-1}, an acceleration of 2 m s^{-2} and is 8 m ahead of B. At the same instant, B has a speed of 20 m s^{-1} and an acceleration of 1 m s^{-2}. Find **(i)** the times after this instant when B overtakes A and when A overtakes B, **(ii)** the distance between these two events.

Answers

Exercise 1A

1 (a) Set A is the set of units used in the measurement of length. **(b)** Set B is the set of quadrilaterals.

(c) Set C is the set of organs in the human digestive system. **(d)** Set D is the set of countries in South-east Asia.

(e) Set E is the set of multiples of 5. **(f)** Set F is the set of letters in the word *train*.

2 (a) $P = \{a, e, i, o, u\}$ **(b)** $Q = \{$red, orange, yellow, green, blue, indigo, violet$\}$

(c) $R = \{$Mercury, Venus, Earth, Mars, Jupiter, Saturn, Uranus, Neptune$\}$

(d) $S = \{$January, March, May, July, August, October, December$\}$ **(e)** $T = \{h, i, s, t, o, r, y\}$ **(f)** $U = \{1, 2, 3, 4, 6, 12\}$

3 (a) $A = \{1, 3, 5, 7, ...\}$ **(b)** $B = \{5, 6, 7, 8, 9, 10, 11, 12\}$ **(c)** $C = \{1, 4, 9, 16\}$ **(d)** $D = \{6, 8, 10, ...\}$ **(e)** $E = \{6, 9, 12\}$

(f) $F = \{(1, 1), (2, 4), (3, 7)\}$ **4 (a)** True because $2 \in \{1, 2, 3, 4\}$. **(b)** True because $2 \notin \{4, 6, 8, 10, 12, 14\}$.

(c) False because $31 \notin \{11, 13, 17, 19, 23\}$. **(d)** False because $9 \in \{4, 9, 16\}$. **5 (a)** $6 \in P$ **(b)** $10 \notin P$ **(c)** $7 \in Q$

(d) $12 \notin Q$ **(e)** $8 \notin R$ **(f)** $3 \in R$ **(g)** $25 \in S$ **(h)** $40 \in S$ **6 (a)** 6 **(b)** 10 **(c)** 1 **(d)** 6 **(e)** 10

7 (a) $H = \emptyset$ **(b)** $J = \emptyset$ **(c)** $K \neq \emptyset$ **(d)** $M = \emptyset$ **8 (a)** $A = B$ **(b)** $C \neq D$ **(c)** $E = F$ **(d)** $G \neq H$

9 $A = \{10, 11\}, B = \{10, 20, 40\}, C = \{12, 18, 24, 30, 36, 42, 48\}$ **10** $n(\varepsilon) = 11, n(P) = 6, n(Q) = 2$

Exercise 1B

1 (a) $A \subseteq B$ **(b)** $A \nsubseteq B$ **(c)** $A \subseteq B$ **2 (a)** true **(b)** true **(c)** false **3 (a)** $X \subset Y$ **(b)** $X \not\subset Y$ **(c)** $X \subset Y$

4 (a) true **(b)** true **(c)** true **(d)** false **(e)** false **(f)** false **5 (a)** $\emptyset, \{1\}, \{2\}, \{3\}, \{1, 2\}, \{1, 3\}, \{2, 3\}, \{1, 2, 3\}$

(b) $\emptyset, \{a\}, \{b\}, \{c\}, \{d\}, \{a, b\}, \{a, c\}, \{a, d\}, \{b, c\}, \{b, d\}, \{c, d\}, \{a, b, c\}, \{a, b, d\}, \{a, c, d\}, \{b, c, d\}, \{a, b, c, d\}$

6 (a) 128 **(b)** 512

Exercise 1C

2 (a) $\{1, 4, 6, 8, 9, 10\}; 6$ **(b)** $\{t, r, i\}; 3$ **(c)** $\{1, 2, 3, 4\}; 4$ **(d)** $\{31, 32, 34, 35, 37, 38, 40\}; 7$ **3 (a)** 17 **(b)** 40

(c) 76 **(d)** 11 **4 (a)** $\{2, 3\}$ **(b)** $\emptyset$ **(c)** $\{5, 7\}$ **(d)** $\{1, 4, 5, 6, 7, 8, 9, 10\}$ **5 (a)** $\{3\}$ **(b)** $\emptyset$ **(c)** $\{2, 5\}$

(d) $\{4, 6, 8, 9\}$ **6** $\{6, 7, 8, 9\}$ **7 (a)** 2 **(b)** 2 **(c)** 0 **8 (a)** $\{1, 2, 3, 4, 5, 7, 8\}$ **(b)** $\{1, 2, 4, 8\}$

(c) $\{1, 4, 6, 8, 9, 10\}$ **(d)** $\{6, 9, 10\}$ **9 (a)** $\{3, 4, 6, 9, 12, 15, 16\}$ **(b)** $\{2, 3, 5, 6, 7, 9, 11, 12, 13, 15\}$

(c) $\{4, 6, 8, 9, 10, 12, 14, 15, 16\}$ **(d)** $\{2, 4, 6, 7, 8, 9, 10, 11, 12, 13, 14, 15, 16\}$ **10 (a)** 7 **(b)** 6 **(c)** 6

11 (a) $\{4, 6\}$ **(b)** $\{3, 4, 5, 6, 7, 9\}$ **(c)** $\{4, 5, 7, 8\}$ **(d)** $\{2, 3, 8, 9\}$ **13 (a)** $\{a, b, c, d, e\}$ **(b)** $\{d, e, f\}$ **(c)** $\{d, e\}$

(d) $\{a, b, c, d, e, f\}$ **(e)** $\{f, g\}$ **(f)** $\{a, b, c, g\}$ **(g)** $\{d, e, f, g\}$ **(h)** $\{a, b, c\}$ **(i)** $\{a, b, c, f, g\}$ **(j)** $\{g\}$

14 (a) $A \cap B'$ **(b)** $A' \cup B$ **16** 14 **17** 22 **18 (b)** 17 **19 (a)** 12 **(b)** 50 **(c)** 8 **(d)** 10 **20 (a) (i)** $4; 0$ **(ii)** $18; 14$

(b) (i) $6; 0$ **(ii)** $22; 16$ **(c) (i)** $0; 3$ **(ii)** $12; 15$ **(d) (i)** $0; 12$ **(ii)** $18; 30$ **21 (a)** $p = 75 - x$ **(b)** 90 **(c)** 35 **(d)** 5

22 (a) 2 **(b) (i)** $\{p, q\}$ **(ii)** $\{r, u, v\}$ **23 (a)** $\{a, d\}$ **(b)** $\{a, c, d, f\}$ **(c)** $\{a, c, d, f\}$

Exercise 1D

3 (a) $(B \cap C) \cap A'$ **(b)** $(A' \cap B) \cup C$ **(c)** $(A \cup C) \cap B$ **(d)** $(A \cap B) \cup (B \cap C) \cup (A \cap C)$ **4 (a)** $\{b, c, d, f, g\}$

(b) $\{b, c, d\}$ **(c)** $\{b, c, f\}$ **(d)** $\{e, f, g\}$ **(e)** $\{b, c, e, f, g\}$ **(f)** $\{e\}$ **5 (b)** 6 **(c)** $\{4, 6, 7\}$ **7 (a)** 7 **9 (a)** 38 **(b)** 16 **(c)** 16

10 (a) 33 **(b)** 4 **(c)** 32 **11 (a)** 7 **(b)** 2 **12 (a)** 10 **(b)** 14 **(c)** 48 **13 (b)** 54 **(c)** 38

Exercise 1E

1 14 **2 (a)** 62 **(b)** 30 **3 (a)** 5 **(b)** 10 **(c)** 27 **4 (a)** 15 **(b)** 90 **6 (a)** 8 **(b)** 16 **(c)** 40 **7 (a)** 75 **(b)** 12

(c) 165 **(d)** 15 **8 (a)** 61 **(b)** 158 **9 (a)** 12 **(b)** 39 **(c)** 32 **10 (a) (i)** 11 **(ii)** 10 **(iii)** 26 **(b)** 38

Revision Exercise 1

1 (a) 2 **(b)** 5 **(c)** $\{p\}$ **(d)** $\{t, w\}$ **(e)** $\{r, v\}$ **2** $A = \{a\}, B = \{a, b, c, d\}, C = \{e, f\}$ **3 (a) (i)** 33 **(ii)** 85 **(iii)** 38
(b) (i) $\{25, 36, 49\}$ **(ii)** $\{12, 60, 72, 84, 96\}$ **(iii)** $\{16, 64, 81\}$ **(c)** $\{12, 16, 60, 72, 84, 96\}$ **4 (a)** $\{6, 7, 18, 19\}$
(b) $\{11, 13, 17\}$ **5 (a)** $\{4, 8, 12, 16, 20, 24, 28\}$ **(b)** 5 **(c)** $A \cap B = C$ **6 (a)** $\emptyset, \{a\}, \{b\}, \{a, b\}$ **(b) (i)** A **(ii)** B
7 (a) R **(b)** 24 **8 (a)** 40 **(b)** 25 **9 (c)** $(A \cap C) \cup (B \cap C)$ **10 (a)** $A \cap B \neq \emptyset; B \cap C \neq \emptyset; A \cap C = \emptyset$ **12 (a)** 23
(b) 25 **(c)** 3 **(d)** 15 **13 (a)** 11 **(b)** $\frac{7}{13}$ **(c)** $-2, 4$ **14 (a)** 14 **(b)** $(H \cup G)'$ **15 (a)** 30 **(b)** 50 **(c)** 30
16 (b) 6 **(c)** 2 **17** $x = 6$; 16 **18 (a)** 18 **(b)** 5; 150

Exercise 2A

1 (a) This is a function because every member in set A is linked to only one member in set B.

(b) This is a function because every member in set C is linked to only one member in set D.

(c) This is not a function because the member '5' in set E is linked to three members, 2, 3, and 4, in set F.

(d) This is not a function because the member '3' in set G is linked to two members, '6' and '9', in set H.

(e) This is a function because every member in set I is linked to only one member in set J even though the number '9' in set J is not linked to any member in set I.

(f) This is not a function because not every member in set K is linked to the members in set L, i.e., the member 'February' in set K is not linked to any member in set L.

2 (a) The domain is {oxygen, hydrogen, salt, sugar}. 'Gas' is the image of 'oxygen' and 'hydrogen', and 'solid' is the image of 'salt' and 'sugar'. The range is {gas, solid}. **(b)** The domain is $\{1, 2, 3, 4, 5\}$. 'Even number' is the image of 2 and 4, and 'odd number' is the image of 1, 3 and 5. The range is {even number, odd number}.

3 (a) $7, -5, -3, 15$ **(b)** $-15, 0, 0, -15$ **4** $\{1, 3, 9\}$ **5** $\{-1, 3, 5\}$ **6** $4, \frac{1}{2}, 2, 5$ **7** $1, 2.5$ **8** 2
9 (a) $-1, 6$ **(b)** 3 **10 (a)** $\frac{1}{4}, 8$ **(b)** 4 **11** $\{-3, -1, 0, 1, 3\}$ **12** $\{1, -2, -\frac{2}{3}\}$ **13** $a = -2, b = 3$
14 $c = 7; a = 2, b = -3$ **15** $a = 2, b = -1$ **16 (a)** $1, 4$ **(b)** $-1, 3$ **17 (a)** $-3, 2$ **(b)** $-1, 4$ **18** $\frac{1}{2}$
19 $3a + 1, 3b + 1, 3a + 3b + 1$; No **20** $3a^2 - 3a$ **21 (a)** 2, undefined, $-1, \frac{1}{3}$ **(b)** {all real values of x, $x \neq -1$}
22 (a) {all real values of x, $x \neq 2$} **(b)** {all real values of x, $x \neq -\frac{2}{3}$} **(c)** {all real values of x, $x \neq -2, x \neq 1$}
(d) {all real values of x, $x \neq -3$} **(e)** {all real positive values of x and $x = 0$} **23 (a)** 1 **(b)** 3
24 (a) {$n \geqslant 4$, n is a positive integer} **(b)** $2, 5, 35$ **(c)** Octagon $(n = 8)$
26 (a) is not the graph of a function because there are two values of y for each value of x.

(b) is the graph of a function because there is only one value of y for each value of x. It is a one-to-one function.

(c) is not the graph of a function because there are two values of y for each value of x.

(d) is the graph of a function because there is only one value of y for each value of x. It is a many-to-one function.

Exercise 2B

1 (a) fg: $x \rightarrow 3x + 3$; gf: $x \rightarrow 3x + 13$. **(b)** fg: $x \rightarrow -2x - 1$; gf: $x \rightarrow 13 - 2x$. **(c)** fg: $x \rightarrow x^2 - 6x + 11$; gf: $x \rightarrow 1 - x^2$
(d) fg: $x \rightarrow \frac{15-x}{3-x}$, $x \neq 3$; gf: $x \rightarrow \frac{3}{1-x}$, $x \neq 1$ **(e)** fg: $x \rightarrow \frac{2x+1}{1-x}$, $x \neq 1$; gf: $x \rightarrow \frac{2-3x}{1-3x}$, $x \neq \frac{1}{3}$
2 (a) fg: $x \rightarrow x^2 + 6x + 7$; gf: $x \rightarrow x^2 + 1$ **(b)** $x = -1$ **3** $x = -1$ **4** $x = -\frac{1}{2}$ **5** 3; 7 **6** 2; 3 **7** $-4; 5\frac{1}{2}$
8 fg: $x \rightarrow \frac{6}{x} - 5$, $x \neq 0$; $\frac{3}{5}$ **9** $a = 4$ **10** $a = 2, b = -3$ **11** $a = -2, b = 3$ **12** $b = 3(a - 1)$
13 f^2: $x \rightarrow x + 2$ f^3: $x \rightarrow x + 3$ f^4: $x \rightarrow x + 4$ f^n: $x \rightarrow x + n$
14 f^2: $x \rightarrow \frac{x}{1-2x}$, $x \neq 1, \frac{1}{2}$ f^3: $x \rightarrow \frac{x}{1-3x}$, $x \neq 1, \frac{1}{2}, \frac{1}{3}$ f^4: $x \rightarrow \frac{x}{1-4x}$, $x \neq 1, \frac{1}{2}, \frac{1}{3}, \frac{1}{4}$ f^n: $x \rightarrow \frac{x}{1-nx}$, $x \neq 1, \frac{1}{2}, \frac{1}{3}, \frac{1}{4}, \frac{1}{5}, \ldots, \frac{1}{n}$
15 f^2: $x \rightarrow x$, $x \neq 1$ f^3: $x \rightarrow \frac{x}{x-1}$, $x \neq 1$ f^4: $x \rightarrow x$, $x \neq 1$ f^{10}: $x \rightarrow x$, $x \neq 1$ f^{11}: $x \rightarrow \frac{x}{x-1}$, $x \neq 1$ **16** $4, 4$
17 (a) f^2: $x \rightarrow \frac{x+4}{1-2x}$, $x \neq -1, \frac{1}{2}$ **(b)** 5 **18** f^2: $x \rightarrow -\frac{1}{x+1}$, $x \neq -2, -1$; f^3: $x \rightarrow -\frac{x+2}{2x+1}$, $x \neq -2, -1, -\frac{1}{2}$; $x = -1$

19 $a = 5, b = -3$ **20** $a = -3$ **21** $5\frac{1}{3}$ **22** g: $x \to x - 2$ **23** g: $x \to 3x$ **24** g: $x \to 2x - 3$ **25** f: $x \to x + 1$

26 f: $x \to x^2 + 1$ **27** f: $x \to \frac{x-2}{x+2}, x \neq -2$ **28 (a)** fg **(b)** gf **(c)** f^2 **(d)** gff **29 (a)** fg **(b)** gf **(c)** f^3 **(d)** gff

Exercise 2C

1 (a) has no inverse because it is a many-to-one function, i.e., –2 and 2 map onto 8, –1 and 1 map onto 2.

(b) has an inverse because it is a one-to-one function, i.e., only one value of x maps onto one value of y.

(c) has no inverse because it is a many-to-one function, i.e., 2 and 4 map onto 1.

(d) has an inverse because it is a one-to-one function, i.e., only one value of x maps onto one value of $i(x)$.

(e) has an inverse because it is a one-to-one function, i.e., only one value of x maps onto one value of y.

(f) has no inverse because it is a many-to-one function, i.e., there are two values of x that map onto the same value of y.

2 (a) f^{-1}: $x \to \frac{x-4}{3}$ **(b)** g^{-1}: $x \to \frac{5-3x}{2}$ **(c)** h^{-1}: $x \to \frac{5}{x} - 1, x \neq 0$ **(d)** i^{-1}: $x \to \frac{3}{x-2}, x \neq 2$ **(e)** j^{-1}: $x \to \frac{3x+1}{x-2}, x \neq 2$

3 –6, 1 **4** f: $x \to \frac{4}{3-x}, x \neq 3$ **5** g: $x \to \frac{3-5x}{1+x}, x \neq -1$ **6** –4 **7** 5.5 **8** 7 **9 (a)** 3 **(b)** g^{-1}: $x \to \frac{x+3}{x-1}, x \neq 1$

10 (a) $c = 2, d = -3$ **(b)** 3 **(c)** f^{-1}: $x \to \frac{3x+2}{x-1}$ **(d)** 1 **11** 1, 3 **12** –5, 2 **13** 5

14 f$^{-1}(x) = \frac{1+2x}{x}$ ($x \neq 0$); f$^2(x) = \frac{x-2}{5-2x}$ ($x \neq \frac{5}{2}$); 2, $\frac{5}{3}$ **15** 3, –7 **16 (a)** f^{-1}: $x \to \frac{3-x}{2x}, x \neq 0$; **(b)** ff^{-1}: $x \to x$;

(c) f^{-1}f: $x \to x$; ff^{-1} = f^{-1}f **17 (a)** f^{-1}: $x \to \frac{2x+3}{1-x}, x \neq 1$ **(b)** f^{-1}f^{-1}: $x \to -\frac{x+9}{3x+2}, x \neq -\frac{2}{3}$ **(c)** f^2: $x \to -\frac{2x+9}{3x+1}, x \neq -\frac{1}{3}$

(d) (f^2)$^{-1}$: $x \to -\frac{x+9}{3x+2}, x \neq -\frac{2}{3}$ (f^2)$^{-1}$ = f^{-1}f^{-1} **18 (a)** f^{-1}: $x \to x + 4$ **(b)** g^{-1}: $x \to \frac{x+2}{3}$ **(c)** f^{-1}g^{-1}: $x \to \frac{x+14}{3}$

(d) g^{-1}f^{-1}: $x \to \frac{x+6}{3}$ f^{-1}g^{-1} ≠ g^{-1}f^{-1} **19 (a)** (fg)$^{-1}$: $x \to \frac{3-x}{6}$ **(b)** g^{-1}f^{-1}: $x \to \frac{3-x}{6}$ (fg)$^{-1}$ = g^{-1}f^{-1}

20 (a) (gf)$^{-1}$: $x \to \frac{x-3}{x-6}, x \neq 6$ **(b)** f^{-1}g^{-1}: $x \to \frac{x-3}{x-6}, x \neq 6$ (gf)$^{-1}$ = f^{-1}g^{-1}

21 (a) (fg)$^{-1}$: $x \to \frac{2x-2}{3x}, x \neq 0$ **(b)** f^{-1}g^{-1}: $x \to \frac{x-5}{x+1}, x \neq -1$ (fg)$^{-1}$ ≠ f^{-1}g^{-1}

22 (a) The domain of f^{-1} is $0 \leq x \leq 9$. The range of f^{-1} is $-2 \leq$ f$^{-1}(x) \leq 4$.

(b) The domain of f^{-1} is $0 \leq x \leq 4$ The range of f^{-1} is $0 \leq$ f$^{-1}(x) \leq 6$.

(c) The domain of f^{-1} is $2 \leq x \leq 4$ The range of f^{-1} is $1 \leq$ f$^{-1}(x) \leq 6$.

(d) The domain of f^{-1} is $-8 \leq x \leq 8$ The range of f^{-1} is $-4 \leq$ f$^{-1}(x) \leq 4$.

23 (b) The domain of f^{-1} is $0 \leq x \leq 6$; The range of f^{-1} is $0 \leq$ f$^{-1}(x) \leq 3$.

24 (a) 1, 2 **(c)** The domain of f^{-1} is $-1 \leq x \leq 2$. The range of f^{-1} is $\frac{1}{2} \leq$ f$^{-1}(x) \leq 2$. **26** 3; $2.5 \leq x \leq 7$.

Exercise 2D

1 (a) 8 **(b)** $\frac{1}{2}$ **(c)** 0.5 **(d)** 27 **2 (a)** 5 **(b)** 7 **(c)** 0 **3** 4, 1, 3 **4** 6, 6, 0, 24 **5** 1, –3, –1, 1 **6** 1, 4 **7** $\frac{1}{4}, \frac{1}{2}$

8 $\frac{4}{5}$, 4 **9** The range of y is $0 \leq y \leq 4$. **10** The range of y is $0 \leq y \leq 5$. **11** The minimum value of y is 0 when $x = -3$.

12 $x = -2, 1$ **13 (a)** Range is $0 \leq y \leq 6$ **(b)** Range is $0 \leq y \leq 1$ **(c)** Range is $y > 0$ **14 (c)** $2 \leq y \leq 9$

15 (a) $-3 \leq y \leq 4$ **(b)** $0 \leq x \leq 3$ **16 (a)** $-1 \leq y \leq 4$ **(b)** 1, 5 **(c)** $1 \leq x \leq 5$ **17** A(5, 0), B(2, 3) **18** $x = \frac{3}{4}, y = 1\frac{2}{3}$

Revision Exercise 2

1 (a) 1 **(b)** 2, $-\frac{5}{3}$ **2** {0, 1, 2}; No **3** $-1 \leq x \leq 3$ **4** $a = 3, b = -5$; $2\frac{1}{2}, 2\frac{1}{2}$ [f(x) = x] **5** –5

6 (a) [$(7n + x)^2 \div 7 = 7n^2 + 2nx$, remainder $\frac{x^2}{7}$]; g(5n + x) = g(x)

8 f^3: $x \to \frac{x}{7x-27}, x \neq 3, \frac{9}{2}, \frac{27}{7}$ f^6: $x \to \frac{x}{-182x+729}, x \neq 3, \frac{9}{2}, \frac{27}{7}, \frac{81}{20}, \frac{243}{61}, \frac{729}{182}$

9 (a) $a = 3, b = -2$ **(b)** f^3: $x \to 27x - 26$ **(c)** f^4: $x \to 81x - 80$ f^5: $x \to 243x - 242$ **10** g: $x \to x^2 - 2$; gf^{-1}

11 (b) $4\frac{1}{2}$; $5\frac{1}{2}$; 4 **12** p = 5; **(a)** 1 **(b)** $\frac{3x-5}{7-x}, x \neq 7$ **(c)** –1, 5 **13 (a) (i)** k = 2 **(ii)** $\frac{3x-6}{5-x}, a = 3, b = -6, c = 5$

(b) (i) 1.41 **(ii)** $0 \leq x \leq 1.6$ **15** $x = 1$ **16** 13.4 units **17** $x = 3, y = -2; x = 2\frac{1}{5}, y = -3\frac{1}{5}$

Maths Booster   **2** $0 \leq y \leq 3$ **3** Since $|a| < 1$, $1 - a^2 > 0$, Since $|b| < 1$, $1 - b^2 > 0$,

$(1 - a)^2 (1 - b)^2 > 0$, $a^2 + b^2 < 1 + a^2 b^2$ $(a + b)^2 < (1 + ab)^2$, $|a + b| < |1 + ab|$, $\left|\frac{a+b}{1+ab}\right| < 1$

Exercise 3A

1 (a) maximum   (b) minimum   (c) maximum   (d) minimum   **2** (a) min $= -2$ when $x = 3$ (b) max $= 3$ when $x = 4$
(c) max $= 0$ when $x = 2$ (d) min $= 2$ when $x = -6$ **3** (a) min $= -8$ when $x = 1$ (b) max $= 5$ when $x = -3$
(c) min $= 0$ when $x = -5$ (d) max $= 6$ when $x = 0$ (e) min $= 5$ when $x = -\frac{1}{2}$ (f) max $= -12$ when $x = \frac{4}{3}$
4 (a) min $= -10$ where $x = 3$ (b) min $= -13$ where $x = -2$ (c) max $= 3$ where $x = -1$ (d) max $= 2\frac{1}{4}$ where $x = -\frac{1}{2}$
(e) min $= -2\frac{1}{4}$ where $x = -1\frac{1}{2}$ (f) min $= c - b^2$ where $x = -b$ **5** min $\left(\frac{1}{4}, -4\frac{1}{8}\right)$ **6** max $\left(-\frac{1}{4}, 3\frac{1}{8}\right)$
7 $-2\left(x + \frac{1}{4}\right)^2 + 5\frac{1}{8}$; max $= 5\frac{1}{8}$, $x = -\frac{1}{4}$ **8** $k = -3$ **9** $a = -3, b = -6$ **10** (a) range: $f(x) \geqslant -4$ (b) range: $g(x) \geqslant 3$
(c) range: $h(x) \leqslant 11$ (d) $i(x) \leqslant 1$ **11** (a) $-5 \leqslant f(x) \leqslant 4$ (b) $-45 \leqslant g(x) \leqslant 5$ **12** $0 \leqslant h(t) \leqslant 11\frac{1}{4}$ **13** 14.25 cm; 3.5 sec

Exercise 3B

1 (a) $-5, 2$ (b) $-6, \frac{1}{2}$ (c) $-\frac{3}{2}, 5$ (d) $-\frac{2}{3}, 5$ **2** (a) $0.65, -4.65$ (b) $0.44, 4.56$ (c) $1.14, -2.64$ (d) $1.40, -0.90$
3 (a) $1.18, -0.43$ (b) $1.18, -0.85$ (c) $1.28, -1.88$ (d) $0.32, 6.32$ **4** (a) no real roots   (b) two equal real roots
(c) two different real roots   (d) two different real roots   **5** (a) -11 (b) $2, -1$ (c) $6, -6$ (d) $0, 8$
6 (a) $q < \frac{17}{4}$ (b) $q < \frac{4}{3}$ (c) $q > -\frac{8}{3}$ (d) $q > 3$ **7** (a) $k < -3$ (b) $k > -1$ (c) $k < \frac{11}{10}$ (d) $k < -1$ **8** $p \leqslant \frac{3}{2}$
9 $0, 4$ **10** $\frac{4}{3}$ **12** $m < 2$ **13** $k > 1$ **14** $t = -2, 1$ **15** $m = \frac{1}{2c}$ **17** $k = -\frac{a}{3}$

Exercise 3C

1 (a) $x < -1$ or $x > 2$ (b) $-3 < x < 2$ (c) $x < -4, x > \frac{1}{3}$ (d) $x \leqslant -\frac{1}{2}$ or $x \geqslant 1$ (e) $\frac{1}{3} \leqslant x \leqslant \frac{1}{2}$ (f) $x < 0$ or $x > 4$
2 $-2 < t < 6$ **3** $-\frac{1}{2} \leqslant p \leqslant 1$ **4** $q < -4$ or $q > 0$ **6** $-1 < x < 2$ or $4 < x < 7$ **7** $-6 < c < 6$ **8** $m < -1$ or $m > \frac{1}{3}$
9 $0 < p < 8$ **10** $q < -2$ or $q > 3$ **11** (a) $-4 < x < -2, 1 < x < 3$ (b) $x \leqslant -2, -1 \leqslant x \leqslant 6, x \geqslant 7$
(c) $-2 \leqslant x \leqslant -1, 2 \leqslant x \leqslant 3$ **12** $-1\frac{1}{2} \leqslant x \leqslant 0, \frac{1}{2} \leqslant x \leqslant 2$ **13** $1 \leqslant x \leqslant 3$

Revsion Exercise 3

1 (a) min $= 22, t = 2$ (b) $22 \leqslant v(t) \leqslant 30$ **2** $y = (x + 1)^2 + 9$; min $= 9, x = -1$ **3** $a = 4, b = -2, c = -5$ **4** $a = -1$ or -2
5 $k = -2$ **6** (b) $312.5 \, \text{m}^2, x = 12.5 \, \text{m}$ **7** $k = 4, -1; x = 4, x = -1$ **9** (a) $p = -4, q = -12$ (b) $r < -16$ **10** (a) $k = \frac{a^2}{b - 2a}$
(b) $p \leqslant -\frac{1}{2}$ **12** (a) $-a \pm \sqrt{3a^2 + 5a - 2}$ (b) $a \leqslant -2$ or $a \geqslant \frac{1}{3}$ **13** (a) $m < -4$ or $m > 4$
(b) $y = 4x + 5, (2, 13); y = -4x + 5, (-2, 13)$ **14** (a) $x \leqslant \frac{1}{2}, x \geqslant 2\frac{1}{3}$ (b) $(1\frac{1}{2}, 6)$ **15** (a) $x \leqslant -\frac{1}{2}$ or $x \geqslant 2\frac{1}{2}$
(b) $(1, -9); (1, 9)$ **16** $2; 1\frac{3}{4}$ **17** (a) $p = -6, q = 8$ (b) $-4 \leqslant x \leqslant -1, 7 \leqslant x \leqslant 10$ **18** $\frac{1}{2} \leqslant x \leqslant 2$
19 $-2 < x < -1, \frac{1}{2} < x < 1\frac{1}{2}$ **20** $4 \leqslant x \leqslant 6$ **21** $\frac{1}{3} \leqslant x \leqslant 1$

Maths Booster   **1** -1 **2** 4   **3** $1 < x < 2, x > 3$ **4** 3   **5** 628

Exercise 4A

1 (a) 81   (b) $\frac{1}{32}$ (c) $\frac{64}{729}$ **2** (a) a^9 (b) a (c) 2^x (d) x^{2n+4} **3** (a) a^4 (b) 3^n (c) a^{10} (d) a^{5n} (e) 5^{2x+3}
(f) 2^{7x} **4** (a) a^8 (b) a^{32} (c) a^3 (d) a^{6n-3} **5** (a) 21^n (b) 24^{3n} **6** (a) 4^n (b) 9^{2n+1} (c) 2^{2n} (d) 3^{6n}
7 (a) 8   (b) 64   (c) 81   (d) 32   **8** (a) 1   (b) 1   (c) 1   (d) 1   (e) 1   **9** (a) $\frac{1}{16}$ (b) 8   (c) $\frac{27}{64}$ **10** (a) 3   (b) $\frac{2}{5}$
(c) $\frac{1}{2}$ **11** (a) 27   (b) 16   (c) $\frac{1}{8}$ (d) $\frac{4}{9}$ (e) $\frac{125}{8}$ (f) 4   (g) $2\frac{1}{4}$ (h) $\frac{1}{243}$ (i) $\frac{1}{8}$ **12** (a) 8   (b) 81   (c) 5
(d) 1   **13** (a) 2^n (b) 1   (c) 1   (d) 5^n **15** (a) $2y^2 - 4y$ (b) $y^2 - \frac{2}{y}$ (c) $8y^2$ (d) $\frac{1}{8}y^2$ **17** (a) 6   (b) -3 (c) 0
(d) $-\frac{3}{4}$ (e) $\frac{3}{5}$ (f) $\frac{1}{3}$ (g) -4 (h) $\frac{2}{3}$ (i) 6   (j) $\frac{1}{2}$ **18** (a) 3   (b) 2   (c) 5   (d) 16   **19** (a) 1, 2   (b) 0, -3
(c) $-1, 1$ (d) 1   **20** $a = 18, b = -2$ **21** $a = 36, n = -2$ **22** (a) $x = -1, y = \frac{1}{2}$ (b) $x = 22, y = -14$ (c) $x = 3, y = 2$

Exercise 4B

1 (a) $\sqrt{14}$ **(b)** $\sqrt{30}$ **(c)** $\sqrt{3}$ **(d)** 4 **(e)** 6 **(f)** 5 **2 (a)** $2\sqrt{2}$ **(b)** $3\sqrt{2}$ **(c)** $5\sqrt{3}$ **(d)** $4\sqrt{2}$ **(e)** $6\sqrt{3}$
(f) $10\sqrt{2}$ **(g)** $8\sqrt{2}$ **(h)** $30\sqrt{2}$ **(i)** $6\sqrt{5}$ **(j)** $15\sqrt{3}$ **(k)** $\sqrt{3}$ **(l)** $\frac{\sqrt{7}}{2}$ **3 (a)** $4\sqrt{2}$ **(b)** $6\sqrt{3}$ **(c)** $-4\sqrt{2}$ **(d)** 0
4 (a) 3.464 **(b)** 8.484 **(c)** 22.36 **(d)** 7.07 **(e)** 5.832 **(f)** 18.71 **5 (a)** 3 **(b)** $\frac{2}{5}$ **(c)** 32 **(d)** 35 **(e)** $\frac{4}{3}$
(f) $\frac{3}{4}$ **(g)** $\frac{9}{2}$ **(h)** $\frac{3}{8}$ **6 (a)** $11+6\sqrt{2}$ **(b)** $9-4\sqrt{5}$ **(c)** $12+2\sqrt{35}$ **(d)** $5-2\sqrt{6}$ **7 (a)** 4, Yes **(b)** $9+6\sqrt{2}$, No
(c) $19-8\sqrt{3}$, No **(d)** 4, Yes **8 (a)** $\frac{\sqrt{3}}{3}$ **(b)** $\sqrt{2}$ **(c)** $\frac{\sqrt{6}}{2}$ **(d)** $2\sqrt{5}$ **(e)** $\frac{\sqrt{6}}{3}$ **(f)** $\frac{\sqrt{3}}{3}$ **(g)** $\frac{5\sqrt{2}}{3}$ **(h)** $\frac{4\sqrt{3}}{5}$
(i) $2\sqrt{3}+1$ **(j)** $2-3\sqrt{2}$ **(k)** $3\sqrt{5}-1$ **(l)** $\frac{3}{2}\sqrt{2}$ **9 (a)** $\sqrt{3}$ **(b)** $\sqrt{2}$ **(c)** $\frac{2\sqrt{2}}{5}$ **(d)** $\frac{\sqrt{5}}{2}$ **(e)** $\frac{\sqrt{2}}{4}$ **(f)** $\frac{3\sqrt{2}}{4}$
(g) $4\sqrt{2}-1$ **(h)** $\frac{3\sqrt{5}-2\sqrt{3}}{5}$ **10 (a)** $\sqrt{5}+\sqrt{2}$ **(b)** $\sqrt{6}-2$ **(c)** $\frac{3-\sqrt{2}}{7}$ **(d)** $\sqrt{6}+2$ **(e)** $\frac{\sqrt{6}+2}{2}$ **(f)** $\frac{3+\sqrt{5}}{2}$
(g) $4+\sqrt{10}$ **11 (a)** 1.414 **(b)** 6.928 **(c)** 14.14 **(d)** 4.472 **(e)** 5.196 **(f)** 5.928 **(g)** 1.447 **(h)** 2.121
12 (a) 20 **(b)** 11 **(c)** 12 **(d)** 7 **(e)** no root **(f)** 4 **(g)** 8 **(h)** 3 **(i)** 5, 29 **(j)** 3, 7

Revision Exercise 4

1 (a) 32 **(b)** $\frac{1}{9}$ **(c)** 64 **2 (a)** $-\frac{1}{2}$ **(b)** $\frac{1}{2}$ **(c)** ± 5 **(d)** 2, 3 **(e)** 2, 3 **(f)** $\frac{1}{2}$ **3** $-6, 2$ **5** $x = 3, y = 2$
6 $p = \frac{1}{3}, q = -4$ **7 (a)** $11\sqrt{3}$ **(b)** $7+4\sqrt{3}$ **(c)** $15-11\sqrt{2}$ **(d)** $-3-7\sqrt{10}$ **8 (a)** $\frac{36-11\sqrt{10}}{2}$ **(b)** $\sqrt{5}-\sqrt{6}$
9 $2\frac{1}{4}$ **10** $a = \pm 2, b = \pm 3$ **11** $\frac{2}{9}$ **12** 4, 9

Maths Booster   **2** $p = 2, q = 4$ **3** $2^n x$; x bacteria, the initial population   **4** 3

Exercise 5A

1 (a) $x = 3, y = 2$ or $x = 1, y = 4$ **(b)** $x = 3, y = 1$ or $x = -3, y = -5$ **(c)** $x = 3, y = -1$ or $x = 1, y = 3$
(d) $x = 4, y = 1$ or $x = -\frac{10}{3}, y = -\frac{8}{3}$ **(e)** $x = 4, y = -1$ or $x = -\frac{1}{2}, y = 2$ **(f)** $x = 3, y = 1$ or $x = \frac{3}{13}, y = -\frac{41}{13}$
(g) $x = 5, y = 8$ or $x = 2, y = -1$ **(h)** $x = 4, y = -1$ or $x = -\frac{47}{13}, y = \frac{20}{13}$ **(i)** $x = 2, y = -1$ or $x = \frac{14}{11}, y = -\frac{5}{11}$
(j) $x = 3, y = 2$ **(k)** $x = 1, y = -\frac{4}{3}$ or $x = 6, y = 2$ **(l)** $x = 3, y = -1$ or $x = -\frac{1}{3}, y = -6$ **2** $(6, 2), (5, 2\frac{1}{2})$
3 $(1, 5), (\frac{5}{2}, 8)$ **4** $(1\frac{1}{2}, -\frac{7}{10})$ **5 (a)** $(0, 2), (4, 6)$ **(b)** $2\sqrt{2}$ unit **6 (a)** $2x - 3y = 3$ **(b)** $(\frac{21}{13}, \frac{1}{13})$ **7** 11 cm, 7 cm
8 $a = 5, b = 20$ or $a = 10, b = 10$ **9** 8, 6 **10** 6, -2

Revision Exercise 5

1 $x = -3, y = 4$ or $x = \frac{12}{5}, y = \frac{2}{5}$ **2** $x = 2, y = 4$ or $x = 21, y = -15$ **3** B(3, 3) **4** Q(0, -5) **5** $(-4\frac{1}{2}, 5)$ **6** $x = 5, y = 10$
7 $u = 3, v = 2$ or $u = -2, v = 4\frac{1}{2}$ **8** $x = 5, y = 7$ **9 (a)** $4x$ **(b)** $x = 1, y = 3$ or $x = \frac{5}{6}, y = \frac{13}{3}$
10 (b) $a = 9, b = 3$ or $a = -11, b = -7$

Maths Booster   **1** $x = 668, y = 667, z = 666$ **2** $w = -5, x = -1, y = 5, z = 1$

Exercise 6A

1 (a) 1 **(b)** 171 **(c)** -16 **2 (a)** 1 **(b)** 41 **(c)** $\frac{7}{27}$ **3 (a)** -15 **(b)** $-\frac{19}{27}$ **(c)** 33 **4** $9p - 53$ **5** -10 **6** 10
7 2, 4 **8** $a = 2, b = -4$ **9** $a = 5, b = -4$ **10** -5 **11** 2, -4 **13** $p - 2q = 6; p = 4, q = -1$ **14** $a = 2, b = 1$ **15** $b = 2$
16 (b) $r = 6$ **(c)** $p = -4, q = 1$

Exercise 6B

1 $x + 4$ is a factor; $x + 2$ is not a factor **4** $k = 3$ **5** $m = 0$ **6** $p = 15$ **7** $a = -2, b = -7$
8 $a = 11; b = -29$ **9** $p = -1, q = -9$ **10** $a = -4, b = -3$ **11** $p = -2, q = 0$ **12** $a = -4, b = 2$ **13** $k = 3$

Exercise 6C

1 $x + 1, x - 1$ **2** $x - 2, x - 5$ **3** $2x - 1, 2x + 1$ **4** **(a)** $(x - 1)(x - 1)(x - 2)$ **(b)** $(x + 1)(x - 2)(x - 3)$ **(c)** $(x - 1)(x^2 + 2)$
(d) $(x - 2)(x + 3)(x - 3)$ **(e)** $(x + 1)(x^2 - x + 1)$ **(f)** $(x - 1)(x + 1)(3x + 2)$ **(g)** $(x + 2)(x - 2)(2x - 3)$
(h) $(x - 1)(2x - 1)(3x - 2)$ **5** $p = -6; x - 1, x - 2$ **6** $a = -1, b = -2; x - 1$ **7** $a = -4, b = 6; (x - 3)(x - 2)(x + 1)$
8 $x + 1, x + 2$ **9** $A = 3, B = 1; 3x^3 - 8x^2 + 15x + 26; (x + 1)(3x^2 - 11x + 26)$

Exercise 6D

1 **(a)** $1, -1, -2$ **(b)** $-1, -2, -3$ **(c)** $-1, -3, 4$ **(d)** $2, -\frac{1}{2}, \frac{3}{2}$ **(e)** $2, \frac{1}{2}, -3$ **(f)** -3 **2** **(a)** $-1, 2.79, -1.79$
(b) $0.5, -3.73, -0.27$ **(c)** $-2, -0.78, 1.28$ **(d)** $-2, -0.41, 2.41$ **3** $(x - 2)(2x + 1)(2x + 3); 2, -\frac{1}{2}, -\frac{3}{2}$ **4** $1, -3, 2; 3; -1, 4$
5 $1, -2, \frac{1}{2}$ **6** $(-1, -1), (-2, -8), (3, 27)$

Revision Exercise 6

1 3 **2** $m = -3, 2$ **3** 23 **4** 6 **5** $b = a - \frac{2}{3}$ **6** $a = 3, R = 11; a = 7, R = 43$
7 **(a)** $b = -1$ **(b)** $c = 8, R = 10$ **(c)** $t = -6, 7$ **8** **(a)** **(i)** $p = 3, -6$ **(ii)** $x + 3$ is a factor **(b)** **(i)** -33 **(ii)** $a = 2$
9 $-2p - 38; p = -19$ **10** **(a)** $a = \frac{1}{6}$ **(b)** $[b = \frac{2}{p}]$ **11** $a = 2, -3, 4$ **12** $a = 4$
13 $1, 1, -2; -1, -1, -4;$ [equation is $(x + 2)^3 - 3(x + 2) + 2 = 0$] **15** $p = 1, 2, -3$ **16** $(x - 1)(x^2 - 2px - q)$ **17** $3, \frac{1}{2}, -\frac{2}{3}$

Maths Booster Ans 1

Exercise 7A

1 **(a)** $\log_4 16 = 2$ **(b)** $\log_7 21 = x$ **(c)** $\log_2 4 = \frac{1}{2}$ **(d)** $\log_3 81 = 4$ **(e)** $\log_{10} 1\,000 = 3$ **(f)** $\log_x 64 = 3$
(g) $\log_2(\frac{1}{8}) = -3$ **(h)** $\log_{10} 0.1 = -1$ **(i)** $\log_x 0.3 = -3$ **2** **(a)** 81 **(b)** $\frac{1}{25}$ **(c)** $\frac{1}{8}$ **(d)** 2 **(e)** 10 **(f)** 9 **(g)** 4
(h) -2 **(i)** $\frac{1}{2}$ **3** **(a)** $\frac{1}{8}$ **(b)** 66 **(c)** 4 **(d)** $\frac{1}{3}$ **(e)** 3 **(f)** 2 **4** **(a)** 2 **(b)** 6 **(c)** 5 **(d)** -2 **(e)** -4 **(f)** -1
(g) $\frac{1}{2}$ **(h)** $\frac{1}{3}$ **(i)** $\frac{2}{3}$ **(j)** $\frac{3}{2}$ **(k)** $\frac{3}{4}$ **(l)** $-\frac{2}{3}$ **(m)** -3 **(n)** -2 **(o)** 0 **(p)** 0 **(q)** 1 **(r)** 1
5 $3^{r+4s}, 3^{2r-2s}; r = \frac{2}{5}, s = \frac{9}{10}$

Exercise 7B

1 **(a)** $3\log_a x + \log_a y$ **(b)** $2\log_a x - \frac{1}{2}\log_a y$ **(c)** $\frac{1}{2}(3\log_a x + 1 - 2\log_a y)$ **2** **(a)** $2\log_a P + 3\log_a Q + \log_a R$
(b) $2\log_a P + \frac{1}{2}\log_a Q - \log_a R$ **(c)** $\log_a P - \log_a Q - \frac{1}{2}\log_a R$ **3** **(a)** $2p + q$ **(b)** $\frac{1}{2}(p + q)$ **(c)** $3p - q$ **(d)** $3 + p - 2q$
4 $\frac{1}{2}(1 + a - 3b)$ **5** $\log_a x = \frac{1}{5}(2p + q); \log_a y = \frac{1}{5}(p - 2q); \log_a xy = \frac{1}{5}(3p - q)$ **6** **(a)** 2.727 **(b)** -0.203 **(c)** 0.203
(d) 4.192 **(e)** 3.786 **(f)** 3.989 **(g)** 1.668 **(h)** 2.465 **(i)** -1.262 **7** **(a)** 0.921 **(b)** 1.13 **(c)** 1.486 **(d)** 1.633
(e) 0.774 **(f)** 0.283 **(g)** 1.356 **(h)** 1.921 **(i)** 0.791 **8** **(a)** 2 **(b)** 4 **(c)** -4 **(d)** -3 **(e)** $\frac{1}{2}$ **(f)** $\frac{1}{3}$ **(g)** 2
(h) -1 **(i)** $-\frac{1}{2}$ **9** **(a)** 3 **(b)** 0 **(c)** 2 **(d)** 4 **10** **(a)** 3 **(b)** 1 **(c)** $4, -1$ **(d)** $3, 5$ **(e)** $-\frac{1}{2}, 3$ **(f)** 8 **(g)** 1
(h) 5 **11** 4 **12** 49 **13** 100 **14** 2 **15** $\frac{2}{3}$ **16** **(a)** 3^{2a+3b} **(b)** $3^{1+a+\frac{1}{2}b}$ **(c)** $3^{2+\frac{1}{2}a-2b}$ **17** **(a)** 3^{3p+2q} **(b)** 3^{p-q}
18 $2^{2a+2b}; 2^{3a-2b}; a = \frac{2}{5}, b = \frac{21}{10}$ **19** **(a)** $x = 2.2, y = 6.8$ **(b)** $x = 2.5, y = 20$

Exercise 7C

1 (a) $\frac{1}{m}$ (b) $\frac{3}{m}$ (c) $\frac{2}{1+m}$ (d) $\frac{3m}{4}$ (e) $\frac{5+m}{3}$ (f) $\frac{6+m}{2(2+m)}$ **2** (a) $\frac{1}{t}$ (b) $\frac{2}{3t}$ (c) t (d) $\frac{1+t}{t}$ [Hint: $18 = 3 \times 6$]
(e) $\frac{1-t}{2t}$ [Hint: $2 = 6 \div 3$] (f) $\frac{t-1}{t}$ [Hint: $0.5 = 3 \div 6$] **3** (a) $\frac{1}{p+q}$ (b) $\frac{p+q}{p}$ (c) $\frac{1+p+q}{q}$ (d) $\frac{1+p}{1+q}$ (e) $\frac{q-p}{1+p}$
(f) $\frac{2+p+q}{p-q}$ **4** (a) 1 (b) 12 (c) 12 (d) $-\frac{2}{3}$ **6** (a) $\frac{3}{2}$ (b) $\frac{2}{3}$ (c) $-\frac{2}{3}$ (d) $-\frac{1}{2}$ **7** (a) 5 (b) $\frac{9}{4}$ (c) $-\frac{1}{2}$
(d) 1 **8** (a) $8, \frac{1}{8}$ (b) $32, \frac{1}{32}$ (c) 2, 64 (d) 3, 81 **9** $y = 2x$ **10** 5 **11** $x = 2, y = 1$

Exercise 7D

1 (a) 1.56 (b) –1.88 (c) 0.0855 (d) 6.98 (e) 0.453 (f) 0.169 **2** (a) 1.58 (b) –0.631 (c) 0.841 (d) 0.708
(e) 0.534 (f) 6.34 **3** (a) 2.90 (b) 209 (c) 0.0158 (d) 0.148 (e) 1.94 (f) –13.3 **4** (a) 1.07 (b) 1.64
(c) 0.225 (d) 1.27 **5** (a) 0.535 (b) 0.613 (c) 2.59 (d) –0.367 **6** (a) 0.827 (b) –0.868 (c) –0.756 (d) –1.71
(e) 5.17 (f) 1.08 **7** (a) 1.66 (b) 0.183 (c) 12.5 (d) –0.197 **8** (a) 9 (b) $\frac{2}{9}$

Exercise 7E

1 (a) 1.46 (b) 0.585 (c) 1.79 (d) 3.81 (e) 0.0803 (f) 1.20 (g) 0.617 (h) 5.42 (i) 0.136 (j) 0.754
2 (a) 15.8 (b) 5.59 **3** (a) 73.5 (b) 59.6 **4** (a) 13.2 (b) 34.7 **5** (a) 80 (b) 26.4 (c) 5.81; 18
6 (a) 2 443 342 (b) 1988 **7** (a) $5036.34 (b) in the 15th year (c) $15 000 **8** $a = 2.67, b = 1.58$
9 $a = 0.845, b = 0.2$

Exercise 7F

1 (a) 1.1, 1.5 (b) (i) 2.7 (ii) 1.7 (c) (1, 0)
2 The two graphs have the same shape. The graph of $y = \ln(x - 1)$ is the image of the graph of $y = \ln x$ under translation $\binom{1}{0}$.
4 $x \approx 2.5$ **5** $\ln(x - 1) = -\frac{1}{2}x + \frac{3}{2}$; $x \approx 2.35$ to 2.40 **6** (b) $\lg(x + 1) = -x + 3$ (c) Draw $y = -x + 3$
7 $\ln x = -x + 2, a = -1, b = 2$

Exercise 7G

1 (a) 2.4, 4.6 (b) (i) 1.8 (ii) 0.8 (c) (0,1)
2 The two graphs have the same shape. Both graphs pass through the point (0, 1) and are positive for all values of x.
For $x > 0$, 4^x increases faster than 3^x as x increases. However $x < 0$, 4^x decreases faster than 3^x as x decreases.
3 (a) 2.2; 0.8 (b) (i) 0.7 (ii) 2.1 (c) (0,1) **4** The two graphs are reflections of each other on the y-axis.
6 $x \approx -0.3$ **7** $x \approx 1.27$

Revision Exercise 7

1 (a) 4 (b) 64 (c) 2.83 **2** (a) 6 (b) 2 **3** (a) 5.69 (b) 1.55 (c) 5.66 **4** (a) 4, 12 (b) 2 **5** (a) $x = 64, y = 16$
(b) $x = \frac{9}{4}, y = \frac{3}{4}$ (c) $x = 15, y = \frac{1}{2}$ (d) $x = 3, y = 2$ **6** (a) $\frac{1}{7}$ (b) $\frac{3}{2}$ (c) 0.166 **7** (a) 1.10 (b) $p = 3, q = 2$
(c) $\frac{1}{25}(u + v)(2u - 3v)$ **8** (a) $\frac{1}{16}$ (b) 64 **10** (a) 8 (b) 7 **11** 11.5 **12** ≈5 **13** $\frac{2a+b}{1+a+b}$ **14** $x > 3$
15 $p = 6, q = \frac{1}{2}$ **16** $x = 0.70 - 0.75$ **17** (1,0), (0.1,0) **18** range: $f(x) > 0$ $f^{-1}: x \to \frac{1}{2}\ln\frac{x}{3}$ **19** (b) 2.58
(c) $\log_2 x = -x + 2.58$; $p = -1, q = 2.58$ (d) $y = -x + 2.58$ (e) 1.8

Maths Booster **1** $\frac{2m+n}{1-m}$ **2** 24

Exercise 8A

1 (a) $y = x - 2$ (b) $y = -\frac{3}{2}x + \frac{11}{2}$ (c) $y = \frac{5}{7}x + \frac{27}{7}$ (d) $y = -\frac{3}{2}x - \frac{5}{2}$ **2** (a) $y = \frac{16}{x^2} + 5$ (b) $y = 10x^{-3}$ (c) $y = \frac{2x}{4x-1}$

(d) $y = x - \frac{5}{6}x^2 + \frac{7}{6}$ **3** $y = \frac{2x-3}{x+2}$ **4** (a) $y = 3x^2 + 2x - 5$ (b) $-2\frac{2}{3}, 2$ **5** (a) $\lg y = \frac{1}{2}x + \frac{1}{2}$ (b) $y = 10^{\frac{x+1}{2}}$ (c) -3

6 $y = -\frac{1}{x} + 5$ **7** $y = \frac{1}{2}x^3 - 3x$ **8** (a) $x = \pm 3$ (b) $y = \frac{3}{4}x^2 - x - \frac{7}{4}$ (c) $-1, \frac{7}{3}$ **9** (a) $y = 2\sqrt{x} + \frac{4.5}{\sqrt{x}}$ (b) 2.7

10 (a) $y = 0.625x^2 + 1.25x$ (b) 2.8 **11** (a) $y = -16x^2 + \frac{95}{x}$ (b) 1.3

Exercise 8B

1 (a) $\frac{y}{x} = bx + a$; plot $\frac{y}{x}$ against x; $m = b, c = a$ (b) $y\sqrt{x} = ax + b$; plot $y\sqrt{x}$ against x; $m = a, c = b$

(c) $y = b(\frac{1}{x^2}) + a$; plot y against $\frac{1}{x^2}$; $m = b, c = a$ (d) $xy = \frac{1}{a}(x^2) - \frac{b}{a}$; plot xy against x^2; $m = \frac{1}{a}, c = -\frac{b}{a}$

(e) $\frac{y}{x} = -\frac{b}{a}x + \frac{1}{a}$; plot $\frac{y}{x}$ against x; $m = -\frac{b}{a}, c = \frac{1}{a}$ (f) $x(y - 1) = by + a$; plot $x(y - 1)$ against y; $m = b, c = a$

(g) $\lg y = \lg a(x) - \lg b$; plot $\lg y$ against x; $m = \lg a, c = -\lg b$

(h) $\lg y = b \lg(x + 3) + \lg a$; plot $\lg y$ against $\lg(x + 3)$; $m = b, c = \lg a$

2 (a) $\lg y = \lg b(x) + \lg a$ (b) $a = 10^{1.15} = 14; b = 10^{0.45} = 2.8$ (c) $y = 10^{2.5} = 316$

3 (a) $\lg y = b \lg x + \lg a$ (b) $a = 10; b = 1.45$ (c) 22 **4** $\frac{1}{y} = -\frac{b}{a}(\frac{1}{x^2}) + \frac{1}{a}$; $a = 5, b = -80$ **5** (a) $xy = -by + a$

(b) $a = 8.5, b = 2.1$ (c) 0.12 **6** $\frac{y}{x} = bx + a$; (a) $a = 2.3, b = 1.5$ (b) 1.75 **7** $a = -6, b = \frac{3}{2}$ **8** $A = 10^5, n = -2$

9 $A = 10^5, b = \frac{1}{10}$ **10** $p = 2, q = 5$ **11** $c = 5, d = 2$ **12** $a = 4.6, b = 2$ **13** $p = 2, q = 6$ **14** $a = \frac{1}{9}, b = \frac{1}{4}$

15 $a = 100, b = 3.16$

Exercise 8C

1 (a) AB = 3, BC = 4, AC = 5; right-angled triangle (b) AB = $\sqrt{37}$, BC = $\sqrt{37}$, AC = $\sqrt{98}$; isosceles triangle

(c) AB = $\sqrt{40}$, BC = $\sqrt{65}$, AC = $\sqrt{37}$; neither **2** 5 units **4** $-6, 4$ **5** $-11, 9$ **6** 4.47 units **7** (a) Yes, at B

(b) $(-1,2)$ [midpoint of AC] (c) 5 units **8** 5 units **9** (a) $(1\frac{1}{2},1)$ (b) $(-3,2)$ (c) $(2p,-p)$ (d) $(a,a+b)$

10 C$(2\frac{1}{2},1\frac{1}{2})$, D$(4,-2)$, E$(5\frac{1}{2},-5\frac{1}{2})$ **11** Q$(5,2)$ **12** $a = -1, b = 10$ **13** D$(-9,-8)$ **14** C$(5,0)$, D$(-1,-3)$

16 No; B is $(4,-1)$

Exercise 8D

1 (a) Yes (b) No **2** (a) AB and CD; BC and AD (b) parallelogram **3** $k = 5$ **4** $t = 19$ **5** (a) Yes (b) No

6 Yes because $m_{AB} \times m_{BC} = -1$ **7** (a) 6 (b) $2,-4$ **8** $k = 6$ **9** (a) $\frac{1}{2}$ (b) $-\frac{5}{7}$ **10** (a) $m_{AB} \times m_{BC} = -1$ (b) 7

11 (a) (i) $(3\frac{1}{2},5)$ (ii) $-\frac{3}{4}$ (b) $6p + 8q = 61$ **12** (b) 4 **13** (a) $2x + y = 1$ (b) $3x - y = -5$ (c) $2y = x - 3$

(d) $3x - 4y = 8$ **14** $y + 5x = -3; 5y - x = 11$ **15** (a) $y = 3x + 8$ (b) $y = \frac{2}{3}x$ (c) $x + y = 7$ **16** $x - 2y = 1$

17 (a) $5y - 3x = 30$ (b) $(-10,0)$ (c) 34 units^2 **18** (a) $h = 4$ (c) M$(2,6)$, P$(5,2)$, Q$(6\frac{1}{2},0)$ (d) 2:1

19 (a) D$(7,12)$, Q$(4,8)$ (b) PR: $y = x + 4$, CD: $3x + 4y = 69$ (c) R$(7\frac{4}{7},11\frac{4}{7})$ (d) QD = 5 units; DR = $\frac{5}{7}$ units

(e) $1\frac{11}{14}$ units^2

Revision Exercise 8

1 $y = \frac{1}{2}x^2 + x - 4$ **2** $y = \frac{4}{5-x}; \frac{1}{5}$

3 $\lg y = \frac{3}{2}b \lg x + \frac{1}{2}\lg a$ Plot $\lg y$ against $\lg x$ and obtain a straight line graph; gradient = $\frac{3}{2}b$ and ln y-intercept = $\frac{1}{2}\lg a$

4 $p = 10, q = -4$ **5** $A = 10^3; k = 0.09$ **6** $\lg p = -n \lg v + \lg a$; $a = 10, n = 1.5$ **7** $\lg y = b \lg(\sqrt{x} - 1) - \lg a$; $a = 4, b = 0.7$

8 $a = 0.25, b = 0.125; x = \sqrt[3]{6.5} = 1.87, y = \sqrt{7.25} = 2.69$ **9** (a) B$(4,5)$ (b) D$(5,2)$, F$(7,-4)$ **11** E$(1,6)$, B$(-11,0)$, D$(13,12)$

12 4 **13 (a)** $\frac{3}{b+1}, \frac{4}{b-6}$ **(c)** 2, 3 **14 (a)** A(–5,0), B(5,0), C(0,5) **15 (a)** (1,3) **(b)** $\frac{1}{2}$ **(c)** $y + 2x = 5$ **16** $3x + 2y = 12$

17 [line is $y - 1 = m(x - 3)$ i.e. $y - mx = 1 - 3m$; A is $(\frac{3m-1}{m}, 0)$, B is $(0, 1 - 3m)$ AC is $y = -\frac{1}{m}(x - \frac{3m-1}{m})$ so C is $(0, \frac{3m-1}{m^2})$

BD is $y - (1 - 3m) = -\frac{1}{m}(x)$ so D is $(m(1 - 3m), 0)$, Gradient of CD is $\dfrac{\frac{3m-1}{m^2}}{-m(1-3m)} = \frac{1}{m^3}$

18 (a) [consider point of intersection of diagonals] **(b)** [diagonals perpendicular] **(c)** [AB perp to AD so $\frac{y_4-y_1}{x_4-x_1} \times \frac{y_2-y_1}{x_2-x_1} = -1$

multiply out to get $y_2y_4 + x_2x_4 = x_1(x_2 + x_4) - x_1^2 + y_1(y_2 + y_4) - y_1^2$ and substitute from (a)]

19 (a) B(–3,0), C(2,0) **(b)** BD: $x + 3y + 3 = 0$; CD: $x - 2y - 2 = 0$ **(c)** D(0,–1) **(d)** $\sqrt{2}:1$

20 (a) 4 **(b)** AB: $x + 2y = 20$; B(0,10) **(c)** [Perpendicular bisector: $y = 2x + 5$; OC: $y + 3x = 0$] C(–1,3) **(d)** 2:1

Exercise 9A

1 (a) 0.8 rad **(b)** 1.2 rad **(c)** 5 rad **2 (a)** 60° **(b)** 120° **(c)** 720° **(d)** 330° **(e)** 45.8° **(f)** 71.6° **(g)** 229.2°
(h) 716.2° **3 (a)** 0.6632 rad **(b)** 2.478 rad **(c)** 1.056 rad **(d)** 10.56 rad **4 (a)** $\frac{3}{4}\pi$ rad **(b)** 3 rad **(c)** $1\frac{1}{9}$ rad
(d) $\frac{\pi}{8}$ rad **5 (a)** 0.909 **(b)** 0.969 **(c)** –34.2 **(d)** 0.598 **(e)** 0.866 **(f)** –0.707 **(g)** 1 **(h)** 1 **6** 0.068

Exercise 9B

1 (a) 4.8 cm **(b)** 15.36 cm **(c)** 25.42 cm **2** 1.2 rad **3** 6 cm **4** 12.8 cm **5** 0.5 rad **6** 1.14 rad **7 (a)** 12 cm
(b) 8π cm **8** 2.7 m s⁻¹ **9 (a)** 1.55 rad **(b)** 15.5 cm **10 (a)** 1.85 rad **(b)** 22.1 m **11 (a)** 7.79 cm **(b)** 1.79 rad
(c) 0.93 cm

Exercise 9C

1 (a) 20 cm² **(b)** 41.9 cm² **(c)** $\frac{7}{2}\pi$ or 11 cm² **2** 0.5 rad **3** 10 cm **4** 11.2 cm **5 (a)** 10 cm **(b)** 0.3 rad
6 40 cm, 1.2 rad; 24 cm, $3\frac{1}{3}$ rad **7 (a)** 3730 cm² **(b)** 256 cm **8 (a)** 5 cm **(b)** 0.4 rad **(c)** 4.8 cm² **9 (c)** 3 cm
(d) 2 rad **10 (a)** 18.85 cm² **(b)** 15.59 cm² **(c)** 3.26 cm² **12** 14.68 cm² **13 (a)** 0.927 rad **(b)** 22.35 cm²
14 (a) 1.05 rad **(b)** 123.3 cm² **15 (a)** 4.47 cm **(b)** 0.841 rad **(c)** 11.5 cm **(d)** 11.0% **16 (a)** 1.85 rad
(b) 11.2 cm² **(c)** 0.28

Revision Exercise 9

1 (a) 2.08 rad **(b)** 25 cm **(c)** 3.98 cm **2 (c)** $3 \leqslant r \leqslant 4$ **3** 12.93 cm **4** 18.82 cm²
5 (a) $\frac{10}{9}\pi$ rad s⁻¹ **(b)** 0.52 m s⁻¹
6 48.33 cm² **7 (a)** 2.46 rad **(b)** 0.292 **8** 43.2 cm² **9** 6.17 cm² **10 (a)** $\frac{2}{3}\pi$ rad **(b)** 1.63 cm² **11** 3; 2 rad
12 [total area of sectors = $2 \times \frac{1}{2} \times \frac{x^2}{9}\theta + \frac{1}{2} \times \frac{x^2}{9} \times (\pi - \theta)$; area of rhombus = $x^2\sin\theta$]; 0.77, 2.37 **13** 10:1

Maths Booster **1** π cm **2** 2.5 rad

Exercise 10A

1 (a) 19.5°, 160.5° **(b)** 40.4°, 319.6° **(c)** 49.0°, 229.0° **(d)** 110.5°, 249.5° **(e)** 194.5°, 345.5° **(f)** 141.0°, 321.0°
(g) 186.8°, 353.2° **(h)** 220.5°, 319.5° **(i)** 76.7°, 283.3° **(j)** 123.7°, 303.7° **(k)** 34.9°, 145.2° **(l)** 98.0°, 262.0°
(m) 150.4°, 209.6° **(n)** 61.6°, 241.6° **(o)** 61.1°, 298.9° **2 (a)** 26.7°, 153.3° **(b)** 129.1°, 65.1°
3 (a) 0°, 23.6°, 156.4°, 180°, 360° **(b)** 18.4°, 198.4°, 161.6°, 341.6° **(c)** 18.4°, 116.6°, 198.4°, 296.6°
(d) 90°, 138.6°, 221.4°, 270° **(e)** 39.2°, 140.8°, 219.2°, 320.8° **(f)** 210°, 221.8°, 318.2°, 330° **(g)** 117.7°, 202.3°

(h) $170.5°, 350.5°$ **(i)** $0°, 19.5°, 160.5°, 180°, 360°$ **(j)** $36.9°, 143.1°, 216.9°, 323.1°$ **(k)** $39.2°, 140.8°, 219.2°, 320.8°$
(l) $210°, 41.8°, 138.2°, 330°$ **(m)** $109.5°, 250.5°$ **(n)** $112.3°, 347.7°$ **(o)** $168.6°, 251.4°$ **4** $35.3°, 144.7°, 215.3°, 324.7°$
5 $158.2°, 338.2°$ **6** $39.2°, 140.8°, 219.2°, 320.8°$ **7 (a)** $200.5°, 339.5°$ **(b)** $15.7°, 164.3°$ **(c)** $129.8°, 230.2°$
(d) $126.7°, 306.7°$

Exercise 10B

1 $120°, 180°$ **4** $4; 8$ **6** 4 **11** 3 **12** 4 **13** $6; 12$ **14** 2 **15 (a)** $21.0°, 69.0°, 201.0°, 249.0°$
(b) $18.2°, 101.8°, 138.2°, 221.8°, 258.2°, 341.8°$ **(c)** $112.6°$ **(d)** $29.4°$ **(e)** $24.1°, 155.9°, 204.1°, 335.9°$ **(f)** $252.1°$
(g) none   **(h)** $80.8°, 170.8°, 260.8°, 350.8°$ **(i)** $62.7°, 207.3°$ **(j)** $92.4°, 147.6°, 332.4°$ **(k)** $110.9°, 159.1°, 290.9°, 339.1°$
(l) $73.1°$ **(m)** $55.2°$ **(n)** $67.5°, 157.5°, 247.5°, 337.5°$ **(o)** $9.7°, 80.3°, 135°, 189.7°, 260.3°, 315°$ **(p)** $120°, 180°$
(q) $114.7°, 155.3°, 294.7°, 335.3°$ **(r)** $115.7°$ **(s)** $65.3°, 114.7°, 245.3°, 294.7°$ **(t)** $174.9°$ **(u)** $271.1°$ **(v)** $83.6°, 276.4°$
16 (a) $24.1°$ **(b)** $58.6°, 148.6°, 238.6°, 328.6°$ **(c)** $82.8°$ **(d)** $66.3°, 123.7°, 246.3°, 303.7°$ **(e)** $222.3°, 77.7°$

Exercise 10D

1 $70.5°, 289.5°$ **2** $90°, 228.6°, 311.4°$ **3** $19.5°, 160.5°$ **4** $30°, 150°, 210°, 330°$ **5** $30°, 150°$ **6** $45°, 71.6°, 225°, 251.6°$
7 $54.7°, 125.3°, 234.7°, 305.3°$ **8** $30°, 90°, 150°$ **9** $19.5°, 41.8°, 138.2°, 160.5°$ **10** $48.2°, 180°, 311.8°$
11 $0°, 101.5°, 258.5°, 360°$ **12** $60°, 120°, 240°, 300°$

Revision Exercise 10

1 (a) $58.3°, 148.3°, 238.3°, 328.3°$ **(b)** $56.3°, 236.3°$ **2** 2 **5 (a)** $72.3°$ **(b)** $48.6°, 90°, 131.4°$ **(c)** $63.4°, 146.3°$
6 (a) $9.7°, 80.3°, 189.7°, 260.3°$ **(b)** $53.1°, 90°, 126.9°, 270°$ **(c)** $84.3°, 275.7°$ **8** 3 **9 (a)** $155°$ **(b)** $159.4°$
(c) $18.4°, 116.6°$ **10 (i)** 3 **(ii)** 1 **11** $1 \leq y \leq 2$ **12** $5; 8$ **13 (a)** $30°, 150°$ **(b)** $32.3°, 147.7°, 212.3°, 327.7°$
14 $0°, 30°, 150°, 180°, 210°, 330°, 360°$ **15 (a)** $30°, 150°$ **(b)** $60°, 120°, 240°, 300°$ **16** 3 **17** 2.3
18 (a) $[AB = 2r \sin \theta, BC = 2r \cos \theta]$ **(b)** max $\frac{\pi r^2}{2}$ when $\theta = 0$, min $r^2 (\frac{\pi}{2} - 1) \approx 0.57r^2$ when $\theta = 45°$ **(c)** $25.9°, 64.1°$
19 (a) 1.46 **(b)** $2.76r^2$ **(c)** 69% **20** 0.97 rad

Maths Booster $H = 1600$ m, $K = 1000$ m

Exercise 11A

1 (a) 10 **(b)** 20 **2 (a)** 40 **(b)** 20 **(c)** 1120 **3** 20 **4** 360 **5** 630 **6** 336 **7** 343 **8** $10\,000$ **9** 120 **10** 120

Exercise 11B

1 (a) 120 **(b)** 720 **(c)** 336 **(d)** 90 **2 (a)** 9 **(b)** 6 **3** 24 **4** 720 **5** 840 **6** 720 **7 (a)** 720 **(b)** 720 **8** $40\,320$
9 2880 **10** 12

Exercise 11C

1 (a) 70 **(b)** 1225 **(c)** $\frac{5}{2}$ **2 (a)** 7 **(b)** 6 **(c)** 20 **3** 126 **4** $270\,725$ **5** $230\,230$ **6** 60 **7** 60 **8** $11\,760$
9 5400 **10** $1740, 1060$

Revision Exercise 11

1 69 184 **2** 40 320, 30 **3** 86 400 **4** 362 880, 2 880 **5** 220 **6** 52 920 **7** 96 **8 (a)** 12 **(b)** 12 **9** 310
10 (a) 28 **(b)** 3^{28}

Maths Booster **(a)** 8 **(b)** 0

Exercise 12A

1 (a) $x^4 - 8x^3 + 24x^2 - 32x + 16$ **(b)** $8x^3 - 36x^2 + 54x - 27$ **(c)** $32x^5 + 80x^4 + 80x^3 + 40x^2 + 10x + 1$
(d) $x^5 - \frac{5}{2}x^4 + \frac{5}{2}x^2 - \frac{5}{2}x^2 + \frac{5}{16}x - \frac{1}{32}$ **(e)** $x^6 + 6x^4 + 15x^2 + 20 + \frac{15}{x^2} + \frac{6}{x^4} + \frac{1}{x^6}$ **(f)** $\frac{x^4}{256} - \frac{x^3}{8} + \frac{3x^2}{2} - 8x + 16$
2 (a) $1 - 10x + 40x^2 - 80x^3 + 80x^4 - 32x^5$ **(b)** $16 - 96x + 216x^2 - 216x^3 + 81x^4$ **(c)** $64 - 96x + 60x^2 - 20x^3 + \frac{15x^4}{4} - \frac{3x^5}{8} + \frac{x^6}{64}$
(d) $1 - 3x^2 + 3x^4 - x^6$ **3 (a)** $32 - 80x + 80x^2 - 40x^3$ **(b)** $1 - 14x + 84x^2 - 280x^3$ **(c)** $1 - 4x + 7x^2 - 7x^3$
(d) $1\,024 - 640x - 160x^2 - 20x^3$ **4 (a)** $81x^4 - 216x^3y + 216x^2y^2 - 96xy^3 + 16y^4$ **(b)** $x^5 - 5x^3 + 10x - \frac{10}{x} + \frac{5}{x^3} - \frac{1}{x^5}$
5 $a^5 + 5a^4b + 10a^3b^2 + 10a^2b^3 + 5ab^4 + b^5$; $\frac{45}{512}$ **6** 0.941 480 **7 (a)** $1 + 3x + 3x^2 + x^3$, $1 - 3x + 3x^2 - x^3$
(b) $2 + 6x^2$; 14 **8** 194 **9 (a)** $1 + 4x + 6x^2 + 4x^3 + x^4$, $1 - 4x + 6x^2 - 4x^3 + x^4$ **(b)** $8x + 8x^3$; 0.080 008
10 (a) $x^5 + 5x^3 + 10x + \frac{10}{x} + \frac{5}{x^3} + \frac{1}{x^5}$, $x^5 - 5x^3 + 10x - \frac{10}{x} + \frac{5}{x^3} - \frac{1}{x^5}$ **(b)** $10x^3 + \frac{20}{x} + \frac{2}{x^5}$ **(c)** $90\frac{1}{16}$
11 $1 - 4x + 6x^2 - 4x^3 + x^4$; $1 - 4x + 8x^2$ **12** $1 + \frac{3x}{2} - \frac{9x^2}{4}$ **13 (a)** $16 - 32x + 24x^2$ **(b)** $81 - 54x + \frac{27}{2}x^2$; $-3\,456$; $3\,888$
(c) $8 - 4x - 6x^2$ **(d)** 3 **14 (a)** $1 + 5x + 10x^2 + 10x^3$ **(b)** $1 + 5x + 5x^2 - 10x^3$ **15 (a)** $1 + 8x + 24x^2 + 32x^3 + 16x^4$
(b) $1 - 3x + 3x^2 - x^3$; $1 + 5x + 3x^2$ **16** $1 + 6x + 12x^2 + 8x^3$; $16 - 16x + 6x^2 - x^3 + \frac{x^4}{16}$; 102 **17** $-\frac{7}{2}$
18 $1 + 5x + 10x^2 + 10x^3$; $32 - 80x + 80x^2 - 40x^3$; -120 **19** $1 + 3ax + 3a^2x^2 + a^3x^3$; $b^4 + 4b^3x + 6b^2x^2 + 4bx^3 + x^4$
20 (a) (i) $1 + 3ax + 3a^2x^2 + a^3x^3$ **(ii)** $1 + 4bx + 6b^2x^2 + 4b^3x^3 + b^4x^4$ **(b)** $\frac{17}{7}, -\frac{4}{7}$ or $-1, 2$

Exercise 12B

1 (a) $1 + 10x + 45x^2$ **(b)** $x^{12} - 6x^{11} + \frac{33x^{10}}{2}$ **(c)** $x^9 - 9x^7 + 36x^5$ **2 (a)** $7\,920$ **(b)** $-3\,240$ **(c)** 126
3 (a) $-70, 168$ **(b)** -350 **4** $-\frac{160}{27}, \frac{20}{3}; -\frac{100}{9}$ **5 (a)** $1 - 8x + 24x^2 - 32x^3$ **(b)** $1 - 8x + 28x^2$; $-\frac{1}{8}$ **6** 20 **7** 9, $\frac{2}{3}$
8 6, 3 **9** 7 **10 (a)** $-1\,792x^2$ **(b)** $1\,120$ **11 (a)** $-\frac{99}{4}$ **(b)** $\frac{231}{16}$ **12** $1 - 8x + 28x^2$; 0.992 03
13 $1 - 20x + 180x^2 - 960x^3 + 3360x^4$; 0.886 28 **14** 0.968 44 **15** $1 + 10x + 55x^2 + 210x^3$; $\frac{64}{25}$

Revision Exercise 12

1 (a) $1 - 15x + 90x^2 - 270x^3$ **(b)** $1 + 35x + 525x^2 + 4\,375x^3$; 90 **2** $a^6 + 6a^5\frac{x}{b} + 15a^4\frac{x^2}{b^2}$; 2, ±3, ±64x
3 $1 - 10x + 40x^2$; 2, 7, -13 **4 (a)** $1 + 10x + 40x^2 + 80x^3 + 80x^4 + 32x^5$; $1 - 10x + 40x^2 - 80x^3 + 80x^4 - 32x^5$
(b) $20x + 160x^3 + 64x^5$ **(c)** 0.020 000 160 000 064 **5** 10, 10 **6** $1 - 5p + 10p^2 - 10p^3 + 5p^4 - p^5$; $1 - 5x + 5x^2 + 10x^3$; 0.01
7 sixth **8 (i)** $64 + 192x^2 + 240x^4 + 160x^6$ **(ii)** 48 **9** $\frac{1}{5}$ or $\frac{1}{45}$ **10** $\frac{7}{9}, -\frac{35}{3}; -7$ **11** $-\frac{1}{2}, 12$
12 $1 + 6ax + 15a^2x^2$; $\frac{1}{2}, -3$ or $-\frac{1}{2}, 3$ **13** 28:5 **14** 3, -2 **15** 8

Maths Booster **1** fourth; 280 **2** 7, -1 **3 (a)** $1 + 5x + 10x^2 + 10x^3 + 5x^4 + x^5$, $1 + 5x^2 + 10x^4 + 5x^8 + x^{10}$
(c) $1 + 5x + 15x^2 + 35x^3$ **4** $7\frac{1}{2}$

Exercise 13A

2 $-2\mathbf{a}, \frac{1}{2}\mathbf{a}, 3\mathbf{a}$ **3 (a)** $\frac{3}{2}\mathbf{a}$ **(b)** $\mathbf{a}$ **(c)** $-\frac{1}{2}\mathbf{a}$ **4 (a)** $-\mathbf{a}$ **(b)** $-\mathbf{b}$ **(c)** $-\mathbf{c}$ **(d)** $2\mathbf{c}$, **(e)** $2\mathbf{b}$ **5** Collinear **6** 5 **7** 13
8 $(\sqrt{5}, 2)$ or $(-\sqrt{5}, 2)$

Exercise 13B

2 (a) $\mathbf{a}+\mathbf{b}$ **(b)** $-\mathbf{a}-\mathbf{b}$ **4** The parallelogram is a rhombus. **5 (a)** $\mathbf{b}-\mathbf{a}$ **(b)** $\frac{1}{2}(\mathbf{b}-\mathbf{a})$ **(c)** $\frac{1}{2}(\mathbf{a}+\mathbf{b})$ **6 (a)** $\frac{1}{2}\mathbf{p}$
(b) $\mathbf{q}-\mathbf{p}$ **(c)** $\frac{3}{4}\mathbf{q}$ **(d)** $\frac{3}{4}\mathbf{q}-\frac{1}{2}\mathbf{p}$ **7 (a)** $\mathbf{b}-\mathbf{a}$ **(b)** $2\mathbf{a}$ **(c)** $\mathbf{b}+2\mathbf{a}$ **(d)** $\mathbf{b}+\mathbf{a}$ **8 (a)** $\frac{3}{2}\mathbf{b}$ **(b)** $\mathbf{a}+\frac{3}{2}\mathbf{b}$
(c) $\mathbf{a}+\frac{1}{2}\mathbf{b}$ **9 (a)** $\frac{1}{2}\mathbf{a}$ **(b)** $\mathbf{b}-\frac{1}{2}\mathbf{a}$ **(c)** $\frac{1}{3}\mathbf{b}-\frac{1}{6}\mathbf{a}$ **(d)** $\frac{1}{3}\mathbf{a}+\frac{1}{3}\mathbf{b}$ **10 (a)** $\mathbf{p}-2\mathbf{q}$ **(b)** $\frac{1}{2}(\mathbf{p}-2\mathbf{q})$ **(c)** $\frac{3}{2}\mathbf{p}$

Exercise 13C

1 $3,-4$ **2** $2,-3$ **3** $-3,2$ **4** $2,-3$ **5** $1:2$ **6** $18; 1:4$ **7** 3 **8** $3; 1:-2$ **9 (a)** $1; 1:2$ **(b)** -5
10 (a) $\frac{1}{3}(5\mathbf{a}+6\mathbf{b})$ **(b)** $\frac{\mathbf{a}}{3}$ **(c)** $\frac{1}{2}(4\mathbf{a}+5\mathbf{b})$ **(d)** $5\mathbf{a}+7\mathbf{b}$ **(e)** $-9\mathbf{a}-14\mathbf{b}$ **11 (a)** $\mathbf{a}-2\mathbf{b}, 3\mathbf{a}+\mathbf{b}$ **(b)** $\frac{1}{3}(6\mathbf{a}+2\mathbf{b})$
(c) $\overrightarrow{OG}=\frac{1}{3}(6\mathbf{a}+2\mathbf{b}), \overrightarrow{GQ}=\frac{1}{3}(3\mathbf{a}+\mathbf{b}); 2:1$ **(d)** 2 **12 (a)** $\overrightarrow{QP}=\overrightarrow{AP}-\overrightarrow{AQ}=\mathbf{a}+\frac{2}{3}(\mathbf{b}-\mathbf{a})-\frac{2}{3}\mathbf{b}=\frac{\mathbf{a}}{3}$ **13** $\frac{1}{4},\frac{4}{5},1:3,4:1$
14 (a) (i) $(1-p)\mathbf{a}+\frac{1}{2}(1+p)\mathbf{b}$ **(ii)** $q\mathbf{a}+q\mathbf{b}$ **(b)** $\frac{1}{3},\frac{2}{3}; 2:1, 2:1$ **15 (a)** $\frac{2}{3}(1-q)\mathbf{a}+q\mathbf{b}; (1-p)\mathbf{a}+\frac{p}{3}\mathbf{b}$ **(b)** $\frac{3}{7},\frac{1}{7}$
(c) $1:6, 3:4$ **16** $[\overrightarrow{DE}=\frac{4\mathbf{a}-\mathbf{b}}{20}, \overrightarrow{DA}=\frac{4\mathbf{a}-\mathbf{b}}{4}]; 1:4$ **17 (a)** $\frac{p}{3}(2\mathbf{a}+\mathbf{b}); \frac{2}{5}(1-q)\mathbf{a}+q\mathbf{b}$ **(b)** $\frac{1}{2},\frac{1}{6}$ **(c)** $1:1, 1:5$
18 (a) $\frac{p}{2}\mathbf{a}+\frac{p}{2}\mathbf{b}; (1-q)\mathbf{a}+\frac{2q}{3}\mathbf{b}$ **(b)** $\frac{4}{5},\frac{3}{5}$ **(c)** $4:1$ **(d)** $(1+k)\mathbf{a}-k\mathbf{b}; \frac{1}{2}$ **19 (a)** $(1+p)\mathbf{a}+2p\mathbf{c}; \frac{3q}{2}\mathbf{a}+(1-q)\mathbf{c}$
(b) $\frac{1}{8}; \frac{3}{4}; 1:7, 3:1$ **(c)** $\frac{3}{8}[\overrightarrow{BF}=r\mathbf{a}+(2r-1)\mathbf{c}, \overrightarrow{CE}=\frac{(3\mathbf{a}-2\mathbf{c})}{2}$ hence $r: 2r-1=3:-2]$ **(d)** $1:4$
20 $\frac{1}{2}(\mathbf{a}+\mathbf{b}); (p-pq)\mathbf{a}+\frac{3p}{2}\mathbf{b}; \frac{5}{6},\frac{2}{5}; 5:1, 2:3$ **21** $\frac{2p+1}{3}\mathbf{c}; (1-\frac{q}{2})\mathbf{a}+q\mathbf{c}; \frac{5}{8},\frac{3}{4}$ **22** 4 **23** $5\mathbf{a}-\mathbf{b}, \mathbf{a}-\frac{\mathbf{b}}{2}, 13\mathbf{a}-2\mathbf{b}; 1:2$
24 $\frac{9\mathbf{a}+\mathbf{b}}{5}, \frac{15\mathbf{a}-7\mathbf{b}}{4}, 7\mathbf{a}-5\mathbf{b}; 3:5$

Exercise 13D

2 $-\mathbf{i}+5\mathbf{j}, 3\mathbf{i}-3\mathbf{j}, -2\mathbf{i}-2\mathbf{j}$ **3 (a)** $-3\mathbf{i}-\mathbf{j}, -4\mathbf{i}+\mathbf{j}$ **(b)** $6\mathbf{i}+2\mathbf{j}$ **(c)** $\sqrt{40}, 18.4°$ **4 (a)** $\sqrt{5}, 116.6°$ **(b)** $\sqrt{18}, 315°$
(c) $\sqrt{13}, 56.3°$ **(d)** $\sqrt{20}, 206.6°$ **5 (a)** $-5\mathbf{i}-2\mathbf{j}$ **(b)** $\binom{-15}{20}, \binom{-17\frac{1}{2}}{14}$ **6** $7\mathbf{i}$ **7** $3\mathbf{i}+6\mathbf{j}$ **8 (a)** $\frac{3\mathbf{i}-4\mathbf{j}}{5}, \frac{\mathbf{i}+3\mathbf{j}}{\sqrt{10}}$
(b) $\frac{-3\mathbf{i}+4\mathbf{j}}{5}, \frac{4\mathbf{i}+3\mathbf{j}}{5}$ **9 (a)** $\frac{3\mathbf{i}+\mathbf{j}}{\sqrt{10}}$ **(b)** $\frac{-\mathbf{i}+2\mathbf{j}}{\sqrt{5}}$ **(c)** $\mathbf{i}+5\mathbf{j}$ **(d)** $9\mathbf{i}-6\mathbf{j}$ **(e)** $-4\mathbf{i}+3\mathbf{j}$ **(f)** $\sqrt{26}$ **(g)** $\sqrt{117}$ **(h)** 5
10 (a) $\mathbf{i}-4\mathbf{j}$ **(b)** $\mathbf{i}+3\mathbf{j}$ **(c)** $2\mathbf{i}+7\mathbf{j}$ **(d)** $2\mathbf{i}-\mathbf{j}$ **11** $(1,-1)$ **12** $\mathbf{i}+7\mathbf{j}$ **13** $\mathbf{i}-\mathbf{j}$ **14** $-11\mathbf{i}+3\mathbf{j}$ **15 (a)** $-\mathbf{i}+4\mathbf{j}, 4\mathbf{i}-2\mathbf{j}$
(c) $\sqrt{61}, 309.8°$ **16** $10\mathbf{i}+19\mathbf{j}$ **17** $6\mathbf{i}+\mathbf{j}$ **19** -2 **21 (a)** $\sqrt{10}$ m s$^{-1}, 71.6°$ **(b) (i)** $2\mathbf{i}+4\mathbf{j}$ **(ii)** $4\mathbf{i}+10\mathbf{j}$
(iii) $\mathbf{i}+\mathbf{j}+t(\mathbf{i}+3\mathbf{j})$ **(c)** 6 secs **22** $7\mathbf{i}-5\mathbf{j}; 5$ sec **23 (a)** $5\mathbf{i}-\mathbf{j}$ **(c)** $-\frac{1}{2}; x+2y=3$ **24** $-1; x+y=0$
25 (a) $\mathbf{i}-3\mathbf{j}$ **(b)** $5\mathbf{i}+5\mathbf{j}$ **(c)** 5 **26** $\frac{4}{3}$ **27** $-1\frac{1}{2}$ **28 (a)** $2\mathbf{i}+2\mathbf{j}; 4\mathbf{i}+5\mathbf{j}; 5\mathbf{i}+7\mathbf{j}$ **(b)** $\frac{4}{5},\frac{2}{5}; 4:1$
29 (a) $m_1m_2=-1$ **(b)** $-\frac{3}{2},\frac{2}{3}$ **31 (a)** $-\frac{3}{2},\frac{2}{k+1}$ **(b)** 2 **32** $7, 3$

Exercise 13E

1 (a) 5.83 km h$^{-1}, 031°$ **(b)** 9.4 m s$^{-1}, 013°$ **(c)** 13.6 m s$^{-1}, 068.5°$ **(d)** 69.3 km h$^{-1}, 080°$ **2** $036.8°$
3 10.8 m s^{-1} at $21.8°$ to line of ship **4** 155.2 km h^{-1} at $015°$ **5 (a)** 2.2 km h^{-1} at $63.5°$ to bank **(b)** 0.2 km
6 229.1 km h^{-1} at $341°$ **7** $53.1°$ to bank, 6 min **8 (a)** $081.9°$ **(b)** 170 km h^{-1} **(c)** 1.76h **(d)** $278.1°$ **(e)** 1.34 h
9 A to B, 153 km h^{-1}; B to A 238 km h^{-1} **10** $056.4°; 42$ min **11 (a)** 20 km h^{-1} **(b)** 200 km h^{-1} **(c)** $354.3°$ **(d)** 90 min
12 (a) 103.9 m **(b)** 69.3 s **13 (a)** $006.6°$ **(b)** 43.2 min **(c)** $173.4°, 37.7$ min **14 (a)** 120 **(b)** 70.2 km

Exercise 13F

1 250 km h$^{-1}, 126.9°$ **2** 72.1 km h$^{-1}, 303.7°$ **3** 32.8 km h$^{-1}, 077.6°$ **4** 108.2 km h$^{-1}, 236.3°$
5 33.3 km h^{-1} in direction $064.7°$ **6** 832 km h$^{-1}, 018.7°$ **7** $018.8°; 16.5$ min **8** 19.2 km h$^{-1}, 231.3°$
9 (a) 15.7 km h^{-1}, direction $174.1°$ **(b)** 1 h 55 min **10** $284.5°$ **11** 17.4 km h$^{-1}, 036.7°$ **12 (a)** $100.5°$ **(b)** $13\,26$ h
13 3.6 m s$^{-1}, 77°; 3.5$ m s$^{-1}, 83.8°$

Revision Exercise 13

1 $(\mu - 4)\mathbf{p} + (\mu + 1)\mathbf{q}, -3\mathbf{p} + 3\mathbf{q}; 1\frac{1}{2}$ **2** $\frac{2}{5}(1-q)\mathbf{a} + \frac{2}{5}q\mathbf{b}; -\frac{4p}{5}\mathbf{a} + \frac{4}{5}\mathbf{b}; \frac{1}{4}, \frac{1}{2}$ **3 (a)** $(1-\lambda)\mathbf{p} + 3\lambda\mathbf{q}$

(b) $2(1-\mu)\mathbf{p} + 2\mu\mathbf{q}; \frac{1}{2}, \frac{3}{4}; \frac{1}{2}(\mathbf{p}+3\mathbf{q})$ **4** $\frac{1}{2}(\mathbf{a}+\mathbf{b}), \frac{4}{5}(\mathbf{a}+\mathbf{b}), -\frac{1}{5}\mathbf{a} + \frac{4}{5}\mathbf{b} - \frac{4}{5}\mathbf{a} + \frac{16}{5}\mathbf{b}, [\overrightarrow{RP} = 4\overrightarrow{AR}] \ 1:4; 4$

5 $2, -\frac{2}{3}; 0, 90°$ **6 (a)** $\frac{p}{2}\mathbf{a} + \frac{p}{2}\mathbf{b}; (1-q)\mathbf{a} + \frac{2q}{3}\mathbf{b}; 4:1$ **(b)** $1:1$ **(c)** $5:3:2$ **7** $\frac{1}{7}(17\mathbf{a} + 27\mathbf{b}), \frac{1}{5}(\mathbf{a}+12\mathbf{b}), -5\mathbf{a} - \mathbf{b}; \frac{3}{7}$

8 (a) 96 m   **(b)** 28°   **9** 165.5°, 194 km h⁻¹; 85 km h⁻¹ from 087.8°   **10** 1 h 46 min   **11** 079.8°   **12** 103°; 1 hr 52 min

13 (a) 041°   **(b)** 1 hr 59 min   **14 (a)** 60° with bank (against current)   **(b)** directly across   **(c)** $t_A = \frac{80\sqrt{3}}{3}$ s, $t_B = 48$ s

(d) 144 m   **15 (a)** 148 km h⁻¹   **(b)** 112.1°, 337.9° or 157.9°, 292.1°   **16 (a)** 024.3°   **(b)** 11 04h

17 19.5 km h⁻¹ from 081.2°; 25.7 km h⁻¹   **18** 061.3°; 5.41 min   **19 (a)** 339.7°   **(b)** 1.46 h   **(c)** 200.3°   **20 (a)** 038.2°

(b) 108 km   **21 (a) (i)** 093.8°   **(ii)** 36 min   **(b)** 26 km h⁻¹, 67.4°   **22** $4\sqrt{2}$ (= 5.66) km h⁻¹ from the SE

23 (a) 22.9 km h⁻¹ on 109.1°   **(b)** 109.1°   **(c)** 45.8 km   **24 (a)** 36.9° $(\sin^{-1}\frac{3}{5})$ **(b)** $\frac{7V}{20}$ **25 (a)** 482.7 m s⁻¹

(b) 124.9°   **(c)** 325.1°   **(d)** 3 h 35 min   **26 (a) (i)** 50.3°   **(ii)** 310 km h⁻¹   **(b) (i)** 2.8 m s⁻¹   **(ii)** 21.8°

27 (a) (i) 15 m s⁻¹, 066.9°   **(ii)** 4.355   **(b)** 23.02 km h⁻¹, 356.8°

Exercise 14A

1 (a) 1×2 **(b)** 2×1 **(c)** 2×2 **(d)** 2×3 **(e)** 4×2 **2 (a)** $(3 \ \ 5)$ **(b)** $\begin{pmatrix} 2 \\ 5 \end{pmatrix}$ **(c)** $\begin{pmatrix} 3 & -4 \\ -4 & 1 \end{pmatrix}$ **(d)** $\begin{pmatrix} 1 & 4 \\ 1 & 4 \\ -3 & 8 \end{pmatrix}$

(e) $\begin{pmatrix} 4 & -2 & 0 & 2 \\ 5 & 5 & 2 & 4 \\ 4 & -7 & 4 & 1 \end{pmatrix}$ **3 (a)** $(2 \ \ 1)$ **(b)** $\begin{pmatrix} 2 \\ 5 \end{pmatrix}$ **(c)** $\begin{pmatrix} 1 & 3 \\ 1 & 3 \end{pmatrix}$ **(d)** $\begin{pmatrix} -1 & -2 & 3 \\ 2 & -1 & 0 \end{pmatrix}$ **(e)** $\begin{pmatrix} 2 & -6 & 2 & 2 \\ -3 & 5 & -2 & 2 \\ 0 & 3 & 2 & -3 \end{pmatrix}$

4 (a) $\begin{pmatrix} 3 & 0 & 3 \\ 6 & 3 & 9 \\ 0 & 3 & 3 \end{pmatrix}$ **(b)** $\begin{pmatrix} -8 & 4 & -2 \\ 6 & -2 & 0 \end{pmatrix}$ **(c)** $\begin{pmatrix} 2 & 8 \\ 5 & -1 \end{pmatrix}$ **(d)** $\begin{pmatrix} 5 & 8 \\ 11 & 6 \end{pmatrix}$ **(e)** $\begin{pmatrix} 1 & -\frac{3}{2} \\ 4 & -2 \\ \frac{11}{2} & 1 \end{pmatrix}$ **5(b)** $\begin{pmatrix} -1 & 3 \\ 4 & 0 \end{pmatrix}$

6 $\begin{pmatrix} 2 & 3 \\ 7 & 9 \end{pmatrix}; \begin{pmatrix} 8 & 9 \\ 3 & 3 \end{pmatrix};$ No   **7 (a)** $1 \times 2; 2 \times 1; 2 \times 2$ **(b)** $AB = (1); BA = \begin{pmatrix} 3 & 6 \\ -1 & -2 \end{pmatrix}; AC = (10 \ \ 7); CB = \begin{pmatrix} 5 \\ 9 \end{pmatrix}$

8 $x = 9; y = \frac{5}{4}$ **9** $m = 2; n = 7$ **10 (a)** 4, −11;   **(b)** 2, 3;   **(c)** 1, −1   **11 (a)** $\begin{pmatrix} 50 & 28 & 22 \\ 70 & 33 & 22 \end{pmatrix}$

(b) \$74.40; \$90.40; \$164.80   **12 (a)** $\begin{matrix} A \\ B \\ C \\ D \end{matrix} \begin{pmatrix} 1\,400 \\ 1\,700 \\ 1\,750 \\ 2\,100 \end{pmatrix}$ **(b)** $\begin{matrix} X & Y & Z \\ (43 & 45 & 37) \end{matrix}$

Exercise 14B

1 (b) $AB = \begin{pmatrix} 4 & 7 \\ 8 & 15 \end{pmatrix}; BA = \begin{pmatrix} 3 & 4 \\ 11 & 16 \end{pmatrix}; AB \neq BA$

4 $A^{-1} = \begin{pmatrix} 3 & -2 \\ -4 & 3 \end{pmatrix}; B^{-1}$ does not exist; $C^{-1} = \begin{pmatrix} 1 & 1 \\ 1 & 2 \end{pmatrix}; D^{-1} = \begin{pmatrix} 2 & -\frac{3}{2} \\ -3 & \frac{5}{2} \end{pmatrix}; E^{-1} = \begin{pmatrix} \frac{5}{7} & -\frac{4}{7} \\ -\frac{2}{7} & \frac{3}{7} \end{pmatrix}; F^{-1} = \begin{pmatrix} 2 & 1 \\ 2 & -3 \end{pmatrix}$

5 (a) 3   **(b)** $\begin{pmatrix} \frac{2}{7} & -\frac{3}{7} \\ \frac{1}{7} & \frac{2}{7} \end{pmatrix}$ **6 (a)** 3   **(b)** $\begin{pmatrix} \frac{1}{2} & -\frac{3}{8} \\ 0 & \frac{1}{4} \end{pmatrix}$ **(c)** $\begin{pmatrix} \frac{1}{24} & -\frac{1}{4} \\ \frac{3}{8} & \frac{3}{4} \end{pmatrix}$ **7 (a)** $\begin{pmatrix} 3 & -\frac{11}{2} \\ -1 & 2 \end{pmatrix}$ **(b)** $\begin{pmatrix} \frac{3}{2} & -\frac{19}{2} \\ -\frac{1}{2} & \frac{7}{2} \end{pmatrix};$ No

10 (a) $A^2 = \begin{pmatrix} 7 & 4 \\ 12 & 7 \end{pmatrix}$ **(b)** $B^2 = \begin{pmatrix} 1 & 3 \\ 3 & 10 \end{pmatrix}$ **(c)** $(AB)^2 = \begin{pmatrix} 11 & 50 \\ 20 & 91 \end{pmatrix}$ **(d)** $A^2B^2 = \begin{pmatrix} 19 & 61 \\ 33 & 106 \end{pmatrix};$ No

Exercise 14C

1 $\begin{pmatrix} 4 & \frac{1}{2} \\ 3 & \frac{7}{2} \end{pmatrix}$ **2** $\begin{pmatrix} 1 & 0 \\ \frac{9}{5} & \frac{12}{5} \end{pmatrix}$ **3** $\begin{pmatrix} 0 & 1 \\ 2 & 3 \end{pmatrix}$ **4** $\begin{pmatrix} 2 & 1 \\ 4 & 0 \end{pmatrix}$ **5** $\begin{pmatrix} 2 & 3 \\ 1 & 1 \end{pmatrix}$ **6** $\begin{pmatrix} 3 & -5 \\ 4 & 2 \end{pmatrix}$ **7** $x = 2, y = 1$ **8** $x = -1, y = 3$

9 $x = \frac{1}{2}, y = 2$ **10** $x = 3, y = -1$ **11** $(5, -2)$ **12** $(\frac{1}{2}, -4)$

Revision Exercise 14

1 (a) $\begin{pmatrix} 4 & 5 \\ 13 & 8 \end{pmatrix}$ (b) $\begin{pmatrix} 5 & 15 \\ -3 & 3 \end{pmatrix}$ **2** $\begin{pmatrix} 3 & 4 \\ 2 & 2 \end{pmatrix}$ **3** (a) $\begin{pmatrix} 17 & 20 \\ -6 & -17 \end{pmatrix}$ (b) $\begin{pmatrix} 11 \\ 5 \end{pmatrix}$ **4** (a) $2 \times 2, 2 \times 1, 1 \times 2$

(b) $AB = \begin{pmatrix} 10 \\ 18 \end{pmatrix}$; $CA = (20 \quad 14)$; $BC = \begin{pmatrix} 12 & 24 \\ -4 & -8 \end{pmatrix}$; $CB = (4)$ **7** $x = 5, y = 13$ **8** $x = 1, y = 2$ **9** $a = \frac{1}{3}, b = -1, c = 4$

10 (a) 2 (b) $\begin{pmatrix} \frac{5}{2} & -\frac{1}{2} \\ -4 & 1 \end{pmatrix}$ **11** (a) $\begin{pmatrix} -2 & -1 \\ -5 & -4 \end{pmatrix}$ (b) $\begin{pmatrix} \frac{4}{3} & -\frac{1}{3} \\ -\frac{5}{3} & \frac{2}{3} \end{pmatrix}$ **12** (a) 2 (b) $\begin{pmatrix} \frac{3}{2} & -\frac{5}{2} \\ -1 & 2 \end{pmatrix}$ (c) $\begin{pmatrix} 26 & 35 \\ 14 & 19 \end{pmatrix}$ **13** (a) 6

(b) 10 (c) $\begin{pmatrix} -\frac{5}{2} & 2 \\ \frac{3}{2} & -1 \end{pmatrix}$ **14** (a) $x = 3, y = 2$ (b) $\begin{pmatrix} 36 \\ 2 \end{pmatrix}$ **15** $x = -2, -3; y = 13, 23$ **16** (a) -2 (b) $\begin{pmatrix} \frac{-x-3}{2} & \frac{x+1}{2} \\ \frac{x+2}{2} & -\frac{x}{2} \end{pmatrix}$

17 (a) $x + 3y = -3, 4x - 2y = 16$ (b) $x = 3, y = -2$ **18** $x = 4, y = -3$ **19** $(\frac{1}{2}, 2)$ **20** $\begin{pmatrix} 7\,000 \\ 7\,500 \\ 7\,800 \\ 8\,900 \\ 9\,550 \end{pmatrix}$ Mon
Tue
Wed; \$40 750
Thu
Fri

Exercise 15A

1 (a) 5 (b) $8x$ (c) 0 (d) $6x$ (e) $6x - 1$ (f) $3x^2 - 2x - 1$ (g) $-6x$ (h) $2x - 2$ (i) $-\frac{4}{x^2}$ (j) $6x - \frac{1}{x^2}$
(k) $3x^2 - 12x + 12$ (l) $2x - \frac{2}{x^3}$ (m) $x^4 + x^3 + x^2 + x$ (n) $2x - 2 + \frac{3}{x^2}$ (o) $\frac{4}{x^2} - \frac{2}{x^3}$ (p) $-\frac{2}{x^2} + \frac{2}{x^3} + \frac{3}{x^4}$ (q) $1 + \frac{1}{\sqrt{x}}$
2 $6t - 4$ **3** $9r^2 - 4r + 1$ **4** $18t - 12$ **5** 6 **6** 2 **7** -4 **8** $(\frac{2}{3}, \frac{2}{9}), (-\frac{2}{3}, \frac{34}{9})$ **9** $(0, -5), (2, -7)$ **10** $1, -\frac{2}{3}$ **11** $(2, -38)$
12 $1, -\frac{3}{2}$ **13** $\frac{1}{3}, -\frac{1}{2}$ **14** $8s - 12; 2$ **15** $2, -1; 6$ **16** $3, -2$ **17** $10, -13$ **18** $x \le -1$ or $x \ge 2$ **19** $\frac{4}{5}, -\frac{9}{5}$
20 $4mp^2 + 2np; 4, -2$

Exercise 15B

1 (a) $5(x - 3)^4$ (b) $21(3x - 1)^6$ (c) $-6(5 - 2x)^2$ (d) $40(4x - 5)^9$ (e) $16(4x - 3)^3$ (f) $3(2x - 1)(x^2 - x + 1)^2$
(g) $5(-1 - 4x)(3 - x - 2x^2)^4$ (h) $-\frac{1}{(x-2)^2}$ (i) $\frac{12}{(1-3x)^2}$ (j) $\frac{-8}{(3+2x)^2}$ (k) $4(1 + \frac{1}{x^2})(x - \frac{1}{x})^3$ (l) $\frac{-2x}{(x^2+3)^2}$
(m) $\frac{-8(2x-1)}{(x^2-x-1)^2}$ (n) $na(ax + b)^{n-1}$ (o) $\frac{-16}{(2x-3)^5}$ (p) $\frac{3(3+4x)}{(1-3x-2x^2)^4}$ (q) $3(2 + \frac{1}{2x^2})(2x - \frac{1}{2x})^2$ **2** (a) $6(2t - 1)^2$
(b) $1\frac{1}{2}, -\frac{1}{2}$ **3** -96 **4** $t + \frac{3}{5}(1 - t)^2 = \frac{3t^2 - t + 3}{5}; 1, -\frac{2}{3}$ **5** $\frac{6}{(4-2r)^2}; \frac{1}{2}(r = -1), -\frac{1}{2}$ $(r = 5)$ **6** (a) $2 + \frac{4}{(x+1)^2}$ (b) 3
7 -6 **8** $(1, -\frac{1}{2}), (-3, \frac{1}{2})$ **9** $(2, 1)$ **10** (a) $\frac{12}{(1-4t)^2}$ (b) $-\frac{1}{4}, \frac{3}{4}$ **11** (a) $3 - \frac{2}{(1+2t)^2}$ (b) $\frac{1}{2}, -\frac{3}{2}$ **12** $-2, -4\frac{1}{2}$
13 $4, -3$ **14** $1, -2$

Exercise 15C

1 (a) $12x^2 - 10x; 24x - 10$ (b) $6(2x - 7)^2; 24(2x - 7)$ (c) $-16(1 - 4x)^3; 192(1 - 4x)^2$ (d) $-\frac{1}{x^2}; \frac{2}{x^3}$ (e) $2x + \frac{1}{x^2}; 2 - \frac{2}{x^3}$
(f) $\frac{3}{(2-x)^2}; \frac{6}{(2-x)^3}$ (g) $4x^3 - 2x + \frac{2}{x^3}; 12x^2 - 2 - \frac{6}{x^4}$ **2** $6t + \frac{4}{t^3}; 6 - \frac{12}{t^4}$ **3** ± 3 **4** $1, -2$ **5** $3, -2$ or $-3, 2$ **6** $-4; 4$
7 $\frac{1}{(2-x)^4}; \frac{2}{(2-x)^3}$ **8** $\frac{2}{3}, 6; 3\frac{1}{3}$ **9** $x \ge \frac{2}{3}$

Exercise 15D

1 (a) $(x - 2)(3x - 2)$ (b) $2x(2x^2 - 1)$ (c) $x(5x^3 + 3x - 2)$ (d) $(x + 1)(x - 2)^2(5x - 1)$ (e) $x^4(1 - 2x)(5 - 14x)$
(f) $-(1 - x)(3 - x)^2(9 - 5x)$ (g) $x(x^2 - x - 1)^2(8x^2 - 5x - 2)$ (h) $2x(x^2 - 3)^2(4x^2 - 3)$ (i) $2(3x - 2)(12x^2 - 4x - 3)$
(j) $2(x^2 + 1)(2x + 1)^2(7x - 2x + 3)$ (k) $\frac{1}{2}x^{-\frac{1}{2}}(x^3 - 1)(13x^3 - 1)$ (l) $(\sqrt{x} - 1)(2\sqrt{x} - 1)$ (m) $2(1 - 2x)^2(1 - 8x)$
(n) $\frac{1}{2}(x - 1)^{-\frac{1}{2}}(x + 1)^3(9x - 7)$ (o) $(x + 1)^2(5x^2 - 2x - 7) = (x + 1)^3(5x - 7)$ (p) $6(3x - 1)(2x + 3)^2(5x + 2)$
2 5 **3** 2 **4** $(4x + 1)(x + 1)^2; 6(x + 1)(2x + 1)$ **5** $(2x - 1)^3(10x - 1); 16(2x - 1)^2(5x - 1)$ **6** $0, 1, \frac{2}{5}$
7 $2(x + 1)(x + 2)^2(3x^2 + 5x + 1)$

Exercise 15E

1 (a) $\dfrac{2}{(x+2)^2}$ (b) $\dfrac{1}{(x+2)^2}$ (c) $\dfrac{5}{(2x+1)^2}$ (d) $\dfrac{(-3x^2+4x+3)}{(x^2+1)^2}$ (e) $\dfrac{x^2-2x-2}{(x-1)^2}$ (f) $\dfrac{(-x^2+2x)}{(1-x)^2}$ (g) $\dfrac{(x-4)}{2(x-2)^{\frac{3}{2}}}$ (h) $\dfrac{2(x+1)}{(2x+1)^{\frac{3}{2}}}$

(i) $\dfrac{x^2(x^2+3)}{(x^2+1)^2}$ (j) $\dfrac{-2}{(x^2-2)^{\frac{3}{2}}}$ (k) $\dfrac{3x^2+2x}{(3x+1)^2}$ (l) $\dfrac{1}{(2-x)^2}$ (m) $\dfrac{3+8x-3x^2}{(x^2+1)^2}$ (n) $\dfrac{(1-2x-x^2)}{(x^2+1)^2}$ **2** $\dfrac{1}{(x+1)^2}$; $-2(x+1)^{-3}$

3 $\dfrac{4}{(2x-1)^3}$ **4** $\dfrac{3}{(2x+3)^2}$; $\dfrac{-12}{(2x+3)^3}$ **5** $\dfrac{3}{(x^2+3)^{\frac{3}{2}}}$; $\dfrac{-9x}{(x^2+3)^{\frac{5}{2}}}$ **6** $\dfrac{1}{2x^{\frac{1}{2}}(x+1)^{\frac{3}{2}}}$ **7** $\dfrac{-1}{(x+1)^{\frac{1}{2}}(x-1)^{\frac{3}{2}}}$ **8** $0, 4$ **9** 3 **10** $\dfrac{(x+2)}{2(x^2+x+1)^{\frac{3}{2}}}$; $x=-2$

Revision Exercise 15

1 (a) $3(x-5)^2$ (b) $-10(1-2x)^4$ (c) $\dfrac{8}{(1-4x)^2}$ (d) $12x(2x^2-1)^2$ (e) $3(-3-4x)(1-3x-2x^2)^2$ (f) $\dfrac{2x-1}{(x-x^2)^2}$

(g) $3(2+\frac{1}{x^2})(2x-\frac{1}{x})^2$ (h) $\frac{1}{2}-\frac{1}{x^3}$ (i) $1+\frac{4}{x^2}$ (j) $-\frac{3}{2}-\dfrac{6}{(1-3x)^2}$ **2** $0 \le x \le 2$ **3** ± 8 **4** (a) $(x-1)^2(3-2x)(13-10x)$

(b) $\dfrac{1-x}{2\sqrt{x}(1+x)^2}$ **5** -8 or 8 **6** $4-\dfrac{2}{(1-2x)^2}$; $\dfrac{-8}{(1-2x)^3}$ **7** $6x^2-4, 12x; 4$ **8** 5 or $1\frac{1}{4}$ **9** $-2, -5$ **10** (a) $2, -3$

(b) [gradient $= -3\frac{1}{2}$] **11** $\dfrac{-3x}{2\sqrt{1-x}}$; $\dfrac{3(x-2)}{4(1-x)^{\frac{3}{2}}}$; $(0,2)$ **12** $-3, 5$ **13** $\frac{7}{3}, -2; 26, -26$ **14** $3, -1$ **15** $-3 < x < 1$

16 $\frac{2}{3} \le x \le 4$ **18** $-\sqrt{2}$

Maths Booster **1** e^x

Exercise 16A

1 (a) $y+6x=-11, 6y-x=45$ (b) $y-6x=-4, 6y+x=13$ (c) $y-5x=4, 5y+x=-6$ (d) $y=5x+3, 5y+x=-11$

(e) $x+y=-4, x-y=0$ (f) $3y+x=5, y-3x=-5$ (g) $y-2x=-3, 2y+x=1$ (h) $y-x=-4, y+x=-8$

(i) $y=8x-11, 8y+x=42$ (j) $y-2x=-3, 2y+x=-1$ (k) $y=8x+11, 8y+x=55\frac{1}{2}$ (l) $2y=2x+3, 2y+2x=1$

2 $4y-4x=3; (-\frac{3}{4},0)$ **3** (a) $(-1,2)$ (b) $4y=x+9$ **4** (a) $y=x$ (b) $(2,2)$ **5** (a) $y+x=7$ (b) $(\frac{4}{3},\frac{17}{3})$

(c) $y+7x=15$ **6** [Normal is $18y+8x=35$]; $-\frac{53}{44}$ **7** $y=8x-12, 3y=8x-12; (\frac{4}{3},0)$ **8** (a) (i) $2y+x=3$ (ii) $(\frac{3}{2},\frac{3}{4})$

(b) $(\frac{1}{4},\frac{47}{16})$

Exercise 16B

1 (a) (i) max at $x=-3$ (ii) 16 (b) (i) min at $x=1\frac{1}{2}$ (ii) $-\frac{9}{4}$ (c) (i) max at $x=-1$, min at $x=1$ (ii) $0, -4$

(d) (i) pt of inf at $x=0$ (ii) -2 (e) (i) max at $x=-3$, min at $x=2$ (ii) $85, -40$ (f) (i) max at $x=0$, min at $x=\frac{1}{3}$

(ii) $1, \frac{26}{27}$ (g) (i) pt of inf at $x=0$, min at $x=1$ (ii) $1, 0$ (h) (i) max at $x=-5$, min at $x=5$ (ii) $-10, 10$ (i) none

(j) (i) pt of inf at $x=2$ (ii) 10 (k) none (l) (i) min at $x=2$, min at $x=-2$ (ii) $8, 8$

(m) (i) max at $x=1$, min at $x=3$ (ii) $0, 4$ (n) (i) min at $x=\frac{5}{6}$ (ii) $-\frac{49}{12}$ (o) (i) min at $x=0$ (ii) 0

(p) (i) min at $x=0$, max at $x=-\frac{2}{3}$ (ii) $1, \frac{31}{27}$ (q) (i) max at $x=-1$, min at $x=\frac{5}{3}$ (ii) $2, -\frac{202}{27}$

(r) (i) pt of inflexion at $x=-1$ (ii) -5 (s) none (t) (i) min at $x=2$, max at $x=0$ (ii) $3, -1$ (u) (i) min at $x=2$

(ii) 12 (v) (i) max at $x=\frac{2}{3}$, min at $x=\frac{8}{3}$ (ii) $-\frac{2}{3}, 7\frac{1}{3}$ **2** (a) 1 (b) min **3** (a) 3 (b) $(-2,16)$

4 (a) 2 (b) min at $x=1$, max at $x=-\frac{7}{3}$ **5** (a) Max $(0,1)$, min $(\frac{4}{3},-\frac{5}{27})$ (b) $(\frac{2}{3},\frac{11}{27})$ **6** (a) 1 (b) $5, 3$ **7** 1

8 (a) $2, -3$ (b) min at $x=2$, max at $x=-1$ **9** (a) $-\frac{1}{3}$ (b) $\frac{1}{2}$; min at $60°, 300°$; max at $109.5°, 250.5°$

10 $r=0$, max; $r=\frac{4}{\pi}$, min **11** $-8 < a < 8$; $x=-1$, min; $x=-4$, max **12** min at $(\frac{3}{2},4)$

Exercise 16C

1 $7\frac{3}{4}$ **2** 25 **3** 14 **4** $\frac{145}{27}$ **5** $-\frac{2}{3}$ **6** 2 **7** 10 **8** (b) 3 **9** 5 **10** $66\frac{2}{3}$ **11** (b) $5, 2$ **12** (b) $12; 576\pi$

13 (a) $y=mx+3-2m$ (b) $3-2m$ (d) $-\frac{3}{2}$ **14** (b) 2 **15** (a) $\$(30x-\frac{3x^2}{4}-50)$ (b) 20 **16** (a) $10t, 100-20t$

(c) 4; 44.7 km **17 (b)** $\pi^2(8r^2 - 2r^3)$; $\frac{8}{3}$ **18 (b)** 5 **(c)** 86.6 cm² **19 (a)** $x^2 + 25$; $x^2 - 6x + 25$ **(b)** $1\frac{1}{2}$ **20** 4; $\sqrt{3}$:4

21 (a) $-1, 2$ **(b)** $(1-t)\mathbf{i} - (2t+3)\mathbf{j}$ **(c)** -1 **(d)** $\sqrt{5}$ **22 (c)** 3; 45π cm² **23 (a)** $10 - 2t, 4t$ **(b)** $28t^2 - 80t + 100$

(c) $\frac{10}{7}$ **(d)** 6.5 cm **24 (b)** $20(3x^2 - x^3)$ **(c)** 2 **(d)** 80 cm² **25 (b)** $\frac{576 - 96x + (\pi+4)x^2}{\pi}$; 6.72 cm

26 $\frac{1}{4}(7x^2 - 4kx + k^2)$; 4:5 **27 (a)** $50 - 5x + \frac{3x^2}{4}$ **(b)** $3\frac{1}{3}$ **28** $\frac{2}{27}m^3[x = \frac{2}{3}]$ **29** $\frac{4}{\sqrt{3}}$; $\frac{256}{3\sqrt{3}}$

Exercise 16D

1 0.175 **2** 2.8 **3** 0.16 **4** 6.4 **5** 0.12 **6** 0.495 **7** 9% **8** -0.5 **9 (a)** 5% **(b)** 10% **10 (b)** $1\frac{1}{3}$% **11** $\frac{4\pi}{3}$

12 (a) $24k$ **(b)** $150k$% **13** $3p$ **14** 0.005 75 **15** 0.5% **16** 6; 0.002 86 **17** 3; 0.004 **18** $-6, 2$ **19** 0.005

20 1.0225, 0.9775 **21** 0.03 **22** 0.01 increase

Exercise 16E

1 20.1 cm² s⁻¹ **2** 0.106 cm s⁻¹ **3 (a)** 314 cm³ s⁻¹ **(b)** 62.8 cm² s⁻¹ **4** 1.59 cm s⁻¹ **5** 2 cm² s⁻¹ **6** 54π cm² s⁻¹

7 1.19 cm s⁻¹ **8** 2400 **9** 0.4 **10** 0.75 **11** 41.89 cm³ s⁻¹ **12** 96 cm³ s⁻¹ **13** 0.637 cm s⁻¹ **14** 1.59 cm s⁻¹

15 -0.125 **16** 0.018 units s⁻¹ **17** 1.02 cm s⁻¹ (increasing) **18 (a)** $56x - 4x^2$ **(b)** 2 **(c)** -10 cm² s⁻¹ **19** $\frac{25}{7\pi}$ cm s⁻¹

20 (c) 2.39 cm s⁻¹ **21 (c)** 2.5 cm² s⁻¹ **22 (a)** $\left[\frac{dL^2}{dt} = \frac{dL^2}{dL} \times \frac{dL}{dt}\right]$ **(c)** $x^2 - 5x + 25$ **(d)** 11 **(e)** $\frac{11}{14}$ cm s⁻¹

Revision Exercise 16

1 $x < -1$ or $x > 5$ **2** $1\frac{1}{2}$ **3** 0.05 **4 (a)** $\frac{6}{x^2}$; $\frac{3p}{8}$ **(b)** 2.4 **5** 0.012 cm² s⁻¹; 5 km **6** $\frac{60 - 2r - \pi r}{2}$; 8.40; maximum

7 $\frac{78p}{43}$% **8** $V = x^3$; $A = 6x^2$; $\frac{dV}{dx} = 3x^2$, $\frac{dA}{dx} = 12x$ **(a)** 300 cm³ s⁻¹ **(b)** 0.12 cm² **9** 17.3 **10** $\frac{100 - 3x}{4}$; 18.83 minimum

11 $\frac{3}{4}$ **12** $y = \frac{27 - 4x^3}{\pi x^2}$ $[A = 4 \times 2x^2 + 4x^2 + (4x^2 - \pi x^2) + \pi x^2 + 2\pi xy]$ **(a)** $\frac{3}{2}$ **(b)** 54, $\frac{6}{\pi}$; minimum

13 (a) $\frac{6 + 5b - 2b^2}{2}$ **(b)** $1\frac{1}{4}$ **14** $\sqrt{100 - h^2}$; $\frac{4000\pi}{3\sqrt{3}}$ **15 (a)** $L = 4r, \theta = 2$, max **16** $(0, 2 - 3m)$, $(\frac{3m-2}{m}, 0)$; 12 $[m = -\frac{2}{3}]$

17 10 cm, $6\frac{2}{3}$ cm, 4 cm **18** -4% **19** 8 cm **20** $1, -2, -7, -3$ **21** $x = -1$, min; $x = 0$, pt of inf. **22 (b)** $\pi r^2(22 - 3r)$

(c) $\frac{10}{3}[r = \frac{44}{9}]$ **23 (b)** $-\frac{2}{3}$% **24 (b)** 2.11 cm s⁻¹ **25 (a)** $\left[\frac{PQ}{x-5} = \frac{20}{x}\right]$ **(b) (i)** 2.78 cm s⁻¹ **(ii)** 1 cm s⁻¹

(c) $-\frac{3200}{x^3}$ cm s⁻¹ [If PQ = h, $\frac{d(\frac{dh}{dt})}{dt} = \frac{d(\frac{dh}{dt})}{dx} \times \frac{dx}{dt}$] **26 (a)** $\frac{80}{x}$ **(b)** $x^2 + \frac{6400}{x^2} - 80$; $4\sqrt{5}(\approx 8.9)$; $4\sqrt{5}$

27 $(4,4)$; $\frac{1}{2}(\sqrt{8}\, x - \frac{x^2}{2})$ [A is $(2, \sqrt{8})$, B is $(x, \frac{x^2}{4})$]; 2 $[x = 2\sqrt{2}\,]$

Maths Booster 4

Exercise 17A

1 (a) $2x^2 + c$ **(b)** $x^4 + c$ **(c)** $-7x + c$ **(d)** $x^3 + c$ **(e)** $3x - \frac{x^2}{2} + c$ **(f)** $\frac{4x^5}{5} + c$ **(g)** $\frac{x^6}{3} + c$ **(h)** $\frac{x^3}{3} - 3x + c$

(i) $x - \frac{x^2}{2} - \frac{x^3}{3} + c$ **(j)** $\frac{x^3}{3} - \frac{x^2}{8} + c$ **(k)** $x - \frac{3x^2}{2} - \frac{4x^3}{3} + c$ **(l)** $\frac{x^6}{6} - x^3 + c$ **(m)** $-\frac{1}{x^2} + c$ **(n)** $\frac{x^3}{3} + 2x^2 + 4x + c$

(o) $\frac{x^4}{4} - x^3 + \frac{3x^2}{2} - x + c$ **(p)** $x + \frac{1}{9x^3} + c$ **(q)** $4x - 2x^2 + \frac{x^3}{3} + c$ **(r)** $\frac{x^3}{3} + \frac{1}{x} + c$ **(s)** $\frac{x^3}{3} - \frac{x^2}{2} - 6x + c$ **(t)** $\frac{x^2}{2} - \frac{1}{x} + c$

(u) $-\frac{1}{3x} - \frac{1}{6x^2} + c$ **(v)** $\frac{x^4}{4} - \frac{x^3}{3} + x^2 - 2x + c$ **(w)** $-\frac{2}{x^2} + x + c$ **(x)** $6x^{\frac{2}{3}} + \frac{x^3}{3} + c$ **(y)** $x + \frac{2x^{\frac{3}{2}}}{3} + c$ **(z)** $\frac{x^2}{2} - 2x^{\frac{1}{2}} + c$

(2) $\frac{x^2}{2} - 2x^{1/2} + c$ **2 (a)** $\frac{x^2}{2} - 4x + c$ **(b)** $-\frac{3}{y} + c$ **(c)** $\frac{x}{3} + c$ **(d)** $2x + \frac{1}{x} + c$

(e) $\frac{3x^2}{2} - 2x + c$ **(f)** $\frac{t^2}{3} + c$ **(g)** $-\frac{4}{y} + c$ **(h)** $-\frac{1}{u} - \frac{1}{u^2} + c$ **3 (a)** $-\frac{1}{u} - \frac{1}{2u^2} + c$ **(b)** $3r^3 - 6r^2 + 4r + c$

(c) $p^3 - \frac{11p^2}{2} + 6p + c$ **(d)** $x - \frac{3x^2}{2} + x^3 - \frac{x^4}{4} + c$ **(e)** $\frac{2t^2}{3} - t + \frac{1}{3t} + c$ **(f)** $\frac{s^3}{3} - s - \frac{1}{4s} + c$ **(g)** $2s - \frac{5s^2}{2} - 4s^3 + c$

(h) $\frac{x^3}{12} + \frac{x^2}{4} + \frac{x}{4} + c$ **(i)** $\frac{x^4}{3} - \frac{x^2}{4} + c$ **(j)** $y - 2y^2 + \frac{4y^3}{3} + c$ **(k)** $\frac{t^4}{2} - 2t^2 + \frac{t}{3} + c$ **(l)** $\frac{4x^3}{4} + 6x - \frac{9}{4x} + c$

(m) $2t - \frac{1}{t} + \frac{2}{3t^3} + c$ **(n)** $\frac{3p^4}{2} + \frac{5p^3}{3} - 3p^2 + c$

Exercise 17B

1 $y = x^2 - x + 4$ **2 (a)** $y = \frac{x^3}{3} - \frac{x^2}{2} + \frac{1}{6}$ **(b)** max at $(0, \frac{1}{6})$, min at $(1,0)$ **3** $1\frac{1}{2}$ **4** $9\frac{1}{2}$ **5** $y = \frac{x^3}{3} + \frac{x^2}{2} + 3x + \frac{35}{6}$
6 $y = \frac{3x^2}{2} - 2x + 4$ **7 (a)** $y = \frac{x^3}{3} - 2x^2 + 3x - 1$ **(b)** min at $(3,1)$, max at $(-1, 6\frac{1}{3})$ **8** $-3; -\frac{1}{6}$ **9** $6\frac{1}{4}$ **10** 53   **11** 17
12 (a) $y = x^3 - x^2 - x + 1$ **(b)** max at $(-\frac{1}{3}, \frac{32}{27})$, min at $(1,0)$ **(c)** $x < \frac{1}{3}$ **13** $-4; y = \frac{2t^3}{3} + \frac{3t^2}{2} - 5t + 2$ **14** $u = 3t - \frac{3t^2}{2} + 4$

Exercise 17C

1 (a) 3 **(b)** $-\frac{1}{2}$ **(c)** 3   **(d)** 6   **(e)** $2\frac{1}{2}$ **(f)** 0   **(g)** $\frac{2}{3}$ **(h)** $-12\frac{2}{3}$ **(i)** $13\frac{1}{2}$ **(j)** $b - a$ **(k)** $\frac{7t^3}{3} - 3t$ **(l)** $-\frac{2}{3}$
(m) -2 **(n)** $\frac{17}{72}$ **(o)** 7   **(p)** 20   **(q)** $4\frac{1}{2}$ **(r)** 28   **(s)** $8\frac{5}{6}$ **(t)** 1   **(u)** $-\frac{16}{3}$ **(v)** $7\frac{1}{2}$ **(w)** 32   **(x)** $2\frac{2}{3}$
2 $-2, 10$ **3** $-3, 4$ **4** $1\frac{1}{2}$ **5** -2 **6** 2   **7 (a)** $5\frac{1}{3}$ units^2 **(b)** $4\frac{1}{2}$ units^2 **(c)** $\frac{7}{6}$ units^2 **(d)** $10\frac{2}{3}$ units^2
(e) $3\frac{1}{3}$ units^2 **(f)** 3 units^2 **(g)** 8 units^2 **(h)** $8\frac{2}{3}$ units^2 **8** $\frac{1}{3}$ units^2 **9 (a)** $8\frac{2}{3}$ units^2 **(b)** $17\frac{1}{3}$ units^2
[curve is symmetrical about y-axis]   **10** 4   **11** 4   **12** $23\frac{1}{3}$ **13** $1\frac{5}{6}$ **14** $9\frac{1}{3}$ **15** $20\frac{2}{3}$ **16 (a)** $2, -3, -2$
(b) $3\frac{1}{6}$ units^2 **17 (a)** 6   **(b) (i)** 21   **(ii)** 3   **(iii)** 3   **18 (a)** $(1,3)$ **(b)** 13 units^2 **19 (a)** $(1,3), (2,0), (4,0)$
(b) $7\frac{1}{3}$ units^2 **20 (a) (i)** $(0,4)$ **(ii)** 2   **(c)** 8 units^2

Exercise 17D

1 36   **2** $5\frac{1}{6}$ units^2 **3** $(-2,5), (3,5); 20\frac{5}{6}$ units^2 **4** $1, 2; \frac{1}{2}$ units^2 **5 (a)** $\frac{4}{3}$ **(b)** $10\frac{2}{3}$ units^2 **(c)** $5\frac{1}{3}$ units^2
(d) $\frac{1}{12}$ units^2 **(e)** $\frac{9}{8}$ units^2 **(f)** $\frac{1}{6}$ units^2 **(g)** $10\frac{2}{3}$ units^2 **(h)** $4\frac{1}{2}$ units^2 **(i)** $4\frac{1}{2}$ units^2 **6 (a)** $(0,-1), (0,3)$
(b) (i) $10\frac{2}{3}$ units^2 **(ii)** $2\frac{1}{3}$ units^2 **7 (a)** $y = x^2 - 4x + 3$ **(b)** $(0,3), (5,8)$ **(c)** $20\frac{5}{6}$ units^2 **8 (b)** $3y + x = 0, \frac{10}{3}$
(c) $\frac{500}{81}$ units^2 **9 (a)** $(-2,0)$ **(b)** $1\frac{1}{3}$ units^2 **10 (a)** $(1,0)$ **(b)** $y = 2x - 2$ **(c)** $1:1$ [both $\frac{1}{2}$]   **11 (a)** $(1,1)$ **(b)** $7:25$
12 (b) $y = 4x, y = -2x + 9$ **(c)** $1\frac{1}{2}; 2\frac{1}{4}$ units^2 **13 (a)** $(-1,4), (3,8); y = x + 5$ **(b)** $10\frac{2}{3}$ units^2 **14 (a)** $-4, 1$
(b) $20\frac{5}{6}$ units^2 **15** $11\frac{1}{3}$ units^2

Revision Exercise 17

1 $-4, y = \frac{x^2}{2} - 4x + 11$ **2 (a)** -2 **(b)** $\frac{7}{8}$ **3** $1:7$ **4 (a)** $(-1,5), (2,2)$ **(b)** $4:3$ **5 (a)** $(2,9)$ **(b)** $y = \frac{9x}{2}$ **(c)** 27 units^2
6 $1:7$ **7 (a)** $(1,0)$ **(b)** $\frac{2}{3}$ units^2 **8 (a)** $(0,4), (2,0), (1,3)$ **(b)** $13:10$ **9 (a)** Area above x-axis = area below
(b) (i) 18   **(ii)** 2   **(iii)** 4   **10 (a)** $(12,6)$ **(b)** 36 units^2 [Use $x\,dy$]   **11 (a)** $4y = 5x - 3$ **(b)** $(\frac{3}{5}, 0)$ **(c)** $(1,0)$
(d) $\frac{9}{40}$ units^2 **(e)** $9:49$ **12** $0; 3, -1$ **13** $\frac{8}{3}$

Exercise 18A

1 (a) $3\cos 3x$ **(b)** $\frac{1}{2}\cos\frac{x}{2}$ **(c)** $-\frac{1}{4}\sin\frac{x}{4}$ **(d)** $3\sec^2 3x$ **(e)** $-\cos x \operatorname{cosec}^2 x$ **(f)** $\sin x + x\cos x$
(g) $2x^2\cos 2x + 2x\sin 2x$ **(h)** $-4x\sin(2x^2 - 1)$ **(i)** $-\cos(\frac{\pi}{3} - x)$ **(j)** $\frac{1}{2}\sec^2\frac{x}{2}$ **(k)** $x\cos x$ **(l)** $\frac{1 - 2\sin x}{(2 - \sin x)^2}$
(m) $-6\sin 2x\cos^2 2x$ **(n)** $\cos x - x\sin x - 2\cos 2x$ **(o)** $3\cos 3x\cos 2x - 2\sin 3x\sin 2x$
(p) $2\sin 2x\cos 2x(4 + \sin^2 2x)^{-\frac{1}{2}}$ **(q)** $18x\cos^2(1 - 3x^2)\sin(1 - 3x^2)$ **(r)** $\sec^2 2x(\tan 2x)^{-\frac{1}{2}}$ **2 (a)** $-3\sin 3x$
(b) $\frac{1}{3}\cos\frac{x}{3}$ **(c)** $-4x\sin(2x^2 - 1)$ **(d)** $6\sin^2 2x\cos 2x$ **(e)** $\frac{1}{3}\sec^2(\frac{x}{3} - 2)$ **(f)** $\frac{1}{2}\cos\frac{x}{2}\cos 2x - 2\sin\frac{x}{2}\sin 2x$
(g) $\frac{-2\cos x}{(1 + \sin x)^2}$ **(h)** $2x\tan\frac{x}{2} + \frac{1}{2}x^2\sec^2\frac{x}{2}$ **(i)** $-2x\sin x^2$ **(j)** $\cos 2x - \sin x - x(2\sin 2x + \cos x)$
3 $2\cos 2x, -4\sin 2x \,(= 4y)$ **4** $-$ **5** $[\frac{d^2y}{dx^2} = -4(A\cos 2x + B\sin 2x)]; -3, 2$ **6** $1.11, 4.25$
7 $2(\sin x + \cos 2x)(\cos x - 2\sin 2x)$ **8** $\frac{\pi}{6}, \frac{5\pi}{6}$ $(0.52, 2.62)$ **9** $\frac{1}{(1 + \cos x)}; \frac{\sin x}{(1 + \cos x)^2}$ **10 (a)** $2.03, 5.18$ **(b)** $\frac{\pi}{6}, \frac{5\pi}{6}; \sqrt{3}, -\sqrt{3}$
11 $y = x, x + y =$ **12** $x + y = \frac{\pi}{2}$

Exercise 18B

1 (a) $-\frac{1}{2}\cos 2x + c$ (b) $\frac{1}{4}\sin 4x + c$ (c) $-2\cos\frac{x}{2} + c$ (d) $-\cos 3x + c$ (e) $\frac{1}{3}\tan 3x + c$ (f) $\frac{1}{2}\sin 2x + \cos x + c$
(g) $-\cos x + \sin x + c$ (h) $2\sin(\frac{x}{2}+\frac{\pi}{4}) + c$ (i) $\frac{1}{5}\sin 5x + c$ (j) $\cos(\frac{\pi}{4}-x) + c$ (k) $2\tan\frac{x}{2} + c$ (l) $\frac{1}{2}\sin 2x + \cos x + c$
(m) $\frac{1}{2}\sin 2x + \tan x + c$ (n) $-2\cos x - \frac{1}{4}\cos 2x + c$ 2 (a) 1 (b) 1 (c) 1 (d) 1 (e) 0 (f) 2 (g) 0.47 (h) $\frac{2}{3}$
(i) 2 (j) 0 (k) $-\frac{1}{4}$ 3 $-\frac{1}{\theta}+\frac{1}{4}\sin 2\theta + 1 + \frac{2}{\pi}$ 4 2 5 $\frac{\sin x}{(1+\cos x)^2}; \frac{1}{2}$ 6 (a) $\frac{\pi}{4}$ (b) 0.59 7 $\frac{1}{2}$

Exercise 18C

1 (a) $\frac{(2x-3)^3}{6} + c$ (b) $\frac{1}{10}(2x+5)^5 + c$ (c) $-\frac{1}{2}(x-2)^{-2} + c$ (d) $\frac{2}{3}(x-3)^{\frac{3}{2}} + c$ (e) $-\frac{1}{3}(3x-2)^{-1} + c$ (f) $(2x+3)^{\frac{1}{2}} + c$
(g) $(2x+3)^{\frac{1}{2}} + c$ (h) $-\frac{1}{16}(3-4x)^4 + c$ (i) $-(3-2x)^{\frac{1}{2}} + c$ (j) $\frac{1}{15}(3x+2)^5 + c$ (k) $\frac{3}{16}(4x-1)^{\frac{4}{3}} + c$ (l) $(2x-5)^{\frac{1}{2}} + c$
(m) $\frac{3}{16}(4x-1)^{\frac{4}{3}} + c$ (n) $\frac{1}{2}(1-2x)^{-1} + c$ 2 (a) 1 (b) $\frac{112}{9}$ (c) 2 (d) 14 (e) $-\frac{4}{3}$ (f) $8\frac{2}{3}$ (g) 2 (h) $\frac{85}{4}$
3 $\frac{1}{20}$ 4 12 5 $\frac{2}{3}$

Exercise 18D

1 (a) $\frac{1}{x}$ (b) $\frac{2}{x}$ (c) $\frac{3}{3x-1}$ (d) $\cot x$ (e) $\frac{1+\sec^2 x}{x+\tan x}$ (f) $-2\tan 2x$ (g) $-2\tan x$ (h) $\frac{1}{2}\cot\frac{x}{2}$ (i) $\frac{4(x-1)}{2x^2-4x-1}$
(j) $\frac{1}{2x-5}$ (k) $-\frac{1}{2x}$ (l) $1 + \ln x$ (m) $\frac{1-2\ln x}{x^3}$ (n) $\frac{\cos x - x\sin x}{x\cos x} = \frac{1}{x} - \tan x$ (o) $-\frac{1}{x}\sin(\ln x)$ (p) $\frac{1}{x}\ln 3x^2$
(q) $2x\ln(x-1) + \frac{x^2+1}{x-1}$ (r) $\frac{2}{x}\ln x$ (s) $\frac{-3\sin 3x}{\cos 3x} = -3\tan 3x$ (t) $\ln 2x + \frac{x-1}{x}$ (u) $\frac{1+\cos x}{x+\sin x}$ (v) $\frac{4x+5}{2x^2+5x-3}$
(w) $\frac{7}{(x-4)(x+3)}$ 3 $\frac{12x-1}{(3x+1)(2x-1)}$ 4 $\frac{3}{x^2-x-2}$ 5 $\frac{1-\cos x}{x-\sin x}, \frac{2}{\pi}$ 6 $\frac{-1}{1-\cos x}$ 7 $\frac{-1}{1+\sin x}$

Exercise 18E

1 (a) $4e^{4x}$ (b) $5e^{5x-1}$ (c) $-3e^{5-3x}$ (d) $2xe^{x^2}$ (e) $-\sin x\,e^{\cos x}$ (f) $e^x + xe^x$ (g) $2e^{-\frac{x}{2}} - (x-2)e^{-\frac{x}{2}}$ (h) ae^{ax-b}
(i) $2(x+1)e^{x^2+2x-1}$ (j) $e^x(\cos x + \sin x)$ (k) $-e^{-x}$ (l) $\frac{xe^x}{(x+1)^2}$ (m) $xe^{-x}(2-x)$ (n) $e^x + e^{-x}$ (o) $-2e^{-x}\cos x$
(p) $e^{-2x}(-1-6x)$ (q) $e^{2x}(2\ln x + \frac{1}{x})$ (r) $\frac{-e^x}{(e^x-1)^2}$ (s) $\frac{e^x(x^2-x-1)}{(x-1)^2}$ (t) $2e^{2x}(\cos 2x - \sin 2x)$ (u) $\frac{e^x(x-1)}{x^2}$
(v) $x^2e^{2x}(2x+3)$ (w) $2e^{2x} - 2e^{-2x}$ 2 $(1,e^3); 5e^3, -e^3$ 3 $x < 3\frac{1}{2}$ 4 $e^{3x}(1+3x); 3e^{3x}(2+3x)$; min at $x = -\frac{1}{3}$ 5 $0, -1$
6 min at $x = -1$, max at $x = 3$ 7 $e^x(\cos x - \sin x); -2e^x\sin x$; max at $x = \frac{\pi}{4}$; min at $x = \frac{5\pi}{4}$
8 $2e^x\cos x; 2e^x(\cos x - \sin x)$; max at $x = \frac{\pi}{2}$, min at $x = \frac{3\pi}{2}$ 9 $[\frac{dy}{dx} = e^x(\sin x + \cos x); \frac{d^2y}{dx^2} = 2e^x\cos x]$ 10 2
11 $a^x\ln a$ 12 $\cos x - \sin x$

Exercise 18F

1 (a) $\frac{1}{3}e^{3x} + c$ (b) $-e^{-x} + c$ (c) $-e^{2-x} + c$ (d) $\frac{1}{2}e^{2x} + 2x - \frac{1}{2}e^{-2x} + c$ (e) $-\frac{1}{3}e^{-3x} + c$ (f) $-\frac{1}{2}e^{1-2x} + c$
2 (a) $\frac{1}{4}(e^4 - 1)$ (b) $e - 1$ (c) $e^4 - e^2$ (d) $\frac{1}{2}(e^5 - e)$ (e) $e^4 - 1$ (f) $\frac{1}{2}(e^{-2} - e^{-4})$ (g) $2(e-1)$ (h) $e^3 - e$
3 $\frac{1}{3}(10 - e^{-3t})$ 4 $\frac{1}{2}(e^2 - 2e + 1)$ 5 $x - e^{-x} + c$ 6 (a) $y = \frac{1}{2}e^{2x}$ (b) $\frac{1}{4}(e^2 - 1)$

Revision Exercise 18

1 $2\cos x - x\sin x$ 2 $\frac{3}{5}$ 3 $\frac{\pi^2}{8} - 1$ 4 (a) $\frac{(\cos x + x\sin x)}{\cos^2 x}$ (b) $\frac{2\cos x}{(1-\sin x)^2}$ (c) $\frac{1}{(\sin x+\cos x)^2}\left[= \frac{1}{1+\sin 2x}\right]$ 5 -4 6 4
7 $0, \frac{3\pi}{2}; 1, 0$ 8 0.01 9 1 10 (a) $\frac{1}{2}(e - e^{-1})$ (b) $2e(e-1)$ (c) $\frac{1}{k}(e^{kb} - e^{ka})$ (d) $e^5 - e^3$ (e) $\frac{1}{2}(e - \frac{1}{e})$ 11 $-\frac{2}{\pi}$
12 $\frac{1}{2}(1 - e^{-2})$ units^2 13 (a) $(1,e^{-1})$ (b) $2(e^{-1} - e^{-2})$ (0.47) 14 Min at $x = -1$, max at $x = 2$ 15 $2x - x^2 - 1$
16 $\frac{3x+2}{2x(x+1)}$ 17 e; max 18 0.005 20 -1 21 -1 23 $4xe^{2x}; \frac{1}{4}(e^2 + 1)$
24 $[\frac{dy}{dx} = -x(2\ln x + 1)$ but $x = 0$ is not possible; only value is $\ln x = -\frac{1}{2}]$ max; $\frac{1}{2e}$ 26 $2\ln 3$ units^2
27 (c) $\frac{1}{2}(e^x - e^{-x}); \frac{1}{4}(e^{2x} - 2 + e^{-2x})$ (e) $e - \frac{1}{e}$

Exercise 19A

1 (a) 4 **(b)** $-4\,\text{m s}^{-1}$ **2 (a)** $-2\,\text{m s}^{-1}$ **(b)** 1 s **(c)** 2 s **(d)** $2\,\text{m s}^{-2}$ **3 (a)** 6 m **(b)** $-5\,\text{m s}^{-1}$ **(c)** $2\frac{1}{2}$ s
(d) 2 s and 3 s **(e)** $6\frac{1}{2}$ m **4 (a)** 24 **(b)** 1 s and 4 s **(c)** 4 **(d)** 1 s and 4 s **(e)** $-18, 18$ **5 (a)** -5 m, $-4\,\text{m s}^{-1}$
(b) 2 s, -9 m **(c)** 5 s **(d)** $2\,\text{m s}^{-2}$ **6 (a)** $-1, 12$ **(b)** 1 s and 2 s **(c)** $1\frac{1}{2}$ s **7 (a)** 3 **(b)** 2 s **(c)** $3\,\text{cm s}^{-1}$
8 $31\,\text{m s}^{-1}; 49$ m **9 (a)** 2 s **(b)** $18\,\text{m s}^{-2}$ **(c)** 34 m **10 (a)** $12\,\text{m s}^{-1}$ **(b)** $49\frac{1}{3}$ m **11 (a)** 68 m **(b)** $62\,\text{m s}^{-2}$
12 (a) $0; 6$ s **(b)** $48, -48\,\text{m s}^{-2}$ **(c)** 288 m

Exercise 19B

1 200m **2 (a)** 275 m **(b)** $\frac{55}{7}\,\text{m s}^{-1}$ **(c)** 18.75 s **3** $\frac{55}{3}$ s, $\frac{400}{3}$ m **4** $1\,\text{km min}^{-1} = \frac{50}{3}\,\text{m s}^{-1}$ **5 (a)** 6 300 m
(b) $0.07\,\text{m s}^{-2}$ **(c)** 666 m **6** 45 s, 900 m from start **7** $2.5\,\text{m s}^{-2}$, $\frac{5}{6}\,\text{m s}^{-2}$, $5\,\text{m s}^{-1}$ **8** 18 s, 150 s **9 (a)** $4.5\,\text{m s}^{-1}$;
11.25 m **(b)** $8\,\text{m s}^{-1}; 55$ m **(c)** $3 + 0.5t\,\text{m s}^{-1}; 3t + 0.25t^2$ m **10** $22\,\text{m s}^{-1}, 260$ m, 302.5 m **11** $20\,\text{s}; 20\,\text{m s}^{-1}$ **12** 16m; 4 s
13 (a) $\frac{5}{3}\,\text{m s}^{-2}$ **(b)** $\frac{71}{6}\,\text{m s}^{-1}$ **(c)** 20 m **14** $\frac{8}{3}\,\text{m s}^{-1}$; $\frac{160}{3}$ m **15** $10\,\text{m s}^{-1}, 15$ m **16 (a)** $\frac{10}{3}$ **(b)** $\frac{5}{3}$ m
17 (a) 4 s **(b)** 24 m

Revision Exercise 19

1 8 **2 (a)** $30\,\text{cm s}^{-1}; 42\,\text{cm s}^{-2}$ **3 (a)** $9\,\text{m s}^{-1}$ **(b)** $12\,\text{m s}^{-1}$ **(c)** $8\,\text{m s}^{-1}$ **4** $v = t^2 - 4t + 3; 15, 3\,\text{s}; -\frac{4}{3}$ m
5 (a) $\left[\frac{PQ}{x-5} = \frac{20}{x}\right]$ **(b) (i)** $2.78\,\text{cm s}^{-1}$ **(ii)** $1\,\text{cm s}^{-1}$ **(c)** $-\frac{3200}{x^3}\,\text{cm s}^{-1}$ **6** $5; 9\frac{1}{3}$ **7 (a)** $20\,\text{m s}^{-1}$ **(b)** 32 m
8 $4, -3; 4$ m **9 (b)** ± 4 units from O **10** 8 s; $\frac{16}{3}$ s **11 (a)** 9 m **(b)** $4\,\text{m s}^{-1}$ **12 (a)** 4 **(b)** $2\frac{1}{2}\,\text{m s}^{-2}$ **(c)** 20 m
13 $S_1 = 4.8V, S_2 = \frac{625 - V^2}{5}; V = 9, 15; t = 16$ s **14 (b)** $t_3 = 3t_2$ **(c)** 19.2, 5.2, 15.6 **15 (a)** 80 s **(b)** $15\,\text{m s}^{-1}$ **(c)** $17.5\,\text{m s}^{-1}$
16 (a) 16 **(b)** 14.2 **17** $\frac{2V}{3}, \frac{3V}{4}$; second train **18** $30; \frac{1}{8}$ **19** 6 s **20 (a)** 10 s **(b)** $22, 24\,\text{m s}^{-1}$ **(c)** $\frac{20}{3}$ s

Maths Booster **1** $\sqrt{20}$ s

Revision Paper 1

1 (a) (ii) 24 **2** (a) B = {16, 27, 38, 49, 50} C = {13, 18, 23, 28, 33, 38, 43, 48} (b) (i) 3 (ii) 18 (iii) 1 (iv) 17
3 (a) (i) 5 (ii) $-1, 4$ (b) $-\frac{5}{2}, 4$ **4** (a) $0 \leqslant f(x) \leqslant 4$ (b) $-5 \leqslant f(x) \leqslant 4$ (c) $-1 \leqslant f(x) \leqslant 3$
5 (b) $-1 \leqslant y \leqslant 1, 4 \leqslant y \leqslant 6$ **6** (a) $-\sqrt{5} \leqslant k \leqslant \sqrt{5}$ (b) $6 + 4x - 2x^2$ **7** (a) $\frac{3}{2}$ (b) 2^{n+3} (c) $2\frac{1}{4}$
8 (a) $2\frac{1}{4}$ (b) 3 **9** $x = 2, y = 1; x = -9, y = -\frac{25}{3}$ **10** (b) $-2 < x < 2$

Revision Paper 2

1 (a) $(A \cup C) \cup (A \cup C)'$ (b) 4 **2** (a) (i) $a = 2, b = 3$ (ii) $-4, 2\frac{1}{2}$ (b) $-1 < x < 2$ **4** $x < -\frac{1}{2}$
5 (a) (i) $-3 < x < 2$ (ii) $6\frac{1}{4}$ (b) $f^2: x \to \frac{x}{4x+9}, x \neq -\frac{9}{4}$; $f^3: x \to \frac{x}{13x+27}, x \neq -\frac{27}{13}$ (c) 1 **6** (a) 0, 1 (b) $11\sqrt{3}$
7 $-1, \frac{1}{2}$ **8** $x = -0.16, y = 1.23; x = -2.70, y = -0.47$ **9** $(-\frac{1}{4}, -\frac{3}{2})$

Revision Paper 3

1 (a) $a = -13, b = 6; (x - 2)(x + 3)(2x - 1)$ (b) -5 **2** (a) $2, 2, \frac{1}{2}$ (b) 3 **3** (a) 1 **4** (a) 0.57 (b) $2\frac{1}{2}$
5 (a) $0, -2$ (b) (i) 1.24 (ii) 1.65 **6** (a) 2 rad (b) 4 cm **7** (a) 11.3 cm (b) 40 cm^2
8 (a) A(0,1) (b) $y = 10x^{\frac{3}{4}}$ (c) 640 **9** $a = 4.7, n = 1.5$ **10** (a) $y = e^{5-2x}$ (b) 11 weeks (c) $2, 2, -3$

Revision Paper 4

1 $a = -3, b = -11; (x - 3)$ **2** $x = -\frac{1}{2}, -\frac{1}{4}, 1, \theta = 45°, 153.4°, 166°$ **3** (a) $y = \frac{10}{x^2}$ (b) $\frac{1}{9}$ **4** (a) 4.42 (b) 1.10
5 0.535 **6** (a) 4.322 (b) 0.161 **7** (a) $p = 5, q = -3$ (b) $6\frac{1}{3}$ **8** (a) $\frac{3\sqrt{2}}{2} \pi$ cm (b) $(9\pi - 18)$ cm^2
9 (a) 3π unit (b) 18 units^2

Revision Paper 5

1 (b) 109.9°, 166.1°, 283.9°, 346.1° **2** 4 **3** 40 **4** (a) 40 320 (b) 576 **5** (a) 6 048 (b) $2, -1$
6 $1 + 12x + 54x^2, 16 - 32x + 24x^2; 504$ **7** (a) $\mathbf{i} + 7\mathbf{j}$ (b) 109.4° **8** $\frac{m}{2}(\mathbf{a}+\mathbf{b}), k\mathbf{a} + (\frac{1-k}{3})\mathbf{b}$; (a) $\frac{1}{4}, \frac{1}{2}$ (b) 1:1, 1:3
9 (a) $\begin{pmatrix} 7 & 2 \\ 14 & 9 \end{pmatrix}$ (b) $\begin{pmatrix} 2 & 1 \\ 16 & 2 \end{pmatrix}$ (c) $\begin{pmatrix} 4 & 3 \\ 4 & 0 \end{pmatrix}$ **10** (a) $5, 2$ (b) $3, -1$

Revision Paper 6

1 (b) 70.5°, 180°, 289.5° **2** 5 **3** 362 880; 2 880 **4** (a) 126 (b) 120 **5** (a) $1 - 8x + 24x^2$
(b) $32 - 80x + 80x^2; 1\ 488$ **6** $5, -3$ **7** (a) $\mathbf{b} - \mathbf{a}, \frac{2}{3}(\mathbf{b} - \mathbf{a}), \frac{1}{3}\mathbf{a} + \frac{2}{3}\mathbf{b}, \mathbf{b} - \frac{2}{3}\mathbf{a}$ (c) $\frac{4}{7}, \frac{6}{7}$ (d) 6:1, 4:3
8 (a) 10.3 km h^{-1} in direction 283.1° (b) 8.1 km h^{-1} (c) 1 hr 44 min **9** $5, 2, 13$ **10** (a) 2 (b) $\begin{pmatrix} 2 & -\frac{1}{2} \\ -3 & 1 \end{pmatrix}$
(c) $\begin{pmatrix} 10 & 6 \\ 36 & 22 \end{pmatrix}$

Revision Paper 7

1 (a) $2x - \frac{1}{2x^3}$ (b) $\frac{-5}{(x+2)^2}$ (c) $2(x - 2)(5x - 9)(2x - 3)^2$ **2** (a) $3y = x - 4$ (b) $12, -12$
3 (a) $x < -1$ or $x > 3$; min at $x = 3$, max at $x = -1$ (b) $(\frac{a+b}{2})^2$ **4** (a) 0.50 units^2 (b) 2.26 cm^3.s^{-1} (c) 2
5 (a) $2x - \frac{3}{x} + c$ (b) 9 (c) $2\sqrt{10} - 2\sqrt{5}$ **6** $4\frac{5}{6}$ **7** (b) $y = 1 + ex$ (c) (0,1) (d) $\frac{e}{2} - 1$ **8** (a) $\frac{4}{x^2-4}$
(b) $-\frac{1}{4} \ln 3$ **9** (a) 4 s (b) -4 m s^{-1} (c) -9 m **10** (a) 660 m (b) 2.4 m s^{-2} (c) 18.75 sec

Revision Paper 8

1 (a) $\frac{2x^2+1}{x(x^2+1)}$ (b) $\frac{1-2\ln x}{x^3}$ (c) $\frac{-(x+2)e^{-x}}{(x+1)^2}$ **2** $2, -3; 2y + 25x = 28$ **3** (a) $\frac{1}{2}$ (b) 3.2 cm s^{-1} **4** 4
5 (a) $\frac{1}{10}$ (b) $-\frac{2}{3}$ (c) $\frac{1}{2} + \frac{1}{2e^2} - \frac{1}{e}$ **6** $8\frac{1}{6}$ **7** (a) $y = x - \frac{x^2}{2} - \frac{2x^3}{3} + 2$ (b) min at $(-1, \frac{7}{6})$, max at $(\frac{1}{2}, \frac{55}{24})$
(c) $6y + 12x = 23$ **8** (a) $3 \tan^2 x \sec^2 x$ (b) $[\tan^4 x = (\sec^2 x - 1)^2 = \sec^4 x - 2 \sec^2 x + 1 = [\sec^2(1 + \tan^2 x) \dots]$
(c) $\frac{\pi}{4} - \frac{2}{3}$ $[\int \tan^4 x \, dx = \int (\sec^2 x \tan^2 x - \sec^2 x + 1)dx = \frac{1}{3} \tan^3 x - \tan x + x + c]$ **9** (a) 12 (b) $-\frac{4}{e}$ (c) $36(1 - \frac{1}{e})$
10 (a) $\frac{1}{2}, 5; 74.75$ m (b) 2 and 8 sec; 150 m